D1194955

FREQUENCY ANALYSIS, MODULATION AND NOISE

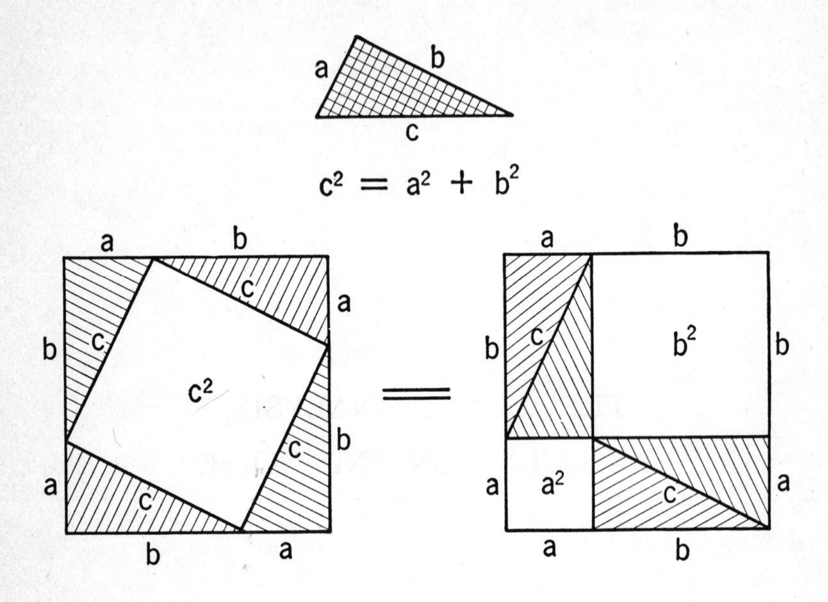

(Frontispiece.)

FREQUENCY ANALYSIS, MODULATION and NOISE

by

Stanford Goldman, Ph.D.

Professor of Electrical Engineering
Syracuse University

DOVER PUBLICATIONS, INC.
NEW YORK

Published in Canada by General Publishing Company, Ltd., 30 Lesmill Road, Don Mills, Toronto, Ontario.
Published in the United Kingdom by Constable and Company, Ltd., 10 Orange Street, London WC 2.

This Dover edition, first published in 1967, is an unabridged and unaltered republication of the work originally published by the McGraw-Hill Book Company, Inc., in 1948.

International Standard Book Number: 0-486-61845-5
Library of Congress Catalog Card Number: 67-26485

Manufactured in the United States of America
Dover Publications, Inc.
180 Varick Street
New York, N. Y. 10014

PREFACE

For several years, the author taught radio engineering in out-of-hour courses to the engineers of the Electronics Receiver Division of the General Electric Company. In developing these courses it was found that there was no textbook available dealing with many of the subjects with which a radio engineer should be familiar. The present book has been written in answer to this need. It gives a comprehensive discussion of the important subjects of Fourier integral analysis, modulation and random noise. A companion volume entitled "Transformation Calculus and Radio Transients" will deal with transient solutions of radio circuit problems with the aid of Laplace transforms.

Most of the material in the present book has never before been treated in any textbook. Some has not appeared even in the periodical literature and is original with the author.

To a considerable extent the different groups of chapters can be read independently. It has been assumed that many readers will want to use the book as a reference volume, and an attempt has been made to make it possible for the reader with a reasonably good background to get considerable information on any particular subject by reading only those sections dealing with that particular subject. The prerequisite training for reading the book is a knowledge of calculus and a good general knowledge of radio engineering.

In writing a book of this character the author has, of course, drawn upon previous writers in various fields of mathematics and of radio engineering. Where the work of specific persons is used, credit is given in the course of the text.

The author is indebted to many of his friends and associates for encouragement and assistance in the preparation of the manuscript, especially to A. W. Sear, R. B. Dome, Max Scherberg, and J. F. McAllister, Jr. He also wishes to thank I. J. Kaar and C. G. Fick for arranging for the General Electric Company's sponsorship of the work. Finally, he wishes to thank E. R. Kretzmer and T. P. Cheatham for valuable advice and criticism.

STANFORD GOLDMAN

CAMBRIDGE, MASS.
February, 1948

PREFACE

For [illegible] years the author [illegible] engineering [illegible] course in the [illegible] of the [illegible] Division of the General Electric Company. In developing [illegible] it was found that there was no textbook available dealing with [illegible] the subjects with which a [illegible] engineer should be familiar. The present book has been written in answer to this need. It gives a comprehensive discussion of the important subjects of [illegible] integral [illegible] calculation and [illegible] [illegible] [illegible] [illegible] [illegible]. The [illegible] [illegible] [illegible] [illegible] [illegible] solutions of [illegible] problems [illegible] the [illegible] of Laplace transform.

Most of the material [illegible] the present book has never before [illegible] in any textbook [illegible] has not appeared even in the [illegible] literature and is original with the author.

[illegible] [illegible] [illegible] [illegible] [illegible] of [illegible] and independently. It has been assumed that many [illegible] want to use the [illegible] and [illegible] attempt [illegible] made to make [illegible] as possible [illegible] with a reasonably good [illegible] [illegible] [illegible] [illegible] particular [illegible] [illegible] [illegible] [illegible] [illegible] [illegible] [illegible] [illegible] [illegible] knowledge [illegible] engineering.

[illegible] [illegible] [illegible] [illegible] [illegible] [illegible] [illegible] engineering. Where [illegible] [illegible] [illegible] [illegible] used [illegible] given [illegible] of the text.

The author is indebted to many of his friends and associates [illegible] encouragement and assistance in the preparation of the manuscript, especially to [illegible] [illegible] R. [illegible] [illegible] [illegible], and [illegible] McAllister, Jr. He also wishes to thank [illegible] and [illegible] [illegible] the General Electric Company [illegible] [illegible]. Finally, he wishes to thank [illegible] [illegible] [illegible] [illegible] valuable advice and criticism.

[illegible]

[illegible], Mass.
[illegible], 19[illegible]

CONTENTS

INTRODUCTION

The Phenomena of Mathematics. Every educated person in the Western World knows that there are physical phenomena, biological phenomena, and natural phenomena of many other kinds. Comparatively few, however, consider that mathematics also has its phenomena. Most people think of mathematics merely as a compact and exact method of expressing ideas, *i.e.*, as an abbreviated language. To be sure, the expression of ideas in mathematical language is a shorthand method of systematizing thought, and certainly it tends to discourage loose thinking and to encourage quantitative work. However, if mathematics were limited to its use as a language, it would never have outgrown its short pants as a tool of science. Surprising as it may seem, the chief importance of mathematics lies in the existence and usefulness of certain phenomena of mathematics.

A short consideration of this point of view of mathematical phenomena is now in order. Consider, for instance, the Fourier series expansion, the fact that any arbitrary periodic function can be shown to consist of a simple sine wave and its harmonics taken with proper phase angles. This is the type of fact that we call a phenomenon of mathematics. Even though its truth can be proved, it had to be discovered. It is not a consequence of the use of mathematics as an abbreviated language. We shall have many occasions to show that this particular mathematical phenomenon is very useful in radio engineering.

The existence of complex quantities that obey the laws of the algebra of real quantities is another phenomenon of mathematics. Their applications in radio engineering are not so obvious as those of Fourier analysis, but once established they are no less important, as the widespread use of the idea of *impedance* testifies.

The student might question to what extent differential and integral calculus deal with mathematical phenomena, rather than with ordinary logic. To clarify this situation, it may be pointed out that the existence of derivatives and integrals generally follows from logical considerations alone; but the fact that the derivatives and integrals of simple functions are usually also simple functions, this simplicity being the basis of the usefulness of calculus, is clearly a phenomenon of mathematics.

In years to come, new mathematical phenomena with radio applications will no doubt be discovered, and new applications for known mathematical phenomena will likewise come to light. However, a wealth of mathematical phenomena applicable to radio is already known, and certain of these will be first the subject matter and then the tools of the present book.

Rigor and Vigor in Mathematics. Modern mathematics has been based upon a logical foundation whose depths are magnificent. This type of thoroughgoing analysis is called rigorous mathematics.

Rigorous mathematics has a rightful place of honor in human thought. However, it has wisely been said that vigor is more important than rigor in the use of mathematics by the average man. In the particular case of this volume, the amount of rigor will be used that is necessary for a thorough understanding of the subject at hand by a radio engineer; but when it appears that rigor will confuse rather than clarify the subject for an engineer, we shall trust in the correctness of the results established by rigorous methods by the pure mathematicians and use them without the background of a rigorous proof.

The Debt of Radio to Mathematics. Although it is not generally appreciated even by radio engineers, radio owes its very existence to mathematics. In 1866, the British scientist James Clerk Maxwell showed that a so-called "displacement current" must exist in space for the differential equations of the electromagnetic field to be consistent. He thus arrived at the famous set of differential equations that bear his name. He then was able to predict by solving these equations that electromagnetic radiation should exist. These deductions of Maxwell were a subject of much scientific controversy for the next 20 years. In 1886–1888 Hertz undertook an elaborate experimental program to verify Maxwell's mathematical deductions and thereby for the first time in history generated and detected radio waves.

The Aims of This Book. While the language and methods of the present book are mathematical, its fundamental aim is not the teaching of mathematics but rather the exposition and clarification of certain fields of radio. Mathematics is used only as a means to this end. It so happens, however, that, for the problems at hand, mathematics is such a powerful tool that it is worth while spending many chapters in developing the student's mathematical knowledge and facility.

CHAPTER I

FOURIER SERIES

1.1 Introduction. There is one phenomenon of mathematics that is perhaps more widely used in radio engineering than any other—the phenomenon of Fourier series expansion. Its importance is so fundamental that many who never heard of a Fourier series nevertheless know about its most salient feature, namely, the existence of harmonics. In this and the following chapter we shall develop the theory of Fourier series and shall learn how to use it in the solution of a variety of radio problems.

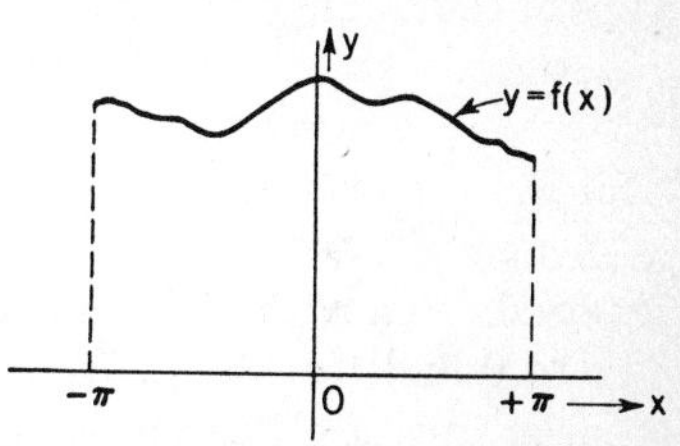

Fig. 1. A function defined in the interval from $-\pi$ to $+\pi$.

The fundamental fact upon which the use of Fourier series is based is that any[1] function $f(x)$ (see Fig. 1) defined in the interval from $-\pi$ to $+\pi$ can be expanded in a series of trigonometric functions such that

$$f(x) = \frac{a_0}{2} + (a_1 \cos x + b_1 \sin x) + (a_2 \cos 2x + b_2 \sin 2x) + (a_3 \cos 3x + b_3 \sin 3x) + \cdots + (a_n \cos nx + b_n \sin nx) + \cdots \quad (1)$$

or, in compact form

$$f(x) = \frac{\omega_0}{2} + \sum_{n=1}^{n=\infty} (a_n \cos nx + b_n \sin nx) \quad (1a)$$

In this series the a's and b's are constants whose values we shall soon determine. The series of sines and cosines on the right side of Eq. (1) or (1a) is known as a Fourier series.

It can be proved, although we shall not do so here[2] that, so long as $f(x)$ has only a finite number of discontinuities and a finite number

[1] Subject only to exceptions of no importance in engineering.

[2] Proofs are given in many texts on function theory, for example, H. S. Carslaw, "Theory of Fourier Series and Integrals," Chap. VII, or Whittaker and Watson, "Modern Analysis," Sec. 9.42.

of maxima and minima in the interval from $-\pi$ to $+\pi$, and provided that

$$\int_{-\pi}^{+\pi} |f(x)|\, dx$$

is finite, then a Fourier expansion is always possible. It is by no means necessary for the function to be expressible by a single equation in the

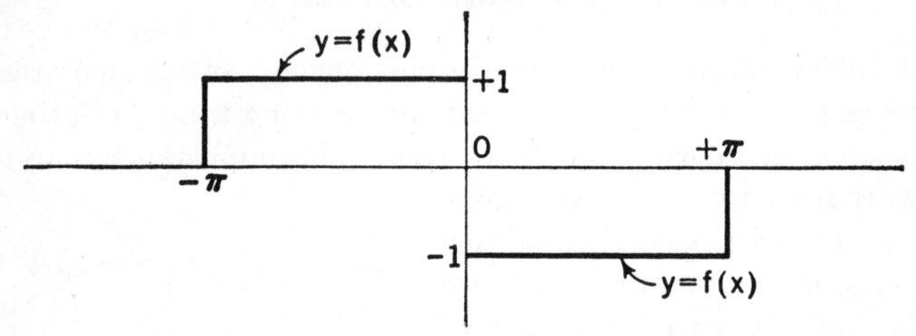

FIG. 2. A square-wave function.

interval. Thus the function shown in Fig. 2, which is $f(x) = 1$ from $-\pi$ to 0 and $f(x) = -1$ from 0 to $+\pi$, can readily be expressed in a Fourier series. Fourier series expansions are thus possible for a much wider variety of functions than Taylor series expansions, the latter requiring that the function be continuous and have continuous derivatives of all orders.

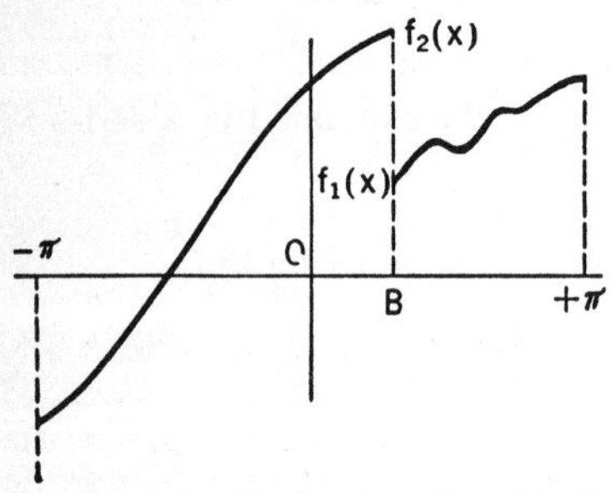

FIG. 3. A function having a discontinuity at $x = B$.

It should be pointed out that if there is a point of discontinuity, such as that shown at B in Fig. 3, the Fourier series will converge to

$$\tfrac{1}{2}[f_1(x) + f_2(x)]$$

where $f_1(x)$ and $f_2(x)$ are the two different values that the function approaches as it comes to B from the positive and negative directions. Furthermore, for the values $x = +\pi$ and $x = -\pi$, the Fourier series converges to

$$\tfrac{1}{2}[f(+\pi) + f(-\pi)]$$

If $f(\pi) = f(-\pi)$, these are then no different from ordinary points.

The series (1) can be expressed as a single series of sines or of cosines, if phase angles are introduced. Thus it can be expressed as

$$f(x) = \frac{a_0}{2} + A_1 \cos (x + \phi_1) + A_2 \cos (2x + \phi_2) + \cdots + A_n \cos (nx + \phi_n) + \cdots \quad (2)$$

where

$$A_n = \sqrt{a_n^2 + b_n^2} \tag{3}$$

and

$$\phi_n = \tan^{-1}\left(\frac{-b_n}{a_n}\right) \tag{4}$$

1.2 Values of the Fourier Coefficients. In order that the series expansion in Eq. (1) should be useful we must be able to determine the values of the a's and b's. We shall now see how to do this.

To find a_0, we multiply through Eq. (1) by dx and integrate from $-\pi$ to $+\pi$. Thus

$$\int_{-\pi}^{+\pi} f(x)\,dx = \int_{-\pi}^{+\pi} \frac{a_0}{2}\,dx + \int_{-\pi}^{+\pi} a_1 \cos x\,dx + \int_{-\pi}^{+\pi} b_1 \sin x\,dx + \cdots + \int_{-\pi}^{+\pi} a_n \cos nx\,dx + \int_{-\pi}^{+\pi} b_n \sin nx\,dx + \cdots = \int_{-\pi}^{+\pi} \frac{a_0}{2}\,dx = a_0\pi \tag{5}$$

since all the other integrals of the series terms vanish. Therefore

$$a_0 = \frac{1}{\pi}\int_{-\pi}^{+\pi} f(x)\,dx \tag{6}$$

To find any other a coefficient, such as a_n, we multiply through Eq. (1) by $\cos nx\,dx$ and integrate from $-\pi$ to $+\pi$. Thus

$$\int_{-\pi}^{+\pi} f(x) \cos nx\,dx = \int_{-\pi}^{+\pi} \frac{a_0}{2} \cos nx\,dx + \int_{-\pi}^{+\pi} a_1 \cos x \cos nx\,dx + \int_{-\pi}^{+\pi} b_1 \sin x \cos nx\,dx + \cdots \tag{7}$$

Now

$$\int_{-\pi}^{+\pi} \sin px \cos qx\,dx = 0 \tag{8}$$

if p and q are any integers whatever, and

$$\int_{-\pi}^{+\pi} \cos px \cos qx\,dx = 0 \tag{9}$$

if p is any integer not equal to q. If $p = q$, then

$$\int_{-\pi}^{+\pi} \cos^2 px\,dx = \pi \tag{10}$$

Therefore all integrals, excepting one, on the right side of Eq. (7) will vanish. As a result, we have

$$\int_{-\pi}^{+\pi} f(x) \cos nx \, dx = \int_{-\pi}^{+\pi} a_n \cos^2 nx \, dx = a_n \pi \qquad (11)$$

or

$$a_n = \frac{1}{\pi} \int_{-\pi}^{+\pi} f(x) \cos nx \, dx \qquad (12)$$

In a similar manner, in order to find b_n, we multiply through Eq. (1) by $\sin nx \, dx$ and integrate from $-\pi$ to $+\pi$. We then find

$$b_n = \frac{1}{\pi} \int_{-\pi}^{+\pi} f(x) \sin nx \, dx \qquad (13)$$

with the aid of the equations

$$\int_{-\pi}^{+\pi} \sin px \sin qx = 0 \qquad (14)$$

if $p \neq q$ and

$$\int_{-\pi}^{+\pi} \sin^2 px \, dx = \pi \qquad (15)$$

Equations (6), (12), and (13) give us the values of the Fourier coefficients.[1]

By an entirely similar process, it can be shown that, if a function is defined in the interval from 0 to 2π, it can be expanded into a Fourier series of the same form as Eq. (1), only this time the coefficients are given by the formulas

[1] Looking over the derivation of Eq. (6) and comparing it with Eq. (1), we see that $a_0/2$ is just the average value of $f(x)$. Since each sine and cosine term in Eq. (1) has an average value of zero between $-\pi$ and $+\pi$, these terms are eliminated by the integration process of Eq. (5), which is essentially an averaging process.

The derivation of the formulas (12) and (13) for a_n and b_n is carried out by what may be called a "weighted" averaging process. Each term on the right of Eq. (1) when multiplied by one of the sine or cosine functions has an average value of zero in the range from $-\pi$ to $+\pi$, unless that particular sine or cosine function is also a factor of the term. In this way all terms are eliminated except that involving the particular sine or cosine function in question. Equations (8) to (10), (14), and (15) thus supply a means of segregating any desired term from Eq. (1) for special consideration. A similar mathematical phenomenon also occurs in the expansion of a function in a series of any of the types of what are known as orthogonal functions.

$$a_n = \frac{1}{\pi}\int_0^{2\pi} f(x)\cos nx\,dx \tag{16}$$

$$b_n = \frac{1}{\pi}\int_0^{2\pi} f(x)\sin nx\,dx \tag{17}$$

Earlier mathematicians such as d'Alembert, Euler, and Clairaut had employed special Fourier series before the time of Fourier, and had even used Eqs. (6), (12), and (13) for the calculation of the Fourier coefficients. However, the great advance made by Fourier was in pointing out that the possibility of the expansion into a Fourier series is not limited to a few special functions but is a general phenomenon true for arbitrary functions. Fourier used the type of series that now bears his name in a number of classical investigations on the conduction of heat. The first of these was presented to the French Academy in 1807.[1]

1.3 Some Examples of Fourier Expansions. *a.* Let us now consider a few examples of Fourier expansions. First we shall find the Fourier expansion of the function shown in Fig. 2. This function is

$$\begin{aligned} y &= 1 \quad (\text{in the range } -\pi \le x \le 0) \\ y &= -1 \quad (\text{in the range } 0 \le x \le \pi) \end{aligned}$$

According to Eq. (6), we then have

$$\begin{aligned} a_0 &= \frac{1}{\pi}\int_{-\pi}^{+\pi} f(x)\,dx = \frac{1}{\pi}\int_{-\pi}^{0} (+1)\,dx + \frac{1}{\pi}\int_0^{\pi} (-1)\,dx \\ &= \frac{\pi}{\pi} - \frac{\pi}{\pi} = 0 \end{aligned} \tag{18}$$

According to Eq. (12),

$$\begin{aligned} a_n &= \frac{1}{\pi}\int_{-\pi}^{+\pi} f(x)\cos nx\,dx \\ &= \frac{1}{\pi}\int_{-\pi}^{0} (+1)\cos nx\,dx + \frac{1}{\pi}\int_0^{\pi} (-1)\cos nx\,dx \\ &= \frac{1}{\pi}\frac{\sin nx}{n}\bigg|_{-\pi}^{0} - \frac{1}{\pi}\frac{\sin nx}{n}\bigg|_0^{\pi} = 0 + 0 = 0 \end{aligned} \tag{19}$$

[1] For an interesting historical review of the mathematical side of Fourier series, see H. S. Carslaw, "Theory of Fourier Series and Integrals."

According to Eq. (13),

$$\begin{aligned} b_n &= \frac{1}{\pi}\int_{-\pi}^{+\pi} f(x)\sin nx\,dx \\ &= \frac{1}{\pi}\int_{-\pi}^{0}(+1)\sin nx\,dx + \frac{1}{\pi}\int_{0}^{\pi}(-1)\sin nx\,dx \\ &= \frac{-1}{n}\frac{\cos nx}{\pi}\bigg|_{\pi}^{0} + \frac{1}{\pi}\frac{\cos nx}{n}\bigg|_{0}^{\pi} \\ &= -\frac{1}{\pi n} - \frac{1}{\pi n} - \frac{1}{\pi n} - \frac{1}{\pi n} = \frac{-4}{\pi n} \quad \text{(if } n \text{ is odd)} \\ &= -\frac{1}{\pi n} + \frac{1}{\pi n} + \frac{1}{\pi n} - \frac{1}{\pi n} = 0 \quad \text{(if } n \text{ is even)} \end{aligned} \tag{20}$$

Therefore

$$f(x) = \frac{-4}{\pi}\left(\sin x + \frac{\sin 3x}{3} + \frac{\sin 5x}{5} + \cdots\right) \tag{21}$$

is the Fourier expansion of the function shown in Fig. 2.

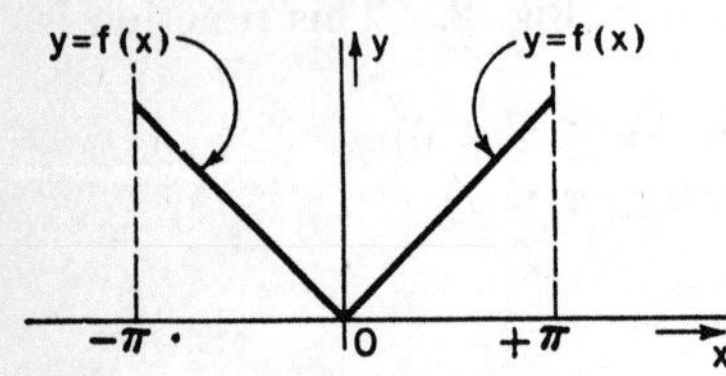

FIG. 4. A triangular-wave function.

b. Next let us expand the function shown in Fig. 4. This function is

$$y = -x \quad (\text{from } -\pi \text{ to } 0)$$

and

$$y = +x \quad (\text{from } 0 \text{ to } \pi)$$

Thus

$$\begin{aligned} a_0 &= \frac{1}{\pi}\int_{-\pi}^{+\pi} f(x)\,dx = \frac{1}{\pi}\int_{-\pi}^{0} -x\,dx + \frac{1}{\pi}\int_{0}^{\pi} x\,dx \\ &= 0 + \frac{\pi^2}{2\pi} + \frac{\pi^2}{2\pi} + 0 = \pi \end{aligned} \tag{22}$$

$$\begin{aligned} a_n &= \frac{1}{\pi}\int_{-\pi}^{+\pi} f(x)\cos nx\,dx \\ &= \frac{1}{\pi}\int_{-\pi}^{0} -x\cos nx\,dx + \frac{1}{\pi}\int_{0}^{\pi} x\cos nx\,dx \end{aligned} \tag{23}$$

Now, integrating by parts,

$$\begin{aligned} \int x\cos nx\,dx &= x\frac{\sin nx}{n} - \int \frac{\sin nx}{n}\,dx \\ &= x\frac{\sin nx}{n} + \frac{\cos nx}{n^2} \end{aligned} \tag{24}$$

Therefore

$$a_n = \frac{-1}{\pi}\left(x\frac{\sin nx}{n} + \frac{\cos nx}{n^2}\right)\Bigg|_{-\pi}^{0} + \frac{1}{\pi}\left(\frac{x \sin nx}{n} + \frac{\cos nx}{n^2}\right)\Bigg|_{0}^{\pi}$$

$$\left.\begin{aligned} &= \frac{1}{\pi}\left(-\frac{1}{n^2} - \frac{1}{n^2} - \frac{1}{n^2} - \frac{1}{n^2}\right) = -\frac{4}{\pi n^2} \text{ (when } n \text{ is odd)} \\ &= \frac{1}{\pi}\left(+\frac{1}{n^2} - \frac{1}{n^2} + \frac{1}{n^2} - \frac{1}{n^2}\right) = 0 \quad \text{(when } n \text{ is even)} \end{aligned}\right\} \tag{25}$$

Furthermore,

$$b_n = \frac{1}{\pi}\int_{-\pi}^{+\pi} f(x) \sin nx \, dx$$

$$= \frac{1}{\pi}\int_{-\pi}^{0} -x \sin nx \, dx + \frac{1}{\pi}\int_{0}^{\pi} x \sin nx \, dx \tag{26}$$

Now

$$\int x \sin nx \, dx = -x\frac{\cos nx}{n} + \int \frac{\cos nx}{n} dx$$

$$= \frac{-x \cos nx}{n} + \frac{\sin nx}{n^2} \tag{27}$$

Therefore

$$b_n = \frac{-1}{\pi}\left(-x\frac{\cos nx}{n} + \frac{\sin nx}{n^2}\right)\Bigg|_{-\pi}^{0} + \frac{1}{\pi}\left(\frac{-x \cos nx}{n} + \frac{\sin nx}{n^2}\right)\Bigg|_{0}^{\pi}$$

$$\left.\begin{aligned} &= \frac{1}{\pi}\left(-\frac{\pi}{n} + \frac{\pi}{n}\right) = 0 \qquad \text{(when } n \text{ is odd)} \\ &= \frac{1}{\pi}\left(+\frac{\pi}{n} - \frac{\pi}{n}\right) = 0 \qquad \text{(when } n \text{ is even)} \end{aligned}\right\} \tag{28}$$

Thus

$$f(x) = \frac{\pi}{2} - \frac{4}{\pi}\left(\cos x + \frac{1}{3^2}\cos 3x + \frac{1}{5^2}\cos 5x + \cdots\right) \tag{29}$$

is the Fourier expansion for the function shown in Fig. 4.

Exercises

1. Find the Fourier expansion of the half sine wave shown in the figure.

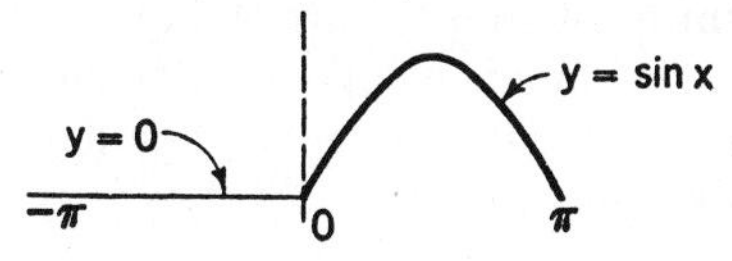

2. Expand the function

$$f(x) = \epsilon^x \text{ from } 0 \text{ to } 2\pi$$

into a Fourier series.

Answer:

$$f(x) = \frac{\epsilon^{2\pi} - 1}{\pi}\left(\frac{1}{2} + \sum_{n=1}^{\infty} \frac{\cos nx}{1+n^2} - \sum_{n=1}^{\infty} \frac{n \sin nx}{1+n^2}\right)$$

(Sokolnikoff)

3. With the aid of Eq. (29), show that

$$1 + \frac{1}{3^2} + \frac{1}{5^2} + \frac{1}{7^2} + \cdots = \frac{\pi^2}{8}$$

1.4 Fourier Expansions of Periodic Functions. Let us suppose that the functions shown in Fig. 2 and 4 are periodic, as represented in Fig. 5, *i.e.*, that every value of the function is repeated after each 2π interval. Then the Fourier expansions of Eqs. (21) and (29) will continue to be valid throughout the whole range in which the functions are periodic. This is true because, if x is increased by 2π, every term on the right side of Eqs. (21) and (29) has again the same value; and since $f(x)$ has a period of 2π, it also has again the same value. Periodic functions may therefore be represented throughout their whole range by a single Fourier series.

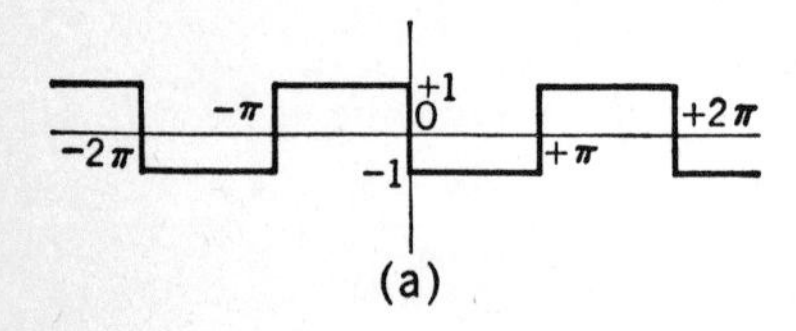

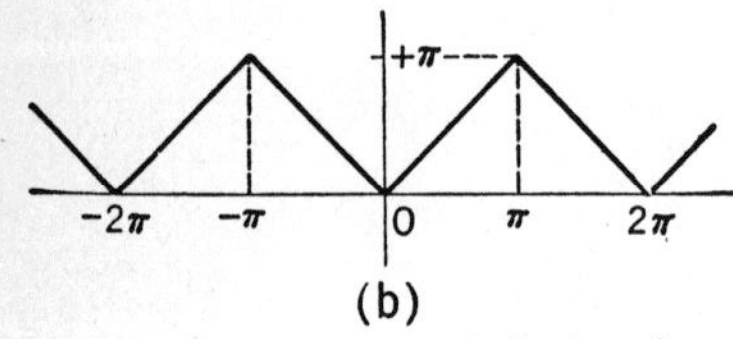

Fig. 5. Examples of periodic functions.

Since every periodic function of the various types that arise in engineering can be represented by a single Fourier series, we know that every engineering quantity arising from periodic excitation can be represented by a Fourier series whose fundamental period is the period of the excitation. Thus, we know that the steady-state current from a generator can consist only of a direct-current component plus fundamental and harmonic components of the period of rotation of the generator. Likewise, we know that the rectified current arising from an alternating current must consist only of a direct-current component plus fundamental and harmonic components of the period of the exciting current. These statements, of course, assume that the excitation is purely periodic, *i.e.*, that it repeats itself exactly.

The foregoing are important physical facts that must follow from the mathematical phenomenon of Fourier series. Another such consequence is the presence of interference from a broadcast transmitter at harmonics of its carrier frequency.

1.5 Odd and Even Functions. *If $f(x)$ in Eq. (1) is an odd function, i.e., if*

$$f(-x) = -f(x) \tag{30}$$

then all the a_n's vanish and the Fourier series consists of sine terms alone. We have already come across a case of this kind in the case of Fig. 2, (or Fig. 5*a*) and have found the Fourier expansion [Eq. (21)] to consist of sine terms alone. To prove the truth of this phenomenon in the general case, consider the equation

$$\begin{aligned} a_n &= \frac{1}{\pi}\int_{-\pi}^{+\pi} f(x)\cos nx\,dx \\ &= \frac{1}{\pi}\int_{-\pi}^{0} f(x)\cos nx\,dx + \frac{1}{\pi}\int_{0}^{\pi} f(x)\cos nx\,dx \end{aligned} \tag{31}$$

Since

$$\cos\theta = \cos(-\theta) \tag{32}$$

for any value of θ, it follows that

$$\int_{-\pi}^{0} f(x)\cos nx\,dx = -\int_{0}^{\pi} f(x)\cos nx\,dx \tag{33}$$

provided that $f(-x) = -f(x)$. Substituting Eq. (33) into Eq. (31), we see that all the a_n's vanish in this case. Furthermore,

$$a_0 = \frac{1}{\pi}\int_{-\pi}^{+\pi} f(x)\,dx = \frac{1}{\pi}\int_{-\pi}^{0} f(x)\,dx + \frac{1}{\pi}\int_{0}^{\pi} f(x)\,dx = 0 \tag{34}$$

if $f(-x) = -f(x)$, so that a_0 also vanishes. The Fourier expansion of an odd function thus consists of sine terms alone.

Next, let us consider $f(x)$ to be an even function, i.e.,

$$f(-x) = f(x) \tag{35}$$

In this case all the b_n's vanish, and the Fourier series consists of cosine terms alone, plus a possible constant. We have seen an example of such a function in Fig. 4 (or Fig. 5*b*) and have found the Fourier expansion [Eq. (29)] to contain only cosine terms plus a constant.

To prove the general theorem, consider the equation

$$b_n = \frac{1}{\pi}\int_{-\pi}^{+\pi} f(x)\sin nx\,dx$$
$$= \frac{1}{\pi}\int_{-\pi}^{0} f(x)\sin nx\,dx + \frac{1}{\pi}\int_{0}^{\pi} f(x)\sin nx\,dx \tag{36}$$

Since

$$\sin\theta = -\sin(-\theta) \tag{37}$$

for all values of θ, it follows that, if $f(-x) = f(x)$, then

$$\int_{-\pi}^{0} f(x)\sin nx\,dx = -\int_{0}^{\pi} f(x)\sin nx\,dx \tag{38}$$

so that all the b_n's vanish. The Fourier expansion of $f(x)$ will then consist only of cosine terms plus perhaps a constant.

The student will, of course, realize that by no means all functions are either even or odd. The Fourier expansions of functions in general will therefore contain both sine and cosine terms. It is interesting to note, however, that, according to Eq. (1*a*), every function capable of Fourier expansion must consist of the sum of an even part plus an odd part since

$$f(x) = \underbrace{\frac{a_0}{2} + \sum_{n=1}^{n=\infty} a_n \cos nx}_{\text{even part}} + \underbrace{\sum_{n=1}^{n=\infty} b_n \sin nx}_{\text{odd part}} \tag{39}$$

This fundamental fact concerning the composition of functions has not generally been considered very important by engineers, but in the opinion of the author an appreciation of its value is likely to grow. It is worth while noting that it follows directly from the elementary identity

$$f(x) \equiv \underbrace{\frac{f(x) + f(-x)}{2}}_{\text{even part}} + \underbrace{\frac{f(x) - f(-x)}{2}}_{\text{odd part}} \tag{40}$$

Equation (40) also gives a very simple means for separating a function into its even and odd parts.

In practical Fourier analysis, it is desirable to choose the origin so that the function to be expanded is either even or odd, provided that the function has the necessary symmetry to make such a choice possible. The calculation of either the b or the a coefficients is thus eliminated.

Exercise

Show that sinh x is the odd part of e^x and cosh x is the even part. Draw a graph of e^x, cosh x, and sinh x from $x = -3$ to $x = +3$, and compare with Fig. 9.

1.6 Functions Whose Expansions Contain Only Odd or Only Even Harmonics—Symmetry. The subject of odd and even functions discussed in the preceding section should not be confused with the subject of functions whose expansions contain only odd or only even harmonics. Regarding this latter matter, we shall now prove a useful theorem.

If a function $f(x)$, having a period 2π, is such that

$$f(x + \pi) = -f(x) \tag{41}$$

then the function has only odd harmonics in its Fourier expansion. If

$$f(x + \pi) = +f(x) \tag{42}$$

then the function has only even harmonics in its Fourier expansion.

The proof of Eqs. (41) and (42) is as follows:

Let a_n and b_n be the Fourier coefficients of the nth harmonic. Then

$$a_n = \int_0^{2\pi} f(x) \cos nx\,dx = \int_0^{\pi} f(x) \cos nx\,dx + \int_{\pi}^{2\pi} f(x) \cos nx\,dx \tag{43}$$

$$b_n = \int_0^{2\pi} f(x) \sin nx\,dx = \int_0^{\pi} f(x) \sin nx\,dx + \int_{\pi}^{2\pi} f(x) \sin nx\,dx \tag{44}$$

Now

$$\left.\begin{aligned} \cos [n(x + \pi)] &= \cos nx \cos n\pi - \sin nx \sin n\pi \\ &= \cos nx \qquad \text{(if } n \text{ is even)} \\ &= -\cos nx \qquad \text{(if } n \text{ is odd)} \end{aligned}\right\} \tag{45}$$

$$\left.\begin{aligned} \sin [n(x + \pi)] &= \sin nx \cos n\pi + \cos nx \sin n\pi \\ &= \sin nx \qquad \text{(if } n \text{ is even)} \\ &= -\sin nx \qquad \text{(if } n \text{ is odd)} \end{aligned}\right\} \tag{46}$$

Let us designate as case A

$$f(x + \pi) = -f(x) \tag{47}$$

and as case B

$$f(x + \pi) = +f(x) \tag{48}$$

Then

$$\left.\begin{aligned}\int_{\pi}^{2\pi} f(x)\cos nx\,dx &= \int_0^{\pi} f(x)\cos nx\,dx \quad \begin{matrix}(\text{case } A,\ n \text{ odd})\\(\text{case } B,\ n \text{ even})\end{matrix}\end{aligned}\right\} \tag{49}$$

$$\left.\begin{aligned}\int_{\pi}^{2\pi} f(x)\cos nx\,dx &= -\int_0^{\pi} f(x)\cos nx\,dx \quad \begin{matrix}(\text{case } A,\ n \text{ even})\\(\text{case } B,\ n \text{ odd})\end{matrix}\end{aligned}\right\} \tag{50}$$

Likewise,

$$\left.\begin{aligned}\int_{\pi}^{2\pi} f(x)\sin nx\,dx &= \int_0^{\pi} f(x)\sin nx\,dx \quad \begin{matrix}(\text{case } A,\ n \text{ odd})\\(\text{case } B,\ n \text{ even})\end{matrix}\end{aligned}\right\} \tag{51}$$

$$\left.\begin{aligned}\int_{\pi}^{2\pi} f(x)\sin nx\,dx &= -\int_0^{\pi} f(x)\sin nx\,dx \quad \begin{matrix}(\text{case } A,\ n \text{ even})\\(\text{case } B,\ n \text{ odd})\end{matrix}\end{aligned}\right\} \tag{52}$$

Therefore

$$\left.\begin{aligned}a_n &= \int_0^{2\pi} f(x)\cos nx\,dx = 2\int_0^{\pi} f(x)\cos nx\,dx\\ &\qquad\qquad\qquad\qquad (\text{case } A,\ n \text{ odd})\\ b_n &= \int_0^{2\pi} f(x)\sin nx\,dx = 2\int_0^{\pi} f(x)\sin nx\,dx\ (\text{case } B,\ n \text{ even})\end{aligned}\right\} \tag{53}$$

while

$$\left.\begin{aligned}a_n &= \int_0^{2\pi} f(x)\cos nx\,dx = 0 \qquad (\text{case } A,\ n \text{ even})\\ b_n &= \int_0^{2\pi} f(x)\sin nx\,dx = 0 \qquad (\text{case } B,\ n \text{ odd})\end{aligned}\right\} \tag{54}$$

We have thus proved that if $f(x + \pi) = -f(x)$, which is called case A, then $f(x)$ has only odd harmonics, since the coefficients of the even harmonics are zero. Likewise, if $f(x + \pi) = +f(x)$, which we call case B, then $f(x)$ has only even harmonics.

We can also separate a function very conveniently into parts consisting of its odd harmonics and its even harmonics, respectively, with the aid of an identity similar to Eq. (40), as follows:

$$f(x) \equiv \underbrace{\frac{f(x) + f(x + \pi)}{2}}_{\text{even harmonics}} + \underbrace{\frac{f(x) - f(x + \pi)}{2}}_{\text{odd harmonics}} \tag{55}$$

At this point we wish to introduce some definitions concerning symmetry properties.

Definitions: A function $f(x)$ is symmetrical about b if

$$f(b + x) = f(b - x) \tag{56}$$

Thus even functions are symmetrical about zero.

A function $f(x)$ is antisymmetrical about b if

$$f(b + x) = -f(b - x) \tag{57}$$

Thus odd functions are antisymmetrical about zero.

A periodic function $f(x)$ of period $2T$ is mirror-symmetrical if

$$f(x + T) = -f(x) \tag{58}$$

An examination of the symmetry properties of the sines and cosines of the harmonic frequencies shows that the cosines of the odd

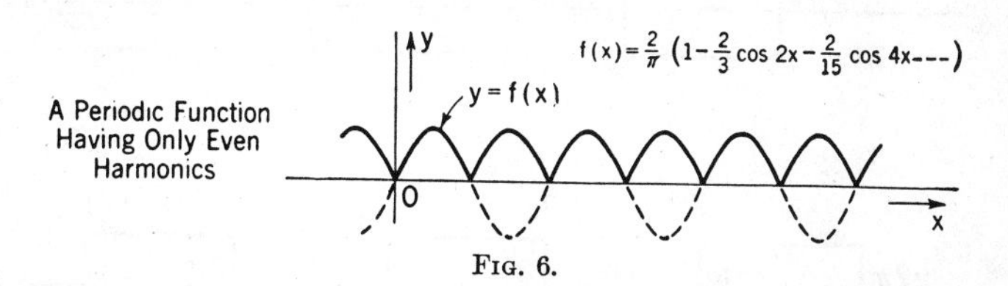

Fig. 6.

harmonics are antisymmetrical about $+\pi/2$, while the cosines of the even harmonics are symmetrical about $+\pi/2$. On the other hand, the sines of the odd harmonics are symmetrical about $+\pi/2$, while the sines of the even harmonics are antisymmetrical about $+\pi/2$. A consideration of these facts in conjunction with Fig. 9 allows us to draw the following conclusions:

1. A necessary and sufficient condition that a function have only even harmonics in its Fourier expansion is that the actual fundamental

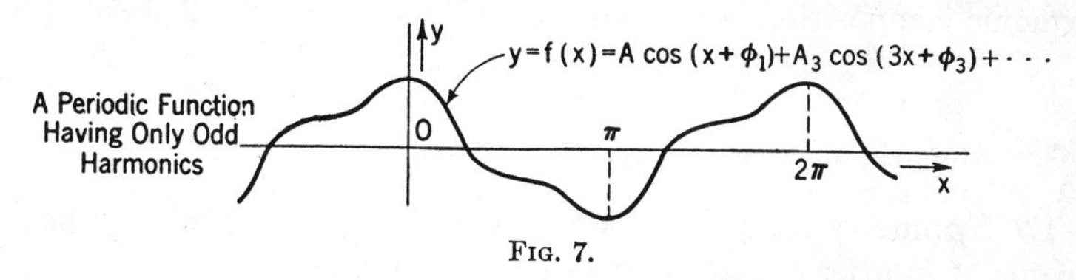

Fig. 7.

frequency of repetition be twice the fundamental used for formal Fourier expansion. As an example, the rectified current of a full-wave rectifier shown in Fig. 6 has a repetition frequency twice as high as that of the sine wave from which it was derived and therefore has only even harmonics in its Fourier expansion.

2. A necessary and sufficient condition that a function have only odd harmonics in its Fourier expansion is that it be mirror-symmetrical. An example of such a function is the output of a push-pull amplifier

shown in Fig. 7, which consequently has only odd harmonics in its Fourier expansion.

3. While the oddness or evenness of a periodic function may change with a shift of the origin, the absence of particular harmonics is unchanged by such a shift.[1] Every radio engineer will realize that this agrees with his experience, for harmonics have a real existence quite independent of any choice of origin. A function that is changed

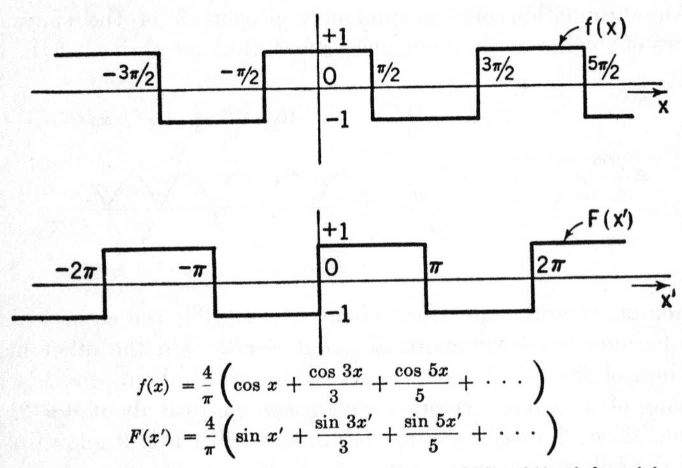

$$f(x) = \frac{4}{\pi}\left(\cos x + \frac{\cos 3x}{3} + \frac{\cos 5x}{5} + \cdots\right)$$

$$F(x') = \frac{4}{\pi}\left(\sin x' + \frac{\sin 3x'}{3} + \frac{\sin 5x'}{5} + \cdots\right)$$

FIG. 8. A function which changes from even to odd by shift of the origin.

from even to odd by a shift of origin is shown in Fig. 8. Note that the harmonic composition is unchanged. (See also Exercise 2 of Sec. 1.9.)

Exercise

Give a formal proof of the above items 1, 2, and 3.

1.7 Symmetry Analysis of a Function. Any function $f(x)$ that is capable of Fourier expansion may be expressed as

$$\begin{aligned} f(x) = \frac{a_0}{2} &+ a_1 \cos x + a_2 \cos 2x + \cdots \\ &+ b_1 \sin x + b_2 \sin 2x + \cdots \end{aligned} \tag{59}$$

[1] It is only in exceptional cases that an odd function can be made an even function, and vice versa, by a shift in origin as shown in Fig. 8. A general type of odd function as shown in Fig. 9*m* cannot be made even by a shift in origin, nor can a general type of even function as shown in Fig. 9*i* be made odd (see Exercises 1 and 2 of Sec. 1.7).

We have already shown that such a function consists of an even part

$$f_1(x) = \frac{a_0}{2} + a_1 \cos x + a_2 \cos 2x + \cdots \tag{60}$$

and an odd part

$$f_2(x) = b_1 \sin x + b_2 \sin 2x + \cdots \tag{61}$$

In order to evaluate the a and b coefficients it is necessary to carry through an integration process. This may be difficult if the original function is not expressed in a convenient analytical form. However, $f_1(x)$ and $f_2(x)$ can easily be obtained from the original function by graphical means without any integration operation. This is done with the aid of Eq. (40). Thus

$$f_1(x) = \frac{f(x) + f(-x)}{2} \tag{62}$$

$$f_2(x) = \frac{f(x) - f(-x)}{2} \tag{63}$$

Equations (62) and (63) make it possible to plot $f_1(x)$ and $f_2(x)$ from the curves of $f(x)$ and $f(-x)$ by the mere addition and subtraction of ordinates.

It is possible to continue the separation of a function into its parts having various types of symmetry by using either the Fourier series expansions or functional equations similar to Eqs. (62) and (63). The latter are especially suitable for graphical analysis. The forms and properties of various symmetrical parts are tabulated in Fig. 9 and are there illustrated for the case of a general type of function, *i.e.*, one not having any special symmetry. In the figure are shown both the functional forms of the various symmetrical components and also their series expansions. These formulas hold for all functions and are therefore useful for reference purposes.

Exercises

1. Show that an odd function having only odd harmonics can be made an even function by shifting the origin by an amount $\pi/2$.

2. Show that an even function having only odd harmonics can be made an odd function by shifting the origin by an amount $\pi/2$.

1.8 Change of the Interval of Expansion. So far we have restricted our Fourier expansions to functions defined in the interval from $-\pi$ to $+\pi$ or from zero to 2π. We can very easily transform these expansions, however, for functions defined in the interval from $-T/2$ to

$$f(x) = (a) = (e) = (c) + (d) = (g) + (h) = (k) + (1) + (p) + (q)$$

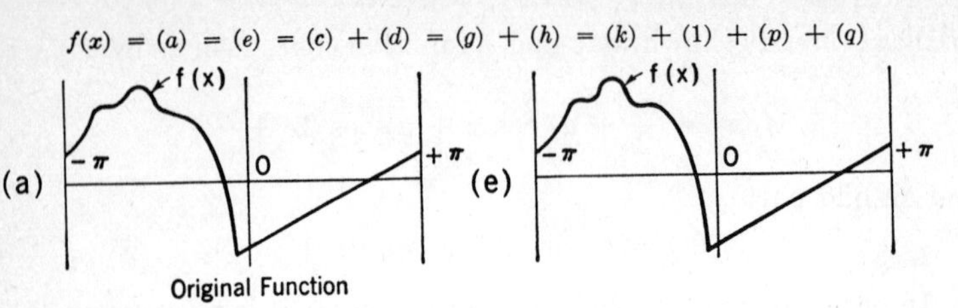

$$\text{Original function} \equiv f(x) = \frac{a_0}{2} + \sum_{n=1}^{\infty} (a_n \cos nx + b_n \sin nx)$$

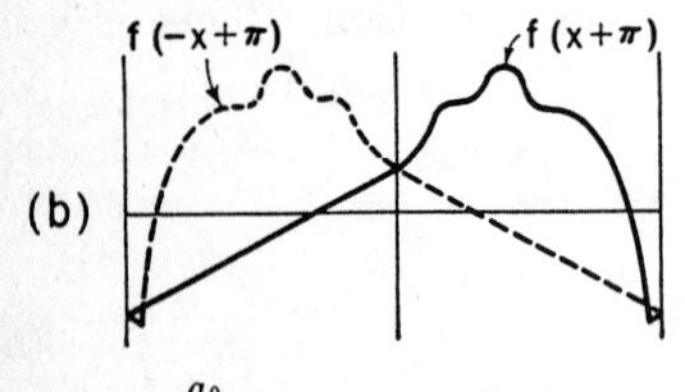

$$f(x + \pi) = \frac{a_0}{2} - a_1 \cos x - b_1 \sin x + a_2 \cos 2x + b_2 \sin 2x + \cdots$$

$$f(-x + \pi) = \frac{a_0}{2} - a_1 \cos x + b_1 \sin x + a_2 \cos 2x - b_2 \sin 2x + \cdots$$

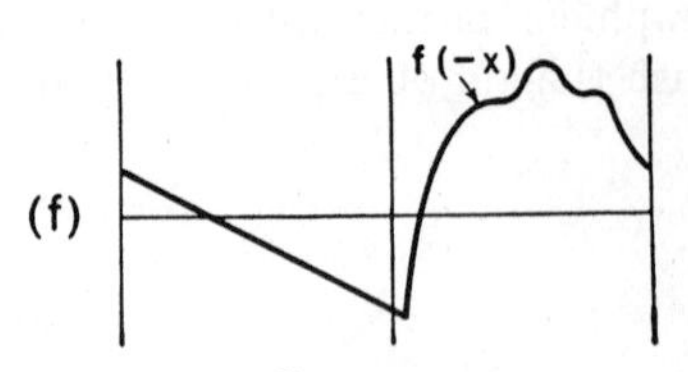

$$f(-x) = \frac{a_0}{2} + \sum_{n=1}^{\infty} (a_n \cos nx - b_n \sin nx)$$

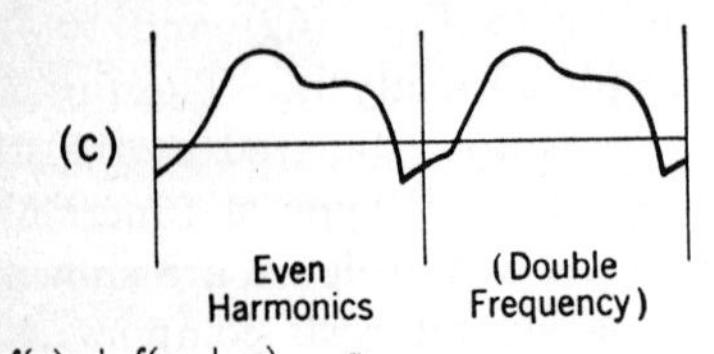

$$\frac{f(x) + f(x + \pi)}{2} = \frac{a_0}{2} + a_2 \cos 2x + b_2 \sin 2x + \cdots$$

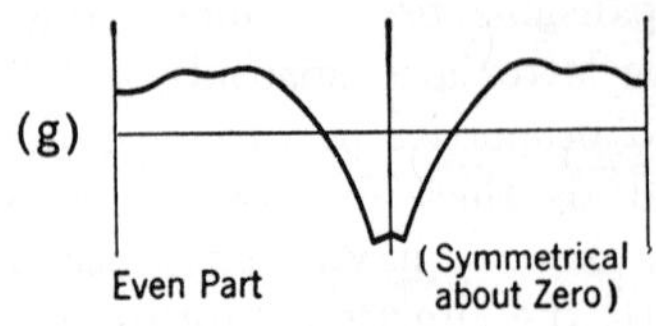

$$\frac{f(x) + f(-x)}{2} = \frac{a_0}{2} + a_1 \cos x + a_2 \cos 2x + \cdots$$

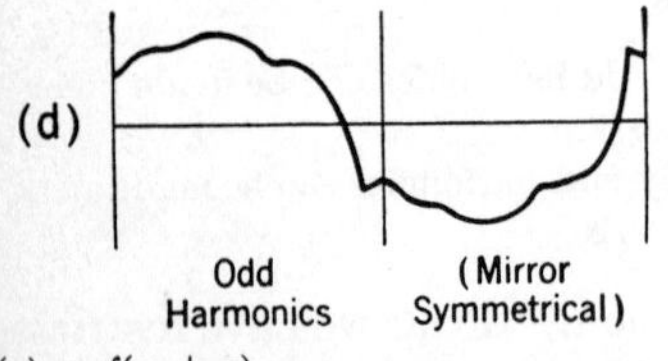

$$\frac{f(x) - f(x + \pi)}{2} = a_1 \cos x + b_1 \sin x + a_3 \cos 3x + b_3 \sin 3x + \cdots$$

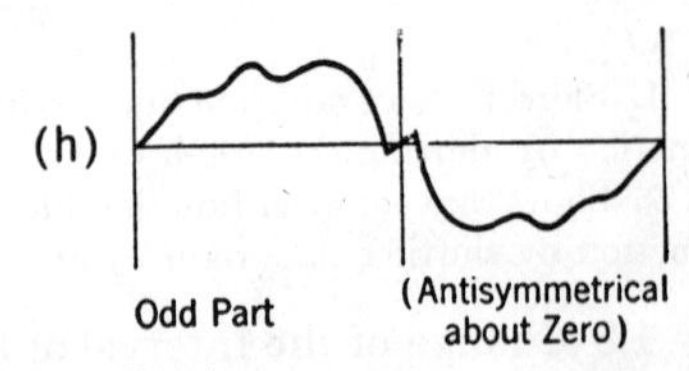

$$\frac{f(x) - f(-x)}{2} = b_1 \sin x + b_2 \sin 2x + b_3 \sin 3x + \cdots$$

FIG. 9. Symmetry analysis of a function.

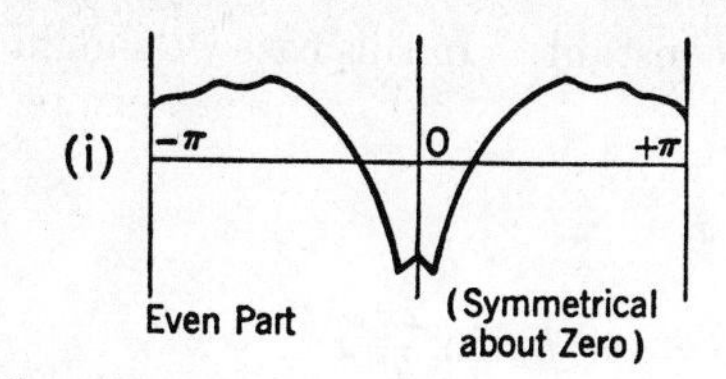

$$\frac{f(x) + f(-x)}{2} = \frac{a_0}{2} + a_1 \cos x + a_2 \cos 2x + \cdots$$

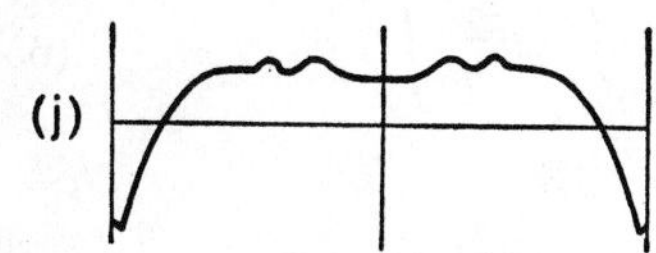

$$\frac{f(x+\pi) + f(-x+\pi)}{2} = \frac{a_0}{2} - a_1 \cos x + a_2 \cos 2x - a_3 \cos 3x + \cdots$$

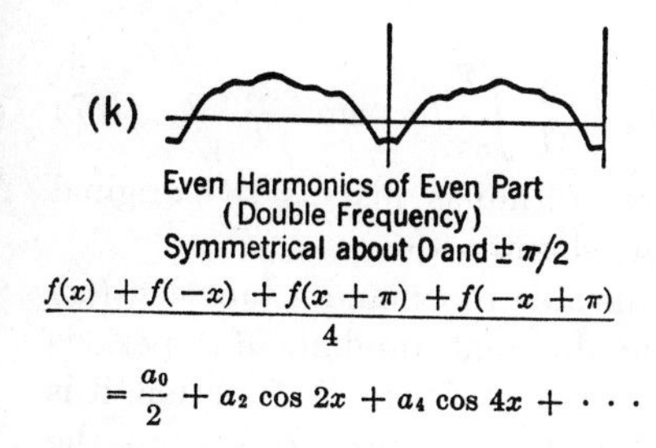

$$\frac{f(x) + f(-x) + f(x+\pi) + f(-x+\pi)}{4} = \frac{a_0}{2} + a_2 \cos 2x + a_4 \cos 4x + \cdots$$

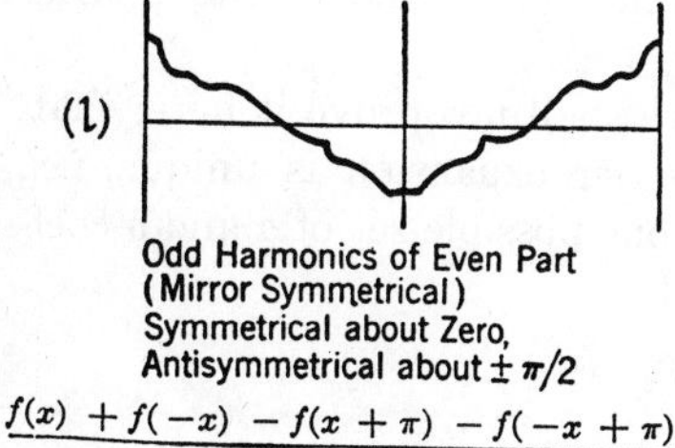

$$\frac{f(x) + f(-x) - f(x+\pi) - f(-x+\pi)}{4} = a_1 \cos x + a_3 \cos 3x + \cdots$$

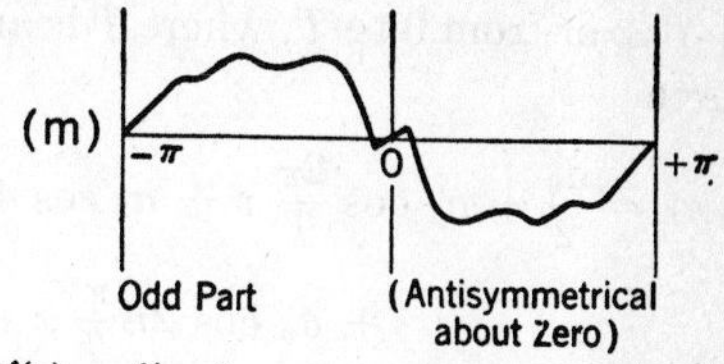

$$\frac{f(x) - f(-x)}{2} = b_1 \sin x + b_2 \sin 2x + b_3 \sin 3x + \cdots$$

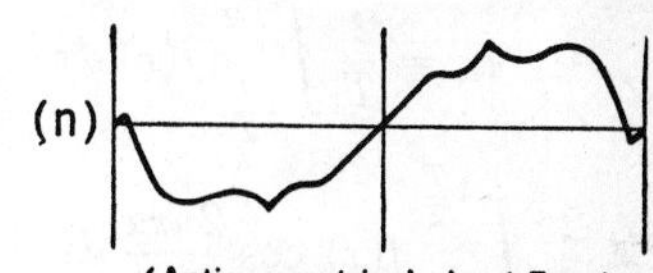

$$\frac{f(x+\pi) - f(-x+\pi)}{2} = -b_1 \sin x + b_2 \sin 2x + b_3 \sin 3x + \cdots$$

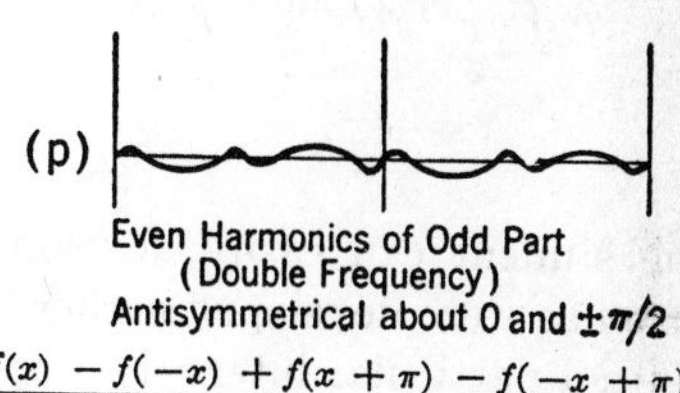

$$\frac{f(x) - f(-x) + f(x+\pi) - f(-x+\pi)}{4} = b_2 \sin 2x + b_4 \sin 4x + \cdots$$

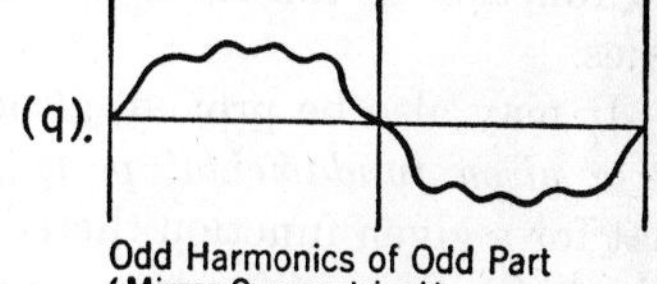

$$\frac{f(x) - f(-x) - f(x+\pi) + f(-x+\pi)}{4} = b_1 \sin x + b_3 \sin 3x + \cdots$$

FIG. 9. (*Contined*).

$+T/2$ or from 0 to T, where T is any constant. In this case we should have

$$f(x) = \frac{a_0}{2} + a_1 \cos \frac{2\pi}{T} x + a_2 \cos 4 \frac{\pi}{T} x + \cdots + a_n \cos 2n \frac{\pi}{T} x + \cdots + b_1 \sin \frac{2\pi}{T} x + b_2 \sin 4 \frac{\pi}{T} x + \cdots + b_n \sin 2n \frac{\pi}{T} x + \cdots \quad (64)$$

where

$$a_0 = \frac{2}{T} \int_{-\frac{T}{2}}^{+\frac{T}{2}} f(x)\, dx \quad \text{or} \quad a_0 = \frac{2}{T} \int_0^T f(x)\, dx \quad (65)$$

$$a_n = \frac{2}{T} \int_{-\frac{T}{2}}^{+\frac{T}{2}} f(x) \cos \frac{2n\pi x}{T}\, dx \quad \text{or} \quad a_n = \frac{2}{T} \int_0^T f(x) \cos \frac{2n\pi x}{T}\, dx \quad (66)$$

$$b_n = \frac{2}{T} \int_{-\frac{T}{2}}^{+\frac{T}{2}} f(x) \sin \frac{2n\pi x}{T}\, dx \quad \text{or} \quad b_n = \frac{2}{T} \int_0^T f(x) \sin \frac{2n\pi x}{T}\, dx \quad (67)$$

The student can easily develop these formulas just as the original formulas were developed earlier in the chapter.

In a particular interval we are thus able to expand a function $f(x)$ into different Fourier series, having different fundamental periods (see exercise below). However, in the case of a periodic function, it is of course only possible to use the same Fourier series to express the value of the function over the whole range, provided that the period of the function is the same as the fundamental period of the Fourier series.

It may also be proved, although we shall not prove it here, that, *for a given fundamental period*, a Fourier expansion is unique, *i.e.*, that for a given function there is only one possible set of a and b coefficients for a given fundamental period.

Exercise

Expand the saw-tooth function

$$f(x) = x \qquad \text{(from } -\pi \text{ to } +\pi\text{)}$$

into a Fourier series.

Answer:

$$f(x) = 2(\sin x - \tfrac{1}{2}\sin 2x + \tfrac{1}{3}\sin 3x - \tfrac{1}{4}\sin 4x + \cdots)$$

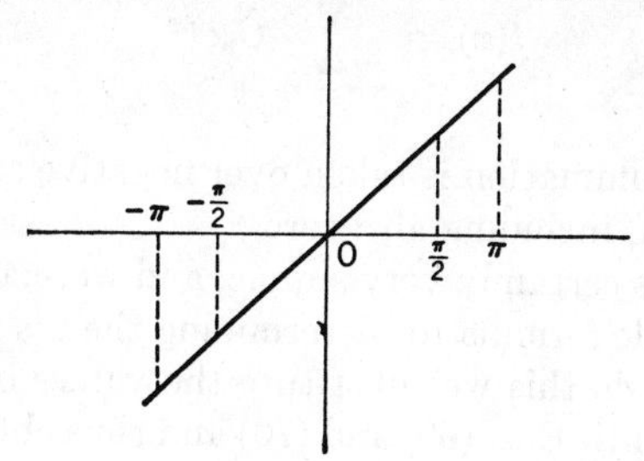

If $-\pi/2$ to $+\pi/2$ is used as the fundamental period of expansion, the Fourier series will be

$$f(x) = \sin 2x - \frac{1}{2}\sin 4x + \frac{1}{3}\sin 6x + \cdots + (-1)^{n-1}\frac{1}{n}\sin 2nx + \cdots$$

In the range from $-\pi/2$ to $+\pi/2$ there are thus two Fourier expansions. The latter expansion, however, does not hold outside the range $-\pi/2 < x < +\pi/2$.

1.9. Complex Form of Fourier Series. The Fourier expansion (1) or (1*a*) and its auxiliary formulas (6), (12), and (13) can be put into much simpler and more elegant form with the use of complex exponentials. In order to do this, we shall first express the general term of Eq. (1), namely,

$$a_n \cos nx + b_n \sin nx$$

in complex exponential form, using the exponential expressions for the cosine and sine.[1] Accordingly,

$$a_n \cos nx + b_n \sin nx = a_n \frac{\epsilon^{jnx} + \epsilon^{-jnx}}{2} + b_n \frac{\epsilon^{jnx} - \epsilon^{-jnx}}{2j}$$

$$= \frac{a_n - jb_n}{2}\epsilon^{jnx} + \frac{a_n + jb_n}{2}\epsilon^{-jnx} \tag{68}$$

Consequently, if we write

$$C_n = \frac{a_n - jb_n}{2} \tag{69}$$

$$C_{-n} = \frac{a_n + jb_n}{2} \tag{70}$$

and

$$C_0 = \frac{a_0}{2} \tag{71}$$

[1] These expressions follow from the Euler identity

$$\epsilon^{j\theta} = \cos\theta + j\sin\theta$$

Eq. (1*a*) becomes

$$f(x) = \sum_{n=-\infty}^{n=+\infty} C_n \epsilon^{jnx} \tag{72}$$

We note that the summation is taken over negative as well as positive integral values of n, including also zero.

The form (72) is certainly very simple, and we shall now show that there is also a simple formula for determining the C's from the original function $f(x)$. To do this we substitute the values of a_n and b_n from Eqs. (12) and (13) into Eqs. (69) and (70) and thus obtain

$$\begin{aligned} C_n &= \frac{a_n - jb_n}{2} = \frac{1}{2\pi} \int_{-\pi}^{+\pi} f(x)(\cos nx - j \sin nx)\, dx \\ &= \frac{1}{2\pi} \int_{-\pi}^{+\pi} f(x) \epsilon^{-jnx}\, dx \end{aligned} \tag{73}$$

$$\begin{aligned} C_{-n} &= \frac{a_n + jb_n}{2} = \frac{1}{2\pi} \int_{-\pi}^{+\pi} f(x)(\cos nx + j \sin nx)\, dx \\ &= \frac{1}{2\pi} \int_{-\pi}^{+\pi} f(x) \epsilon^{jnx}\, dx \end{aligned} \tag{74}$$

Furthermore, from Eqs. (6) and (71),

$$C_0 = \frac{a_0}{2} = \frac{1}{2\pi} \int_{-\pi}^{+\pi} f(x)\, dx \tag{75}$$

If we let n take on all positive and negative integral values, including zero, then the three formulas (73), (74), and (75) are all of the same form, namely,

$$C_n = \frac{1}{2\pi} \int_{-\pi}^{+\pi} f(x) \epsilon^{-jnx}\, dx \tag{76}$$

Equations (72) and (76) are thus the only two formulas necessary for the expression of a Fourier expansion in complex form. Compared with them, the usual trigonometric expressions (1), (6), (12), and (13) seem clumsy indeed.

The simplicity of the expression (72) arises from the fact that each harmonic component is expressed in it as the sum of two conjugate[1]

[1] If $z = a + jb$ is a complex quantity, then $a - jb$ is called its complex conjugate quantity and is written as z^* (or $\bar{z}$). The following formulas involving

complex quantities, *i.e.*,

$$C_n\epsilon^{jnx} + C_{-n}\epsilon^{-jnx} = \frac{a_n - jb_n}{2}\epsilon^{jnx} + \frac{a_n + jb_n}{2}\epsilon^{-jnx}$$
$$= a_n \cos nx + b_n \sin nx \tag{77}$$

The sum of these conjugate complex quantities is real, but the complex form allows the information concerning the harmonic phase angles to be contained in it without the necessity of expressing it explicitly.

If the interval of expansion is changed from $-\pi$ to $+\pi$ to a new interval 0 to T, as is done in Sec. 1.8, then formulas (72) and (76) become

$$f(x) = \sum_{n=-\infty}^{n=+\infty} C_n\epsilon^{j\frac{2\pi nx}{T}} \tag{78}$$

$$C_n = \frac{1}{T}\int_0^T f(x)\epsilon^{-j\frac{2\pi nx}{T}}\,dx \tag{79}$$

The complex form of the Fourier expansion is often preferable to the trigonometric form in practical as well as in theoretical work, especially in problems involving differentiation and integration. To illustrate the complex form we shall now work some examples.

Exercises

1. Write the formulas corresponding to Eq. (78) and (79) for the interval T_1 to T_2 instead of 0 to T.

2. Show that if the origin is shifted in the positive direction by an amount x_1, the magnitude of each C_n in the complex Fourier expansion of any function is unchanged, but its phase is decreased by an amount $2\pi nx_1/T$. This is a generalization of conclusion (3) of Sec. 1.6.

1.10 Examples. *a. Square Wave.* In order to compare the use of the complex form of Fourier series with the trigonometric form, let us solve the example already worked out in Sec. 1.3*a*, but this time by

---

complex conjugates may be found useful in solving problems in various parts of the book.

(1) $z \cdot z^* = a^2 + b^2$
(2) $z + z^* = 2a$
(3) $z - z^* = j2b$
(4) $z_1^* + z_2^* = (z_1 + z_2)^*$
(5) $z_1^* \cdot z_2^* = (z_1 \cdot z_2)^*$
(6) $\dfrac{z_1^*}{z_2^*} = \left(\dfrac{z_1}{z_2}\right)^*$
(7) $(z^*)^* = z$
(8) $(z^*)^n = (z^n)^*$
(9) $\dfrac{1}{z^*} = \left(\dfrac{1}{z}\right)^*$
(10) If z is a real quantity, then $z^* = z$
(11) If z is a pure imaginary, then $z^* = -z$
(12) $(R\epsilon^{j\phi})^* = R\epsilon^{-j\phi}$ where R and ϕ are real

using the complex form. In this case (see Fig. 2), the function is

$$f(x) = +1 \qquad \text{(from } -\pi \text{ to } 0)$$
$$f(x) = -1 \qquad \text{(from } 0 \text{ to } \pi)$$

Substituting these values into (76), we get

$$\begin{aligned} C_n &= \frac{1}{2\pi}\int_{-\pi}^{+\pi} f(x)\epsilon^{-jnx}\,dx \\ &= \frac{1}{2\pi}\int_{-\pi}^{0} \epsilon^{-jnx}\,dx - \frac{1}{2\pi}\int_{0}^{\pi} \epsilon^{-jnx}\,dx \\ &= \frac{-1}{2\pi jn}\,\epsilon^{-jnx}\Big|_{-\pi}^{0} + \frac{1}{2\pi jn}\,\epsilon^{-jnx}\Big|_{0}^{\pi} \\ &= \frac{-1}{2\pi jn}(1 - \epsilon^{jn\pi}) + \frac{1}{2\pi jn}(\epsilon^{-jn\pi} - 1) \\ &= \frac{-1}{2\pi jn}(2 - \epsilon^{jn\pi} - \epsilon^{-jn\pi}) \end{aligned} \tag{80}$$

From Eq. (80) it follows that if n is an even integer or zero[1]

$$C_n = 0 \tag{81}$$

since in that case

$$\epsilon^{jn\pi} = \epsilon^{-jn\pi} = 1 \tag{82}$$

On the other hand, if n is an odd integer,

$$\epsilon^{jn\pi} = \epsilon^{-jn\pi} = -1 \tag{83}$$

so that

$$C_n = \frac{-4}{2\pi jn} = \frac{-2}{j\pi n} \tag{84}$$

Substituting Eqs. (81) and (84) into Eq. (72), we get

$$f(x) = -\frac{2}{\pi}\left(\frac{\epsilon^{jx} - \epsilon^{-jx}}{j}\right) - \frac{2}{3\pi}\left(\frac{\epsilon^{j3x} - \epsilon^{-j3x}}{j}\right) - \frac{2}{5\pi}\left(\frac{\epsilon^{j5x} - \epsilon^{-j5x}}{j}\right) - \cdots \tag{85}$$

$$= \frac{-4}{\pi}\left(\sin x + \frac{\sin 3x}{3} + \frac{\sin 5x}{5} + \cdots\right) \tag{86}$$

Equation (86) is the same as Eq. (21) so that the results obtained are the same in either case. The actual manipulation when the com-

[1] The general answer at the right of Eq. (80) becomes indeterminate when $n = 0$. However, in this case we refer back to the original integral and get

$$C_0 = \frac{1}{2\pi}\int_{-\pi}^{+\pi} f(x)\,dx = \frac{1}{2\pi}\int_{-\pi}^{0} dx + \frac{1}{2\pi}\int_{0}^{\pi} (-1)\,dx = 0$$

plex form is used is somewhat simpler since sines and cosines need not be handled separately. Furthermore, the complex form (85) is frequently more convenient for practical use than the trigonometric form (86) in the solution of problems.

b. Pulses of Arbitrary Length. As another example, let us find the Fourier composition of a series of pulses of arbitrary length. Such a series of pulses is shown in Fig. 10*a*. These pulses have a length $t_2 - t_1$ and are repeated at intervals of length T.

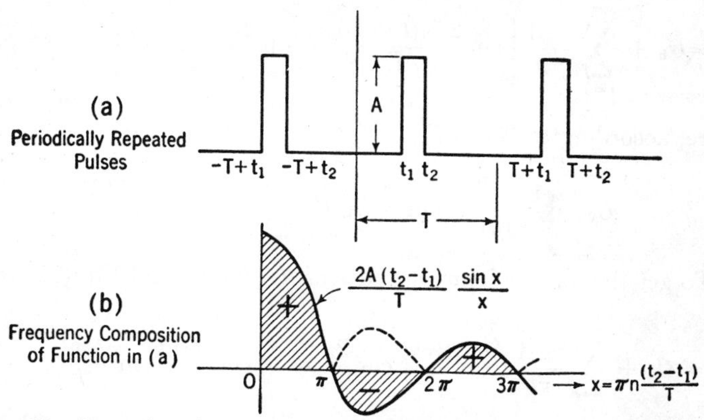

FIG. 10. Properties of periodically repeated narrow pulses. (If $T \gg (t_2 - t_1)$, then for each integral value of n, the function in Fig. 10*a* has a Fourier component whose amplitude is given by the curve in Fig. 10*b*.)

To find the Fourier composition of this series of pulses we use Eqs. (78) and (79). We shall change the variable from x to t, since the independent variable is usually time when this problem is met in practice.

Thus

$$f(t) = A \qquad \text{(from } t_1 \text{ to } t_2\text{)}$$

and

$$f(t) = 0$$

elsewhere in the interval from 0 to T.

Substituting these values into Eq. (79), we obtain

$$\begin{aligned} C_n &= \frac{1}{T}\int_0^T f(t)\epsilon^{-j\frac{2\pi nt}{T}}\,dt \\ &= \frac{A}{T}\int_{t_1}^{t_2} \epsilon^{-j\frac{2\pi nt}{T}}\,dt = \frac{A}{T}\frac{-T}{j2\pi n}\,\epsilon^{-j\frac{2\pi nt}{T}}\Bigg|_{t_1}^{t_2} \\ &= \frac{-A}{j2\pi n}\left(\epsilon^{-j\frac{2\pi nt_2}{T}} - \epsilon^{-j\frac{2\pi nt_1}{T}}\right) \end{aligned} \tag{87}$$

Therefore, the Fourier expansion is

$$f(t) = \sum_{n=-\infty}^{+\infty} \frac{-A}{j2\pi n} \left(\epsilon^{-j\frac{2\pi n t_2}{T}} - \epsilon^{-j\frac{2\pi n t_1}{T}}\right) \epsilon^{j\frac{2\pi n t}{T}} \tag{88}$$

$$= C_0 + \sum_{n=1}^{\infty} \frac{-A}{j2\pi n} \left[\epsilon^{j\frac{2\pi n(t-t_2)}{T}} - \epsilon^{j\frac{2\pi n(t-t_1)}{T}} - \epsilon^{-j\frac{2\pi n(t-t_2)}{T}} + \epsilon^{-j\frac{2\pi n(t-t_1)}{T}}\right]$$

$$= C_0 + \sum_{n=1}^{\infty} \frac{-A}{\pi n} \left[\sin \frac{2\pi n(t - t_2)}{T} - \sin \frac{2\pi n(t - t_1)}{T}\right] \tag{89}$$

where, according to Eq. (87),

$$C_0 = \frac{1}{T} \int_0^T f(t)\, dt = \frac{1}{T} \int_{t_1}^{t_2} A\, dt = \frac{A(t_2 - t_1)}{T} \tag{90}$$

To get the harmonic magnitudes of $f(t)$ we expand Eq. (89) to get

$$f(t) = C_0 + \sum_{n=1}^{\infty} \frac{-A}{\pi n} \left(\sin \frac{2\pi nt}{T} \cos \frac{2\pi nt_2}{T} - \cos \frac{2\pi nt}{T} \sin \frac{2\pi nt_2}{T}\right.$$
$$\left. - \sin \frac{2\pi nt}{T} \cos \frac{2\pi nt_1}{T} + \cos \frac{2\pi nt}{T} \sin \frac{2\pi nt_1}{T}\right)$$

$$= C_0 + \sum_{1}^{\infty} \frac{-A}{\pi n} \left[\left(\cos \frac{2\pi nt_2}{T} - \cos \frac{2\pi nt_1}{T}\right) \sin \frac{2\pi nt}{T}\right.$$
$$\left. - \left(\sin \frac{2\pi nt_2}{T} - \sin \frac{2\pi nt_1}{T}\right) \cos \frac{2\pi nt}{T}\right]$$

$$= C_0 + \sum_{1}^{\infty} \frac{-A}{\pi n} \left\{-2 \sin \left[\frac{\pi n}{T} (t_2 + t_1)\right] \sin \left[\frac{\pi n}{T}(t_2 - t_1)\right] \sin \frac{2\pi nt}{T}\right.$$
$$\left. - 2 \sin \left[\frac{\pi n}{T} (t_2 - t_1)\right] \cos \left[\frac{\pi n}{T} (t_2 + t_1)\right] \cos \frac{2\pi nt}{T}\right\}$$

$$= C_0 + \sum_{1}^{\infty} \frac{2A}{\pi n} \left\{\sin \left[\frac{\pi n}{T} (t_2 - t_1)\right] \cos \left(\frac{2\pi nt}{T} - \phi_n\right)\right\} \tag{91}$$

where

$$\phi_n = \frac{2\pi n}{T} \frac{t_2 + t_1}{2} \tag{92}$$

When $t_1 = -T/2$ and $t_2 = 0$, Eq. (91) reduces to

$$f(t) = \frac{A}{2} + \sum_{1}^{\infty} \frac{2A}{\pi n} \sin \frac{\pi n}{2} \cos \left(\frac{2\pi n t}{T} - \pi n \right)$$

$$= \frac{A}{2} - \sum_{m=1}^{\infty} \frac{2A}{\pi m} \sin \frac{2\pi m t}{T} \tag{93}$$

where m takes on only odd values. This result agrees with Eqs. (21) and (86), the direct-current component being, of course, different by $A/2$ and the value of A in Eq. (93) being equivalent to 2 in Eq. (86).

According to Eq. (91) the magnitude of the nth harmonic is the absolute value of

$$\frac{2A}{\pi n} \sin \frac{\pi n}{T} (t_2 - t_1) \tag{94}$$

A case of particular interest occurs when the repetition period T is much greater than the pulse length $t_2 - t_1$. A diagram showing the frequency distribution of harmonic magnitudes in this case is shown in Fig. 10*b*, where the magnitude given by the expression (94) is plotted as a function of n. The regions marked (−) in the diagram just indicate a 180-deg phase change; but as far as magnitudes are concerned, these portions of the curve may be replaced by the dotted line.

The distribution shows a principal maximum at zero frequency and subsidiary maxima when

$$n = \frac{1}{\pi} \frac{T}{t_2 - t_1} \tan \pi n \frac{t_2 - t_1}{T} \tag{95}$$ [1]

Minima, of zero amplitude, occur when

$$n = \text{a multiple of } \frac{T}{t_2 - t_1} \tag{96}$$

Exercises

1. Find the Fourier expansion of the pulse shown in the figure below, and discuss its properties.

[1] The function $\sin x/x$ has amplitude maxima when $x = \tan x$. This can readily be shown by differentiation.

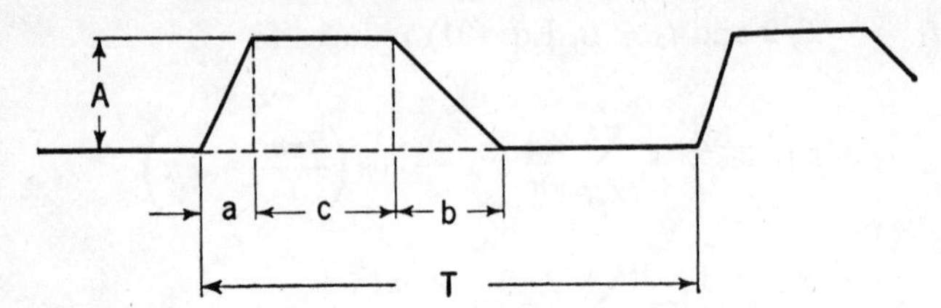

2. In Fig. 10a, move the y axis to the center of one of the pulses so that $t_1 = -t_2$. This makes the series of pulses an even function. Derive the Fourier expansion of this function, and note how simply the expansion is obtained. In practice, it is generally desirable whenever possible to locate the y axis so that the function is either even or odd in order to simplify the Fourier expansion.

1.11 Average Value of the Product of Two Functions Expressed in Terms of Their Fourier Constants. Let $f(x)$ and $g(x)$ be two functions expressible in Fourier series in the interval from 0 to 2π as

$$f(x) = \frac{a_0}{2} + \sum_{n=1}^{\infty} (a_n \cos nx + b_n \sin nx) \tag{97}$$

and

$$g(x) = \frac{A_0}{2} + \sum_{n=1}^{\infty} (A_n \cos nx + B_n \sin nx) \tag{98}$$

Then the average value of the product of the two functions in the interval from 0 to 2π is

$$\frac{1}{2\pi} \int_0^{2\pi} f(x)g(x)\, dx = \frac{a_0 A_0}{4} + \frac{1}{2} \sum_{n=1}^{\infty} (a_n A_n + b_n B_n) \tag{99}$$

That Eq. (99) is the expected answer can readily be seen by substituting Eqs. (97) and (98) into the integral in Eq. (99) and integrating term by term. We then have integrals of the forms

$$\int_0^{2\pi} a_p B_q \cos px \sin qx\, dx$$

$$\int_0^{2\pi} a_p A_q \cos px \cos qx\, dx$$

$$\int_0^{2\pi} b_p B_q \sin px \sin qx\, dx$$

$$\int_0^{2\pi} A a_{0n} \cos nx\, dx$$

and

$$\int_0^{2\pi} a_0 B_n \sin nx\, dx$$

These all vanish except

$$\int_0^{2\pi} a_n A_n \cos^2 nx\, dx = \pi a_n A_n \tag{100}$$

and

$$\int_0^{2\pi} b_n B_n \sin^2 nx\, dx = \pi b_n B_n \tag{101}$$

The foregoing indicates the truth of Eq. (99). A complete proof would require a demonstration of the convergence and integrability of the product series. Such a proof may be found in Carslaw's text, to which reference has previously been made.[1] We shall accordingly assume the truth of Eq. (99). The student can easily show that the equivalent of Eq. (99) in complex form is

$$\frac{1}{2\pi}\int_0^{2\pi} f(x)g(x)\, dx = \sum_{n=-\infty}^{+\infty} c_n C_{-n} \tag{102}$$

where

$$c_n = \frac{a_n - jb_n}{2} \quad \text{and} \quad C_n = \frac{A_n - jB_n}{2}$$

$$c_{-n} = \frac{a_n + jb_n}{2} \quad \text{and} \quad C_{-n} = \frac{A_n + jB_n}{2}$$

As a corollary to Eqs. (99) and (102) we have

$$\frac{1}{2\pi}\int_0^{2\pi} [f(x)]^2\, dx = \frac{a_0^2}{4} + \frac{1}{2}\sum_{n=1}^{\infty} (a_n^2 + b_n^2) \tag{103}$$

or

$$\frac{1}{2\pi}\int_0^{2\pi} [f(x)]^2\, dx = \sum_{n=-\infty}^{+\infty} c_n c_{-n} \tag{104}$$

The foregoing theorems will be of value when we discuss effective values of currents and power consumption in the next chapter.

Exercise

Prove that, for a given fundamental period, the coefficients of a Fourier expansion are unique.

1.12 Convergence of Fourier Series—Differentiation and Integration.[2] In all problems of interest in radio the Fourier series arising by

[1] CARSLAW, H. S., "Theory of Fourier Series and Integrals."

[2] Chapter X of Guillemin's "Communication Networks," Vol. I, contains additional information concerning Fourier series, especially regarding summation formulas. The author is indebted to Guillemin's book for valuable material used in the present chapter.

expansion of a function can be depended upon to converge. However, not all, by any means, converge with the same rapidity. Thus Eq. (21) converges as $1/n$, while Eq. (29) converges as $1/n^2$. In the study of infinite series it is found that a series must vary with n to a higher power than the first in $1/n$ in order to ensure absolute convergence. On this basis, the convergence of the series (21) is not ensured by the coefficients but depends on the properties of the sine factors as well. This difference between series in the rapidity of convergence has an important bearing on their differentiability.

Since there are well-known formulas both for differentiating and integrating $\cos nx$, $\sin nx$, and ϵ^{jnx}, it is always possible to perform formally both differentiation and integration of any Fourier series. However, differentiation of $\cos nx$, $\sin nx$, or ϵ^{jnx} with respect to x will introduce a factor of n multiplying the corresponding term and will thereby decrease the rapidity of convergence. In an analogous manner, integration will make the convergence more rapid. Consequently, the series of derivatives of the Fourier terms will not necessarily converge. On the other hand, the series of integrals of the Fourier terms will always converge to the value of the integral of the function from which the series was derived.

The foregoing does not mean that Fourier series cannot be differentiated, but rather that when they are differentiated the question of convergence should be investigated.

Exercise

Differentiate the series (29), and compare the result with Eq. (21). Is this result to be expected from a comparison of Figs. 4 and 2?

1.13 Harmonic Analysis—Gibbs's Phenomenon. Following the terminology used in music, all terms of the form $A_n \cos (nx + \phi_n)$ are so-called "harmonics" of $A_1 \cos (x + \phi_1)$, the latter being called the fundamental term. The frequencies of the terms are likewise called the harmonic and fundamental frequencies, respectively.

It is often an important technical problem to ascertain the harmonic composition of a given function of interest, say a voltage or current wave form. If the wave form is periodic and is given or can be translated into electrical form, its composition can be determined with the aid of electrical apparatus[1] containing tuned circuit filters of variable frequency. This apparatus gives the amplitude and frequency of the Fourier components. It does not give the phase, but this is often not important.

[1] Such as the wave analyzer manufactured by the General Radio Company.

A numerical method of determining approximate values of the early Fourier coefficients in the analysis of a curve is also available and may be found described elsewhere.[1]

Furthermore, there are several types of mechanical machines available, called harmonic analyzers. These machines[2] give both amplitude

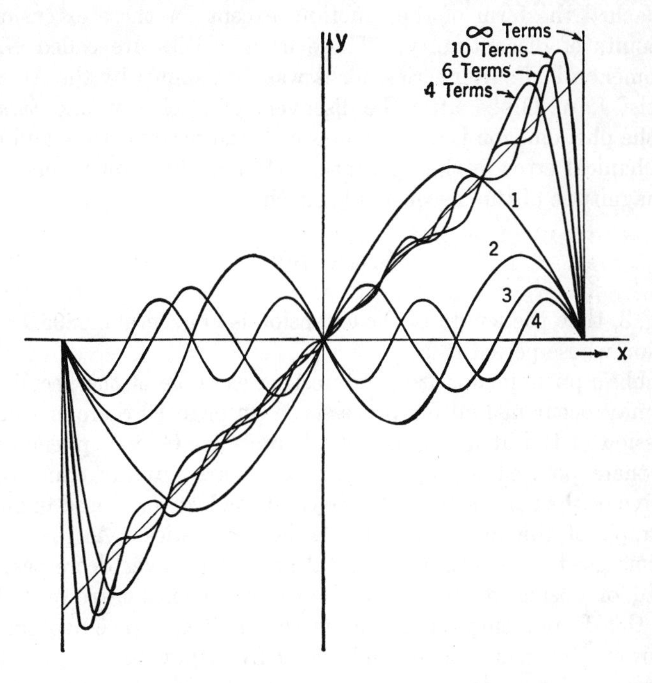

$$y = x = 2\left(\sin x - \frac{\sin 2x}{2} + \frac{\sin 3x}{3} \cdots\right) \quad (-\pi < x < +\pi)$$

FIG. 11. Graphical representation of terms in a Fourier series, and sums of terms, showing appearance of Gibbs's phenomenon.

and phase of the harmonics of a drawn curve. In one apparatus of Michelson and Stratton, harmonics up to $n = 80$ could be determined. The apparatus can also be used to synthesize a curve, if the harmonic composition is given.

A rather curious phenomenon was noted when the apparatus of Michelson and Stratton was used to synthesize the curve given by a

[1] See SOKOLNIKOFF, I. S., and E. S. SOKOLNIKOFF, "Higher Mathematics for Engineers and Physicists," pp. 545–550.

[2] See BUSH, VANNEVAR, Harmonic Analysis, *Encyclopedia Britannica*, 14th ed., for a description of harmonic analyzers.

series such as Eq. (21). As the higher harmonics were added, the synthesized curve approached the form of the original function, except at points of discontinuity. Here little towers appeared, as shown in Fig. 11. As more harmonics were added, these towers pushed closer to the points of discontinuity, so that the infinite series ultimately approached the form of the function, except for these extensions at the points of discontinuity. These irregularities are called Gibbs's phenomenon in Fourier series, for it was first shown by the American scientist J. W. Gibbs, after the discovery of Michelson and Stratton, that the phenomenon is a consequence of Fourier expansion and is not a mechanical error in the apparatus. It may be shown that if D is the magnitude of the discontinuity, such as

$$f_2(x) - f_1(x)$$

in Fig. 3, then the length of the extension is in general $0.0895D$,[1] for a function whose period is 2π.

Gibbs's phenomenon is an interesting example of the peculiarities that may occur in limiting processes. On page 80 there is a further discussion of the little towers that characterize Gibbs's phenomenon. It is there pointed out that these towers are actually equal to the negative of the sum of the terms beyond the last term used in making the graph of the function from its Fourier series. As the number of terms used is increased, the total area of a tower decreases; but, instead of decreasing in height, the tower becomes narrower. However, this is not surprising; for as the limiting process progresses, the tower represents higher and higher frequency terms. The limiting process of summing the Fourier series thus has no necessary effect on the height of the tower even though it continually decreases its area.

It is shown in Chap. IV that Gibbs's phenomenon is of technical importance because of its relation to "overshoot" and sharp cutoff.

1.14 Further Discussion. Before going on to the more practical radio applications of Fourier series, a few general remarks are in order. In the first place it should be pointed out that series expansions of general functions are possible in terms of many other types of functions besides sines and cosines. In fact, series expansions are possible in

[1] CARSLAW, H. S., "Fourier Series and Integrals," p. 294. The limiting value of the extension has an exact value of $[(2/\pi)\mathrm{Si}(\pi) - 1]D$. The function $\mathrm{Si}(x)$ is defined and discussed in Chap. IV.

terms of practically any complete[1] set of orthogonal functions, as well as other sets of functions.[2] However, the predominant importance of Fourier expansions, in mathematics, is due to the simplicity of sines and cosines. Furthermore, in all physical phenomena, including radio, harmonic vibrations (*i.e.*, sines and cosines) are the only kind that always retain their form in every linear system.[3] Thus in electrical circuits, harmonic vibrations retain their form in any circuits in which L, R, and C are independent of amplitude and time. Finally, regarding radio applications, because of the exact periodicity of harmonic vibrations they are the only ones suitable for the series expansion of the periodic functions so important in radio.

In closing this chapter, it will be of interest to note a passage from Rayleigh's "Theory of Sound" concerning the importance of harmonic vibrations in acoustics.

Seeing now that notes are usually compound, and that only a particular sort called tones are incapable of further analysis, we are led to inquire what is the physical characteristic of tones, to which they owe their peculiarity? What sort of periodic vibration is it, which produces a simple tone? According to what mathematical function of the time does the pressure vary in the passage of the ear? No question in acoustics can be more important.

The simplest periodic functions with which mathematicians are acquainted are the circular functions, expressed by a sine or cosine; indeed there are no others at all approaching them in simplicity. They may be of any period, and admitting of no other variation (except magnitude), seem well adapted to produce simple tones. Moreover it has been proved by Fourier, that the most general single-valued periodic function can be resolved into a series of circular functions, having periods which are submultiples of that of the given function. Again, it is a consequence of the general theory of vibration that the particular type, now suggested as corresponding to a simple tone, is the only one capable

[1] The fact that a *complete* set of orthogonal functions is generally required for the expansion of a function makes it clear that these series expansions (including Fourier series) are a distinct phenomenon of mathematics. Thus it cannot be supposed that the possibility of a Fourier expansion is just due to the fact that an infinite number of terms are available so that any function can necessarily be matched by juggling the coefficients. For example, the set of sines and cosines would still be infinite in number if $\sin 3x$ were removed from the set, but it would not be possible to expand the function shown in Fig. 2 or Fig. 5a if $\sin 3x$ were removed from the set.

[2] See WHITTAKER and WATSON, "Modern Analysis," Chap. VIII.

[3] This is due to the fact that $\sin x$ and $\cos x$ are of identical shape and that they may be treated as the real and imaginary components of ϵ^{jx}. The latter is remarkable in that its absolute value is independent of x and is the same as that of its derivative or integral of any order.

of preserving its integrity among the vicissitudes which it may have to undergo. Any other kind is liable to a sort of physical analysis, one part being differently affected from another. If the analysis within the ear proceeded on a different principle from that effected according to the laws of dead matter outside the ear, the consequence would be that a sound originally simple might become compound on its way to the observer. There is no reason to suppose that anything of this sort actually happens. When it is added that according to all the ideas we can form on the subject, the analysis within the ear must take place by means of a physical machinery, subject to the same laws as prevail outside, it will be seen that a strong case has been made out for regarding tones as due to vibrations expressed by circular functions. We are not however left entirely to the guidance of general considerations like these. In the chapter on the vibration of strings, we shall see that in many cases theory informs us beforehand of the nature of the vibration executed by a string, and in particular whether any specified simple vibration is a component or not. Here we have a decisive test. It is found by experiment that, whenever according to theory any simple vibration is present, the corresponding tone can be heard, but, whenever the simple vibration is absent, then the tone cannot be heard. We are therefore justified in asserting that simple tones and vibrations of a circular type are indissolubly connected. This law was discovered by Ohm.

Fundamental Formulas of Chapter I

For the interval $-\pi \leq x \leq +\pi$,

$$
\begin{aligned}
f(x) &= \frac{a_0}{2} + \sum_{n=1}^{\infty} (a_n \cos nx + b_n \sin nx) \\
&= \frac{a_0}{2} + (a_1 \cos x + b_1 \sin x) + (a_2 \cos 2x + b_2 \sin 2x) \\
&\quad + \cdots + (a_n \cos nx + b_n \sin nx) + \cdots \\
&= \frac{a_0}{2} + A_1 \cos (x + \phi_1) + A_2 \cos (2x + \phi_2) + \cdots \\
&\quad + A_n \cos (nx + \phi_n) + \cdots \\
&= \sum_{n=-\infty}^{+\infty} C_n \epsilon^{inx} \qquad (1)
\end{aligned}
$$

where

$$a_0 = \frac{1}{\pi} \int_{-\pi}^{+\pi} f(x)\, dx = 2C_0 \qquad (2)$$

$$a_n = \frac{1}{\pi} \int_{-\pi}^{+\pi} f(x) \cos nx\, dx = C_n + C_{-n} \qquad (3)$$

$$b_n = \frac{1}{\pi} \int_{-\pi}^{+\pi} f(x) \sin nx\, dx = j(C_n - C_{-n}) \qquad (4)$$

$$A_n = \sqrt{a_n^2 + b_n^2} = 2\sqrt{C_n C_{-n}} \qquad (5)$$

$$\phi_n = \tan^{-1} \frac{-b_n}{a_n} \qquad (6)$$

$$C_n = \frac{a_n - jb_n}{2} = \frac{1}{2\pi} \int_{-\pi}^{+\pi} f(x)\epsilon^{-jnx}\, dx \tag{7}$$

$$C_{-n} = \frac{a_n + jb_n}{2} = \frac{1}{2\pi} \int_{-\pi}^{+\pi} f(x)\epsilon^{jnx}\, dx = C_n^* \tag{8}$$

$$C_0 = \frac{a_0}{2} = \frac{1}{2\pi} \int_{-\pi}^{+\pi} f(x)\, dx \tag{9}$$

For the general interval $T_1 \leq x \leq T_2$,

$$\begin{aligned} f(x) &= \frac{a_0}{2} + \left(a_1 \cos \frac{2\pi x}{T_2 - T_1} + b_1 \sin \frac{2\pi x}{T_2 - T_1}\right) \\ &\quad + \cdots + \left(a_n \cos \frac{2\pi n x}{T_2 - T_1} + b_n \sin \frac{2\pi n x}{T_2 - T_1}\right) + \cdots \\ &= \frac{a_0}{2} + \sum_{n=1}^{\infty} \left(a_n \cos \frac{2\pi n x}{T_2 - T_1} + b_n \sin \frac{2\pi n x}{T_2 - T_1}\right) \\ &= \sum_{n=-\infty}^{+\infty} C_n \epsilon^{j\frac{2\pi n x}{T_2 - T_1}} \end{aligned} \tag{10}$$

where

$$a_0 = \frac{2}{T_2 - T_1} \int_{T_1}^{T_2} f(x)\, dx \tag{11}$$

$$a_n = \frac{2}{T_2 - T_1} \int_{T_1}^{T_2} f(x) \cos \frac{2\pi n x}{T_2 - T_1}\, dx \tag{12}$$

$$b_n = \frac{2}{T_2 - T_1} \int_{T_1}^{T_2} f(x) \sin \frac{2\pi n x}{T_2 - T_1}\, dx \tag{13}$$

$$C_n = \frac{1}{T_2 - T_1} \int_{T_1}^{T_2} f(x)\epsilon^{-j\frac{2\pi n x}{T_2 - T_1}}\, dx \tag{14}$$

CHAPTER II

RADIO APPLICATIONS OF FOURIER SERIES

2.1 The Full-wave Rectifier. As a simple example of a radio application of Fourier series, we shall first consider the full-wave rectifier. In Fig. 1*a* is the schematic diagram of a full-wave rectifier, and in Fig. 1*b* is its simplified equivalent circuit, the effect of circuit reactance being neglected. During one half of a cycle of the impressed voltage, the plate of diode 1 is positive with respect to its cathode so that the diode conducts. During the next half cycle, the plate is negative with respect to the cathode so that the diode acts essentially

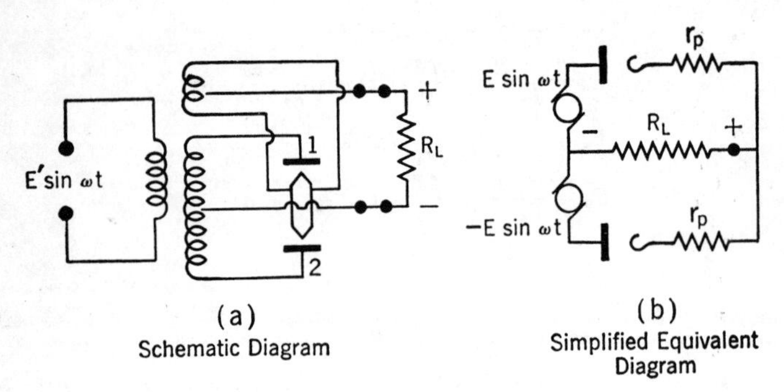

FIG. 1. A full-wave rectifier.

as an infinite impedance and does not conduct. Therefore the current through diode 1 consists of half sine waves as shown in Fig. 2*a*. At the same time current goes through diode 2 during the alternate half cycles as shown in Fig. 2*b*. Since both these currents go through the load R_L, the current through the load is that of a rectified sine wave as shown in Fig. 2*c*.

It is an important practical matter to know the magnitude of the direct-current component of the rectified current going through R_L and also the magnitude of the harmonics. These can readily be deter-

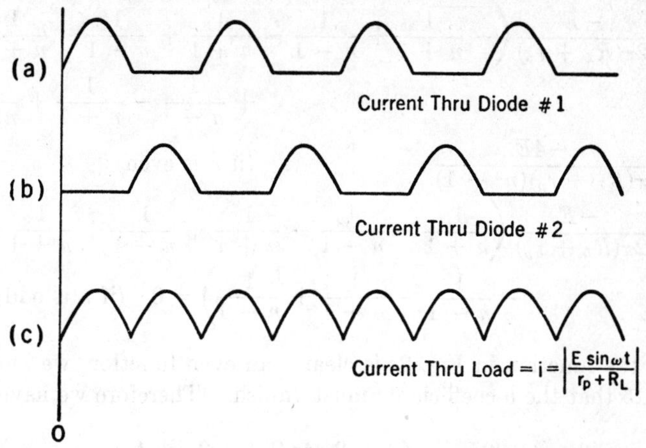

FIG. 2. Currents in various branches of a full-wave rectifier.

mined by expanding the function $\left|\frac{E \sin \omega t}{R_L + r_p}\right|$, representing the rectified current, into a Fourier series. Using Eqs. (6), (12), and (13) of Chap. I, we get

$$a_0 = \frac{1}{\pi}\int_{\omega t=0}^{\omega t=2\pi} f(\omega t)\, d(\omega t) = \frac{1}{\pi}\int_{\omega t=0}^{\omega t=\pi} \frac{E \sin \omega t}{R_L + r_p}\, d(\omega t) + \frac{1}{\pi}\int_{\omega t=\pi}^{\omega t=2\pi}\left(-\frac{E \sin \omega t}{R_L + r_p}\right) d(\omega t)$$

$$= \frac{E}{\pi(R_L + r_p)}\left(-\cos \omega t\Big|_{\omega t=0}^{\omega t=\pi} + \cos \omega t\Big|_{\omega t=\pi}^{\omega t=2\pi}\right)$$

$$= \frac{E}{\pi(R_L + r_p)}(1 + 1 + 1 + 1) = \frac{4E}{\pi(R_L + r_p)} \tag{1}$$

$$a_n = \frac{1}{\pi}\int_{\omega t=0}^{\omega t=2\pi} f(\omega t) \cos n\omega t\, d(\omega t)$$

$$= \frac{1}{\pi}\int_0^{\pi} \frac{E \sin \omega t \cos n\omega t}{R_L + r_p}\, d(\omega t) + \frac{1}{\pi}\int_{\pi}^{2\pi} \frac{-E \sin \omega t \cos n\omega t}{R_L + r_p}\, d(\omega t)$$

$$= \frac{-E}{\pi(R_L + r_p)}\frac{1}{2}\left\{\frac{\cos [(n+1)\omega t]}{n+1} - \frac{\cos [(n-1)\omega t]}{n-1}\right\}\Bigg|_0^{\pi} + \frac{E}{\pi(R_L + r_p)}\frac{1}{2}\left\{\frac{\cos [(n+1)\omega t]}{n+1} - \frac{\cos [(n-1)\omega t]}{n-1}\right\}\Bigg|_{\pi}^{2\pi}$$

$$= \frac{-E}{2\pi(R_L + r_p)}\left(-\frac{1}{n+1} + \frac{1}{n-1} - \frac{1}{n+1} + \frac{1}{n-1} - \frac{1}{n+1} + \frac{1}{n-1} - \frac{1}{n+1} + \frac{1}{n-1}\right)$$

$$= \frac{-4E}{\pi(R_L + r_p)(n^2 - 1)} \qquad \text{(if } n \text{ is even)} \tag{2}$$

$$= \frac{-E}{2\pi(R_L + r_p)}\left(\frac{1}{n+1} - \frac{1}{n-1} - \frac{1}{n+1} + \frac{1}{n-1} + \frac{1}{n+1} - \frac{1}{n-1} - \frac{1}{n+1} + \frac{1}{n-1}\right) = 0 \quad \text{(if } n \text{ is odd)} \tag{3}$$

Since the function in Fig. 2c is clearly an even function, we know by Sec. 1.5 that the b coefficients must vanish. Therefore we have

$$\left|\frac{E \sin \omega t}{R_L + r_p}\right| = \frac{2E}{\pi(R_L + r_p)}\left(1 - \frac{2 \cos 2\omega t}{2^2 - 1} - \frac{2 \cos 4\omega t}{4^2 - 1} - \cdots\right) \tag{4}$$

The direct-current component of the rectified current is thus

$$\frac{2E}{\pi(R_L + r_p)}$$

We note that there are no odd harmonics, a characteristic that would follow even without calculation from the fact that the current in Fig. 2c has a frequency of repetition of ω/π as well as $\omega/2\pi$.*

Exercises

1. Analyze the full-wave rectifier problem, using the complex form of Fourier series instead of the trigonometric form.

2. The current from a half-wave rectifier has the approximate wave form shown in the figure below, which is a series of half sine waves. Find the magnitude of (*a*) direct current; (*b*) fundamental; (*c*) second harmonic.

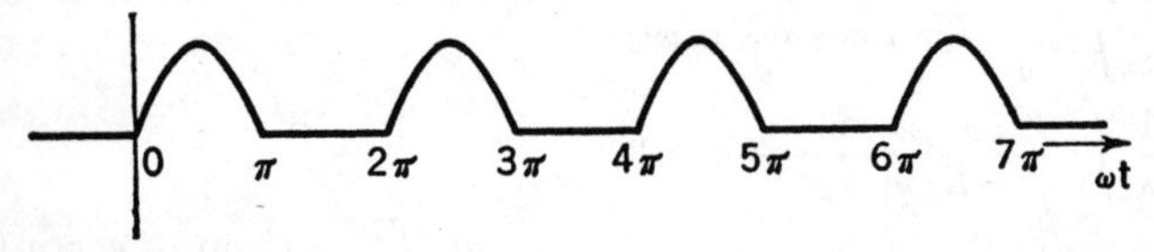

2.2 Saturated Amplifiers. A common occurrence in amplifiers is cutoff or saturation of signal at a given level. Such a situation is depicted in Fig. 3. This condition causes a certain amount of har-

* For an excellent analysis of a variety of types of rectifiers see "Electronics" by Millman and Seely.

monic generation and a certain amount of signal loss at the fundamental frequency. We shall now calculate these amounts.

Suppose that the signal in Fig. 3 is[1] $A \cos \omega t$ except where saturation takes place and that saturation takes place at the level $A \cos \phi$

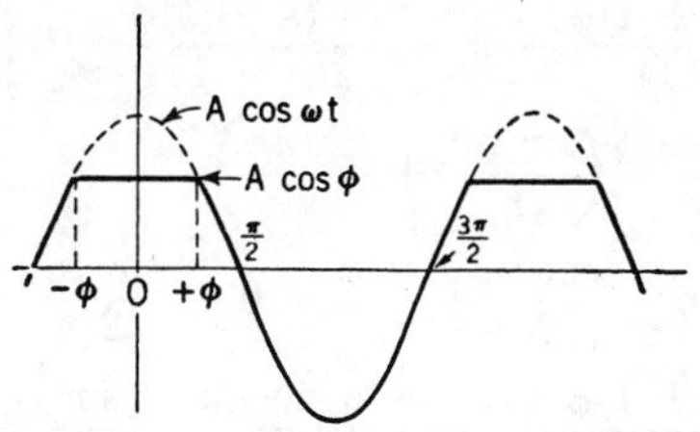

FIG. 3. The phenomenon of saturation.

from $-\phi$ to $+\phi$. Analyzing the resultant signal in a Fourier series, we have

$$a_0 = \frac{1}{\pi}\int_{-\pi}^{+\pi} f(\omega t)\,d(\omega t) = \frac{1}{\pi}\int_{-\pi}^{-\phi} A\cos\omega t\,d(\omega t) + \frac{1}{\pi}\int_{-\phi}^{\phi} A\cos\phi\,d(\omega t) + \frac{1}{\pi}\int_{\phi}^{\pi} A\cos\omega t\,d(\omega t)$$

$$= \frac{A}{\pi}\left(\sin\omega t\Big|_{\omega t=-\pi}^{-\phi} + (\omega t)\cos\phi\Big|_{\omega t=-\phi}^{\phi} + \sin\omega t\Big|_{\omega t=\phi}^{\pi}\right)$$

$$= \frac{A}{\pi}(-\sin\phi + \phi\cos\phi + \phi\cos\phi - \sin\phi)$$

$$= \frac{2A}{\pi}(\phi\cos\phi - \sin\phi) \tag{5}$$

$$a_n = \frac{1}{\pi}\int_{-\pi}^{+\pi} f(\omega t)\cos n\omega t\,d(\omega t)$$

$$= \frac{1}{\pi}\int_{-\pi}^{-\phi} A\cos\omega t\cos n\omega t\,d(\omega t) + \frac{1}{\pi}\int_{-\phi}^{+\phi} A\cos\phi\cos n\omega t\,d(\omega t) + \frac{1}{\pi}\int_{\phi}^{\pi} A\cos\omega t\cos n\omega t\,d(\omega t)$$

$$= \frac{A}{\pi}\left\{\frac{\sin[(n+1)\omega t]}{2(n+1)} + \frac{\sin[(n-1)\omega t]}{2(n-1)}\right\}\Bigg|_{\omega t=-\pi}^{-\phi}$$

[1] The choice of time origin does not affect the relative magnitudes of harmonics and can therefore be chosen to simplify the calculation of Fourier coefficients. We have accordingly used the form $A \cos \omega t$, which makes the function even everywhere, including the region of saturation, thus eliminating the calculation of sine coefficients.

$$+\frac{A\cos\phi}{\pi}\left(\frac{\sin n\omega t}{n}\right)\Bigg|_{\omega t=-\phi}^{+\phi}$$

$$+\frac{A}{\pi}\left\{\frac{\sin[(n+1)\omega t]}{2(n+1)}+\frac{\sin[(n-1)\omega t]}{2(n-1)}\right\}\Bigg|_{\omega t=\phi}^{\pi}$$

$$=\frac{A}{\pi}\left[\frac{-\sin(n+1)\phi}{2(n+1)}-0-\frac{\sin(n-1)\phi}{2(n-1)}-0\right]$$

$$+\frac{A\cos\phi}{\pi}\left(\frac{\sin n\phi}{n}+\frac{\sin n\phi}{n}\right)$$

$$+\frac{A}{\pi}\left[0-\frac{\sin(n+1)\phi}{2(n+1)}+0-\frac{\sin(n-1)\phi}{2(n-1)}\right]$$

$$=\frac{A}{\pi}\left[\frac{-\sin(n+1)\phi}{n+1}+\frac{2\cos\phi\sin n\phi}{n}-\frac{\sin(n-1)\phi}{n-1}\right] \tag{6}$$

Since

$$2\cos\phi\sin n\phi=\sin(n+1)\phi+\sin(n-1)\phi \tag{7}$$

we obtain

$$a_n=\frac{A}{\pi}\left[\frac{\sin(n+1)\phi}{n(n+1)}-\frac{\sin(n-1)\phi}{n(n-1)}\right] \tag{8}$$

When $n = 1$, Eq. (8) breaks down and we must return to the original Fourier equation to obtain

$$a_1=\frac{1}{\pi}\int_{-\pi}^{-\phi}A\cos^2\omega t\,d(\omega t)+\frac{1}{\pi}\int_{-\phi}^{\phi}A\cos\phi\cos\omega t\,d(\omega t)$$
$$+\frac{1}{\pi}\int_{\phi}^{\pi}A\cos^2\omega t\,d(\omega t)$$

$$=\frac{A}{\pi}\left(\frac{\omega t}{2}+\frac{\cos\omega t\sin\omega t}{2}\right)\Bigg|_{-\pi}^{-\phi}+\frac{A\cos\phi}{\pi}(\sin\omega t)\Bigg|_{-\phi}^{\phi}$$
$$+\frac{A}{\pi}\left(\frac{\omega t}{2}+\frac{\cos\omega t\sin\omega t}{2}\right)\Bigg|_{\phi}^{\pi}$$

$$=\frac{A}{\pi}\left(\frac{-\phi}{2}+\frac{\pi}{2}-\frac{\cos\phi\sin\phi}{2}-0\right)$$
$$+\frac{A\cos\phi}{\pi}(\sin\phi+\sin\phi)$$
$$+\frac{A}{\pi}\left(\frac{\pi}{2}-\frac{\phi}{2}+0-\frac{\cos\phi\sin\phi}{2}\right)$$

$$=\frac{A}{\pi}(\pi-\phi+\sin\phi\cos\phi) \tag{9}$$

As a result of Eqs. (5), p. 39 (8), and (9), we have

$$\text{Signal} = f(\omega t) = \frac{A}{\pi}(\phi \cos \phi - \sin \phi) + \frac{A}{\pi}(\pi - \phi + \sin \phi \cos \phi) \cos \omega t$$
$$+ \sum_{n=2}^{\infty} \frac{A}{\pi}\left[\frac{\sin (n+1)\phi}{n(n+1)} - \frac{\sin (n-1)\phi}{n(n-1)}\right] \cos n\omega t \quad (10)$$

If there were no saturation, the signal would be

$$A \cos \omega t \quad (11)$$

Comparing this with Eq. (10), we see that saturation introduces a direct-current component of amount

$$\frac{A}{\pi}(\phi \cos \phi - \sin \phi)$$

It causes a reduction of fundamental of amount

$$A\left(1 - \frac{\pi - \phi + \sin \phi \cos \phi}{\pi}\right)$$

Finally, it introduces harmonics of amount

$$\sum_{n=2}^{\infty} \frac{A}{\pi}\left[\frac{\sin (n+1)\phi}{n(n+1)} - \frac{\sin (n-1)\phi}{n(n-1)}\right] \cos n\omega t$$

In the special case that

$$\phi = \frac{\pi}{2}$$

Eq. (10) gives the output of a half-wave rectifier, but with reversed sign. Thus the output of a half-wave rectifier such as is shown in Fig. 4 is

$$\text{Signal} = \frac{A}{\pi} - \frac{A}{2} \cos \omega t - \frac{2A}{\pi} \sum_{n=2,4,6}^{\infty} \frac{(-1)^{\frac{n}{2}} \cos n\omega t}{(n+1)(n-1)} \quad (12)$$

The algebraic signs in front of the harmonics in Eq. (12) do not have much significance since they represent phase angles that change with a shift in the origin chosen for the time axis.

The saturation of actual amplifiers is, of course, never as perfect as shown in Fig. 3. The above analysis, however, points out the general features of the phenomenon even when the saturation is incomplete.

At the outset of this section, it is stated that saturation causes a certain amount of signal loss at the fundamental frequency. This statement, and in fact the entire analysis leading up Eq. (10), referred to the case shown in Fig. 5*a*, where part of a given signal is removed by

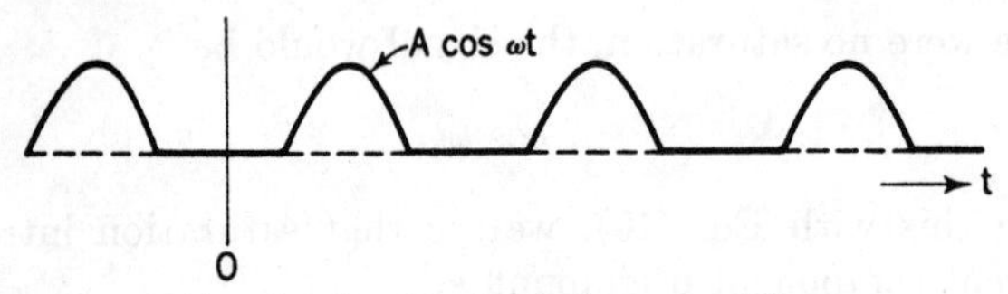

FIG. 4. Output of a half-wave rectifier.

limiting. Suppose now that we consider the somewhat different cases shown in Figs. 5*b* and 5*c*. Here the signal is limited by the peak signal amplitude that the system will pass. In Fig. 5*b* the amplitude is limited only in the positive direction. In the two cases shown in Figs. 5*b* and 5*c* the amount of fundamental actually increases as the signal becomes saturated.

The case of Fig. 5*c* (considered in Exercise 2 below) is of the most practical importance. In this case, for complete saturation (*i.e.*,

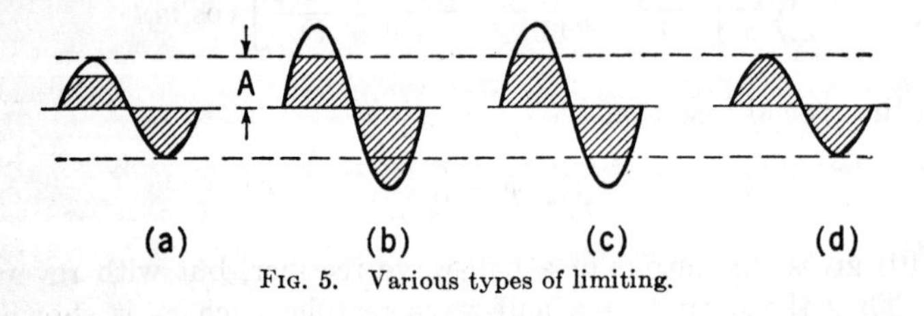

FIG. 5. Various types of limiting.

a square wave), the signal at the fundamental frequency becomes $(4/\pi)A$, which is an increase of about 27 per cent.[1] In addition, the decrease in plate dissipation in the latter case actually makes it possible to use even larger values of A. For these reasons, a push-pull power stage of a radio transmitter is usually operated as shown in Fig. 5*c*, rather than as shown in Fig. 5*d*.

[1] The power increase is

$$\left(\frac{4}{\pi}\right)^2 - 1 = 62\%$$

Exercises

1. Find the harmonic composition of the output of the asymmetrical limiter in Fig. *A*.

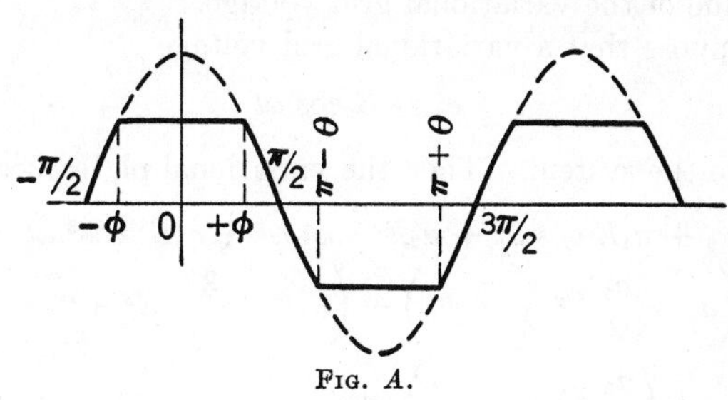

Fig. *A*.

2. Find the harmonic composition of the output of a symmetrical limiter, *i.e.*, when $\theta = \phi$ in Fig. *A*.

2.3 The Generation of Harmonics by Second-power and Higher-order Distortion Terms—Sum and Difference Tones. If a vacuum-tube amplifier is operated over a plane portion of its characteristic i_p, e_p, e_g surface, the variational component of the plate current is exactly similar in shape to the grid voltage. If the plate load is resistive, a grid voltage $E \cos \omega t$ will then give rise to a plate current expressible as $I \cos \omega t$. On the other hand, if there is a reactive component in the plate-circuit impedance, then the expression for the plate current must include a phase change and thus becomes $I \cos (\omega t - \phi)$.

In the foregoing case, we say that the tube is being operated over a linear portion of its characteristics. By this we mean that, for a resistive load,[1] the variational plate current i_p may be expressed as a linear function of the variational grid voltage e_g, so that

$$i_p = a_0 + a_1 e_g \tag{13}$$

As long as only small variational grid voltages and plate currents are under consideration, the above relation (13) will usually hold good. However, when the variational grid voltages and plate currents are large, Eq. (13) is no longer a sufficiently good approximation and the plate current must then be expressed as a power series in terms of the grid voltage,[2] *i.e.*,

$$i_p = a_0 + a_1 e_g + a_2 e_g^2 + a_3 e_g^3 + \cdots \tag{14}$$

[1] We shall limit our analysis to the case of a resistive load in this section. For reactive loads, see the exercises at the end of the chapter.

[2] In a given experimental setup, i_p may be expressed as a function of e_g alone, since variations of e_p that occur as a consequence of variations in i_p are a property of the setup and are therefore included in the constants a_0, a_1, a_2, etc.

Equation (14) means that for a given setup (*i.e.*, given circuit constants and supply voltages) having no reactive components[1] the instantaneous value of the variational plate current depends only on the instantaneous value of the variational grid voltage.

Now suppose that a variational grid voltage

$$e_g = E \cos \omega t \tag{15}$$

is applied to the system. Then the variational plate current is

$$\begin{aligned} i_p &= a_0 + a_1 E \cos \omega t + a_2 E^2 \cos^2 \omega t + a_3 E^3 \cos^3 \omega t + \cdots \\ &= \left(a_0 + \frac{a_2}{2} E^2 + \cdots\right) + \left(a_1 E + \frac{3a_3}{4} E^3 + \cdots\right) \cos \omega t \\ &\quad + \left(\frac{a_2}{2} E^2 + \cdots\right) \cos 2\omega t \\ &\quad + \left(\frac{a_3}{4} E^3 + \cdots\right) \cos 3\omega t + \cdots \end{aligned} \qquad (16)^2$$

The right side of Eq. (16) is a Fourier series, although we have not arrived at it by the conventional method of using Eqs. (6), (12), and (13) of the last chapter. The fact that only cosine terms can be

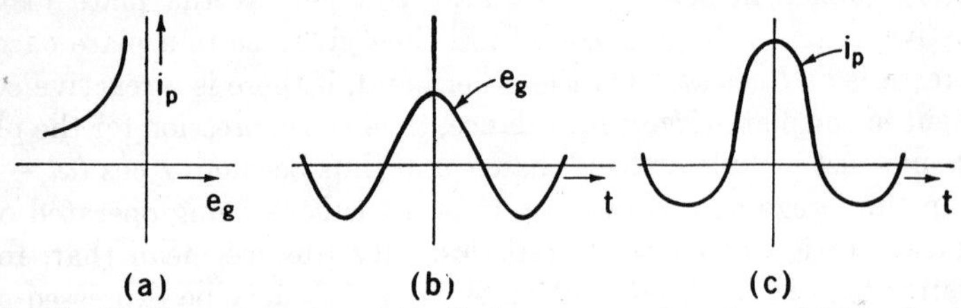

FIG. 6. Nonlinear response and its effect upon wave shape in a resistive circuit.

present is also obvious from the symmetry properties of Fig. 6, which show that i_p is an even function. Equation (16) shows how the second-power coefficient a_2 of Eq. (14) and the higher coefficients $a_3, a_4, \ldots$ give rise to harmonics in i_p. In particular, it shows which coefficients give rise to which harmonics.

If the applied voltage has components of more than one frequency, then sum and difference tones are generated, as well as harmonics, as soon as the operation is nonlinear. While this is not a Fourier series

[1] If there are reactive circuit components present, the instantaneous value of the variational plate current will depend upon the wave shape of the grid voltage as well as upon its instantaneous value, since the stored energy in the reactive components will affect the plate current. Equation (14) can then no longer be used.

[2] Since $\cos^2 x = \frac{1}{2} + \frac{1}{2} \cos 2x$, $\cos^3 x = \frac{3}{4} \cos x + \frac{1}{4} \cos 3x$, etc.

phenomenon, it is closely related to the subject at hand. For example, if

$$e_g = E_1 \cos \omega_1 t + E_2 \cos \omega_2 t \tag{17}$$

and if i_p is given by Eq. (14), then

$$\begin{aligned} i_p = & \left[a_0 + \frac{a_2}{2}(E_1^2 + E_2^2) + \cdots \right] \\ & + (a_1E_1 + \tfrac{3}{4}a_3E_1^3 + \tfrac{3}{2}a_3E_1E_2^2 + \cdots) \cos \omega_1 t \\ & + (a_1E_2 + \tfrac{3}{4}a_3E_2^3 + \tfrac{3}{2}a_3E_1^2E_2 + \cdots) \cos \omega_2 t \\ & + \left(\frac{a_2}{2}E_1^2 + \cdots\right) \cos 2\omega_1 t + \left(\frac{a_2}{2}E_2^2 + \cdots\right) \cos 2\omega_2 t \\ & + (a_2E_1E_2 + \cdots) \cos [(\omega_2 + \omega_1)t] \\ & + (a_2E_1E_2 + \cdots) \cos [(\omega_2 - \omega_1)t] \\ & + \left(\frac{a_3}{4}E_1^3 + \cdots\right) \cos 3\omega_1 t + \left(\frac{a_3}{4}E_2^3 + \cdots\right) \cos 3\omega_2 t \\ & + \left(\frac{3a_3}{4}E_1E_2^2 + \cdots\right) \cos [(2\omega_2 + \omega_1)t] \\ & + \left(\frac{3a_3}{4}E_1E_2^2 + \cdots\right) \cos [(2\omega_2 - \omega_1)t] \\ & + \left(\frac{3a_3}{4}E_1^2E_2 + \cdots\right) \cos [(2\omega_1 + \omega_2)t] \\ & + \left(\frac{3a_3}{4}E_1^2E_2 + \cdots\right) \cos [(2\omega_1 - \omega_2)t] \\ & + \cdots\cdots\cdots\cdots \end{aligned} \tag{18}$$

The terms in Eq. (18) of frequencies $(\omega_2 + \omega_1)/2\pi$ and $(\omega_2 - \omega_1)/2\pi$ are called sum and difference frequencies or sum and difference tones. The terms of frequencies $(2\omega_2 + \omega_1)/2\pi$, $(2\omega_2 - \omega_1)/2\pi$, $(2\omega_1 + \omega_2)/2\pi$, $(2\omega_1 - \omega_2)/2\pi$, etc., may be called sum and difference frequencies of higher order. The difference tone $(\omega_2 - \omega_1)/2\pi$ is employed in the operation of the first detector in a superheterodyne receiver. Otherwise, sum and difference tones usually represent distortion in a system and are eliminated in so far as is possible. It is believed that sum and difference tones represent a more annoying type of audio distortion to the ear than ordinary harmonics in a program.

Exercise

A piece of thyrite is a nonohmic resistor whose voltage-current characteristic may be expressed as

$$i = ke^B$$

If a cosinusoidal voltage

$$e = E \cos \omega t$$

is applied to a particular piece of thyrite having the constants

$$B = 3.57$$
$$k = 1.3 \times 10^{-10}$$

and if $E = 2{,}000$ volts, what is the ratio between the magnitudes of second harmonic and fundamental in the resultant current?

2.4 Push-pull Amplifiers. In the output circuits of a radio transmitter or receiver, it is generally desirable to operate the tubes over a

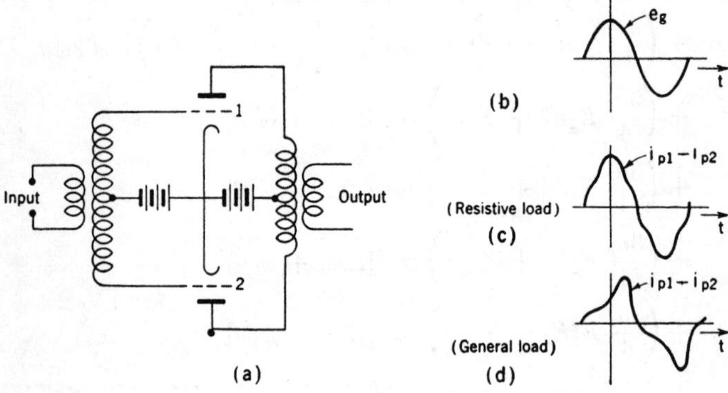

FIG 7. Circuit and wave shapes in a push-pull amplifier.

wide range of their characteristic curves in order to realize maximum output from them. This usually means that the tubes are operated beyond their linear range, and thus harmonics are produced. Since these harmonics represent distortion of the signal, it is desirable to reduce their magnitude as far as possible.

One way to reduce harmonic distortion very considerably is to use a push-pull amplifier, such as is shown in Fig. 7*a*. If the tubes have essentially identical characteristics, balanced midtapped input and output transformers are used, and the effective load is resistive, then the grid voltages and plate currents of the output tubes may be represented as

$$e_{g1} = E \cos \omega t \tag{19}$$
$$e_{g2} = -E \cos \omega t \tag{20}$$

$$
\begin{aligned}
i_{p1} = \left(a_0 + \frac{a_2}{2} E^2 + \cdots\right) + \left(a_1 E + \frac{3a_3}{4} E^3 + \cdots\right) \cos \omega t \\
+ \left(\frac{a_2}{2} E^2 + \cdots\right) \cos 2\omega t \\
+ \left(\frac{a_3}{4} E^3 + \cdots\right) \cos 3\omega t + \cdots \qquad (21)
\end{aligned}
$$

$$
\begin{aligned}
i_{p2} = \left[a_0 + \frac{a_2}{2} (-E)^2 + \cdots\right] \\
+ \left[a_1(-E) + \frac{3a_3}{4} (-E)^3 + \cdots\right] \cos \omega t \\
+ \left[\frac{a_2}{2} (-E)^2 + \cdots\right] \cos 2\omega t \\
+ \left[\frac{a_3}{4} (-E)^3 + \cdots\right] \cos 3\omega t + \cdots \qquad (22)
\end{aligned}
$$

The plate currents i_{p1} and i_{p2} go through the output transformer in opposite directions. Therefore their effective value is

$$
\begin{aligned}
i(t) = i_{p1} - i_{p2} = 2\left(a_1 E + \frac{3a_3}{4} E^3 + \cdots\right) \cos \omega t \\
+ 2\left(\frac{a_3}{4} E^3 + \cdots\right) \cos 3\omega t + \cdots \qquad (23)
\end{aligned}
$$

We thus see that the push-pull arrangement eliminates even harmonics from the output. Since the second harmonic is usually the strongest distortion term, its elimination in the push-pull amplifier causes a marked reduction in distortion.

The fact that even harmonics are eliminated in a push-pull amplifier with any type of load, whether resistive or not, can be seen by consideration of Figs. 7*c* and *d* without the necessity of any series expansion. Since the two sides of the amplifier, 1 and 2, have identical characteristics, the curves in Figs. 7*c* and *d* are mirror-symmetrical. Therefore, by the argument in Sec. 1.6, there are no even harmonics in their series expansions.

Exercise

Which of the sum and difference tones in Eq. (18) are eliminated in a push-pull amplifier?

2.5 Effective Value of Current and Power Consumption in Terms of Harmonic Composition. Suppose we have a periodic current of arbitrary wave shape expressible as

$$i = \frac{a_0}{2} + \sum_{n=1}^{n=\infty} (a_n \cos n\omega t + b_n \sin n\omega t) \tag{24}$$

If this current goes through a resistance R, the power dissipated is

$$P = i^2 R \tag{25}$$

Therefore, by Eq. (103) of Sec. 1.11, the average value of the power dissipated in R is

$$P_{av} = \frac{1}{2\pi} \int_0^{2\pi} i^2 R \, d(\omega t)$$

$$\frac{Ra_0^2}{4} + \frac{1}{2} \sum_{n=1}^{\infty} R(a_n^2 + b_n^2) = Ri_0^2 + \sum_{n=1}^{\infty} Ri_n^2 \tag{26}$$

where

$$i_0 = \frac{a_0}{2} = \text{direct-current component} \tag{27}$$

and

$$i_n = \sqrt{\frac{a_n^2 + b_n^2}{2}} = \text{rms value of } n\text{th harmonic} \tag{28}$$

We conclude from Eq. (26) that each harmonic makes its own separate contribution to the average power dissipated just as though the others were not present. This means that any interaction between harmonics in contributing to the power dissipated averages out to zero over a cycle.

If we define the effective value of the current i as i_{eff}, where

$$i_{eff} = \sqrt{\frac{P_{av}}{R}} \tag{29}$$

then by Eq. (26)

$$i_{eff} = \sqrt{i_0^2 + i_1^2 + i_2^2 + \cdots} \tag{30}$$

In other words, the effective value of a current of arbitrary wave shape is equal to the square root of the sum of the squares of the rms values of its components.

Next suppose that a periodic voltage expressible as

$$e = \frac{A_0}{2} + \sum_{n=1}^{\infty} (A_n \cos n\omega t + B_n \sin n\omega t) \tag{31}$$

is impressed upon a circuit by a power source and that a periodic current of the same fundamental period is made to flow in the circuit. The current may then be expressed as

$$i = \frac{a_0}{2} + \sum_{n=1}^{\infty} (a_n \cos n\omega t + b_n \sin n\omega t) \tag{32}$$

The instantaneous power delivered by the source is then

$$P = ei \tag{33}$$

The average value of the power delivered is then, by Eq. (99) of Sec. 1.11,

$$P_{av} = \frac{1}{2\pi} \int_0^{2\pi} ei \, d(\omega t) = \frac{a_0 A_0}{4} + \frac{1}{2} \sum_{n=1}^{\infty} (a_n A_n + b_n B_n) \tag{34}$$

Thus the average power is equal to the sum of the rms power products of the individual harmonics. This means that the power products between different harmonics average out to zero over a complete cycle. Therefore, if a sinusoidal voltage is impressed upon a nonlinear circuit, the average power drawn from the source is equal to the power product of the voltage and the fundamental component of the current.

Exercises

1. Find the effective value of a square wave of current.

2. Find the effective value of pulses of current of duration t_1 and repetition period T.

2.6 Some General Considerations with Respect to Distortion. A circuit (or network) in which all the resistance, capacitance, and inductance values are independent of the magnitude of the current is called a linear circuit (or network). Such a system is governed by linear differential equations. If the values of the circuit elements also do not vary with time, they may correctly be described as circuit constants, and the linear differential equations that govern the behavior of the system then have constant coefficients.

The steady-state solution of the system corresponds to the particular integral of the differential equations, while the transient solution corresponds to the complementary function. We shall limit our considerations in this section to the steady-state case. When the circuit elements are constants, each separate frequency component in the

applied emf gets an independent response in the circuit current which is distinct from that of every other frequency component.[1] We can thus separate an applied voltage into its frequency components (whether they are harmonically related or not), find the response of the circuit to each frequency component, and then add the results. This is called the principle of superposition (as applied to frequency components).

In any system such as an amplifier, any difference in the wave shape of the output signal from the input signal is called distortion. Now, according to the discussion in the last paragraph, a system whose circuit elements are constants will add no new frequency components not present in the applied emf. Therefore the output can differ from the input only in the relative magnitude and phase of the frequency components already present. Because such systems are governed by linear differential equations, it is customary to describe distortion of the foregoing type, which does not involve the generation of new frequency components, as *linear distortion.* The *principle of superposition* applies to a system having only linear distortion; *i.e.*, the response of each frequency component can be considered independently in such a system.

In the earlier sections of this chapter we dealt with systems in which, either directly or in equivalent form, the values of the circuit elements were not independent of the current. There we found that new frequency components were introduced by the system. When we considered only the case of a single-frequency component in the input, we found only its harmonics in the new components generated. However, when we had more than one-frequency component in the input, we also found sum and difference frequencies in the output. Distortion of this type in which new frequency components are introduced by circuit elements whose values vary with current is called *nonlinear distortion.* In the case of nonlinear distortion, frequency components cannot be treated independently, since their interaction has an important effect. We describe this situation by saying that

[1] This follows from the properties of particular integrals of Type V discussed in the author's "Transformation Calculus." In a system governed by linear differential equations with constant coefficients, the responses to the superposition of voltages $f_1(t)$ and $f_2(t)$ can be added algebraically, when $f_1(t)$ and $f_2(t)$ are superimposed. This is true whether $f_1(t)$ and $f_2(t)$ are single-frequency components or not. This is the origin of the *principle of superposition.* It can be applied without question only if the coefficients of the differential equation are functions neither of amplitude nor of time.

the principle of superposition does not apply to a system having nonlinear distortion.

There is another type of distortion, distinct from the foregoing types, which arises when the value of a circuit element varies with time. An example of such a case is a carbon microphone or a condenser microphone. The value of a circuit parameter in these cases varies with time in accordance with the instantaneous intensity of the impinging sound wave. From the point of view of the differential equations of the circuits these are cases where the circuit coefficients are functions of time, rather than of current. It may be shown[1] that harmonics and sum and difference frequency distortion terms are created in these cases. The presence of sum and difference terms shows that the principle of superposition is not applicable here.

The foregoing gives a general outline of the types of distortion that may arise in electrical systems. It has become customary to describe distortion that consists of changes in the relative magnitudes and phases of the frequency components in the signal but that does not involve the generation of new frequency components as linear distortion. Distortion consisting of the generation of new frequency components is generally described as nonlinear distortion. There is some confusion in these definitions since the *linear* differential equations (with variable coefficients) which govern a system in which the magnitude of a circuit element varies with time are thus said to create nonlinear distortion. However, the confusion is not serious since the designation of nonlinear distortion as that type which involves the generation of new frequency components seems to be accepted everywhere.

Exercises

1. Equivalent plate-circuit theorem. Suppose that a tube is operated over a portion of its characteristics in which the second- and higher-order partial derivatives may be considered as zero. Then find the plate current in terms of the grid voltage, if the plate-circuit impedance has a reactive component. Show that the plate current is still a linear function of the grid voltage but that the constants in the function are complex. Use the complex expressions for current and voltage.

2. Discuss the equivalent circuits of a triode and the location and magnitude of generator voltages in the generation of harmonics. Express the phase lag introduced by plate-circuit reactance in the case of harmonics.

3. Find the effect of external plate-circuit resistance on the generation of harmonics.

[1] See, for instance, Guillemin, "Communication Networks," Vol. I, pp. 403–416.

4. A triode-connected 6L6 with a 10,000-ohm resistive plate load is operated at $E_c = -5$ and $E_B = 300$. Find the approximate values of a_1 and a_2 in Eq. (14) for this setup from the published curves of the 6L6.

5. Show that if a signal consists of the superposition of n different frequency components in the form

$$A_1 \cos(\omega_1 t + \phi) + A_2 \cos(\omega_2 t + \phi_2) + \cdots + A_n \cos(\omega_n t + \phi_n)$$

then the average value of the square of the signal amplitude is

$$\frac{A_1^2 + A_2^2 + \cdots + A_n^2}{2}$$

6. If an oscillator signal $E_1 \cos \omega_1 t$ and a radio-frequency signal $E_2 \cos \omega_2 t$ are simultaneously applied to the grid of a mixer tube having a characteristic equation

$$i_p = a_0 + a_1 e_g + a_2 e_g^2 + a_3 e_g^3$$

find the magnitudes and frequencies of all terms in the plate current.

Consider a superheterodyne receiver with the oscillator designed to operate at 455 kc above the radio-frequency frequency and a frequency scale extending from 540 to 1,700 kc. Suppose that an incoming radio-frequency signal of 1,000 kc is present. At what locations on the tuning scale (corresponding to oscillator frequencies 455 kc higher than the tuning setting) will there be a response from the receiver?

7. If the voltage wave shown in Fig. a is applied to the circuit in Fig. b, find the dissipation in R.

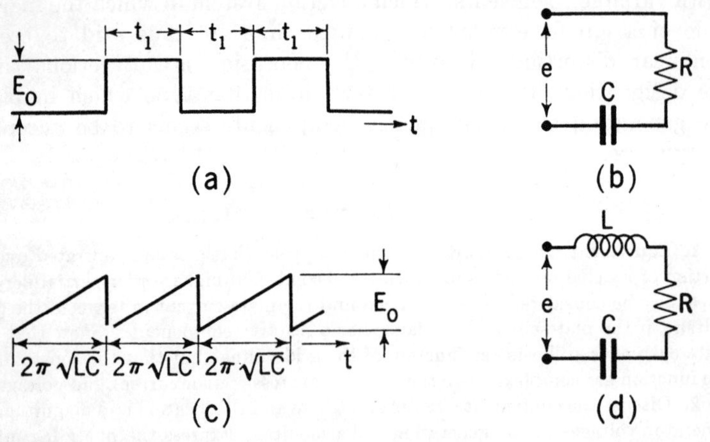

8. If the voltage wave shown in Fig. c is applied to the circuit in Fig. d, find the dissipation in R.

CHAPTER III

FOURIER INTEGRALS

3.1 Origin of the Fourier Integral Formula. In many branches of physics, particularly in radio engineering, the steady-state characteristics of systems or equipment are readily studied and the results are well known; but the study of transient characteristics is a more difficult matter. In this chapter, however, we shall introduce a very powerful tool, the Fourier integral, which allows the behavior of linear systems in the transient state to be described in terms of their steady-state characteristics.

In Fig. 1 is shown a transient signal. We shall now show how this can be considered as the superposition (*i.e.*, algebraic sum) of a large number of steady-state components and thus introduce the Fourier

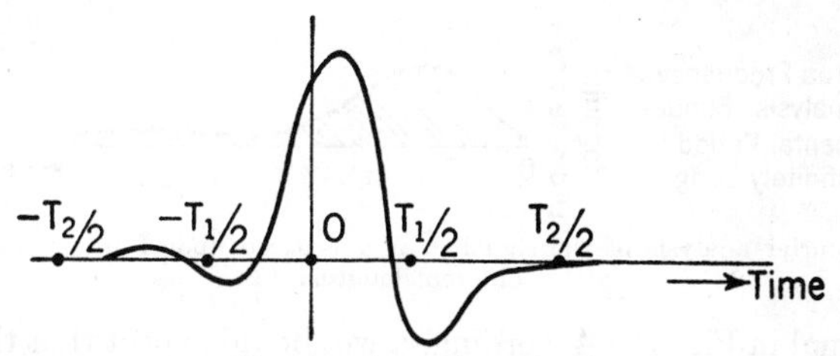

FIG. 1. A transient signal.

integral. First of all, we recall that in Sec. 1.8 we showed that, in the interval from $-T/2$ to $+T/2$, any function, with but few restrictions, may be analyzed into fundamental and harmonic components of the period T. Accordingly, in the range from $-T_1/2$ to $+T_1/2$, the signal in Fig. 1 may be expressed as the sum of components of the frequencies of $1/T_1$ and its harmonics $2/T_1$, $3/T_1$, etc. The relative magnitudes of the various components in this case are shown in Fig. 2*a*. If the length of the expansion interval is now successively increased to T_2, T_3, T_4 and is finally made infinitely long, the respective harmonic amplitude distributions will then be similar to those shown in Fig. 2*b* for T_2 and Fig. 2*c* for $T = \infty$. We note that, as T becomes longer and longer, the frequency spacing between harmonics becomes smaller and smaller. Finally, as T approaches infinity the frequency spacing between harmonics approaches zero and we approach the condition of a continuous distribution of frequency components.

Next, it should be pointed out that, when T becomes infinite, the individual harmonic components become infinitely long, so that they are essentially steady-state components. The graph of Fig. 2c may thus be considered a graph of the (steady-state) frequency composition

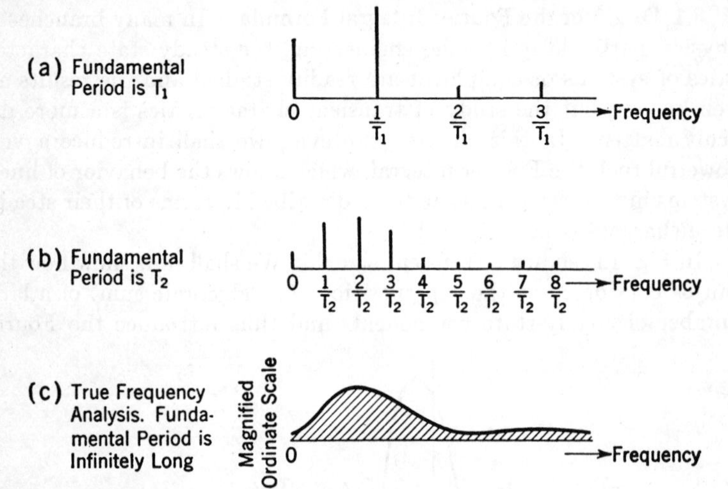

FIG. 2. Fourier analysis of the signal in Fig. 1 based upon fundamental periods of different lengths.

of the signal in Fig. 1. Accordingly, we should expect that the Fourier series expansion formula

$$G(t) = \frac{a_0}{2} + \sum_{n=1}^{\infty} (a_n \cos nt + b_n \sin nt) \tag{1}$$

might go over into an equation of the form

$$G(t) = \int_0^\infty a(\omega) \cos \omega t \, d\omega + \int_0^\infty b(\omega) \sin \omega t \, d\omega \qquad (2)^1$$

[1] The notation $a(\omega)$ and $b(\omega)$ means a that is a function of ω and b that is a function of ω. The zero frequency limits in Eq. (2) take care of the direct-current term in Eq. (1), except for cases in which there is a direct-current term lasting from $-\infty$ to $+\infty$. Such cases represent signals having infinite energy and require special and individual consideration when they arise. The unit step function discussed in the next chapter is such a case.

when the expansion interval is made infinitely long. Such a formula would then give the frequency composition of the function $G(t)$. Now it can be proved[1] that, if $G(t)$ satisfies certain conditions[2] which are actually satisfied by all functions representing radio signals, then $G(t)$ may be represented as shown in Eq. (2), where

$$a(\omega) = \frac{1}{\pi}\int_{-\infty}^{+\infty} G(t)\cos\omega t\,dt \tag{3}$$

and

$$b(\omega) = \frac{1}{\pi}\int_{-\infty}^{+\infty} G(t)\sin\omega t\,dt \tag{4}$$

Thus we have the Fourier integral formula, sometimes called the Fourier integral identity:

$$G(t) = \frac{1}{\pi}\int_0^{\infty}\left[\int_{-\infty}^{+\infty} G(t)\cos\omega t\,dt\right]\cos\omega t\,d\omega + \frac{1}{\pi}\int_0^{\infty}\left[\int_{-\infty}^{+\infty} G(t)\sin\omega t\,dt\right]\sin\omega t\,d\omega \tag{5}$$

With the aid of this formula, we can make frequency analyses of transients, as we shall show.

Equation (5) may also be written

$$G(t) = \frac{1}{\pi}\int_0^{\infty} S(\omega)\cos\left[\omega t + \phi(\omega)\right]d\omega \qquad (6)^3$$

where

$$S(\omega) = \sqrt{\left[\int_{-\infty}^{+\infty} G(t)\cos\omega t\,dt\right]^2 + \left[\int_{-\infty}^{+\infty} G(t)\sin\omega t\,dt\right]^2} \tag{7}$$

[1] See CARSLAW, H. S., "Fourier Series and Fourier Integrals," Chap. X, or WHITTAKER and WATSON, "Modern Analysis," Chap. IX.

[2] These conditions are that the function may have only a finite number of points of discontinuity and a finite number of maxima and minima in any finite interval and that $\int_{-\infty}^{+\infty} |G(t)|\,dt$ shall be finite. This latter condition might at first glance seem to be serious, since it rules out functions with a constant direct-current component. However, if the direct-current component is present only for a finite length of time, which is always the case in practice, the condition is satisfied.

[3] Just as in the corresponding Fourier series case, if $G(t)$ has a point of discontinuity, then the right sides of Eqs. (6), (5), and (2) will give the value

$$\tfrac{1}{2}[G(t+0) + G(t-0)]$$

at the point of discontinuity.

and

$$\tan \phi(\omega) = \frac{-\int_{-\infty}^{+\infty} G(t) \sin \omega t \, dt}{\int_{-\infty}^{+\infty} G(t) \cos \omega t \, dt} \tag{8}$$

If now we plot $S(\omega)$ as a function of ω, it will show the frequency composition of $G(t)$. Such a plot is shown in Fig. 2c.

It may be noted in passing that, if it were not for the Fourier integral formula, there would be no justification for assuming that a nonperiodic function had a frequency composition at all.

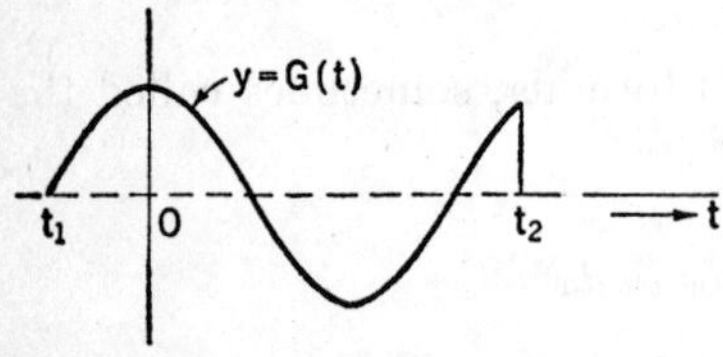

FIG. 3. A cosine wave of a specified length.

3.2 Examples of Frequency Distributions. Suppose that $G(t)$ is a harmonic function $\cos \omega_0 t$ over a small interval and that it is zero everywhere else (see Fig. 3). Let us find the frequency distribution of this function. This is a good function to study, for it will show us how the length of the wave train affects the frequency distribution and will indicate the transition from Fourier integrals to Fourier series.

We begin by calculating the integrals.

$$\int_{-\infty}^{+\infty} G(t) \cos \omega t \, dt = \int_{-\infty}^{t_1} 0 \cos \omega t \, dt + \int_{t_1}^{t_2} \cos \omega_0 t \cos \omega t \, dt + \int_{t_2}^{\infty} 0 \cos \omega t \, dt$$

$$= \int_{t_1}^{t_2} \cos \omega_0 t \cos \omega t \, dt$$

$$= \left[\frac{1}{2(\omega + \omega_0)} \sin (\omega + \omega_0)t + \frac{1}{2(\omega - \omega_0)} \sin (\omega - \omega_0)t \right]_{t_1}^{t_2} \tag{9}$$

In a similar manner,

$$\int_{-\infty}^{+\infty} G(t) \sin \omega t \, dt = \int_{t_1}^{t_2} \cos \omega_0 t \sin \omega t \, dt$$

$$= \left[\frac{-1}{2(\omega + \omega_0)} \cos (\omega + \omega_0)t + \frac{-1}{2(\omega - \omega_0)} \cos (\omega - \omega_0)t \right]_{t_1}^{t_2} \tag{10}$$

With the aid of Eqs. (7), (9), and (10) we can find the value of $S(\omega)$, for all values of ω, except ω_0. When $\omega = \omega_0$,

$$\int_{t_1}^{t_2} \cos \omega_0 t \cos \omega t \, dt = \int_{t_1}^{t_2} \cos^2 \omega_0 t \, dt$$

$$= \int_{t_1}^{t_2} \frac{1 - \cos 2\omega_0 t}{2} dt = \left[\frac{t}{2} - \frac{\sin 2\omega_0 t}{4\omega_0} \right]_{t_1}^{t_2}$$

$$= \frac{t_2 - t_1}{2} - \frac{1}{4\omega_0} (\sin 2\omega_0 t_2 - \sin 2\omega_0 t_1) \quad (11)$$

$$\int_{t_1}^{t_2} \cos \omega_0 t \sin \omega_0 t \, dt = \int_{t_1}^{t_2} \frac{\sin 2\omega_0 t}{2} dt$$

$$= -\frac{1}{4\omega_0} (\cos 2\omega_0 t_2 - \cos 2\omega_0 t_1) \quad (12)$$

With the aid of the foregoing formulas we can find the value of the frequency-distribution function $S(\omega)$ for any length of the wave train.

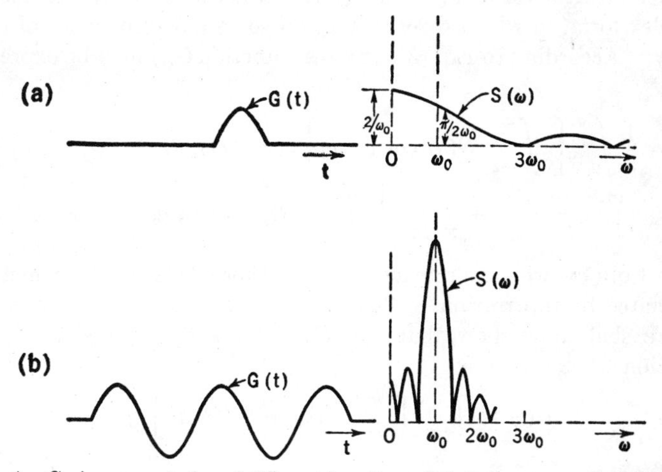

FIG. 4. Cosine wave trains of different lengths and their frequency distributions.

In Fig. 4 is a diagram showing the frequency distributions for wave trains of various lengths. These are obtained by substituting the values of t_2 and t_1 for the wave train under consideration into Eqs. (9), (10), (12), and (7). We see that, the more cycles there are in the periodic wave train, the more peaked is the frequency distribution. As the wave train becomes infinitely long, we approach the case of a Fourier series component. In the latter case, $S(\omega)$ is zero except at ω_0, when $G(t) = A \cos \omega_0 t$. If $G(t)$ is an infinitely long periodic wave train, of period $2\pi/\omega_0$, but not a pure cosine wave, then $S(\omega)$ is zero for all values of ω except ω_0 and its harmonics.

Exercises

1. Plot $S(\omega)$, for a signal $\cos \omega_0 t$ of just one cycle's duration, that is, $t_1 = \pi/2$, $t_2 = 5\pi/2$.

2. Find the frequency composition $S(\omega)$ of the group of two square waves in Fig. *A*. Plot $S(\omega)$ as a function of frequency.

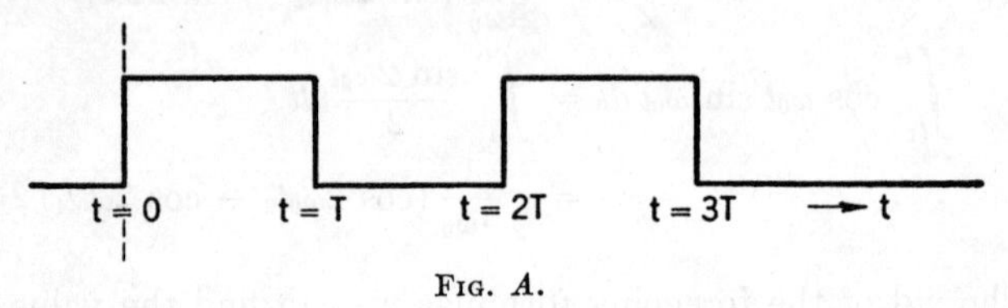

FIG. *A*.

3.3 Complex Form of Fourier Integrals—Fourier Pairs. The Fourier integral formula, given by Eq. (5), can also be expressed in complex form, in which case it takes on some new properties of symmetry. According to Eq. (5), any real function $G(t)$ may be expressed as

$$G(t) = \frac{1}{\pi}\int_0^\infty \left[\int_{-\infty}^{+\infty} G(g)\cos \omega g\, dg\right]\cos \omega t\, d\omega + \frac{1}{\pi}\int_0^\infty \left[\int_{-\infty}^{+\infty} G(g)\sin \omega g\, dg\right]\sin \omega t\, d\omega \tag{13}$$

In Eq. (13) we have replaced with g's those t's of Eq. (5) which are eliminated by integration.

We shall now show that Eq. (13) is exactly equivalent to the equation

$$G(t) = \int_{-\infty}^{+\infty}\left[\int_{-\infty}^{+\infty} G(g)\epsilon^{j2\pi f(t-g)}\, dg\right] df \tag{14}$$

where

$$f = \frac{\omega}{2\pi} \tag{15}$$

To prove this equivalence, we expand Eq. (14) into its real and imaginary parts. Thus

$$\begin{aligned} G(t) &= \int_{-\infty}^{+\infty}\left[\int_{-\infty}^{+\infty} G(g)\epsilon^{j2\pi f(t-g)}\, dg\right] df \\ &= \frac{1}{2\pi}\int_{-\infty}^{+\infty}\left[\int_{-\infty}^{+\infty} G(g)\cos \omega(t-g)\, dg\right] d\omega \\ &\quad + \frac{j}{2\pi}\int_{-\infty}^{+\infty}\left[\int_{-\infty}^{+\infty} G(g)\sin \omega(t-g)\, dg\right] d\omega \end{aligned} \tag{16}$$

Now since

$$\sin \omega(t - g) = - \sin [(-\omega)(t - g)] \tag{17}$$

and

$$\cos \omega(t - g) = + \cos [(-\omega)(t - g)] \tag{18}$$

we have

$$\int_{-\infty}^{+\infty} \left[\int_{-\infty}^{+\infty} G(g) \cos \omega(t - g)\, dg \right] d\omega = 2\int_{0}^{\infty} \left[\int_{-\infty}^{+\infty} G(g) \cos \omega(t - g)\, dg \right] d\omega \tag{19}$$

and

$$\int_{-\infty}^{+\infty} \left[\int_{-\infty}^{+\infty} G(g) \sin \omega(t - g)\, dg \right] d\omega = 0 \tag{20}$$

Therefore Eq. (14) reduces to

$$\begin{aligned} G(t) &= \frac{1}{\pi} \int_{0}^{\infty} \left[\int_{-\infty}^{+\infty} G(g) \cos \omega(t - g)\, dg \right] d\omega \\ &= \frac{1}{\pi} \int_{0}^{\infty} \left[\int_{-\infty}^{+\infty} G(g)(\cos \omega g \cos \omega t + \sin \omega g \sin \omega t)\, dg \right] d\omega \end{aligned} \tag{21}$$

The right side of Eq. (21) is the same as that of Eq. (13). We have thus shown that Eq. (14) is an equivalent expression for the Fourier integral identity.

Next, let us define the function $F(f)$ as

$$F(f) = \int_{-\infty}^{+\infty} \epsilon^{-j2\pi fg} G(g)\, dg \tag{22}$$

Then by Eq. (14) (since $\epsilon^{j2\pi f(t-g)} = \epsilon^{j2\pi ft}\epsilon^{-j2\pi fg}$)

$$G(t) = \int_{-\infty}^{+\infty} \epsilon^{j2\pi ft} F(f)\, df \tag{23}$$

or, writing the same thing in a different way,

$$G(g) = \int_{-\infty}^{+\infty} \epsilon^{j2\pi fg} F(f)\, df \tag{24}$$

Equations (22) and (24) are a pair of remarkable relationships existing between the functions $F(f)$ and $G(g)$. Functions that show these relationships to each other are known as Fourier transforms or *Fourier pairs*, and one is called the *mate* of the other.

The functions $F(f)$ and $G(g)$ are a highly symmetrical development of the functions $S(\omega)$ and $G(t)$ defined at the beginning of the chapter. In a sense, we might also call them a vectorial development. To show this, let us expand Eq. (22) into its real and imaginary parts. Thus

$$F(f) = \int_{-\infty}^{+\infty} G(g) \cos \omega g \, dg - j \int_{-\infty}^{+\infty} G(g) \sin \omega g \, dg \tag{25}$$

Comparing this with Eqs. (3), (4), and (7), we see that

$$\text{Real part of } F(f) = \pi a(\omega) = \text{real part of } F(-f) \tag{26}$$

$$\text{Imaginary part of } F(f) = -\pi b(\omega) = -\text{imaginary part of } F(-f) \tag{27}$$

$$\text{Absolute value of } |F(f)| = S(\omega) = |F(-f)| \tag{28}$$

Thus

$$F(-f) = [F(f)]^* \qquad (29)^1$$

Since $F(f)$ separates the in-phase and quadrature components of $S(\omega)$, it is really a more valuable and certainly a more concise formulation. Equations (22) and (24) are the equivalent in Fourier integral theory of Eqs. (76) and (72), respectively, of Chap. I in the theory of Fourier series.

If we wish to use ω instead of f as the second variable in Eq. (23) or (24), then we can write

$$G(t) = \frac{1}{2\pi} \int_{-\infty}^{+\infty} \epsilon^{j\omega t} \Omega(\omega) \, d\omega \tag{30}$$

where

$$\Omega(\omega) = \int_{-\infty}^{+\infty} \epsilon^{-j\omega t} G(t) \, dt = F(f) \tag{31}$$

Quite recently, R. V. L. Hartley[2] has pointed out that the Fourier integral identity may be written in the following completely symmetrical real form:

$$G(t) = \frac{1}{\sqrt{2\pi}} \int_{-\infty}^{+\infty} \psi(\omega)(\cos \omega t + \sin \omega t) \, d\omega \tag{32}$$

where

$$\psi(\omega) = \frac{1}{\sqrt{2\pi}} \int_{-\infty}^{+\infty} G(t)(\cos \omega t + \sin \omega t) \, dt \tag{33}$$

The reader may show as an exercise that this form can be derived from the earlier forms, Eq. (5) or (13).

The effect of a shift of the origin of $G(t)$ on its Fourier transform $F(f)$ follows easily from Eq. (22). Thus the Fourier transform of

[1] The asterisk in Eq. (29) signifies the complex conjugate.

[2] *Proc. I.R.E.*, March, 1942, p. 144.

$G(t-T)$, where T is a constant, is $\epsilon^{-j2\pi fT}F(f)$. This is the analogue of the result derived in Exercise 2 of Sec. 1.9 for Fourier series.

Just as in the case of Fourier series, the complex formulation of Fourier integrals frequently gives a more simple and rapid solution to practical problems than the separation into trigonometric components. We shall now illustrate the use of the complex formulation by solving an example.

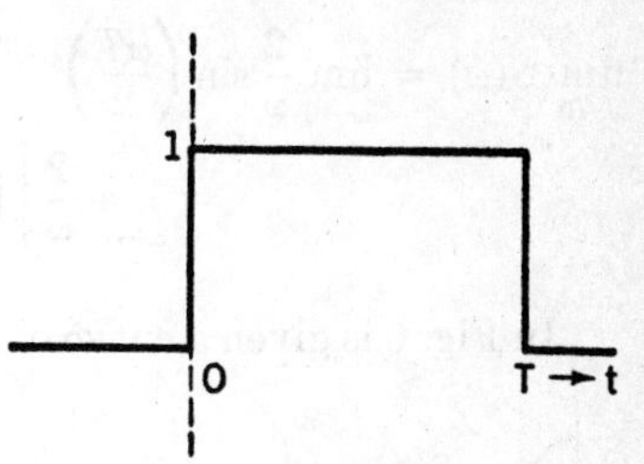

FIG. 5. A rectangular pulse of unit height.

3.4 Frequency Distribution of a Rectangular Pulse. Suppose we have a pulse of arbitrary length, such as is shown in Fig. 5, and we wish to find the frequency distribution of its components. To do this, we use Eqs. (22) and (31) and obtain

$$\Omega(\omega) = F(f) = \int_{-\infty}^{+\infty} \epsilon^{-j\omega g}G(g)\,dg = \int_0^T \epsilon^{-j\omega g}\,dg = \left.\frac{\epsilon^{-j\omega g}}{-j\omega}\right|_0^T$$
$$= \frac{\epsilon^{-j\omega T}-1}{-j\omega} = \frac{1}{\omega}[\sin\omega T + j(\cos\omega T - 1)] \tag{34}$$

Then, by Eq. (28), the frequency distribution

$$S(\omega) = |F(f)| = \frac{1}{\omega}\sqrt{\sin^2\omega T + (\cos\omega T - 1)^2}$$
$$= \frac{\sqrt{2}}{\omega}\sqrt{1-\cos\omega T} = \frac{2}{\omega}\sin\left(\frac{\omega T}{2}\right) \tag{35}$$

The frequency distribution thus has minima of zero amplitude when

$$f = \frac{\omega}{2\pi} = \frac{n}{T} \tag{36}$$

where n is any integer.

The frequency distribution will have maxima when

$$\frac{d}{d\omega}\left[\frac{2}{\omega}\sin\left(\frac{\omega T}{2}\right)\right] = 0 \tag{37}$$

which reduces to

$$\frac{\omega T}{2} = \tan\left(\frac{\omega T}{2}\right) \tag{38}$$

A singular case occurs when $f = 0$. In this case we expand $\sin(\omega T/2)$ in a Maclaurin series and disregard higher power terms as $f \to 0$. Thus

$$\lim_{\omega\to 0} S(\omega) = \lim_{\omega\to 0} \frac{2}{\omega} \sin\left(\frac{\omega T}{2}\right)$$
$$= \lim_{\omega\to 0} \frac{2}{\omega}\left[\left(\frac{\omega T}{2}\right) - \frac{1}{3!}\left(\frac{\omega T}{2}\right)^3 + \cdots\right] = T \quad (39)$$

In Fig. 6 is given a curve of $S(\omega)$ showing the frequency distribution of the components of a rectangular pulse. Comparing this with Fig. 10*b* of Chap. I for the frequency distribution of periodically repeated pulses or comparing Eq. (35) of this chapter with Eq. (94) of Chap. I, we see that the frequency range distributions are similar but that the components are bunched together at the harmonic frequencies in the case of periodically repeated pulses. The transition is shown precisely in Exercise 1 at the end of the chapter.

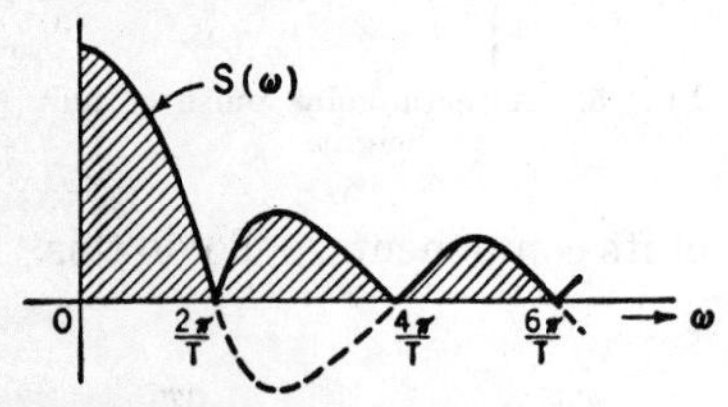

Fig. 6. Frequency distribution of the components of a rectangular pulse.

Equations (34) and (35) show the remarkable simplicity in the use of the complex form of the Fourier integral in this case.

3.5 Odd and Even Functions.[1] Fourier integrals just like Fourier series provide a means for separating a function into its odd and even parts. Starting with Eq. (23) and making use of Eq. (22), we write

$$G(t) = \int_{-\infty}^{+\infty} \epsilon^{j2\pi ft} F(f)\, df \quad (40)$$
$$= \frac{1}{2\pi}\int_{-\infty}^{+\infty} (\cos\omega t + j\sin\omega t)\, F(f)\, d\omega \quad (41)$$
$$= \frac{1}{2\pi}\int_{-\infty}^{+\infty}\int_{-\infty}^{+\infty} [G(g)\cos\omega g\cos\omega t + G(g)\sin\omega g\sin\omega t]\, dg\, d\omega$$
$$+ \frac{j}{2\pi}\int_{-\infty}^{+\infty}\int_{-\infty}^{+\infty} [G(g)\cos\omega g\sin\omega t - G(g)\sin\omega g\cos\omega t]\, dg\, d\omega \quad (42)$$

The imaginary component of Eq. (42) vanishes if $G(t)$ is assumed to be a real function of t. Therefore

[1] Our discussion is limited to the case in which $G(t)$ is a real function of t.

$$G(t) = \frac{1}{2\pi} \int_{-\infty}^{+\infty} \int_{-\infty}^{+\infty} G(g) \cos \omega g \cos \omega t \, dg \, d\omega + \frac{1}{2\pi} \int_{-\infty}^{+\infty} \int_{-\infty}^{+\infty} G(g) \sin \omega g \sin \omega t \, dg \, d\omega \tag{43}$$

The first term on the right of Eq. (43) is the even part of $G(t)$, and the second term is the odd part. This is a consequence of the fact that

$$\cos [\omega(-t)] = \cos \omega t \tag{44}$$

while

$$\sin [\omega(-t)] = -\sin \omega t \tag{45}$$

Since $G(t)$ is assumed to be real, it follows from Eq. (41) that, if $F(f)$ is real,

$$G(t) = \frac{1}{2\pi} \int_{-\infty}^{+\infty} \cos \omega t F(f) \, d\omega \tag{46}$$

so that $G(t)$ is an even function of t. On the other hand, if $F(f)$ is a pure imaginary, then Eq. (41) tells us that

$$G(t) = \frac{1}{2\pi} \int_{-\infty}^{+\infty} j \sin \omega t F(f) \, d\omega \tag{47}$$

so that $G(t)$ is an odd function of t. More generally, if $F(f)$ is complex, its real part gives rise to the even component of $G(t)$, while its imaginary part gives rise to the odd component of $G(t)$.

Let us next expand $F(f)$ into its real and imaginary components. Thus, from Eq. (22),

$$F(f) = \int_{-\infty}^{+\infty} \epsilon^{-j2\pi f g} G(g) \, dg = \int_{-\infty}^{+\infty} G(g) \cos \omega g \, dg - j \int_{-\infty}^{+\infty} G(g) \sin \omega g \, dg \tag{48}$$

We now note also that the real part of $F(f)$ is an even function of ω, and therefore of f, while the imaginary part of $F(f)$ is an odd function of ω and of f. We may therefore conclude that, if $F(f)$ is an even function of (f), then $G(t)$ is an even function of t. On the other hand, if $F(f)$ is an odd function of f, then $G(t)$ is an odd function of t. The converses are also true.

The foregoing facts can frequently be put to use in simplifying calculations. For example, in performing the frequency analysis of the pulse in Fig. 5, in case the origin of time is not fixed by some other condition in the problem, it is convenient to move it to the center of the pulse, thus making the pulse an even function of time. It then follows from the foregoing paragraphs that $F(f)$ will be a pure real quantity, and no vectorial manipulation will be necessary to find the frequency distribution. Thus we would have

$$F(f) = \int_{-\frac{T}{2}}^{+\frac{T}{2}} \epsilon^{-j2\pi fg}\, dg = \frac{\epsilon^{-j2\pi fg}}{-j2\pi f}\Bigg|_{-\frac{T}{2}}^{+\frac{T}{2}} = \frac{\epsilon^{-j2\pi f\frac{T}{2}} - \epsilon^{+j2\pi f\frac{T}{2}}}{-j2\pi f.} = \frac{2}{\omega}\sin\frac{\omega T}{2}$$

Let us now return once more to the general case. $F(f)$, being a complex quantity, may be expressed as

$$F(f) = P(f)\epsilon^{jQ(f)} \tag{49}$$

where $P(f)$ and $Q(f)$ are real. From Eq. (48) it follows that

$$P(f) = P(-f) \tag{50}$$

and

$$Q(f) = \tan^{-1}\frac{-\int_{-\infty}^{+\infty} G(g)\sin\omega g\, dg}{\int_{-\infty}^{+\infty} G(g)\cos\omega g\, dg} = -Q(-f) \tag{51}$$

Therefore $P(f)$ is an even function of f, while $Q(f)$ is an odd function. Now

$$P(f) = P\left(\frac{\omega}{2\pi}\right) = |F(f)| = S(\omega) \tag{52}$$

and

$$Q(f) = \phi(\omega) \tag{53}$$

Therefore Eq. (23) may be rewritten as

$$G(t) = \frac{1}{2\pi}\int_{-\infty}^{+\infty} S(\omega)\epsilon^{j[\omega t+\phi(\omega)]}\, d\omega \tag{54}$$

where

$$S(\omega) = S(-\omega) \tag{55}$$

and

$$\phi(\omega) = -\phi(-\omega) \tag{56}$$

The foregoing symmetry properties are a consequence of the fact that $G(t)$ is a pure real function of t.

Exercises

1. Show that if we write

$$F(f) = \alpha(\omega) + j\beta(\omega)$$

then $\alpha(\omega)$ is even, while $\beta(\omega)$ is odd, provided that $G(t)$ is real.

2. With $\alpha(\omega)$ and $\beta(\omega)$ as defined in Exercise 1, show that

$$\alpha(\omega) = \frac{2}{\pi}\int_0^{\infty} \cos\omega t\left[\int_0^{\infty} \alpha(u)\cos ut\, du\right] dt$$

$$\beta(\omega) = \frac{2}{\pi}\int_0^{\infty} \sin\omega t\left[\int_0^{\infty} \beta(u)\sin ut\, du\right] dt$$

3.6 Tabulation of Fourier Pairs. In a very valuable publication,[1] Campbell and Foster have listed a large number of Fourier pairs that have been worked out by various persons since Fourier first published his work. This tabulation gives the pairs $F(f)$ and $G(g)$ and therefore the frequency analysis of a wide variety of functions. It is extremely useful as a reference table. The text of the monograph also gives much valuable general information concerning Fourier integrals.

Since the Campbell and Foster monograph is available, no extensive table of Fourier pairs is presented in this book. For purposes of illustration, however, listed in Appendix D are those Fourier pairs which are used in the present volume. Thus the pairs derived in Secs. 3.2 and 3.4 are listed as pairs 3 and 4 in the table. When a table is used, it is, of course, unnecessary to derive the pairs as we have done.

Despite the great value of the Campbell and Foster table, it frequently happens that in specific cases, it is simpler to perform the integration in Eqs. (22) and (24) than to try to find the desired form in the table. The greatest value of the table is in those cases where it is a task of extreme difficulty to evaluate the integrals. Most of these cannot be evaluated by ordinary means but require contour integration in the complex plane.

In comparing the results of Sec. 3.5 with Campbell and Foster's discussion of The Elementary Properties of Pairs it should be remembered that our discussion is limited to cases where $G(t)$ is a real function of t.

Exercises

1. Find the frequency distribution of m pulses of length T_1 and repetition period T_2 as shown in the figure. Draw the frequency-distribution functions $S(\omega)$, for $m = 2$ and for $m = 10$.

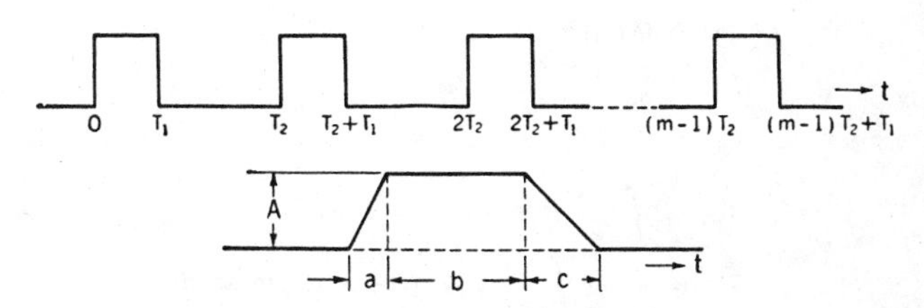

2. Find the frequency distribution of the trapezoidal pulse shown in the figure.

[1] Campbell, G. A., and R. M. Foster, Fourier Integrals for Practical Applications, *Bell Telephone System Mono.* B584. Our notation $F(f)$ and $G(g)$ follows that used by Campbell and Foster.

Fundamental Formulas

$$\omega = 2\pi f \tag{1}$$

$$\begin{aligned}
G(t) &= \int_0^\infty a(\omega)\cos\omega t\,d\omega + \int_0^\infty b(\omega)\sin\omega t\,d\omega \\
&= \frac{1}{\pi}\int_0^\infty \left[\int_{-\infty}^{+\infty} G(g)\cos\omega g\,dg\right]\cos\omega t\,d\omega \\
&\qquad + \frac{1}{\pi}\int_0^\infty \left[\int_{-\infty}^{+\infty} G(g)\sin\omega g\,dg\right]\sin\omega t\,d\omega \\
&= \frac{1}{\pi}\int_0^\infty S(\omega)\cos[\omega t + \phi(\omega)]\,d\omega = \frac{1}{2\pi}\int_{-\infty}^{+\infty} S(\omega)\cos[\omega t + \phi(\omega)]\,d\omega \\
&= \frac{1}{2\pi}\int_{-\infty}^{+\infty} S(\omega)\epsilon^{j[\omega t+\phi(\omega)]}\,d\omega \\
&= \int_{-\infty}^{+\infty}\left[\int_{-\infty}^{+\infty} G(g)\epsilon^{j2\pi f(t-g)}\,dg\right]df \\
&= \int_{-\infty}^{+\infty} \epsilon^{j2\pi ft}F(f)\,df = \frac{1}{2\pi}\int_{-\infty}^{+\infty} \epsilon^{j\omega t}F(f)\,d\omega
\end{aligned} \tag{2}$$

$$a(\omega) = \frac{1}{\pi}\int_{-\infty}^{+\infty} G(t)\cos\omega t\,dt \tag{3}$$

$$b(\omega) = \frac{1}{\pi}\int_{-\infty}^{+\infty} G(t)\sin\omega t\,dt \tag{4}$$

$$\begin{aligned}
S(\omega) = S(-\omega) &= \sqrt{\left[\int_{-\infty}^{+\infty} G(t)\cos\omega t\,dt\right]^2 + \left[\int_{-\infty}^{+\infty} G(t)\sin\omega t\,dt\right]^2} \\
&= |F(f)|
\end{aligned} \tag{5}$$

$$\phi(\omega) = -\phi(-\omega) = \tan^{-1}\left[\frac{-b(\omega)}{a(\omega)}\right] = \tan^{-1}\frac{-\int_{-\infty}^{+\infty} G(g)\sin\omega g\,dg}{\int_{-\infty}^{+\infty} G(g)\cos\omega g\,dg} \tag{6}$$

$$\begin{aligned}
F(f) &= \int_{-\infty}^{+\infty} \epsilon^{-j2\pi ft}G(t)\,dt \\
&= \int_{-\infty}^{+\infty} G(t)\cos\omega t\,dt - j\int_{-\infty}^{+\infty} G(t)\sin\omega t\,dt \\
&= S(\omega)\epsilon^{j\phi(\omega)}
\end{aligned} \tag{7}$$

$$F(-f) = [F(f)]^* \tag{8}$$

$$G(t) = \frac{1}{2\pi}\int_{-\infty}^{+\infty} \epsilon^{j\omega t}\Omega(\omega)\,d\omega \tag{9a}$$

where

$$\Omega(\omega) = \int_{-\infty}^{+\infty} \epsilon^{-j\omega t}G(t)\,dt = F(f) \tag{9b}$$

$$G(t) = \frac{1}{\sqrt{2\pi}}\int_{-\infty}^{+\infty} \psi(\omega)\,(\cos\omega t + \sin\omega t)\,d\omega \tag{10a}$$

where

$$\psi(\omega) = \frac{1}{\sqrt{2\pi}}\int_{-\infty}^{+\infty} G(t)\,(\cos\omega t + \sin\omega t)\,dt \tag{10b}$$

$$\Omega(\omega) = S(\omega)\epsilon^{j\phi(\omega)} \tag{11}$$

CHAPTER IV

RADIO APPLICATIONS AND PHYSICAL INTERPRETATION OF FOURIER INTEGRAL ANALYSIS

4.1 Introduction. The Fourier integral identity

$$G(t) = \frac{1}{\pi} \int_0^\infty S(\omega) \cos [\omega t + \phi(\omega)]\, d\omega \tag{1}$$

expresses any function of t as the integral (*i.e.*, summation) of steady-state frequency components. We shall show in the following sections of this chapter that this gives us a means of reducing problems in transients to steady-state problems. The latter are usually easier to handle.

In the practical use of Fourier integrals in this chapter, the problem involved will usually be to find the effect of a transmission system, with a given frequency characteristic, on a particular signal of interest. The general method of solution will be as follows:

1. Find the frequency composition, $S(\omega)$ or $F(f)$, of the signal of interest.
2. Apply the characteristics of the transmission system to the result of 1, and obtain a resultant frequency composition.
3. Find the signal equivalent to the resultant frequency composition in 2. This is the desired answer.

The foregoing procedure will be illustrated by numerous examples in the following pages. It should be noted in passing that this procedure makes use of the superposition theorem, which, while almost obvious, is derived and made precise in Sec. 4.6.

Although the method is limited to systems to which the superposition theorem applies, *i.e.*, linear systems, this restriction is generally not serious. As a matter of experience, Fourier integral analysis has turned out to be the most powerful method available for investigating the required frequency responses in radio apparatus. At the end of the chapter, after we have worked out several practical examples, we shall look further into the general aspects of the method.

4.2 Frequency Distribution and Selective Circuits—Transients. Let us suppose that a voltage pulse of the form shown in Fig. 1*a* is sent into a frequency-selective network, such as that shown in Fig. 1*b*. The frequency-distribution function of the pulse is shown in Fig. 1*c*, and the frequency response curve of the network is shown in Fig. 1*d*. Now, according to the method outlined in Sec. 4.1, the frequency response curve of the voltage output of the network will be the product of $S(\omega)$ and $Y(\omega)$. This product is shown in Fig. 1*e* and it is obviously sharply peaked at ω_1.

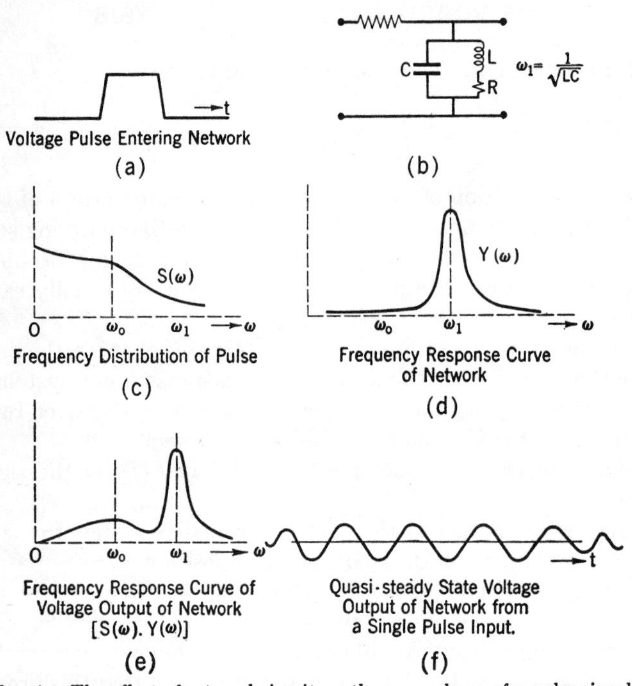

FIG. 1. The effect of a tuned circuit on the wave shape of a pulse signal.

The curve in Fig. 1*e* is much steeper and more sharply peaked at ω_1 than $S(\omega)$ is at ω_0. Let us find the meaning of this. Since the voltage output is so sharply peaked at ω_1, it must consist of a wave train several periods long of frequency $\omega_1/2\pi$. From the orthodox point of view, this output is called the transient response of the tuned circuit due to shock excitation. However, from the point of view of Fourier integral analysis, it is just the ordinary selectivity of the network operating on the frequency distribution of the incoming voltage.

4.3 Distortionless Transmission. We shall next find the conditions under which a signal of arbitrary wave form will be transmitted without distortion through a system. Let the signal be a voltage represented as $G(t)$. Then by Eq. (1)

$$G(t) = \frac{1}{\pi} \int_0^\infty S(\omega) \cos [\omega t + \phi(\omega)] \, d\omega \tag{2}$$

Next let us represent the transfer impedance of the system at any frequency $\omega/2\pi$ as

$$Z(\omega) = |Z(\omega)| \epsilon^{jB(\omega)} \tag{3}$$

The output will then be

$$I(t) = \frac{1}{\pi} \int_0^\infty \frac{S(\omega)}{|Z(\omega)|} \cos [\omega t + \phi(\omega) - B(\omega)] \, d\omega \qquad (4)^1$$

In any signal of technical importance, $S(\omega)$ will have an appreciable value only in a finite frequency range, say from $\omega_1/2\pi$ to $\omega_2/2\pi$, where $\omega_1/2\pi$ may be zero in special cases. We may therefore rewrite Eq. (4) as

$$I(t) = \frac{1}{\pi} \int_{\omega_1}^{\omega_2} \frac{S(\omega)}{|Z(\omega)|} \cos [\omega t + \phi(\omega) - B(\omega)] \, d\omega \tag{5}$$

Suppose now that in the frequency range $\omega_1/2\pi$ to $\omega_2/2\pi$ the transmission of the system is uniform with frequency and the phase shift is proportional to frequency; then we may write

$$|Z(\omega)| = K \tag{6}$$
$$B(\omega) = \omega T \tag{7}$$

where K and T are constants. Substituting these values into Eq. (5) we get

$$\begin{aligned} I(t) &= \frac{1}{\pi K} \int_{\omega_1}^{\omega_2} S(\omega) \cos [\omega(t - T) + \phi(\omega)] \, d\omega \\ &= \frac{1}{K} G(t - T) \end{aligned} \tag{8}$$

Thus the output signal is of exactly the same wave form as the input; but it has its amplitude altered by the factor $1/K$, and it is delayed in time by an amount T. Therefore, a transmission system

[1] If $Z(\omega)$ has the dimensions of an electrical impedance and $G(t)$ is a voltage, then $I(t)$ is a current. The argument of this section is, however, not limited to this particular case. $Z(\omega)$ may represent any type of transfer characteristic, and $G(t)$ and $I(t)$ may be any types of signals. The only limitation is that the dimensions of $G(t)$ shall be equal to the product of the dimensions of $Z(\omega)$ and $I(t)$.

whose transmission characteristics are of the form given by Eqs. (6) and (7) will give distortionless transmission. The foregoing argument shows that Eqs. (6) and (7) are "sufficient" condition for distortionless transmission. If we reverse the line of thought in Eq. (8), it follows that for the transmission system to cause only a change in amplitude and a time delay, but no change in wave shape, the conditions described by Eqs. (6) and (7) are also "necessary." In other words, Eqs. (6) and (7) are the only forms of $|Z(\omega)|$ and $B(\omega)$, that will give a transmitted signal of the form $(1/K)G(t - T)$. The foregoing results could readily have been predicted from the effect that a shift in the origin of time has on the Fourier transform, as discussed in Sec. 3.3.

4.4 Negative Frequencies and Symmetry Properties of the Transmission Characteristics of a System. If we use the complex form of the Fourier integral in making a frequency analysis of a signal $G(t)$, then according to Eq. (23) or Eq. (30) of Chap. III, we write

$$G(t) = \int_{-\infty}^{+\infty} \epsilon^{j2\pi ft} F(f)\, df = \frac{1}{2\pi} \int_{-\infty}^{+\infty} \epsilon^{j\omega t} \Omega(\omega)\, d\omega \tag{9}$$

In either of these forms, $G(t)$ has negative as well as positive frequency components, so that the transmission characteristics of systems for negative frequency components become a matter of interest.

In Eq. (29) of Chap. III it is shown that $F(-f)$ is the complex conjugate of $F(f)$, that is,

$$F(-f) = [F(f)]^* \tag{10}$$

Similarly,

$$\Omega(-\omega) = [\Omega(\omega)]^* \tag{11}$$

Consequently,

$$\begin{aligned} \frac{1}{2\pi} [\epsilon^{j\omega t}\Omega(\omega) + \epsilon^{j(-\omega)t}\Omega(-\omega)] &= \frac{1}{2\pi} \{\epsilon^{j\omega t}\Omega(\omega) + [\epsilon^{j\omega t}\Omega(\omega)]^*\} \\ &= \frac{1}{\pi} S(\omega) \cos [\omega t + \phi(\omega)] \end{aligned} \tag{12}$$

where

$$\Omega(\omega) = S(\omega)\epsilon^{j\phi(\omega)} \tag{13}$$

From Eqs. (1), (9), (12), and (13) it then follows that the use of negative frequencies is a means for combining the amplitude and phase characteristics of the frequency distribution of $G(t)$ into a single complex function.

Suppose now that the signal $G(t)$ enters a transmission system having a frequency characteristic such that at any frequency $\omega/2\pi$ the amplitude is multiplied by a factor $A(\omega)$ and the phase is advanced by an angle $B(\omega)$. Consequently, the component

$$\frac{1}{\pi} S(\omega) \cos [\omega t + \phi(\omega)] \tag{14}$$

will be altered to become

$$\frac{1}{\pi} S(\omega) A(\omega) \cos [\omega t + \phi(\omega) + B(\omega)] \tag{15}$$

It follows from the foregoing that the signal which leaves the system, say $G_1(t)$, may be expressed as

$$\begin{aligned} G_1(t) &= \frac{1}{\pi} \int_0^\infty S(\omega) A(\omega) \cos [\omega t + \phi(\omega) + B(\omega)]\, d\omega \\ &= \frac{1}{2\pi} \int_{-\infty}^{+\infty} \epsilon^{j\omega t} \Omega_1(\omega)\, d\omega \end{aligned} \tag{16}$$

where

$$\Omega_1(\omega) = S(\omega) A(\omega) \epsilon^{j[\phi(\omega)+B(\omega)]} \tag{17}$$

and

$$\Omega_1(-\omega) = [\Omega_1(\omega)]^* \tag{18}$$

From Eqs. (13), (17), and (18) it follows that the transmission characteristic $1/z(j\omega)$ of any system may be expressed in complex form, as

$$A(\omega) \epsilon^{jB(\omega)} = \frac{1}{z(j\omega)} \tag{19}$$

where

$$A(-\omega) = A(\omega) \tag{20}$$

and

$$B(-\omega) = -B(\omega) \tag{21}$$

In other words,

$$z(-j\omega) = [z(+j\omega)]^* \tag{22}$$

Equations (20), (21), and (22) show how the transmission characteristics of a system for negative frequencies can be obtained from the values for positive frequencies.

It follows from the above formulas that, if a signal $\sin \omega t$ entering a system comes out as $A \sin (\omega t + B)$, then a signal $\sin [(-\omega)t]$ entering the system will come out as $A \sin [(-\omega)t - B]$. Since $\sin \omega t = -\sin (-\omega t)$ and $\sin (\omega t + B) = -\sin (-\omega t - B)$, this result agrees with what we know by ordinary common sense must happen.

It is hoped that the foregoing account will make clear to the reader what is really going on physically when negative frequencies are used in the Fourier analysis of a physical problem.

4.5 Bandwidth and Detail in Video and Pulse Amplifiers.[1] Let us next determine the effect of the width of the pass band of a video or pulse amplifier on various elementary types of signals that it may be called upon to transmit. In Fig. 2 are examples of such elementary signals. Figures 2*a* and *b* represent demarcation lines between black

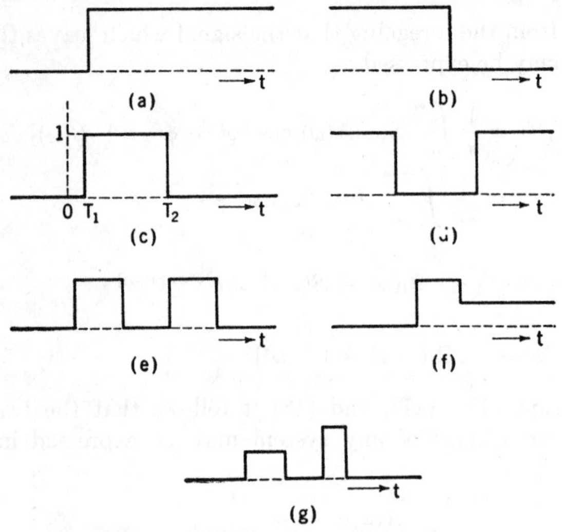

Fig. 2. Elementary signal types.

and white portions of a television picture, while Figs. 2*e*, *f*, and *g* are types of fine picture detail that may commonly occur. Figures 2*c* and *d* would be isolated fine spots or lines in a picture and are therefore not particularly important in television in their own right. However, we shall find that *c* can be used as a convenient means for analyzing all the other types of picture detail. Furthermore, it is the basic signal in pulse amplifiers. We shall therefore begin our analysis by finding the effect of a transmission system on a signal of the type shown in Fig. 2*c*.

Let us assume an amplifier having uniform transmission in the frequency range from zero to $\omega_s/2\pi$ and no transmission above this fre-

[1] The realization of the importance of frequency bandwidth in the transmission of detail and in the transmission of information in general is largely due to H. Nyquist and R. V. L. Hartley.

quency. Furthermore, let us assume that the phase shift of the amplifier is proportional to frequency (within the transmission band) since it has been shown that this is a desirable characteristic for low distortion and since, furthermore, this is a condition which can approximately be obtained in practice. Let us now find the shape of the output signal of such an amplifier when the input is a signal of the type shown in Fig. 2*c*. Since the characteristics of the amplifier are given as a function of frequency, we first transform the input signal into frequency elements so that we can find the effect of the amplifier upon it. Accordingly we use Eq. (30) of Chap. III and write

$$\text{Input signal} \equiv G(t) = \frac{1}{2\pi}\int_{-\infty}^{+\infty} \epsilon^{j\omega t}\Omega(\omega)\,d\omega \tag{23}$$

where

$$\begin{aligned}\Omega(\omega) &= \int_{-\infty}^{+\infty} \epsilon^{-j\omega t}G(t)\,dt = \int_{T_1}^{T_2} \epsilon^{-j\omega t}\,dt = \left.\frac{\epsilon^{-j\omega t}}{-j\omega}\right|_{T_1}^{T_2} \\ &= \frac{\epsilon^{-j\omega T_2} - \epsilon^{-j\omega T_1}}{-j\omega}\end{aligned} \tag{24}$$

The transmission of the amplifier is uniform, say equal to k, from 0 to $\omega_s/2\pi$, and the phase shift is proportional to frequency, say $= -g\omega$, where g is a constant. Therefore, the output signal is[1]

Output signal $\equiv \bar{G}(t)$

$$\begin{aligned}&= \frac{1}{2\pi}\int_{-\omega_s}^{\omega_s} \epsilon^{j\omega(t-g)}\frac{k}{-j\omega}\left(\epsilon^{-j\omega T_2} - \epsilon^{-j\omega T_1}\right)d\omega \\ &= \frac{jk}{2\pi}\int_{-\omega_s}^{\omega_s}\left[\frac{\epsilon^{j\omega(t-g-T_2)} - \epsilon^{j\omega(t-g-T_1)}}{\omega}\right]d\omega \\ &= \frac{jk}{2\pi}\int_{-\omega_s}^{\omega_s}\left\{\left[\frac{\cos\omega(t-g-T_2)}{\omega} - \frac{\cos\omega(t-g-T_1)}{\omega}\right]\right. \\ &\qquad \left. + j\left[\frac{\sin\omega(t-g-T_2)}{\omega} - \frac{\sin\omega(t-g-T_1)}{\omega}\right]\right\}d\omega\end{aligned} \tag{25}$$

Now $\cos(\omega A)/\omega$ is an odd function of ω, while $\sin(\omega A)/\omega$ is an even function of ω, where A is any quantity independent of ω. Therefore

$$\int_{-\omega_s}^{+\omega_s} \frac{\cos\omega A}{\omega}\,d\omega = 0 \tag{26}$$

and

$$\int_{-\omega_s}^{+\omega_s} \frac{\sin(\omega A)}{\omega}\,d\omega = 2\int_0^{\omega_s} \frac{\sin(\omega A)}{\omega}\,d\omega \tag{27}$$

[1] Since we are using the complex form of the Fourier integral, we must include negative as well as positive frequencies.

Thus Eq. (25) becomes

Output signal $\equiv \bar{G}(t)$

$$= -\frac{k}{\pi}\int_0^{\omega_s}\left[\frac{\sin\omega(t-g-T_2)}{\omega}-\frac{\sin\omega(t-g-T_1)}{\omega}\right]d\omega$$

$$= \frac{k}{\pi}\left[\int_0^{\omega_s(t-g-T_1)}\frac{\sin x}{x}\,dx - \int_0^{\omega_s(t-g-T_2)}\frac{\sin x}{x}\,dx\right] \quad (28)$$

Now $\int(\sin x/x)\,dx$ cannot be integrated in closed form in terms of elementary functions, but it can be integrated in a power series. This integral is so important in technical problems that a function Si(x) has been defined by the equation

$$\mathrm{Si}(x) = \int_0^x \frac{\sin x}{x}\,dx \quad (29)$$

and tables of its values have been calculated, as in Table I (page 76). The function Si(x) is called the sine integral of x. Making use of this new function, Eq. (28) may be written as

Output signal $= \bar{G}(t)$

$$= \frac{k}{\pi}\{\mathrm{Si}[\omega_s(t-g-T_1)] - \mathrm{Si}[\omega_s(t-g-T_2)]\} \quad (30)$$

Graphs of Si(x) and of $\bar{G}(t)$ are shown in Fig. 3. Equation (30) is the solution to our problem. We should have arrived at the same answer, of course, if we had used the trigonometric form of the Fourier integral instead of the complex form.

The function Si(x) is fundamental in the theory of pulse transmission as related to bandwidth. In Fig. 3*a* we see that its value is approximately $-\pi/2$ over the range in which $x < 0$ and approximately $+\pi/2$ over the range in which $x > 0$. Around $x = 0$ the function Si$(x)/\pi$ rises from a minimum of -0.59 at $-\pi$ to a maximum of $+0.59$ at $+\pi$. Outside the range $-\pi < x < \pi$ the function $(1/\pi)$Si(x) has slight and rapidly decreasing oscillations about the value -0.5 when $x < -\pi$ and about the value $+0.5$ when $x > +\pi$. At $x = 0$ the rate of rise of $(1/\pi)$Si(x) is $1/\pi$. Let us now see how these properties of Si(x) affect the transmission of picture detail.

Looking at Eq. (30) and Fig. 3*e* we see that the shape of the leading edge of the pulse is essentially

$$\frac{k}{\pi}\left\{\frac{\pi}{2} + \mathrm{Si}[\omega_s(t-g-T_1)]\right\}$$

except for a very slight effect due to the lagging edge. Neglecting this effect we see that the leading edge rises from 0 to $1.09k$ in the

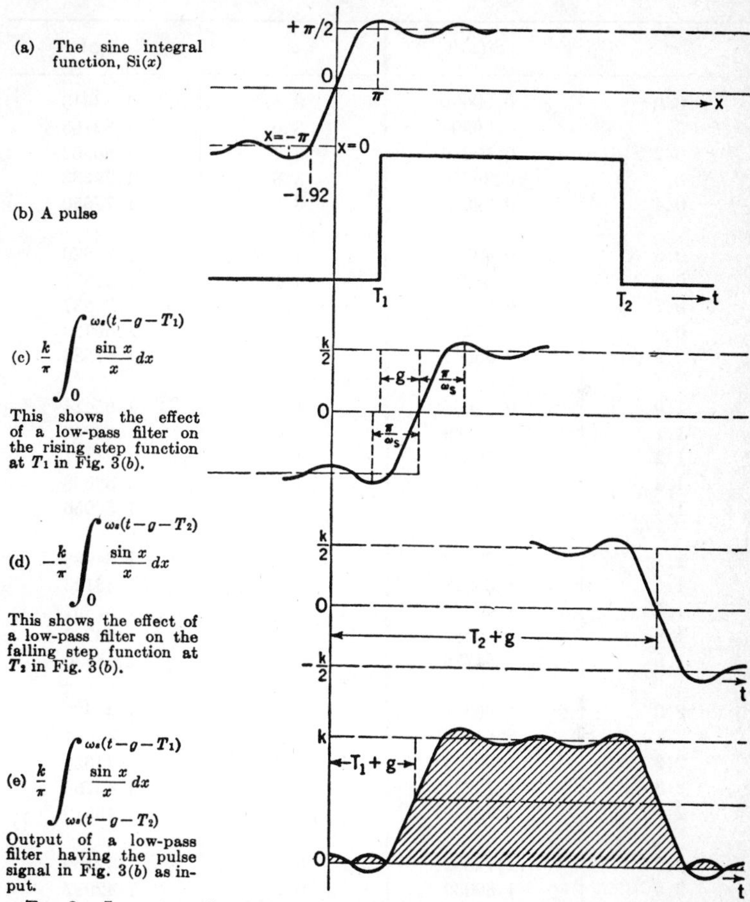

FIG. 3. Important signals in the transmission of step functions and pulses through a low-pass filter having sharp cutoff at $\omega_s/2\pi$. (These figures illustrate the time delay in transmission, the finite rate of rise and fall, anticipatory transients, and overshoot.)

time from $g + T_1 - (1.92/\omega_s)$ to $g + T_1 + (3.14/\omega_s)$. In other words, in a length of time

$$\frac{5.06}{\omega_s} = \frac{0.805}{\text{cutoff frequency}} \tag{31}$$

the signal rises from zero to its maximum value. At $g + T_1$, when the

TABLE I.—SINE INTEGRAL, Si(x)*

$$\mathrm{Si}(x) = \int_0^x \frac{\sin u}{u}\, du$$

x	Si(x)	x	Si(x)
0.0	0.00000	3.5	1.83313
0.1	0.09994	3 6	1.82195
0.2	0.19956	3.7	1.80862
0.3	0.29850	3.8	1.79333
0.4	0.39646	3.9	1.77650
0.5	0.49311	4.0	1.75820
0.6	0.58813	4.1	1.73874
0.7	0.68122	4.2	1.71837
0.8	0.77210	4.3	1.69732
0.9	0.86047	4.4	1.67583
1.0	0.94608	4.5	1.65414
1.1	1.02869	4.6	1.63246
1.2	1.10805	4.7	1.61101
1.3	1.18396	4.8	1.58998
1.4	1.25623	4.9	1.56956
1.5	1.32468	5.0	1.54993
1.6	1.38918	5.1	1.53125
1.7	1.44959	5.2	1.51367
1.8	1.50582	5.3	1.49732
1.9	1.55778	5.4	1.48230
2.0	1.60541	5.5	1.46872
2.1	1.64870	5.6	1.45667
2.2	1.68763	5.7	1.44620
2.3	1.72221	5.8	1.43736
2.4	1.75249	5.9	1.43018
2.5	1.77852	6.0	1.42469
2.6	1.80039	6.1	1.42087
2.7	1.81821	6.2	1.41871
2.8	1.83210	6.3	1.41817
2.9	1.84219	6.4	1.41922
3.0	1.84865	6.5	1.42179
3.1	1.85166	6.6	1.42582
3.2	1.85140	6.7	1.43121
3.3	1.84808	6.8	1.43878
3.4	1.84191	6.9	1.44570

* From PEDERSEN, P. O. Radiation from a Vertical Antenna over Flat Perfectly Conducting Earth, *G. E. C. Gad.*, Copenhagen, Denmark.

TABLE I.—SINE INTEGRAL, Si(x).—(*Continued*)

x	Si(x)	x	Si(x)
7.0	1.45460	11.0	1.57831
7.1	1.46443	11.1	1.56927
7.2	1.47509	11.2	1.56042
7.3	1.48644	11.3	1.55182
7.4	1.49834	11.4	1.54356
7.5	1.51068	11.5	1.53571
7.6	1.52331	11.6	1.52835
7.7	1.53611	11.7	1.52155
7.8	1.54894	11.8	1.51535
7.9	1.56167	11.9	1.50981
8.0	1.57419	12.0	1.50497
8.1	1.58637	12.1	1.50088
8.2	1.59810	12.2	1.49755
8.3	1.60928	12.3	1.49501
8.4	1.61981	12.4	1.49327
8.5	1.62960	12.5	1.49234
8.6	1.63857	12.6	1.49221
8.7	1.64665	12.7	1.49287
8.8	1.65379	12.8	1.49430
8.9	1.65993	12.9	1.49647
9.0	1.66504	13.0	1.49936
9.1	1.66908	13.1	1.50292
9.2	1.67205	13.2	1.50711
9.3	1.67393	13.3	1.51188
9.4	1.67473	13.4	1.51716
9.5	1.67446	13.5	1.52291
9.6	1.67316	13.6	1.52905
9.7	1.67084	13.7	1.53352
9.8	1.66757	13.8	1.54225
9.9	1.66338	13.9	1.54917
10.0	1.65835	14.0	1.55621
10.1	1.65253	14.1	1.56330
10.2	1.64600	14.2	1.57036
10.3	1.63883	14.3	1.57733
10.4	1.63112	14.4	1.58414
10.5	1.62294	14.5	1.59072
10.6	1.61439	14.6	1.59702
10.7	1.60556	14.7	1.60296
10.8	1.59654	14.8	1.60851
10.9	1.58743	14.9	1.61360

TABLE I.—SINE INTEGRAL, Si(x).—(*Continued*)

x	Si(x)	x	Si(x)
15.0	1.61819	19.0	1.51863
15.1	1.62226	19.1	1.51967
15.2	1.62575	19.2	1.52122
15.3	1.62865	19.3	1.52324
15.4	1.63093	19.4	1.52572
15.5	1.63258	19.5	1.52863
15.6	1.63359	19.6	1.53192
15.7	1.63396	19.7	1.53357
15.8	1.63370	19.8	1.53954
15.9	1.63280	19.9	1.54378
16.0	1.63130	20.0	1.54824
16.1	1.62921	20.1	1.55289
16.2	1.62657	20.2	1.55767
16.3	1.62339	20.3	1.56253
16.4	1.61973	20.4	1.56743
16.5	1.61573	20.5	1.57232
16.6	1.61112	20.6	1.57714
16.7	1.60627	20.7	1.58186
16.8	1.60111	20.8	1.58641
16.9	1.59572	20.9	1.59077
17.0	1.59014	21.0	1.59489
17.1	1.58443	21.1	1.59873
17.2	1.57863	21.2	1.60225
17.3	1.57285	21.3	1.60543
17.4	1.56711	21.4	1.60823
17.5	1.56146	21.5	1.61063
17.6	1.55598	21.6	1.61261
17.7	1.55070	21.7	1.61415
17.8	1.54568	21.8	1.61525
17.9	1.54097	21.9	1.61590
18.0	1.53661	22.0	1.61608
18.1	1.53264	22.1	1.61582
18.2	1.52909	22.2	1.61510
18.3	1.62600	22.3	1.61395
18.4	1.52339	22.4	1.61238
18.5	1.52128	22.5	1.61041
18.6	1.51969	22.6	1.60806
18.7	1.51863	22.7	1.60536
18.8	1.51810	22.8	1.60234
18.9	1.51810	22.9	1.59902

TABLE I.—SINE INTEGRAL, Si(x).—(*Continued*)

x	Si(x)	x	Si(x)
23.0	1.59546	24.5	1.53897
23.1	1.59168	24.6	1.53672
23.2	1.58772	24.7	1.54484
23.3	1.58363	24.8	1.53333
23.4	1.57945	24.9	1.53221
23.5	1.57521	25.0	1.53148
23.6	1.57097	50.0	1.55162
23.7	1.56676		
23.8	1.56262		
23.9	1.55860		
24.0	1.55474		
24.1	1.55107		
24.2	1.54762		
24.3	1.54444		
24.4	1.54154		

signal is rising most rapidly, its rate of rise is[1]

$$\text{Max. rate of rise} = \frac{k\omega_s}{\pi} = 2k \text{ times cutoff frequency}$$

$$= \frac{2k}{\text{period of cutoff frequency}} \quad (32)$$

These latter values are probably the most descriptive of the sharpness of the sides of the outgoing pulse.

We note from Fig. 3*e* that there is a time delay, numerically equal to g, between the input and the main output signal. The output, however, shows two additional effects besides those already discussed. These are

1. Overshoot
2. Anticipatory transients

Overshoot is the phenomenon of the signal exceeding its distortionless value before settling down. (There is about 9 per cent overshoot in Fig. 3*e*.) Concerning this phenomenon (as well as that of anticipatory transients, discussed below) we may point out that the frequency components outside the range $-\omega_s < \omega < \omega_s$ (which have not been passed by the amplifier) would just cancel the effect.

[1] The rate of fall of the lagging edge is the same.

Without contradicting the foregoing, we may note, however, that at each edge considered separately, as shown in Fig. 3c or *d*, the 9 per cent overshoot in the pulse only becomes narrower but does not decrease in peak value as the pass band is increased. It therefore continues to exist even when $\omega_s \to \infty$, only it becomes infinitesimally thin. This is then an example of Gibbs's phenomenon in Fourier integrals, and we note that it has the same 9 per cent value as Gibbs's phenomenon in Fourier series[1] (see Sec. 1.13).[2] In the case of a narrow pulse, however, when there is interaction between the edge effects of T_1 and T_2, the overshoots may be eliminated for some pulse widths. This is illustrated by Fig. 6*b*.

Finally, a word should be said about *anticipatory transients*. These constitute the phenomenon of the existence of output signal ahead of the main pulse. If these transients exist beween T_1 and $T_1 + g$, they may just be considered as ordinary transients in the transmission system. However, if they occur before $t = T_1$, they violate the law of cause and effect by letting the effect appear before the cause. This may happen when we have assumed amplitude and phase characteristics of the amplifier that cannot simultaneously be exactly satisfied. In the author's "Transformation Calculus" it is shown that certain particular relations must exist between the amplitude and phase

[1] In the case of a square edge of unit height the frequency components in the pass band add up to $(1/\pi)[\pi/2 + \text{Si}(\omega_s t)]$ as shown in Fig. *A*. It is of interest to consider briefly the properties of Gibbs's phenomenon in this case. The frequency components between ω_s and infinity add up to the curve in Fig. *B*, which is the difference between $1/\pi[\pi/2 + \text{Si}(\omega_s t)]$ and the square edge. As ω_s is made larger, the curve in Fig. *B* is compressed in the horizontal direction, but not in the vertical. Consequently as $\omega_s \to \infty$, the curve in Fig. *B* represents less and less energy, but its maximum amplitude is unaffected. Gibbs's phenomenon thus represents the effect of those frequency components which have been omitted.

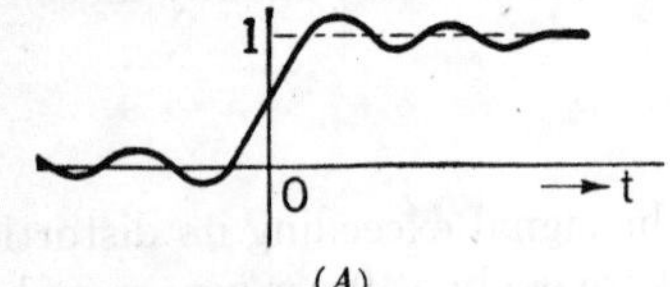

(*A*)

FIG. *A*. Response of a low-pass filter to a unit step.

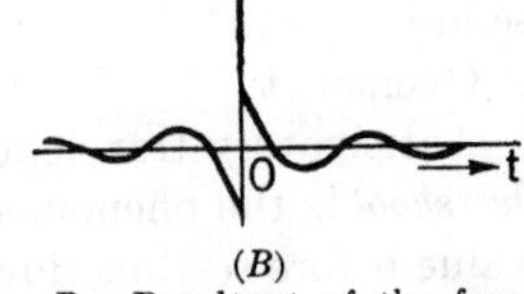

(*B*)

FIG. *B*. Resultant of the frequency components in a unit step which are not passed by the low-pass filter.

[2] The overshoot phenomena discussed here are related to sharp cutoff and are discussed in more detail in Sec. 4.19*a*. Another type of overshoot, that due to the quadrature component in asymmetric sideband transmission, is discussed in Sec. 4.9.

characteristics of a system. In the particular case of our amplifier, if we consider its cutoff characteristics as being due to a low-pass filter, it is found that an infinite number of sections are necessary (and therefore an infinite time delay g) in order to get absolutely sharp cutoff at ω_s. This eliminates the violation of the law of cause and effect.

Despite the foregoing demonstration that our assumed conditions cannot be satisfied exactly, they can be satisfied to a sufficiently close approximation, so that all the principal phenomena described in this section can be observed in practice. Thus the relation between pass band and the sharpness of rise of a pulse can be verified experimentally. Also, the phenomena of overshoot and of oscillations preceding the main pulse can be observed directly in an oscilloscope, and they can be seen as striations in a television picture at a line of demarcation between black and white. Later in this chapter we shall discuss means of reduction of this latter undesired effect.

4.6 The Superposition Theorem of Fourier Integral Analysis. In Eq. (30) we have the analytical expression for the output of a low-pass

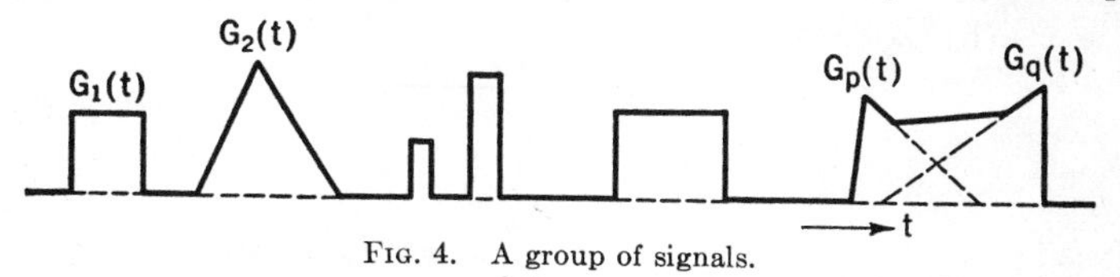

FIG. 4. A group of signals.

video amplifier when the input is a pulse Suppose next that we consider any system in which the input is a group of signals as shown in Fig. 4 and that the individual details in Fig. 4 are called $G_1(t)$, $G_2(t)$, . . . , $G_n(t)$, respectively.[1] In that case,

$$\begin{aligned} F(f) &= \int_{-\infty}^{+\infty} \epsilon^{-j2\pi ft} G(t)\,dt = \int_{-\infty}^{+\infty} \epsilon^{-j2\pi ft}[G_1(t) + G_2(t) + \cdots + G_n(t)]\,dt \\ &= \int_{-\infty}^{+\infty} \epsilon^{-j2\pi ft} G_1(t)\,dt + \cdots + \int_{-\infty}^{+\infty} \epsilon^{-j2\pi ft} G_n(t)\,dt \\ &= F_1(f) + F_2(f) + \cdots + F_n(f) \end{aligned} \tag{33}$$

Suppose, furthermore, that the system[2] causes a phase lag $g(\omega)$ and introduces an amplitude multiplication factor $K(\omega)$ at any fre-

[1] There may be overlap between signals, as shown between $G_p(t)$ and $G_q(t)$ in Fig. 4, without disturbing the following argument. In fact, it is just in such overlap cases that the theorem is most useful.

[2] The assumption that the effect of the system can be completely expressed by a phase shift $g(\omega)$ and an amplitude multiplication factor, $K(\omega)$, is equivalent to assuming that the system is linear.

quency $\omega/2\pi$. Then the output signal is

$$
\begin{aligned}
\text{Output signal} &= \overline{G}(t) \\
&= \frac{1}{2\pi}\int_{-\infty}^{+\infty} \epsilon^{j[\omega t - g(\omega)]} K(\omega)[F_1(f) + F_2(f) + \cdots + F_n(f)]\, d\omega \\
&= \frac{1}{2\pi}\int_{-\infty}^{+\infty} \epsilon^{j[\omega t - g(\omega)]} K(\omega) F_1(f)\, d\omega \\
&\quad + \frac{1}{2\pi}\int_{-\infty}^{+\infty} \epsilon^{j[\omega t - g(\omega)]} K(\omega) F_2(f)\, d\omega + \cdots \\
&\quad + \frac{1}{2\pi}\int_{-\infty}^{+\infty} \epsilon^{j[\omega t - g(\omega)]} K(\omega) F_n(f)\, d\omega \\
&= \overline{G_1}(t) + \overline{G_2}(t) + \cdots + \overline{G_n}(t)
\end{aligned}
\tag{34}
$$

(a) Transmission Characteristics

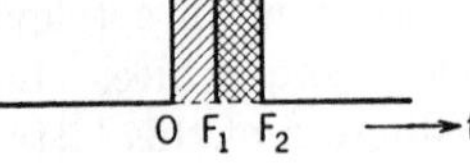

(b) Original Signal

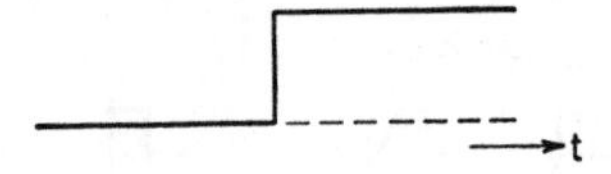

(c) Response to Shaded Transmission System

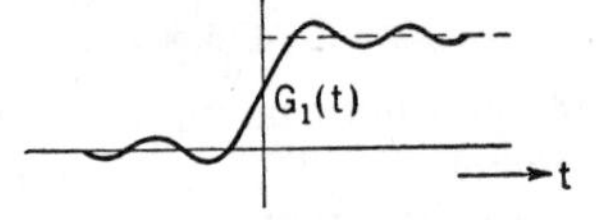

(d) Response to Cross-Hatched Transmission System

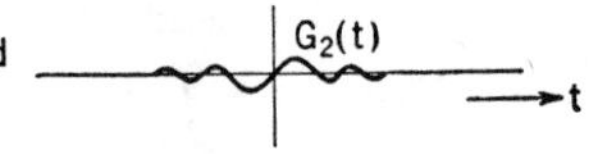

(e) Response to Combined Transmission System

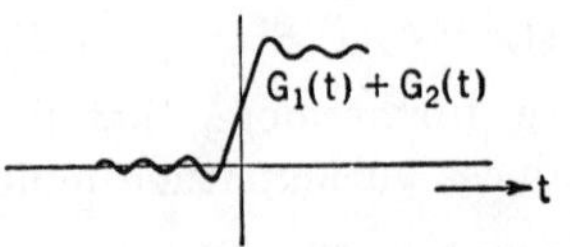

Fig. 5. Illustration of the principle of superposition as applied to frequency ranges.

We see from Eq. (34) that the analytical expression for the output of a group of signals is just the sum of the expressions for the outputs of the individual signals. This we may call the superposition theorem of Fourier integral analysis. We shall find this theorem very useful in the remainder of the chapter. Its use is of course limited, as is everything discussed in this chapter, to linear systems.

In an entirely similar manner, we can show that, if a single signal $G(t)$ going through two different transmission systems of frequency

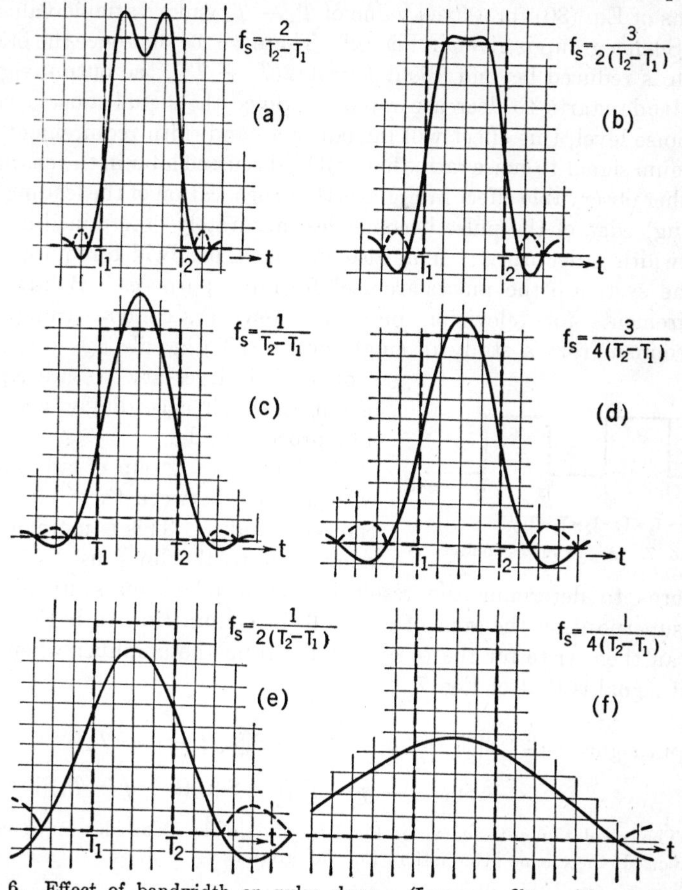

FIG. 6. Effect of bandwidth on pulse shape. (Low-pass filter with cutoff at f_s.)

characteristics $F_1(f)$ and $F_2(f)$ has responses $G_1(t)$ and $G_2(t)$, then the signal obtained when the original signal goes through a transmission system whose response is $F_1(f) + F_2(f)$ will be $G_1(t) + G_2(t)$. This is illustrated in Fig. 5.

4.7 Bandwidth and Detail in Video and Pulse Amplifiers—Bandwidth Requirements. Let us return now to the case of pulses going through a low-pass filter. So far we have said nothing about the important matter of how much bandwidth is required to pass a pulse of given length. Equations (31) and (32) show that the steepness of the sides is proportional to the bandwidth, but the best approach to the question of true bandwidth requirements is a series of actual graphs of Eq. (30) for a fixed value of $T_2 - T_1$ and a variable value of ω_s. Such a group is given in Fig. 6.[1] There we see that once the bandwidth is reduced beyond about $f_s = 1/2(T_2 - T_1)$, the output-signal amplitude starts to decrease rapidly. Since the signal must exceed the noise level, this effect will introduce a bandwidth requirement for optimum signal-to-noise ratio that will be discussed later in the chapter. Another observable effect in Fig. 6 is that the location of the leading (or lagging) edge of the pulse becomes less accurately determined as the bandwidth is decreased. This also will put a bandwidth requirement on the system if the pulses are used for radar purposes. Bandwidth requirements for television purposes, however, cannot readily be determined from a study of single pulses. To handle this question properly it is necessary to study a pair of pulses, which, accordingly, we shall now proceed to do.

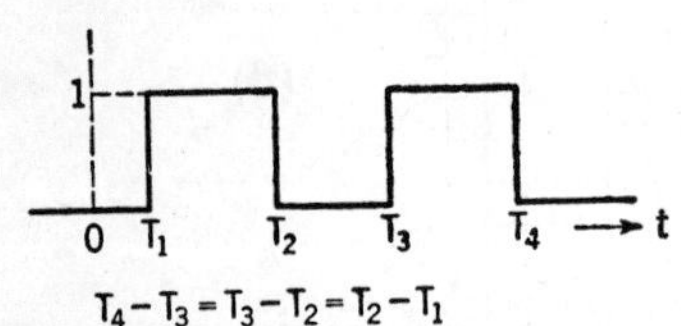

FIG. 7. A pair of test pulses.

In Fig. 7 is a group of two pulses with a space between them equal to the pulse width. This is more or less equivalent to the lines used in test patterns to determine the resolution of a television system. By the superposition theorem of Sec. 4.6, in conjunction with Eq. (30) we can then write for the output signal from the amplifier when the input signal is that of Fig. 7,

$$\text{Output signal} = \frac{k}{\pi}\{\text{Si}[\omega_s(t - g - T_1)] - \text{Si}[\omega_s(t - g - T_2)] + \text{Si}[\omega_s(t - g - T_3)] - \text{Si}[\omega_s(t - g - T_4)]\} \quad (35)$$

[1] The calculation of the curves in Fig. 6 is quite simple. Consider, for example, Fig. 6a. If there is no attenuation, Eq. (30) gives us

$$\begin{aligned} G(t) &= \frac{1}{\pi}\{\text{Si}[\omega_s(t - g - T_1)] - \text{Si}[\omega_s(t - g - T_2)]\} \\ &= \frac{1}{\pi}\{\text{Si}[\omega_s(t - g - T_1)] - \text{Si}[\omega_s(t - g - T_1) - \omega_s(T_2 - T_1)]\} \\ &= \frac{1}{\pi}[\text{Si}(x) - \text{Si}(x - 4\pi)] \end{aligned}$$

where $x = \omega_s(t - g - T_1)$.

The output $G(t)$ is then obtained for a series of values of x from about -2π to $+6\pi$, while the input is just a unit pulse from $x = 0$ to $x = 4\pi$.

With the aid of Eq. (35) the patterns in Fig. 8 have been calculated. As a general conclusion from Fig. 8, we may say that the required bandwidth for good detail is about that of Fig. 8*c*, *i.e.*,

$$f_s = \frac{\omega_s}{2\pi} = \frac{1}{2(T_2 - T_1)} \tag{36}$$

where $T_2 - T_1$ is the width of the smallest detail that it is desired to show in the television picture. If the bandwidth is decreased below this value, the detail rapidly becomes "washed out." The effect of increasing the bandwidth beyond the value given by Eq. (36) is principally to sharpen the sides of the edges.

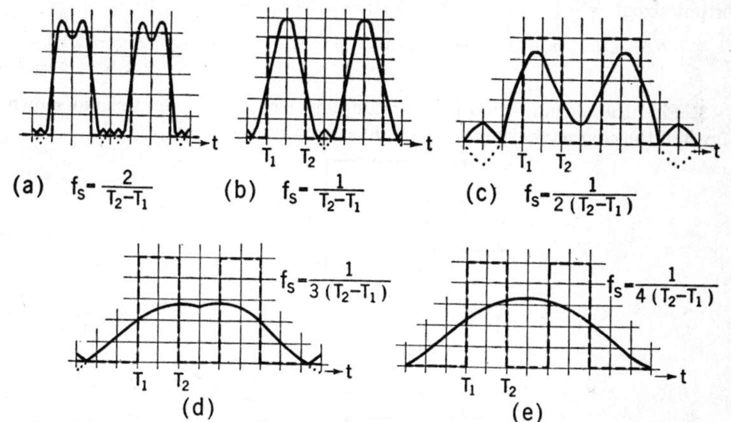

FIG. 8. Effect of bandwidth on the transmission of detail. (Low-pass filter with cutoff at f_s.)

Figure 8 is sufficiently important so that it is worth while considering a numerical example. Suppose that we have two rectangular pulses, each 1 μsec long, and that they are separated by an interval of 1 μsec. If these pulses pass through a transmission system having a bandwidth of 250 kc, we have the case of Fig. 8*e*. In this case the bandwidth is insufficient to show any sign of the detail between the pulses. If the bandwidth is increased to 333 kc, shown in Fig. 8*d*, the detail is still completely hidden but the general broadening of the output starts to show a hint of the existence of two pulses. Next, as the bandwidth is increased from 333 to 500 kc, the detail rather suddenly shows up clearly (see Fig. 8*c*). Further increases of the bandwidth to 1 mc (Fig. 8*b*) and to 2 mc (Fig. 8*a*) have the effect of sharpening the edges of the pulses.

Exercises

1. Find the output signal for the pulses in Fig. 7 if the video amplifier is not low-pass but band-pass from ω_1 to ω_2, with linear phase shift in the pass band as before. Discuss the importance or lack of importance of the very low frequencies.

2. Find the output signal from the low-pass amplifier of Sec. 4.5 for the input signal shown in Fig. *A*.

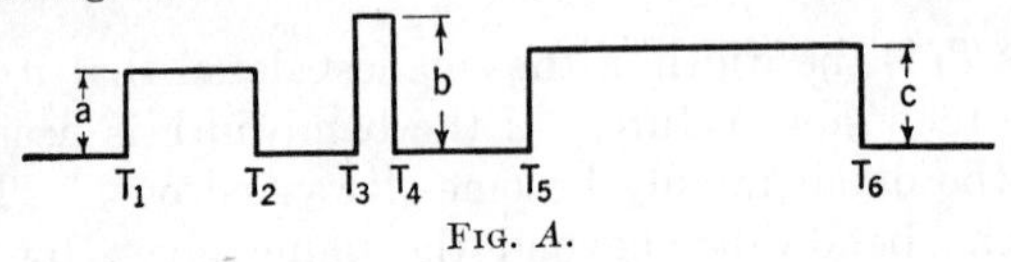

FIG. *A*.

Answer:

$$\text{Output signal} = \frac{k}{\pi}\{a\,\text{Si}[\omega_s(t - g - T_1)] - a\,\text{Si}[\omega_s(t - g - T_2)] + b\,\text{Si}[\omega_s(t - g - T_3)] - b\,\text{Si}[\omega_s(t - g - T_4)] + c\,\text{Si}[\omega_s(t - g - T_5)] - c\,\text{Si}[\omega_s(t - g - T_6)]\}$$

3. Find the output signal from an amplifier having the input signal shown in Fig. *B*, if the characteristics of the amplifier are those shown in Fig. *C*.

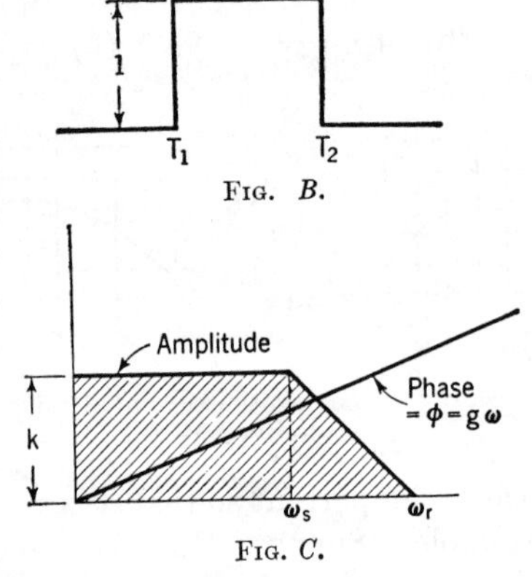

FIG. *B*.

FIG. *C*.

4. In the circuit of Fig. *D*, assume that the input is a voltage pulse of unit height and length $T_2 - T_1$. Find the output by the methods of Fourier integral analysis. The table of integrals in Appendix B may be used.

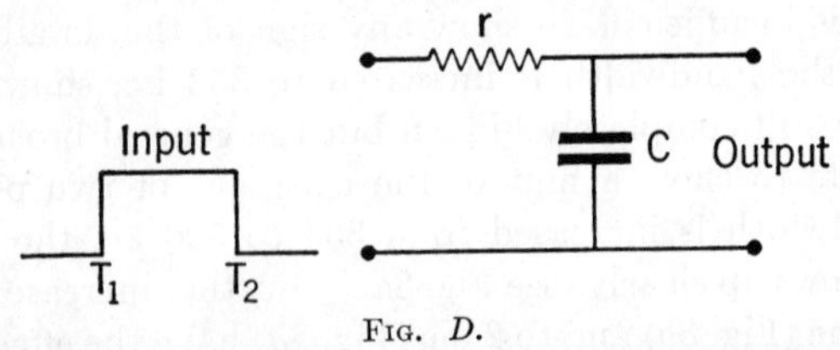

FIG. *D*.

4.8 Bandwidth and Detail in Intermediate-frequency Amplifiers—Symmetrical Sideband Case. Let us next suppose that the detail of

Fig. 2c is used to amplitude-modulate an intermediate-frequency carrier, giving a signal as shown in Fig. 9a.

Let the frequency of the intermediate-frequency carrier be $\omega_c/2\pi$, and suppose that the intermediate-frequency amplifier has uniform transmission, equal to K, from $\omega_c - \omega_p$ to $\omega_c + \omega_q$. Furthermore, assume that the phase shift is linear and symmetrical in the pass band, *i.e.*,

$$\text{Phase lag} = g(\omega - \omega_b) \tag{37}$$

The signal of Fig. 9a is

$$\left.\begin{aligned} G(t) &= \cos \omega_c t \qquad &&\text{(from } T_1 \text{ to } T_2\text{)} \\ G(t) &= 0 &&\text{(elsewhere)} \end{aligned}\right\} \tag{38}$$

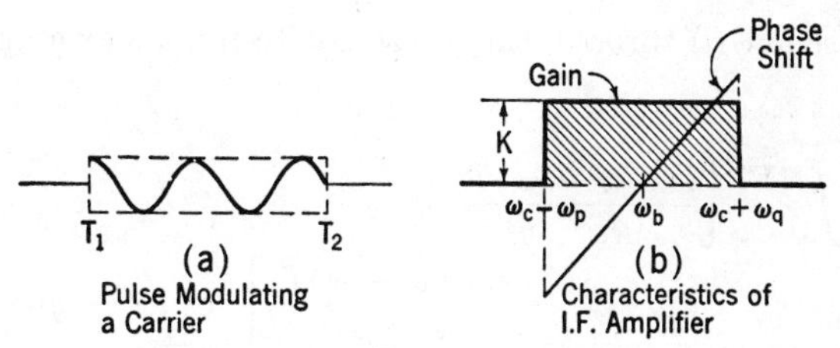

FIG. 9.

We shall analyze this signal with the trigonometric form of the Fourier integral (Eq. (5) of Chap. III) since this is the most convenient in this case. Accordingly the coefficients $a(\omega)$ and $b(\omega)$ are

$$\begin{aligned} a(\omega) &= \frac{1}{\pi}\int_{-\infty}^{+\infty} G(t) \cos \omega t \, dt \\ &= \frac{1}{\pi}\int_{T_1}^{T_2} \cos \omega_c t \cos \omega t \, dt \\ &= \frac{1}{2\pi}\int_{T_1}^{T_2} [\cos (\omega - \omega_c)t + \cos (\omega + \omega_c)t] \, dt \\ &= \frac{\sin (\omega - \omega_c)T_2}{2\pi(\omega - \omega_c)} + \frac{\sin (\omega + \omega_c)T_2}{2\pi(\omega + \omega_c)} - \frac{\sin (\omega - \omega_c)T_1}{2\pi(\omega - \omega_c)} \\ &\qquad - \frac{\sin (\omega + \omega_c)T_1}{2\pi(\omega + \omega_c)} \end{aligned} \tag{39}$$

$$\begin{aligned} b(\omega) &= \frac{1}{\pi}\int_{-\infty}^{+\infty} G(t) \sin \omega t \, dt = \frac{1}{\pi}\int_{T_1}^{T_2} \cos \omega_c t \sin \omega t \, dt \\ &= \frac{1}{2\pi}\int_{T_1}^{T_2} [\sin (\omega - \omega_c)t + \sin (\omega + \omega_c)t] \, dt \\ &= \frac{\cos (\omega - \omega_c)T_1}{2\pi(\omega - \omega_c)} + \frac{\cos (\omega + \omega_c)T_1}{2\pi(\omega + \omega_c)} - \frac{\cos (\omega - \omega_c)T_2}{2\pi(\omega - \omega_c)} \\ &\qquad - \frac{\cos (\omega + \omega_c)T_2}{2\pi(\omega + \omega_c)} \end{aligned} \tag{40}$$

If, as we shall assume, the carrier frequency is very high with respect to the modulation frequency range, the terms with $\omega + \omega_c$ in the denominator become negligible with respect to the others. Therefore, approximately,

$$G(t) = \int_0^\infty a(\omega) \cos \omega t \, d\omega + \int_0^\infty b(\omega) \sin \omega t \, d\omega$$
$$= \int_0^\infty \left[\frac{\sin (\omega - \omega_c) T_2}{2\pi(\omega - \omega_c)} - \frac{\sin (\omega - \omega_c) T_1}{2\pi(\omega - \omega_c)} \right] \cos \omega t \, d\omega$$
$$+ \int_0^\infty \left[\frac{\cos (\omega - \omega_c) T_1}{2\pi(\omega - \omega_c)} - \frac{\cos (\omega - \omega_c) T_2}{2\pi(\omega - \omega_c)} \right] \sin \omega t \, d\omega \quad (41)$$

If now we send $G(t)$ through the intermediate-frequency amplifier, the output is

$$\bar{G}(t) = \frac{K}{2\pi} \int_{\omega_c - \omega_p}^{\omega_c + \omega_q} \left[\frac{\sin (\omega - \omega_c) T_2}{(\omega - \omega_c)} - \frac{\sin (\omega - \omega_c) T_1}{(\omega - \omega_c)} \right] \cos [\omega t - g(\omega - \omega_b)] \, d\omega$$
$$+ \frac{K}{2\pi} \int_{\omega_c - \omega_p}^{\omega_c + \omega_q} \left[\frac{\cos (\omega - \omega_c) T_1}{(\omega - \omega_c)} - \frac{\cos (\omega - \omega_c) T_2}{(\omega - \omega_c)} \right] \sin [\omega t - g(\omega - \omega_b)] \, d\omega \quad (42)$$

To evaluate these integrals, let

$$\omega_1 = \omega - \omega_c \quad (43)$$

and

$$g(\omega_c - \omega_b) = \theta \quad (44)$$

Then

$$\begin{aligned} \cos [\omega t - g(\omega - \omega_b)] &= \cos [\omega_c t - g(\omega_c - \omega_b) + (\omega - \omega_c)t - g(\omega - \omega_c)] \\ &= \cos [(\omega_c t - \theta) + \omega_1(t - g)] \\ &= \cos [\omega_1(t - g)] \cos (\omega_c t - \theta) \\ &\qquad - \sin [\omega_1(t - g)] \sin (\omega_c t - \theta) \end{aligned} \quad (45)$$

and

$$\begin{aligned} \sin [\omega t - g(\omega - \omega_b)] &= \sin [\omega_c t - g(\omega_c - \omega_b) + (\omega_c - \omega_c)t - g(\omega - \omega_c)] \\ &= \sin [(\omega_c t - \theta) + \omega_1(t - g)] \\ &= \sin [\omega_1(t - g)] \cos (\omega_c t - \theta) \\ &\qquad + \cos [\omega_1(t - g)] \sin (\omega_c t - \theta) \end{aligned} \quad (46)$$

Furthermore,

$$d\omega_1 = d\omega \quad (47)$$

Substituting these equations into Eq. (42), we obtain

$$\bar{G}(t) = \frac{K}{2\pi} \int_{-\omega_p}^{+\omega_q} \left(\frac{\sin \omega_1 T_2}{\omega_1} - \frac{\sin \omega_1 T_1}{\omega_1} \right)$$
$$\{\cos [\omega_1(t - g)] \cos (\omega_c t - \theta) - \sin [\omega_1(t - g)] \sin (\omega_c t - \theta)\} \, d\omega_1$$
$$+ \frac{K}{2\pi} \int_{-\omega_p}^{+\omega_q} \left(\frac{\cos \omega_1 T_1}{\omega_1} - \frac{\cos \omega_1 T_2}{\omega_1} \right)$$
$$\{\sin [\omega_1(t - g)] \cos (\omega_c t - \theta) + \cos [\omega_1(t - g)] \sin (\omega_c t - \theta)\} \, d\omega_1$$
$$= \frac{K}{2\pi} \left(\int_{-\omega_p}^{+\omega_q} \left\{ \frac{\sin \omega_1 T_2}{\omega_1} \cos [\omega_1(t - g)] - \frac{\sin \omega_1 T_1}{\omega_1} \cos [\omega_1(t - g)] \right. \right.$$
$$\left. \left. + \frac{\cos \omega_1 T_1}{\omega_1} \sin [\omega_1(t - g)] - \frac{\cos \omega_1 T_2}{\omega_1} \sin [\omega_1(t - g)] \right\} d\omega_1 \right) \cos(\omega_c t - \theta)$$
$$+ \frac{K}{2\pi} \left(\int_{-\omega_p}^{+\omega_q} \left\{ \frac{\sin \omega_1 T_1}{\omega_1} \sin [\omega_1(t - g)] \right. \right.$$
$$- \frac{\sin \omega_1 T_2}{\omega_1} \sin [\omega_1(t - g)] + \frac{\cos \omega_1 T_1}{\omega_1} \cos [\omega_1(t - g)]$$
$$\left. \left. - \frac{\cos \omega_1 T_2}{\omega_1} \cos [\omega_1(t - g)] \right\} d\omega_1 \right) \sin (\omega_c t - \theta)$$
$$= \frac{K}{2\pi} \left\{ \int_{-\omega_p}^{+\omega_q} \left[\frac{\sin \omega_1(t - g - T_1)}{\omega_1} \right. \right.$$
$$\left. \left. - \frac{\sin \omega_1(t - g - T_2)}{\omega_1} \right] d\omega \right\} \cos (\omega_c t - \theta)$$
$$+ \frac{K}{2\pi} \left\{ \int_{-\omega_p}^{+\omega_q} \left[\frac{\cos \omega_1(t - g - T_1)}{\omega_1} \right. \right.$$
$$\left. \left. - \frac{\cos \omega_1(t - g - T_2)}{\omega_1} \right] d\omega_1 \right\} \sin (\omega_c t - \theta)$$
$$= \frac{K}{2\pi} \left[\int_{-\omega_p(t-g-T_1)}^{+\omega_q(t-g-T_1)} \frac{\sin x}{x} \, dx - \int_{-\omega_p(t-g-T_2)}^{+\omega_q(t-g-T_2)} \frac{\sin x}{x} \, dx \right] \cos (\omega_c t - \theta)$$
$$+ \frac{K}{2\pi} \left[\int_{-\omega_p(t-g-T_1)}^{+\omega_q(t-g-T_1)} \frac{\cos x}{x} \, dx - \int_{-\omega_p(t-g-T_2)}^{+\omega_q(t-g-T_2)} \frac{\cos x}{x} \, dx \right] \sin (\omega_c t - \theta) \quad (48)$$

Equation (48) is the solution for the output signal. We shall now analyze its meaning, considering first the case of symmetrical side-band transmission. In this case ω_c is in the middle of the pass band, so that we many write

$$\omega_q = \omega_p = \omega_m \quad (49)$$

and

$$\omega_c = \omega_b \qquad \text{(so that } \theta = 0) \quad (50)$$

where $\omega_m/2\pi$ is one-half the width of the pass band of the intermediate-frequency amplifier. For this case, we note that

$$\int_{-\mu}^{+\mu} \frac{\sin x}{x}\,dx = 2\int_{0}^{\mu} \frac{\sin x}{x}\,dx \tag{51}$$

$$\int_{-\mu}^{+\mu} \frac{\cos x}{x}\,dx = 0 \tag{52}$$

where μ is any quantity whatever. Therefore, in the case of symmetrical sideband transmission,

$$\begin{aligned}\bar{G}(t) &= \frac{K}{\pi}\left[\int_0^{\omega_m(t-g-T_1)} \frac{\sin x}{x}\,dx - \int_0^{\omega_m(t-g-T_2)} \frac{\sin x}{x}\,dx\right] \cos \omega_c t \\ &= \frac{K}{\pi}\{\mathrm{Si}[\omega_m(t-g-T_1)] - \mathrm{Si}[\omega_m(t-g-T_2)]\} \cos \omega_c t \end{aligned} \tag{53}$$

Equation (53) expresses a carrier $\cos \omega_c t$, amplitude-modulated by a signal of exactly the same form as Eq. (30). Thus for the transmission of pulses and detail, an intermediate-frequency amplifier with symmetrical sideband transmission is exactly equivalent to a low-pass video amplifier of one-half the pass band. It is unnecessary to go further into the details of this transmission, since we have already studied it (see Figs. 6 and 8).

Exercises

1. If $G(t)$ has the Fourier transform $F(f)$, show that regardless of the signal shape of $G(t)$, the Fourier transform $\bar{F}(f)$ of $G(t) \cos \omega_v t$ is

$$\bar{F}(f) = \frac{F(f+f_c) + F(f-f_c)}{2} = \frac{F(f_c+f) + [F(f_c-f)]^*}{2}$$

Plot curves of $|F(f)|$ and $|\bar{F}(f)|$ in case $G(t)$ is a pulse such as shown in Fig. 2c.

2. Work out the solution for the problem of the transmission of the pulse-modulated carrier of Fig. 9a through the transmission system in Fig. 9b by using the complex form of the Fourier integral instead of the trigonometric form. Which form allows the solution to be obtained more easily?

4.9 Bandwidth and Detail in Intermediate-frequency Amplifiers—Asymmetrical Sideband Case, Quadrature Components.[1] The case of asymmetrical sideband transmission differs mathematically from the symmetrical case in that the integrals of the type

$$\int_{-a}^{+b} \frac{\cos x}{x}\,dx$$

[1] This problem is dealt with from the standpoint of general modulation theory in Sec. 5.6.

in Eq. (48) no longer vanish. To handle this case we shall define a new function, the cosine integral function. This is defined as

$$\mathrm{Ci}(x) = -\int_x^\infty \frac{\cos x}{x}\,dx \tag{54}$$

A curve of $\mathrm{Ci}(x)$ is shown in Fig. 10, and Table II gives some of its values.[1] With the aid of Eq. (54) we may write

$$\begin{aligned}\int_{-a}^{+b} \frac{\cos x}{x}\,dx &= \int_{-a}^{+a} \frac{\cos x}{x}\,dx + \int_a^b \frac{\cos x}{x}\,dx = \int_a^b \frac{\cos x}{x}\,dx \\ &= \int_{-a}^{\infty} \frac{\cos x}{x}\,dx - \int_b^\infty \frac{\cos x}{x}\,dx = \mathrm{Ci}(b) - \mathrm{Ci}(a)\end{aligned} \tag{55}$$

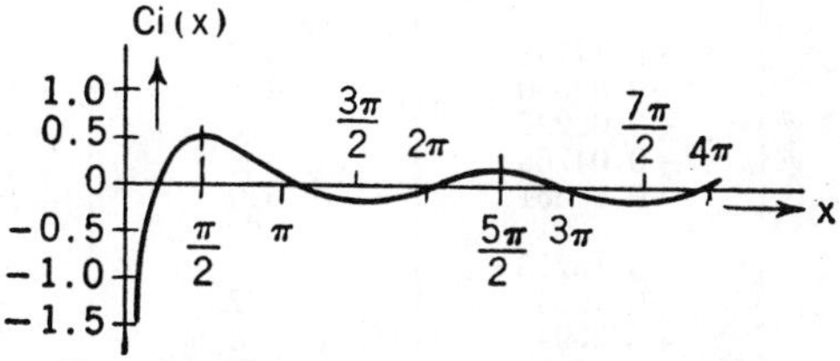

FIG. 10. The cosine integral function, $\mathrm{Ci}(x)$.

We may now write Eq. (48) in the general form

$$\begin{aligned}\bar{G}(t) = \frac{K}{2\pi}\{&\mathrm{Si}[\omega_q(t - g - T_1)] + \mathrm{Si}[\omega_p(t - g - T_1)] \\ &- \mathrm{Si}[\omega_q(t - g - T_2)] - \mathrm{Si}[\omega_p(t - g - T_2)]\}\cos(\omega_c t - \theta) \\ &+ \frac{K}{2\pi}\{\mathrm{Ci}[\omega_q(t - g - T_1)] - \mathrm{Ci}[\omega_p(t - g - T_1)] \\ &- \mathrm{Ci}[\omega_q(t - g - T_2)] \\ &\qquad + \mathrm{Ci}[\omega_p(t - g - T_2)]\}\sin(\omega_c t - \theta)\end{aligned} \tag{56}$$

$$\begin{aligned}&= M\cos(\omega_c t - \theta) + N\sin(\omega_c t - \theta) \\ &\qquad = \sqrt{M^2 + N^2}\cos(\omega_c t + \psi)\end{aligned} \tag{57}$$

In Eq. (57) the quantities M and N are the coefficients of $\cos(\omega_c t - \theta)$ and $\sin(\omega_c t - \theta)$, respectively, in Eq. (56). Thus $\sqrt{M^2 + N^2}$ is the envelope of the output signal, which is the matter of interest, and ψ is an inconsequential intermediate-frequency phase shift.

At this point, we could study the envelope $\sqrt{M^2 + N^2}$ for various input signals and various amounts of asymmetry in the location of

[1] For small values of x, $\mathrm{Ci}(x)$ may be calculated from its series expansion

$$\mathrm{Ci}(x) = C + \log_\epsilon x - \frac{x^2}{2 \cdot 2!} + \frac{x^4}{4 \cdot 4!} + \cdots$$

where $C = 0.5772 \cdots$ is Euler's constant.

TABLE II.—COSINE INTEGRAL, Ci(x)*

$$\mathrm{Ci}(x) = -\int_x^\infty \frac{\cos x}{x}\,dx$$

x	Ci(x)	x	Ci(x)
0.00	$-\infty$	3.6	−0.05797
0.05	−2.4191	3.7	−0.08190
0.10	−1.7279	3.8	−0.1038
0.15	−1.3255	3.9	−0.1235
0.20	−1.0422	4.0	−0.1410
0.25	−0.8247	4.1	−0.1562
0.30	−0.6492	4.2	−0.1690
0.35	−0.5031	4.3	−0.1795
0.40	−0.3788	4.4	−0.1877
0.45	−0.2715	4.5	−0.1935
0.50	−0.17778	4.6	−0.1970
0.55	−0.09530	4.7	−0.1984
0.60	−0.02227	4.8	−0.1976
0.65	+0.04265	4.9	−0.1948
0.70	+0.10051	5.0	−0.1900
0.75	+0.15216	6	−0.06806
0.80	+0.1983	7	+0.07670
0.85	+0.2394	8	+0.1224
0.90	+0.2761	9	+0.05535
0.95	+0.3086	10	−0.04546
1.0	+0.3374	11	−0.08956
1.1	+0.3847	12	−0.04978
1.2	+0.4025	13	+0.02676
1.3	+0.4457	14	+0.06940
1.4	+0.4620	15	+0.04628
1.5	+0.4704		
		20	+0.04442
1.6	+0.4717	25	−0.00685
1.7	+0.4670	30	−0.03303
1.8	+0.4568	35	−0.01148
1.9	+0.4419	40	+0.01902
2.0	+0.4230		
		45	+0.01863
2.1	+0.4005	50	−0.00563
2.2	+0.3751	55	−0.01817
2.3	+0.3472	60	−0.00481
2.4	+0.3173	65	+0.01285
2.5	+0.2859		
		70	+0.01092
2.6	+0.2533	75	−0.00533
2.7	+0.2201	80	−0.01240
2.8	+0.1865	85	−0.001935
2.9	+0.1529	90	+0.009986
3.0	+0.1196		
		95	+0.007110
3.1	+0.08699	100	−0.005149
3.2	+0.05526	110	−0.000320
3.3	+0.02468	120	+0.004781
3.4	−0.004518	130	−0.007132
3.5	−0.03213		

* From JAHNKE-EMDE, "Table of Functions," p. 6.

the carrier in the pass band. However, in order to increase the practical interest in our study we shall consider the somewhat more important pass band shown in Fig. 11.

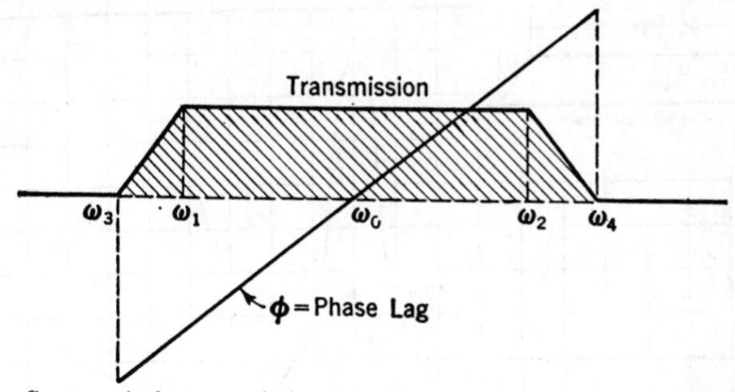

FIG. 11. Symmetrical transmission characteristic of an intermediate-frequency amplifier.

For the case of the transmission characteristics in Fig. 11, it may be shown by the same[1] methods as those used in Sec. 4.8 that M and N in Eq. (57) have the values

$$M = P(t - g - T_1) - P(t - g - T_2) \tag{58}$$

$$N = Q(t - g - T_1) - Q(t - g - T_2) \tag{59}$$

where

$$P(x) = \frac{1}{2\pi x(\omega_1 - \omega_3)} \int_{(\omega_3-\omega_c)x}^{(\omega_1-\omega_c)x} \sin \mu \, d\mu + \frac{\omega_c - \omega_3}{2\pi(\omega_1 - \omega_3)} \int_{(\omega_3-\omega_c)x}^{(\omega_1-\omega_c)x} \frac{\sin \mu}{\mu} \, d\mu + \frac{1}{2\pi} \int_{(\omega_1-\omega_c)x}^{(\omega_2-\omega_c)x} \frac{\sin \mu}{\mu} \, d\mu - \frac{1}{2\pi x(\omega_4 - \omega_2)} \int_{(\omega_2-\omega_c)x}^{(\omega_4-\omega_c)x} \sin \mu \, d\mu + \frac{\omega_4 - \omega_c}{2\pi(\omega_4 - \omega_2)} \int_{(\omega_2-\omega_c)x}^{(\omega_4-\omega_c)x} \frac{\sin \mu}{\mu} \, d\mu \tag{60}$$

$$Q(x) = \frac{1}{2\pi x(\omega_1 - \omega_3)} \int_{(\omega_3-\omega_c)x}^{(\omega_1-\omega_c)x} \cos \mu \, d\mu + \frac{\omega_c - \omega_3}{2\pi(\omega_1 - \omega_3)} \int_{(\omega_3-\omega_c)x}^{(\omega_1-\omega_c)x} \frac{\cos \mu}{\mu} \, d\mu + \frac{1}{2\pi} \int_{(\omega_1-\omega_c)x}^{(\omega_2-\omega_c)x} \frac{\cos \mu}{\mu} \, d\mu - \frac{1}{2\pi x(\omega_4 - \omega_2)} \int_{(\omega_2-\omega_c)x}^{(\omega_4-\omega_c)x} \cos \mu \, d\mu + \frac{\omega_4 - \omega_c}{2\pi(\omega_4 - \omega_2)} \int_{(\omega_2-\omega_c)x}^{(\omega_4-\omega_c)x} \frac{\cos \mu}{\mu} \, d\mu \tag{61}$$

[1] The procedure is simple but lengthy, and it will therefore be omitted here.

Curves of $P(x)$ and $Q(x)$ for various locations[1] of the carrier in the pass band in a particular case of television interest that has been studied by the author[2] are given in Fig. 12. Comparison of Fig. 12

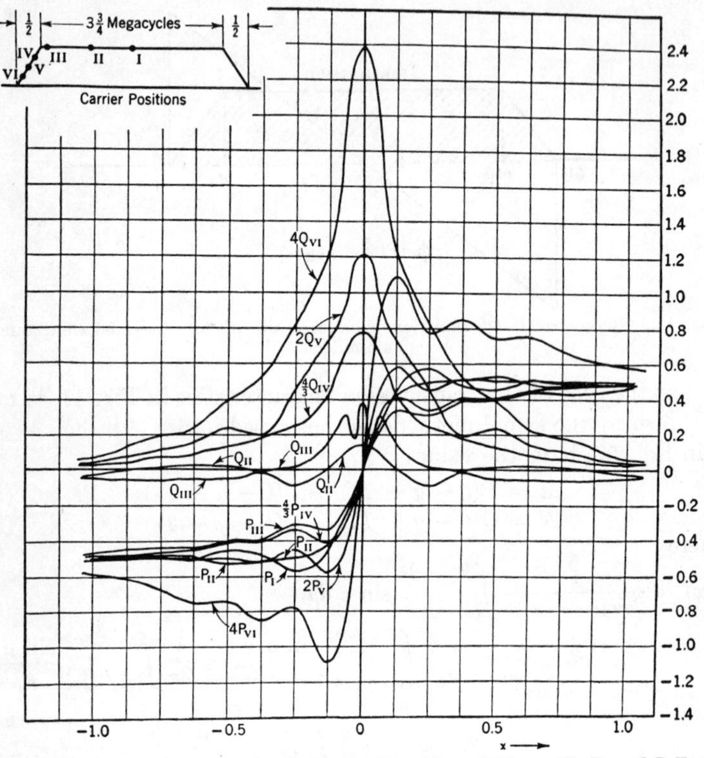

Fig. 12. Graphs of $P(x)$ and $Q(x)$ (normalized). (*From Goldman, S., Proc. I.R.E.*, **27**, *November*, 1939.)

with Fig. 3, and of Eqs. (56) through (61) with Eq. (30) shows that $P(x)$ tends to reproduce the signal, while $Q(x)$ is a pure distortion effect which increases in magnitude with the amount of asymmetry in the

[1] In order to get a clearer picture of what is actually happening, Figs. 12 and 15 show normalized response. In normalization, the values corresponding to position IV are multiplied by $\frac{4}{3}$, those corresponding to position V are multiplied by 2, and those corresponding to position VI are multiplied by 4. This equalizes the signal level for all positions, as might be done with a volume control in a television receiver.

[2] Goldman, Television Detail and Selective-sideband Transmission, *Proc. I.R.E.*, November, 1939, p. 725.

location of the carrier. It is customary to call the $P(x)$ terms the inphase component of the signal and the $Q(x)$ terms the quadrature component, since they are the multipliers of the inphase and quadrature components of the carrier, respectively, in Eq. (57).

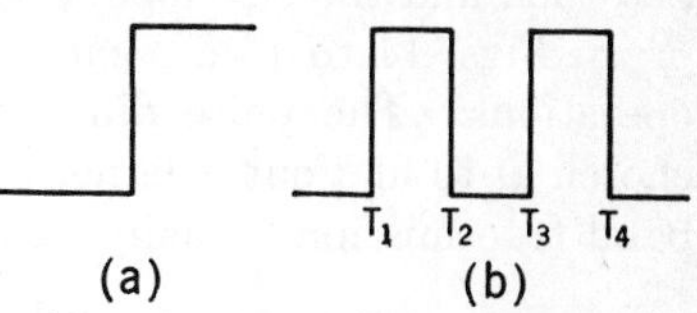

FIG. 13. Television test signals.

Using Eqs. (56) through (61) and Fig. 12, we can readily find the envelope (which is then also the detected video signal) of the output signal for the two important types of input signal shown in Fig. 13. The output corresponding to Fig. 13a will show the sharpness of edges in the picture, while that corresponding to 13b will show the ability of the system to transmit fine detail. In order to find the

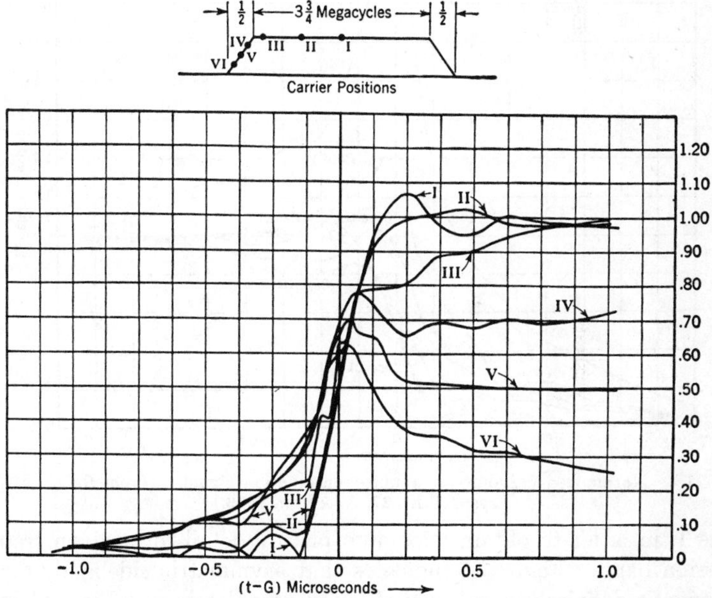

FIG. 14. Response to a unit-step-function signal. (*From Goldman, S., Proc. I.R.E.*, **27**, *November*, 1939.)

response in the case of Fig. 13a we let $T_2 \rightarrow \infty$ in Eqs. (58) and (59). In the case of Fig. 13b we use the superposition theorem of Sec. 4.6 and write

$$M = P(t - g - T_1) - P(t - g - T_2) + P(t - g - T_3) - P(t - g - T_4) \quad (62)$$

$$N = Q(t - g - T_1) - Q(t - g - T_2) + Q(t - g - T_3) - Q(t - g - T_4) \quad (63)$$

and then find the envelope $\sqrt{M^2 + N^2}$.

In Figs. 14 to 16 are shown the results of carrying through such operations. The pulse dimensions and spacing in Fig. 16 were so chosen as to find out whether it is worth while to use asymmetric sideband transmission (usually case V or IV), rather than the symmetric

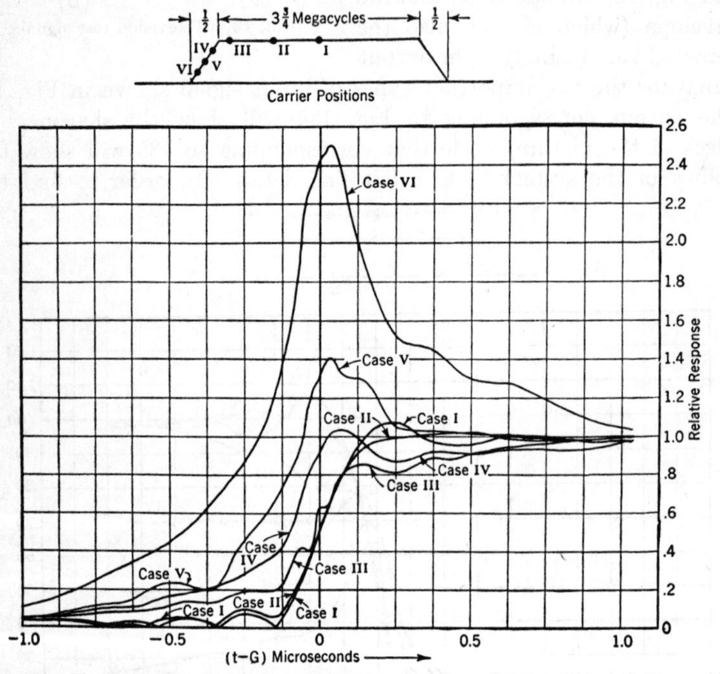

FIG. 15. Normalized response to a unit-step-function signal. (*From Goldman, S., Proc. I.R.E.*, **27**, *November*, 1939.)

case I, in order to obtain maximum picture detail for a given transmission band. Figure 16 indicates that asymmetric sideband transmission is definitely worth while[1] for picture detail, but Figs. 14 and 15 show that it is of no value for showing sharp edges in the case considered here, *i.e.*, when the no-signal carrier level is zero.

We shall, show in the next section, however, that there is an improvement when the no-signal carrier level is not zero.

[1] A comparison of Figs. 16 and 8, if $\omega_s = 2\frac{1}{8}$ mc in the latter, shows that case V requires about half the bandwidth of case I.

The reason for the improvement in detail but not in the sharpness of edges in the asymmetric sideband case is that the quadrature functions $Q(x)$, which produce distortion in the picture, cancel midway

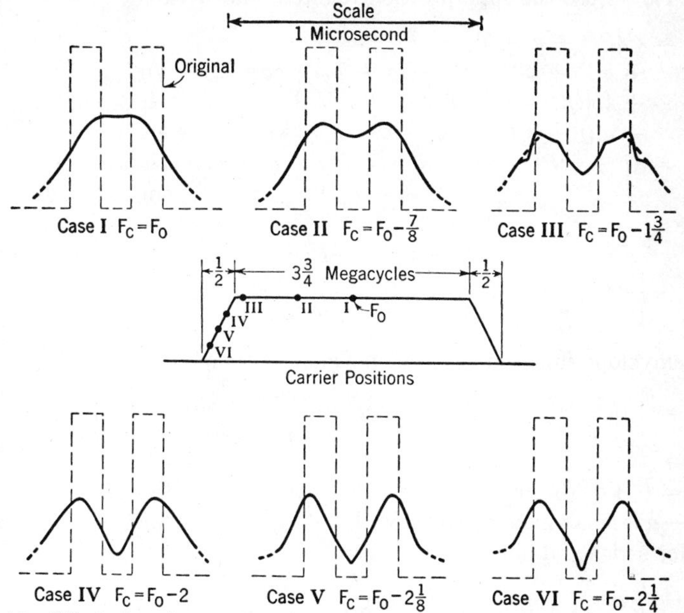

FIG. 16. Effect of carrier position on the reproduction of detail. (*From Goldman, S., Proc. I.R.E.*, **27**, *November*, 1939.)

between the pulses in Fig. 16 but show no cancellation effect in the case of a single sharp edge. It is worthy of note that if $\omega_1 - \omega_3$, the cutoff range on the carrier side, is made too narrow, or if the carrier is moved too close to ω_3 for any reason, then the quadrature distortion becomes so large as to cause a serious reduction in picture quality.

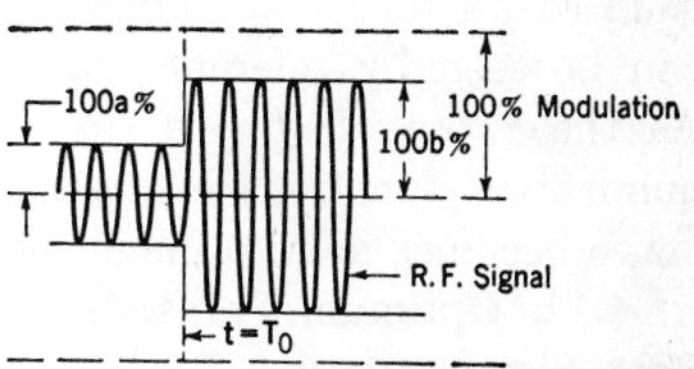

FIG. 17. A step-type signal modulating a carrier.

4.10 The Case in Which the No-signal Carrier Level Is not Zero. The foregoing discussion applied to the case in which the no-signal carrier level is zero. Let us next see what differences result from the use of a no-signal carrier level that is not zero. Accordingly, let us study a signal of the type shown in Fig. 17, which depicts an edge in a television picture. As we have seen, all pulse-type signals can be obtained from this signal with the aid of the superposition theorem.

To find the output signal $\bar{G}(t)$ when the input is the signal shown in Fig. 17, we use the superposition theorem and write

$$\begin{aligned}\bar{G}(t) = & \{b[P(t - g - T_0) - P(-\infty)] \\ & + a[P(+\infty) - P(t - g - T_0)]\} \cos (\omega_c t - \theta) \\ & + \{b[Q(t - g - T_0) - Q(-\infty)] \\ & + a[Q(+\infty) - Q(t - g - T_0)]\} \sin (\omega_c t - \theta) \\ = & [(b + a)P(+\infty) + (b - a)P(t - g - T_0)] \cos (\omega_c t - \theta) \\ & + (b - a)Q(t - g - T_0) \sin (\omega_c t - \theta) \end{aligned} \tag{64}$$

since

$$P(-\infty) = -P(+\infty) \tag{65}$$

and

$$Q(-\infty) = Q(+\infty) = 0 \tag{66}$$

The envelope function, *i.e.*, video signal, is then

$$G(t) = \{[(b + a)P(\infty) + (b - a)P(t - g - T_0)]^2 + [(b - a)Q(t - g - T_0)^2\}^{\frac{1}{2}} \tag{67}$$

If $a = 0$, Eq. (67) reduces to the case depicted in Fig. 14. However, if $b - a$ is small in comparison with $b + a$, we can expand Eq. (67) in a Taylor series and obtain

$$\bar{G}(t) = (b + a) \left\{ P(\infty) + \frac{b - a}{b + a} P(t - g - T_0) + \left[\text{terms in } \left(\frac{b - a}{b + a} \right)^2 \right] \right\} \tag{68}$$

In this case, then, the quadrature functions become of negligible importance. The sharpness of edges in case V is about twice as good as in case I for small changes in the percentage of modulation. This can be seen by reference to Fig. 12 in conjunction with Eq. (68). As the value of $(b - a)/(b + a)$ increases, the importance of the quadrature functions increases with it and the distortion that they cause becomes more pronounced.[1]

4.11. Optimum Transmission Bands for Pulse Receives to Obtain Best Signal-to-noise Ratio. In the design of pulse receivers, it is

[1] It should be noted that only in cases I and V is there a uniform distribution of sideband energy sensitivity vs. frequency. The nonuniformity in the other cases is at relatively low frequencies and shows up in Fig. 12 in the length of time required for the $P(x)$ functions to reach the steady state.

desirable to know the optimum bandwidth for the carrier-frequency (over-all radio frequency plus intermediate frequency) amplifier and

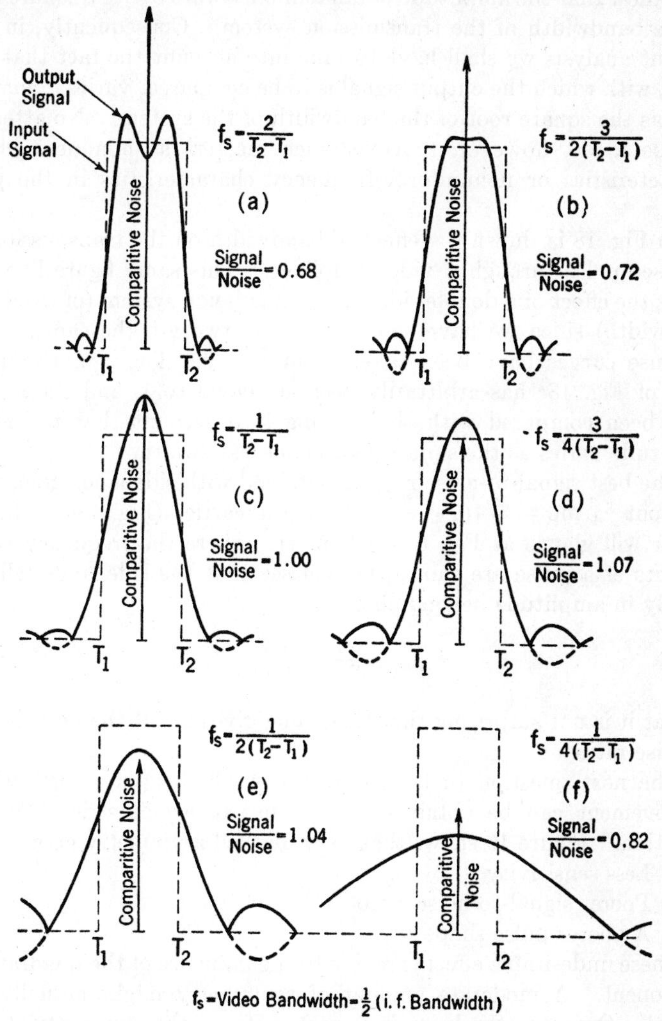

FIG. 18. Bandwidth vs. relative signal-to-noise ratio in pulse amplifiers.

for the low-frequency amplifier. With the aid of the analysis in the preceding sections, we are now in a good position to consider these matters.

The usual objective in the design of a pulse receiver is to get maximum signal-to-noise ratio. Now, in our chapters on noise, we shall show that the amplitude of random noise varies as the square root of the bandwidth of the transmission system. Consequently, in our present analysis we shall have to take into account the fact that the noise, with which the output signal is to be compared, varies in magnitude as the square root of the bandwidth of the system. No attempt will be made, however, to cover such matters as nonlinear phase characteristics or nonuniform frequency characteristics in the pass band.

In Fig. 18 is shown the effect of bandwidth on the transmission of a 1-μsec pulse through a video amplifier. This same figure likewise shows the effect of a double sideband transmission system (of twice the bandwidth) since we have shown that the two are the same. The response curves have been taken from Fig. 6. The signal-to-noise ratio of Fig. 18*c* has arbitrarily been set equal to 1, and the others have been compared with this, taking into account that the noise amplitude varies as the square root of the bandwidth.

The best signal-to-noise ratio is obtained with sidebands going out to about ¾ mc = $3/4(T_2 - T_1)$ from the carrier (Fig. 18*d*). If the reader will glance at Fig. 6 of Chap. III, where the frequency components of a pulse are shown, he will see that the sidebands fall off rapidly in amplitude beyond about

$$f_m = \frac{\omega_m}{2\pi} = \frac{3}{4}\frac{1}{T} \tag{69}$$

so that it is not surprising that this value gives about the best signal-to-noise ratio.

The next question to be considered is whether any worth-while improvement can be obtained by the use of asymmetric sideband reception. Figure 19 shows that very marked asymmetry gives

1. Less sensitivity
2. Poorer signal-to-noise ratio
3. A poorer pulse shape

These undesirable effects are due to the influence of the quadrature component. A moderate amount of asymmetry might actually be helpful. Owing to the large frequency drifts in the apparatus at the radio frequencies at which most pulse transmission takes place at present, actual reception probably changes from the symmetric to the asymmetric type many times every minute. Consequently, it is probably useless to design the apparatus for one rather than the other.

As a general conclusion, we may therefore say that for best signal-to-noise ratio we should use approximately

$$\text{Video pass band} = \frac{3}{4}\frac{1}{T} \tag{70}$$

and, because of upper and lower sidebands,

$$\text{Modulated carrier-frequency pass band} = \frac{3}{4}\frac{2}{T} \tag{71}$$

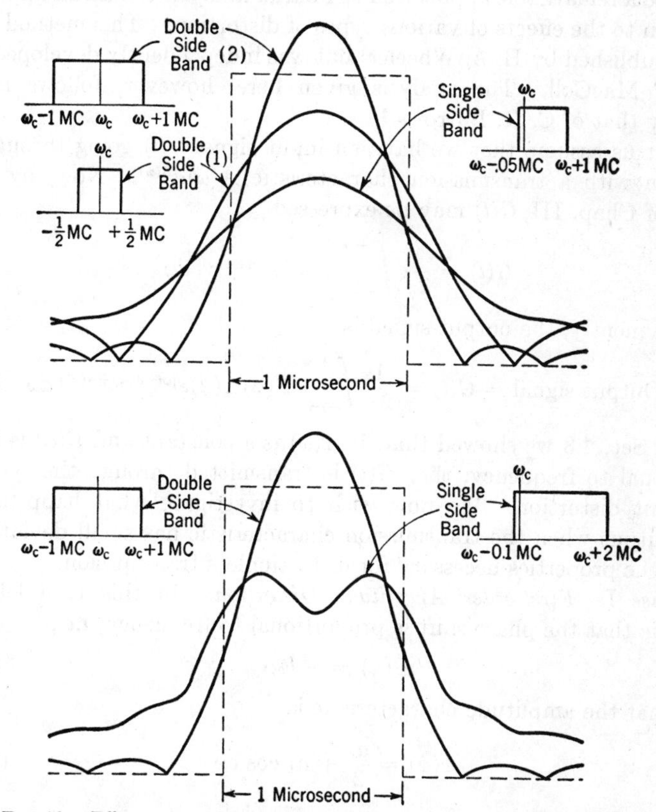

FIG. 19. Effects of asymmetric sideband transmission on pulse reception.

If it is essential to have sharply defined edges for the pulses, *i.e.*, for accurate radar ranging, and if signal-to-noise ratio is not a serious problem, a glance at Fig. 6 of Chap. III shows that good values to use for bandwidth are

$$\text{Video pass band} = \frac{7}{4}\frac{1}{T} \tag{72}$$

$$\text{High-frequency pass band} = \frac{7}{4}\frac{2}{T} \tag{73}$$

Larger high-frequency pass bands than called for by Eqs. (71) and (73) may, of course, be required owing to frequency drift of the equipment.

4.12 The Interpretation of Distortion as Paired Echoes. We come next to a remarkable application of Fourier analysis to find an approximation to the effects of various types of distortion. This method was first published by H. A. Wheeler[1] but was independently developed by L. A. MacColl. The analysis given here, however, follows more closely that of C. R. Burrows.[2]

Let us assume that we have an input signal $G(t)$ going through a system with a transmission characteristic $A(\omega)\epsilon^{jB(\omega)}$. Now, by Eq. (54) of Chap. III, $G(t)$ may be expressed

$$G(t) = \frac{1}{2\pi}\int_{-\infty}^{+\infty} S(\omega)\epsilon^{j[\omega t+\phi(\omega)]}\,d\omega \tag{74}$$

Consequently, the output signal is

$$\text{Output signal} = \bar{G}(t) = \frac{1}{2\pi}\int_{-\infty}^{+\infty} S(\omega)A(\omega)\epsilon^{j[\omega t+\phi(\omega)+B(\omega)]}\,d\omega \tag{75}$$

In Sec. 4.3 we showed that, if $A(\omega)$ is a constant and $B(\omega)$ is proportional to frequency, then $G(t)$ is transmitted through the system without distortion. We now wish to investigate what happens to the output when the transmission characteristic has small deviations from the properties necessary for distortionless transmission.

Case I. *First-order Amplitude Distortion.* In this case let us assume that the phase shift is proportional to frequency, *i.e.*,

$$B(\omega) = -b_0\omega \tag{76}$$

but that the amplitude characteristic is

$$A(\omega) = \frac{a_0}{2} + a_1 \cos c\omega \tag{77}$$[3]

where a_1 is small in comparison with a_0. Such a frequency characteristic is shown in Fig. 20. The value of c is ordinarily so chosen that

[1] *Proc. I.R.E.*, June, 1939, p. 359.

[2] *Proc. I.R.E.*, June, 1939, p. 384.

[3] In Sec. 4.4 it is shown that $A(\omega)$ is an even function of ω, while $B(\omega)$ is an odd function.

most of the frequency components of $G(t)$ lie within the range

$$-\frac{\pi}{c} < \omega < \frac{\pi}{c}.$$

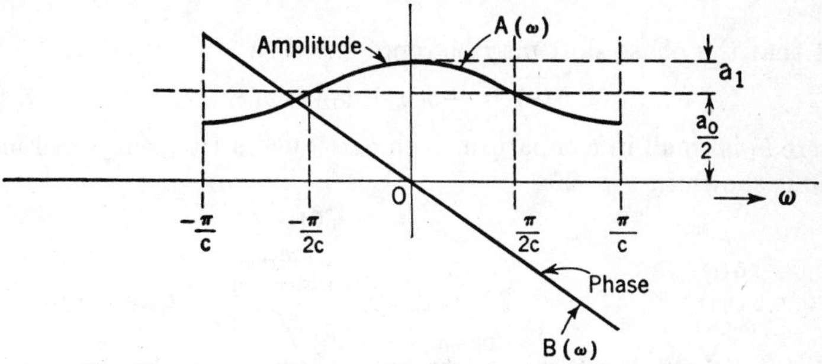

FIG. 20. A nonuniform amplitude-transmission characteristic.

Substituting Eqs. (76) and (77) into Eq. (75), we have

$$\begin{aligned}
\bar{G}(t) &= \frac{1}{2\pi}\int_{-\infty}^{+\infty} S(\omega)\left(\frac{a_0}{2} + a_1 \cos c\omega\right)\epsilon^{j[\omega t - b_0\omega + \phi(\omega)]}\,d\omega \\
&= \frac{1}{2\pi}\int_{-\infty}^{+\infty} S(\omega)\left(\frac{a_0}{2} + \frac{a_1}{2}\epsilon^{jc\omega} + \frac{a_1}{2}\epsilon^{-jc\omega}\right)\epsilon^{j[\omega t - b_0\omega + \phi(\omega)]}\,d\omega \\
&= \frac{a_0}{2}\frac{1}{2\pi}\int_{-\infty}^{+\infty} S(\omega)\epsilon^{j[\omega(t-b_0)+\phi(\omega)]}\,d\omega \\
&\quad + \frac{a_1}{2}\frac{1}{2\pi}\int_{-\infty}^{+\infty} S(\omega)\epsilon^{j[\omega(t-b_0+c)+\phi(\omega)]}\,d\omega \\
&\quad + \frac{a_1}{2}\frac{1}{2\pi}\int_{-\infty}^{+\infty} S(\omega)\epsilon^{j[\omega(t-b_0-c)+\phi(\omega)]}\,d\omega \\
&= \frac{a_0}{2}G(t-b_0) + \frac{a_1}{2}G(t-b_0+c) + \frac{a_1}{2}G(t-b_0-c)
\end{aligned} \tag{78}$$

in which we have used the formula

$$\cos x = \frac{\epsilon^{jx} + \epsilon^{-jx}}{2} \tag{79}$$

Equation (78), as depicted in Fig. 21, shows that in this case the output of the system consists of the main undistorted transmitted signal, $(a_0/2)G(t - b_0)$, plus two "echoes," similar in shape to the undistorted signal but displaced from it on either side by an amount of time $t = c$. These echoes are the terms $(a_1/2)G(t - b_0 + c)$ and $(a_1/2)G(t - b_0 - c)$, respectively, and they represent the distortion in the transmitted signal.

Case II. *First-order Phase Distortion.* In this case we assume that the amplitude characteristic is independent of frequency, *i.e.*,

$$A(\omega) = \frac{a_0}{2} \tag{80}$$

but that the phase shift may be represented as

$$B(\omega) = -b_0\omega + b_1 \sin c_1\omega \tag{81}$$

where b_1 is small in comparison with b_0. Such a frequency characteristic is shown in Fig. 22.

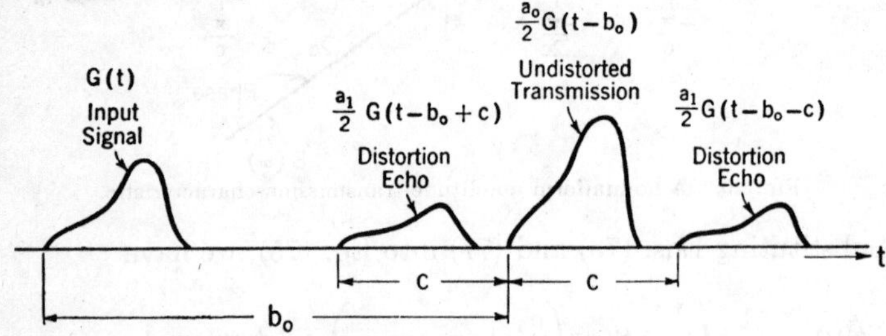

FIG. 21. Illustration of amplitude distortion echoes.

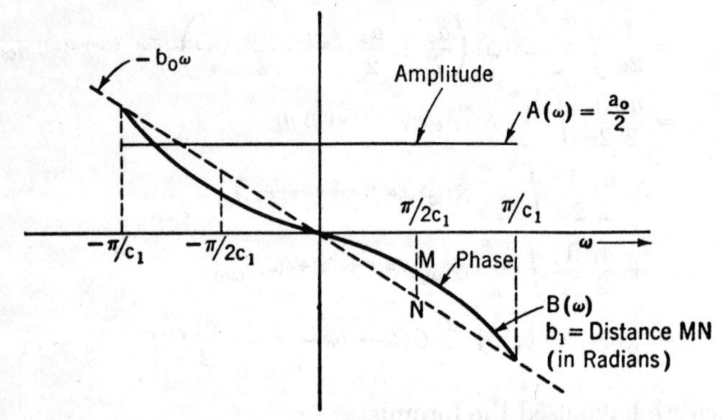

FIG. 22. A nonlinear phase-characteristic.

Substituting Eqs. (80) and (81) into Eq. (75), we have

$$\text{Output signal} = \bar{G}(t) = \frac{1}{2\pi}\int_{-\infty}^{+\infty} S(\omega)\,\frac{a_0}{2}\,\epsilon^{j[\omega t+\phi(\omega)-b_0\omega+b_1\sin c_1\omega]}\,d\omega \tag{82}$$

In Appendix E it is pointed out that

$$\epsilon^{jx\sin\theta} = \sum_{k=-\infty}^{+\infty} J_k(x)\epsilon^{jk\theta}$$

$$= J_0(x) + [J_1(x)\epsilon^{j\theta} + J_{-1}(x)\epsilon^{-j\theta}] + \cdots \quad (83)^1$$

[1] This is Eq. (11) of Appendix E.

If x is small, we may neglect any higher-order terms in the expression on the right in Eq. (83). The functions $J_0(x)$, $J_1(x)$, $J_{-1}(x)$, etc., are types of Bessel functions, which are discussed in Appendix E. Their values as functions of x are given in Fig. 23, and this is all that we need

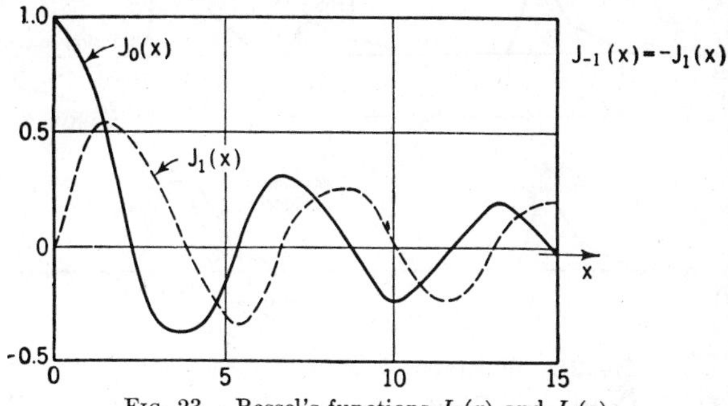

FIG. 23. Bessel's functions $J_0(x)$ and $J_1(x)$.

to know about them for the present. If we use the approximation of Eq. (83) in Eq. (82), we obtain

$$\bar{G}(t) = \frac{1}{2\pi} \int_{-\infty}^{+\infty} S(\omega) \frac{a_0}{2} \epsilon^{j[\omega t + \phi(\omega) - b_0\omega]} [J_0(b_1) + J_1(b_1)\epsilon^{jc_1\omega} + J_{-1}(b_1)\epsilon^{-jc_1\omega}] \, d\omega$$

$$= \frac{a_0}{2} J_0(b_1) G(t - b_0) + \frac{a_0}{2} J_1(b_1) G(t - b_0 + c_1) + \frac{a_0}{2} J_{-1}(b_1) G(t - b_0 - c_1)$$

$$= \frac{a_0}{2} J_0(b_1) G(t - b_0) + \frac{a_0}{2} J_1(b_1) G(t - b_0 + c_1) - \frac{a_0}{2} J_1(b_1) G(t - b_0 - c_1) \quad (84)$$

In the foregoing equation, we have used the known relation in Bessel functions that $J_{-k}(x) = (-1)^k J_k(x)$.

Equation (84) shows that in this case the output of the system consists of the main undistorted transmitted signal $(a_0/2)J_0(b_1)G(t - b_0)$, plus a positive echo $(a_0/2)J_1(b_1)G(t - b_0 + c_1)$, similar in shape to the undistorted transmitted signal but preceding it by a length of time c_1, and a negative echo $(-a_0/2)J_1(b_1)G(t - b_0 - c_1)$, similar in shape to the undistorted transmitted signal but following it by a length of time c_1. This situation is depicted in Fig. 24. In Fig. 24*b* the value of c_1 has been changed to a smaller value c_1' so that there is some juxtaposition of the transmitted signal and its echoes. The composite signal is also shown. This type of distortion is actually more common than the case in which the transmitted signal and its echoes are completely separated.

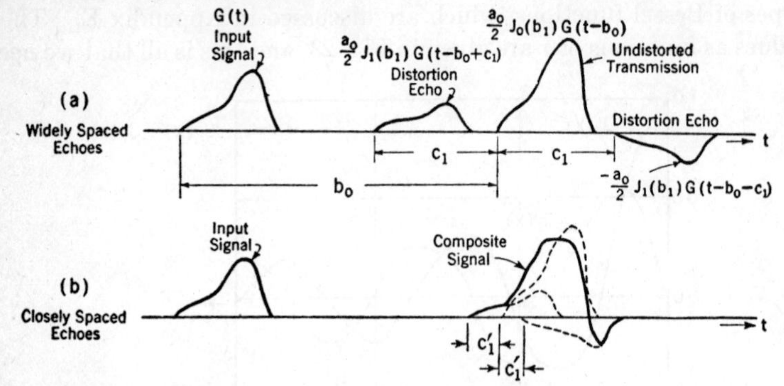

FIG. 24. Illustration of phase-distortion echoes.

Case III. *Combined First-order Amplitude and Phase Distortion.* In this case we assume an amplitude characteristic

$$A(\omega) = \frac{a_0}{2} + a_1 \cos c\omega \tag{85}$$

and a phase characteristic

$$B(\omega) = -b_0\omega + b_1 \sin c_1\omega \tag{86}$$

Proceeding as in the previous cases, we get for the output signal

$$\begin{aligned}
\bar{G}(t) &= \int_{-\infty}^{+\infty} S(\omega)\left(\frac{a_0}{2} + a_1 \cos c\omega\right) \epsilon^{j[\omega t + \phi(\omega) - b_0\omega + b_1 \sin c_1\omega]}\, d\omega \\
&= \int_{-\infty}^{+\infty} S(\omega)\left(\frac{a_0}{2} + \frac{a_1}{2}\epsilon^{jc\omega} + \frac{a_1}{2}\epsilon^{-jc\omega}\right)\epsilon^{[\omega t + \phi(\omega) - b_0\omega]} \\
&\qquad [J_0(b_1) + J_1(b_1)\epsilon^{jc_1\omega} - J_1(b_1)\epsilon^{-jc_1\omega}]\, d\omega \\
&= \frac{a_0}{2} J_0(b_1)G(t - b_0) + \frac{a_0}{2} J_1(b_1)G(t - b_0 + c_1) \\
&\qquad - \frac{a_0}{2} J_1(b_1)G(t - b_0 - c_1) \\
&\quad + \frac{a_1}{2} J_0(b_1)G(t - b_0 + c) + \frac{a_1}{2} J_0(b_1)G(t - b_0 - c) \\
&\qquad + \frac{a_1}{2} J_1(b_1)G(t - b_0 + c + c_1) \\
&\quad - \frac{a_1}{2} J_1(b_1)G(t - b_0 + c - c_1) + \frac{a_1}{2} J_1(b_1)G(t - b_0 - c + c_1) \\
&\qquad - \frac{a_1}{2} J_1(b_1)G(t - b_0 - c - c_1)
\end{aligned} \tag{87}$$

Equation (87) shows the main undistorted transmitted signal $(a_0/2)J_0(b_1)G(t - b_0)$. It also shows four first-order echoes involving

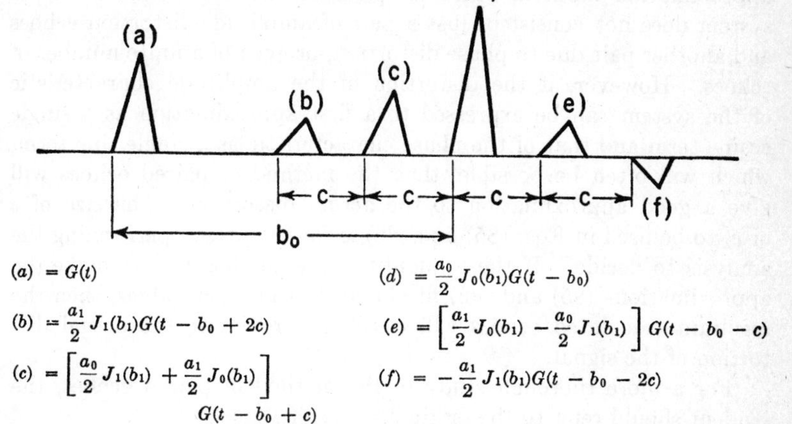

(a) $= G(t)$

(b) $= \frac{a_1}{2} J_1(b_1)G(t - b_0 + 2c)$

(c) $= \left[\frac{a_0}{2} J_1(b_1) + \frac{a_1}{2} J_0(b_1)\right] G(t - b_0 + c)$

(d) $= \frac{a_0}{2} J_0(b_1)G(t - b_0)$

(e) $= \left[\frac{a_1}{2} J_0(b_1) - \frac{a_0}{2} J_1(b_1)\right] G(t - b_0 - c)$

(f) $= -\frac{a_1}{2} J_1(b_1)G(t - b_0 - 2c)$

FIG. 25. Combined amplitude- and phase-distortion echoes according to Eq. (87) (assuming $c_1 = c$).

either $(a_0/2)J_1(b_1)$ or $(a_1/2)J_0(b_1)$. Finally, it shows four second-order echoes involving $(a_1/2)J_1(b_1)$. If a_1 and b_1 are relatively small, these second-order echoes should be negligible. Case III is depicted in Fig. 25, where c_1 is shown equal to c, in order to get a simpler picture.

Discussion of the General Case. In the general case the distortion will not be limited to first-order terms. It is then still possible to expand the distortion terms in $A(\omega)$ and $B(\omega)$ in Fourier series and obtain

$$A(\omega) = \frac{a_0}{2} + \sum_{n=1}^{\infty} a_n \cos nc\omega \tag{88}$$

and

$$B(\omega) = -b_0\omega + \sum_{m=1}^{\infty} b_m \sin mc\omega \tag{89}$$

These values may be substituted in Eq. (75). The result will be a main undistorted signal plus an infinite series of echoes displaced in time from the main signal by multiples of c. All the echoes will be of the original shape, but they will be of varying magnitude, and some will be negative. Such a representation, however, is of more theoretical than practical interest.

In its practical application, the method of paired echoes is an approximation method. The complete distortion of a transmission system does not consist of just a pair of amplitude-distortion echoes and another pair due to phase distortion, or even of a finite number of echoes. However, if the distortion of the amplitude characteristic of the system can be expressed to a first approximation as a single cosine term and that of the phase characteristic as a single sine term, which will often be possible, then the method of paired echoes will give a good approximation to the actual distortion. The size of c or c_1 to be used in Eqs. (85) and (86) is for the person performing the analysis to decide. If these quantities are so chosen as to make the approximations (85) and (86) fit closely to the exact values, then the resultant calculated echoes will closely approximate the actual distortion of the signal.

For a more thorough study of the method of paired echoes, the student should refer to the original paper of Wheeler.[1]

Exercise

A pulse shown in Fig. *a* is sent through a transmission system having the characteristics in Fig. *b*. Find the output.

Note that the main transmitted signal and its echoes are similar, not to the pulse, but to the transmitted signal of a pulse passing through a low-pass filter.

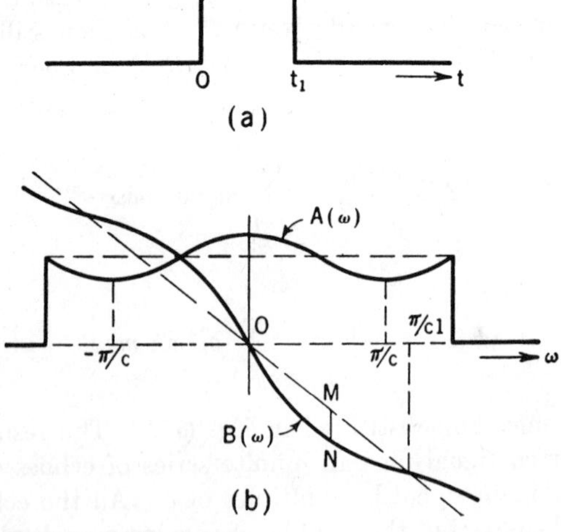

[1] *Proc. I.R.E.*, June, 1939, p. 359.

4.13 The Fourier Integral Energy Theorem. In Sec. 2.5 it is shown that, in the case of a periodic current which can be analyzed by means of a Fourier series, the average power dissipated is equal to the sum of that dissipated by the individual frequency components separately. The interaction between different harmonics thus does not contribute to the average power. It is also shown in the same section that, when an emf, expressible as a Fourier series, is impressed upon a circuit, the power delivered to the circuit is equal to the sum of the powers delivered at the different harmonics. Interaction between a voltage of one harmonic and a current of a different harmonic does not contribute to the average power delivered.

The foregoing propositions were based upon Eq. (102) of Chap. I, namely,

$$\frac{1}{2\pi}\int_0^{2\pi} f(x)g(x)\,dx = \sum_{n=-\infty}^{+\infty} c_n C_{-n} \tag{90}$$

or upon its trigonometric equivalents. A formula corresponding to Eq. (90) can also be derived for Fourier integrals.[1] This is

$$\int_{-\infty}^{+\infty} G_1(t)G_2(t)\,dt = \int_{-\infty}^{+\infty} F_1(f)F_2(-f)\,df \tag{91}$$

where F_1 and G_1 are a Fourier pair, as are also F_2 and G_2. Now according to Eqs. (26) and (27) of Chap. III, we may write

$$F_1(f) = \pi[a_1(\omega) - jb_1(\omega)] \tag{92}$$

$$F_2(-f) = \pi[a_2(\omega) + jb_2(\omega)] \tag{93}$$

Therefore, since

$$df = \frac{1}{2\pi}\,d\omega \tag{94}$$

$$a(-\omega) = a(\omega) \tag{95}$$

and

$$b(-\omega) = -b(\omega) \tag{96}$$

we may rewrite Eq. (91) as

$$\begin{aligned}\int_{-\infty}^{+\infty} G_1(t)G_2(t)\,dt &= \frac{\pi}{2}\int_{-\infty}^{+\infty} \{[a_1(\omega)a_2(\omega) + b_1(\omega)b_2(\omega)] \\ &\qquad + j[a_1(\omega)b_2(\omega) - a_2(\omega)b_1(\omega)]\}\,d\omega \\ &= \pi\int_0^{\infty} [a_1(\omega)a_2(\omega) + b_1(\omega)b_2(\omega)]\,d\omega \\ &= \frac{1}{\pi}\int_0^{\infty} S_1(\omega)S_2(\omega)\cos[\phi_1(\omega) - \phi_2(\omega)]\,d\omega \end{aligned} \tag{97}$$

[1] See the Campbell and Foster table, p. 39 (Table I, part 2, footnote); TITCHMARSH, E. C., "Introduction to the Theory of Fourier Integrals," Oxford, 1937.

For convenient reference, we recall here the defining equations of $a(\omega)$ and $b(\omega)$, namely,

$$a(\omega) = \frac{1}{\pi} \int_{-\infty}^{+\infty} G(t) \cos \omega t \, dt \tag{98}$$

$$b(\omega) = \frac{1}{\pi} \int_{-\infty}^{+\infty} G(t) \sin \omega t \, dt \tag{99}$$

As a corollary to Eq. (97), we have

$$\int_{-\infty}^{+\infty} [G(t)]^2 \, dt = \pi \int_0^{\infty} \{[a(\omega)]^2 + [b(\omega)]^2\} \, d\omega$$
$$= \frac{1}{\pi} \int_0^{\infty} [S(\omega)]^2 \, d\omega \tag{100}$$

Equation (100) is called the Fourier integral energy theorem and was originally derived by Lord Rayleigh. Since the energy of a disturbance $G(t)$ is generally proportional to the square of its amplitude, the Fourier integral energy theorem shows that the total energy of a disturbance is equal to the sum (*i.e.*, integral) of the energies of its frequency components. Incidentally, it shows that cross products of different frequency components do not contribute to the energy.[1]

Equation (100) has a wide variety of applications. For example, with its aid we can study the transfer of power due to various signals in terms of the frequency characteristics alone of the transmission system. This is especially valuable in later chapters when we study the important topics of modulation and noise.

The more general equation, (97), allows us to calculate the energy absorption in terms of frequency components in a system in which a current $I(t)$ is flowing when a voltage $E(t)$ is applied. Equation (97) shows that the energy absorption depends only on the power products of the components of the same frequency and is independent of any interaction between components of different frequencies.

Exercises

1. Calculate the energies in the pulses of Fig. 37, and show that the answer is the same whether $G(t)$ or whether $S(\omega) = |F(f)|$ is used as the basis of calculation.

2. Using Eq. (91), show that

$$\int_{-\infty}^{+\infty} [G^2(t)]^2 \, dt = \int_{-\infty}^{+\infty} F(f)F^*(f) \, df = \int_{-\infty}^{+\infty} |F(f)|^2 \, df$$

This shows that the Fourier integral energy theorem applies to complex as well as real frequency distributions.

[1] This proposition is, of course, limited to systems to which the Fourier integral applies, *i.e.*, linear systems.

4.14 The Principle of Stationary Phase.[1] We come next to a proposition of wide applicability in many branches of radio engineering, as well as in many fields of physics. As a first step in arriving at this proposition, consider a quantity

$$P = \int_M^N U(x) \cos [V(x)]\, dx = \text{Re} \left\{ \int_M^N U(x) e^{jV(x)}\, dx \right\} \qquad (101)^2$$

in which $U(x)$ varies only slowly with x, while $\cos [V(x)]$ goes through a large number of periods within the range of integration. In particular, it is assumed that $U(x)$ changes by only a small fraction of itself, while $V(x)$ changes by 2π. Under these circumstances the value of the above integral usually will be small, for those portions of it in which $\cos [V(x)]$ is negative will tend to cancel those portions in which $\cos [V(x)]$ is positive. An exception will occur, however, if $V(x)$ has any stationary values, *i.e.*, values for which

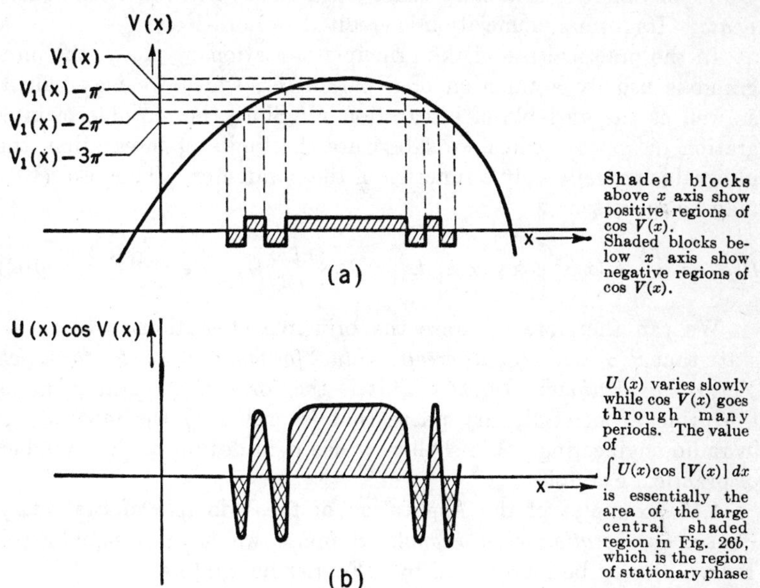

FIG. 26. Graphical illustration of the principle of stationary phase.

$$\frac{d}{dx} [V(x)] = 0$$

[1] See also WATSON, G. N., "Theory of Bessel Functions," 2d ed., Sec. 8.2.

[2] Re stands for "the real part of."

In this case a substantial contribution may be made to the value of P by the portion of the integral in the range of stationary phase. This is shown in Fig. 26*b*, where the shaded areas show contributions of one sign and the crosshatched areas show contributions of the opposite sign. There will, in general, be cancellation of positive against negative areas except for the range of stationary phase.

The proposition that *in an integral of the type of Eq.* 101 *there is general cancellation of positive and negative portions of the integral except for ranges of stationary phase* is called *the principle of stationary phase.* Its formal enunciation is credited to Lord Kelvin.

In the practical use of the principle of stationary phase, the integrand is usually a function of a parameter, which we may call α, as well as the variable of integration x. Since the variable of integration disappears when we substitute the limits of integration, the integral is actually only a function of the parameter. Thus Eq. (101) may be rewritten

$$P(\alpha) = \int_M^N U(x,\alpha) \cos V(x,\alpha)\, dx = \text{Re}\left\{ \int_M^N U(x,\alpha) e^{jV(x,\alpha)}\, dx \right\} \tag{102}$$

We can therefore rephrase the principle of stationary phase to state that $P(\alpha)$ *will have its greatest values for those values of* α *for which* $V(x,\alpha)$ *has stationary values.* This is the form of the statement of the principle of stationary phase that is ordinarily the most useful in radio engineering. We shall now use it in dealing with a number of practical examples.

4.15 Examples of the Application of the Principle of Stationary Phase. *a. Location of a Signal.* Suppose we have a signal $G(t)$. Then $G(t)$ may be represented by a Fourier integral as

$$G(t) = \frac{1}{\pi} \int_0^\infty S(\omega) \cos [\omega t + \phi(\omega)]\, d\omega \tag{103}$$

According to the principle of stationary phase, if $S(\omega)$ *varies only slowly* with ω while $\cos [\omega t + \phi(\omega)]$ goes through a large number of periods, then the major portions of the signal are located where

$$\frac{d}{d\omega} [\omega t + \phi(\omega)] = t + \frac{d\phi}{d\omega} = 0 \tag{104}$$

or

$$t = -\frac{d\phi}{d\omega} \tag{105}$$

Equation (105) gives the approximate location in time of the signal. The situation is depicted in Fig. 27 by the signal $G(t)$. In case $d\phi/d\omega$ varies with ω, then the average value of $d\phi/d\omega$ in the frequency range containing most of the energy of the signal should be used in Eq. (105).

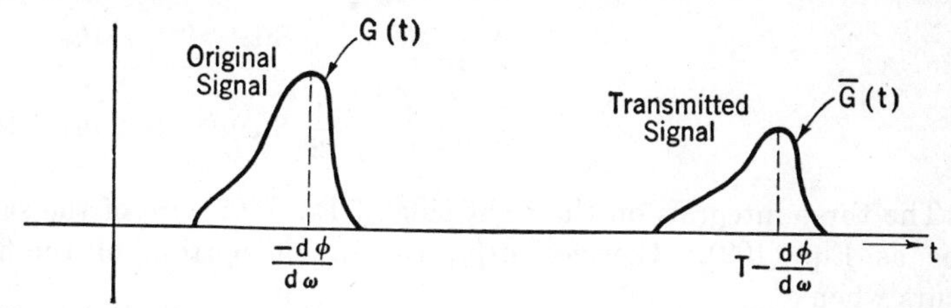

Fig. 27. The location of signals according to the principle of stationary phase.

b. Distortionless Transmission. Next suppose that the signal in Eq. (103) goes through a transmission system with a transmission characteristic whose amplitude is independent of frequency and equal to $1/K$ and whose phase shift is proportional to frequency and equal to $-\omega T$. These are the characteristics of a system having distortionless transmission, as in Sec. 4.3. Then the output is

$$\bar{G}(t) = \frac{1}{\pi K}\int_0^\infty S(\omega)\cos\left[\omega t + \phi(\omega) - \omega T\right]d\omega \tag{106}$$

According to the principle of stationary phase, the major portions of the signal are then located where

$$\frac{d}{d\omega}\left[\omega t + \phi(\omega) - \omega T\right] = t - T + \frac{d\phi}{d\omega} = 0 \tag{107}$$

or

$$t = T - \frac{d\phi}{d\omega} \tag{108}$$

Comparing this with Eq. (105), we see that the phase shift in the transmission system has caused a time delay of amount T for the signal The situation is shown pictorially in Fig. 27.

c. Paired Echoes of Distortion. Let us next consider the paired echoes of distortion discussed in Sec. 4.12. To be specific, let us consider the case of first-order amplitude distortion. The other cases can be treated by exactly similar means. For the case of first-order amplitude distortion, Eq. (78) gives us

$$\bar{G}(t) = \frac{1}{2\pi} \int_{-\infty}^{+\infty} S(\omega) \left(\frac{a_0}{2} + a_1 \cos c\omega \right) \epsilon^{j(\omega t - b_0 \omega)} \, d\omega$$
$$= \frac{1}{2\pi} \int_{-\infty}^{+\infty} \frac{a_0}{2} S(\omega) \epsilon^{j\omega(t-b_0)} \, d\omega$$
$$+ \frac{1}{2\pi} \int_{-\infty}^{+\infty} \frac{a_1}{2} S(\omega) \epsilon^{j\omega(t-b_0+c)} \, d\omega$$
$$+ \frac{1}{2\pi} \int_{-\infty}^{+\infty} \frac{a_1}{2} S(\omega) \epsilon^{j\omega(t-b_0-c)} \, d\omega \quad (109)$$

The three integrals on the right side of Eq. (109) are of the same type as Eq. (102). Consequently, the major portion of the first occurs when

$$\frac{d}{d\omega} [\omega(t - b_0)] = t - b_0 = 0 \qquad \text{or} \qquad t = b_0 \quad (110)$$

of the second when

$$\frac{d}{d\omega} [\omega(t - b_0 + c)] = t - b_0 + c = 0 \qquad \text{or} \qquad t = b_0 - c \quad (111)$$

and of the third when

$$\frac{d}{d\omega} [\omega(t - b_0 - c)] = t - b_0 - c = 0 \qquad \text{or} \qquad t = b_0 + c \quad (112)$$

Thus the principle of stationary phase can be used to locate both the main transmitted signal and its echoes.

In the foregoing example, the original amplitude function was

$$S(\omega) \left(\frac{a_0}{2} + a_1 \cos c\omega \right)$$

Since $\cos c\omega$ varied more than slowly with ω, it was necessary to transfer this factor into the phase portion of the integral, before applying the principle of stationary phase.

d. Spectral Distribution of Frequency Components.[1] The foregoing examples have shown us how to find the location in time of signals under various circumstances. We shall now study an example of locating the principal frequency ranges in the distribution of the components of a signal.

[1] In this connection, see John R. Carson and Thornton C. Fry, Variable Frequency Electrical Circuit Theory, Appendix I, *Bell System Tech. J.*, October, 1937, p. 513. The author first became acquainted with the principle of stationary phase through this article.

Consider a signal (see Fig. 3 of Chap. III)

$$\left.\begin{aligned} G(t) &= \cos \omega_0 t \qquad &\text{(from } T_1 \text{ to } T_2\text{)} \\ G(t) &= 0 \qquad &\text{(elsewhere)} \end{aligned}\right\} \tag{113}$$

In this case the complex frequency-distribution function is

$$F(f) = \int_{-\infty}^{+\infty} G(t)\epsilon^{-j\omega t}\,dt = \int_{T_1}^{T_2} \cos(\omega_0 t)\epsilon^{-j\omega t}\,dt$$
$$= \int_{T_1}^{T_2} \frac{\epsilon^{j\omega_0 t} + \epsilon^{-j\omega_0 t}}{2}\,\epsilon^{-j\omega t}\,dt$$
$$= \int_{T_1}^{T_2} \frac{\epsilon^{-j(\omega-\omega_0)t}}{2}\,dt + \int_{T_1}^{T_2} \frac{\epsilon^{-j(\omega+\omega_0)t}}{2}\,dt \tag{114}$$

According to the principle of stationary phase, the major portion of the first integral on the right side of Eq. (114) is located where

$$\frac{d}{dt}[(\omega - \omega_0)t] = \omega - \omega_0 = 0$$

or

$$\omega = +\omega_0 \tag{115}$$

while the major portion of the second integral is located where

$$\frac{d}{dt}[(\omega + \omega_0)t] = \omega + \omega_0 = 0$$

or

$$\omega = -\omega_0 \tag{116}$$

Equations (115) and (116) thus tell us that the major portions of $F(f)$ for the signal of Eq. (113) are located around ω_0 and $-\omega_0$. The reader can verify this conclusion by referring to Fig. 4 of Chap. III, remembering that

$$S(\omega) = |F(f)| \tag{117}$$

So far we have used the principle of stationary phase for the location of the major portions of a signal both in time and in the frequency spectrum. In the next section we shall use it for locating a signal in space and shall thus develop the important concept of *group velocity*.

4.16 Signals Travel with Group Velocity. If a plane wave of one frequency is traveling through space or an electric wave of one frequency is traveling down a transmission line, either may be represented analytically as

$$A \cos\left[\omega\left(t - \frac{r}{V}\right)\right] \tag{118}$$

where A = amplitude factor
t = time
r = distance traveled
V = velocity of propagation.

The expression (118) is derived and discussed in most elementary texts in physics and radio engineering and is no doubt familiar to the reader. The situation, however, is no longer as simple as that expressed in Eq. (118), if a disturbance[1] $G(t)$, which is made up of the superposition of waves of a band of frequencies, from $\omega_1/2\pi$ to $\omega_2/2\pi$, is traveling down the line, in case the velocity of propagation is different for each frequency. Let us see with what velocity this disturbance is propagated.

The disturbance may be represented by the Fourier integral

$$G(t) = \int_{\omega_1}^{\omega_2} A(\omega) \cos \left[\omega\left(t - \frac{r}{V}\right)\right] d\omega \tag{119}$$

By the principle of stationary phase the major portion of this disturbance is located where

$$\frac{d}{d\omega}\left[\omega\left(t - \frac{r}{V}\right)\right] = \left(t - \frac{r}{V}\right) + \frac{\omega r}{V^2}\frac{dV}{d\omega} = 0 \tag{120}$$

Solving Eq. (120), we obtain for the location of the disturbance

$$r = \frac{t}{\dfrac{1}{V} - \dfrac{\omega}{V^2}\dfrac{dV}{d\omega}} \tag{121}$$

If we call the velocity at which the disturbance is traveling v_G, then we have by the very definition of velocity

$$r = v_G t \tag{122}$$

Comparing Eq. (121) with Eq. (122), we have

$$\frac{1}{v_G} = \frac{1}{V} - \frac{\omega}{V^2}\frac{dV}{d\omega} = \frac{d}{d\omega}\left(\frac{\omega}{V}\right) \tag{123}$$

If we write

$$k = \frac{\omega}{V} = \frac{2\pi}{\lambda} \tag{124}$$

[1] A disturbance is the general term used in wave studies to describe any type of variation, for example, a radio signal.

where λ is the wavelength corresponding to ω, we can transform Eq. (123) into the standard form as derived by Rayleigh,

$$v_G = \frac{d\omega}{d(\omega/V)} = \frac{d(kV)}{dk} = V + k\frac{dV}{dk} \tag{125}$$

v_G, the velocity at which the disturbance as a whole is traveling, is called the *group velocity*. On the other hand, V, the velocity at which the phase of a wave of one frequency moves down the line, is called the *phase velocity* or *wave velocity*.

Phase velocity can be determined by measuring the steady-state characteristics of a line, such as the wavelength of standing waves, and we can study the variation of this phase velocity with frequency. However, the velocity at which a disturbance travels down the line, *i.e.*, the velocity at which *energy* travels down the line, is ordinarily the *group velocity*.

If the phase velocity is independent of frequency, Eq. (125) tells us that it is then equal to the group velocity. It is probably for this reason that the distinction between phase velocity and group velocity was not at first recognized. An interesting historical case may be cited in this connection. When Michelson first measured the velocity of light in a medium other than air (he used carbon bisulphide) by a method that actually measured the time required for light to travel between two points, he found that the measured velocity differed markedly from the figure obtained by dividing the velocity of light in air by the known index of refraction of carbon bisulphide for the color used. The difficulty was resolved when Gibbs and Rayleigh pointed out that the velocity of light determined by the index of refraction method was the phase velocity, while Michelson measured the velocity at which light energy actually traveled, *i.e.*, the group velocity. They then calculated the difference term, $k\, dV/dk$ [see Eq. (125)] from the known variation of the index of refraction with frequency and found that it accounted for the discrepancy.

4.17 Criteria on The Phase Characteristics of Video and Pulse Amplifiers. In earlier sections of this chapter we studied the way in which bandwidth affects the output of video and pulse amplifiers. In particular, we made approximate determinations of the bandwidth necessary to transmit various amounts of detail and to allow the accurate location of sharp edges of pulses. In this section we shall attempt to establish criteria for the requirements in transmission phase characteristics to do the same things.

a. Criteria for Detail. In Sec. 4.7 we found that a frequency bandwidth of

$$f_s = \frac{1}{2 \times \text{pulse length}} \tag{126}$$

is sufficient to pass fine detail of equal pulses and spaces. However, a bandwidth of

$$f_{s1} = \frac{1}{4 \times \text{pulse length}} \tag{127}$$

completely washes out the detail. We now propose to study this case in terms of distortion and paired echoes and by analogy with it derive corresponding criteria for the phase characteristic. Accordingly, we shall now study the echoes corresponding to Eq. (127).

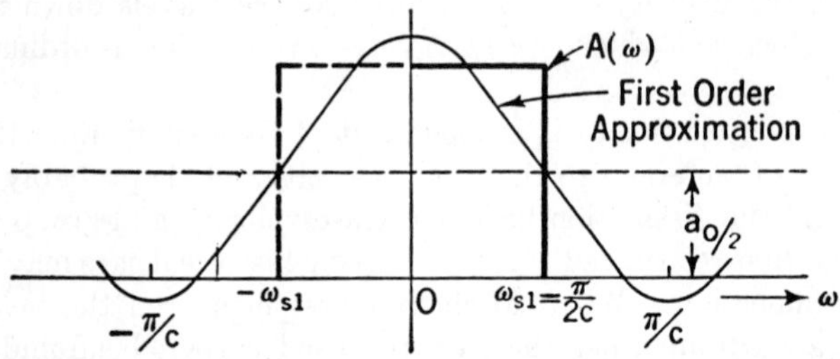

FIG. 28. Amplitude vs. frequency characteristic of a low-pass filter and its first-order approximation.

In Fig. 28 is shown the frequency characteristic corresponding to Eq. (127). We shall consider only the first-order amplitude-distortion echoes corresponding to Fig. 28 and accordingly shall consider only the fundamental in the Fourier expansion of Fig. 28. Referring to Fig. 8 of Chap. I and Fig. 20 of this chapter, we see that the magnitude of the fundamental distortion term is $(4/\pi)(a_0/2)$. If we now refer to Eq. (78) of this chapter, we see that the echoes corresponding to this fundamental will be $2/\pi$ times as large as the undistorted signal and will be displaced from it by a time

$$c = \frac{\pi}{2\omega_{S1}} = \frac{\pi}{4\pi f_{S1}} = \text{original pulse length} \tag{128}$$

by Eq. (127). The situation is depicted in Fig. 29.

Although the transmitted signal in Fig. 29 shows a similarity to the original signal, the detail is entirely due to the distortion echoes and is therefore fortuitous. For our purposes, in accordance with Eq. (127) we shall assume that a pair of positive echoes of 63 per cent (*i.e.*, $2/\pi$) of the size of the undistorted signal and displaced from it by the pulse length will completely wash out the signal detail.

Let us next consider the phase-distortion echoes. In this case we have one obvious difference from the amplitude-distortion case in that one of the echoes is negative. With equal pulse lengths and spaces as shown in Fig. 29 this would have the effect of the negative distortion eliminating the positive distortion when the echoes were displaced from the main signal by the pulse length as called for in Eq. (128). It therefore appears that a larger displacement can be tolerated for the phase-distortion echoes. If the displacement is made equal to $3/2$ times the pulse length, the picture becomes about as bad as that of Fig. 29*d*. Accordingly, we shall assume that a com-

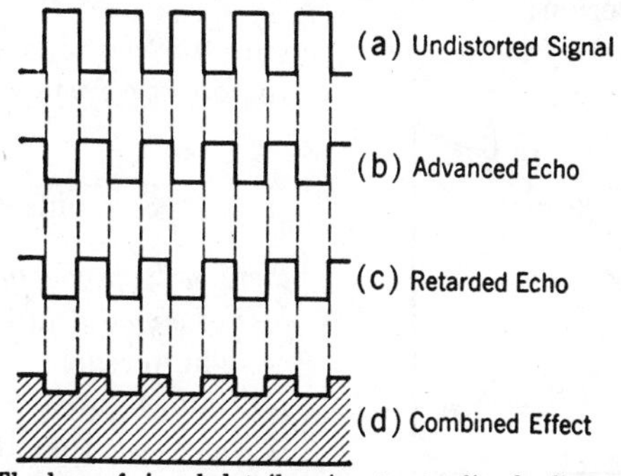

FIG. 29. The loss of signal detail owing to amplitude-distortion echoes.

plete loss of detail due to phase distortion will result from phase-distortion echoes of magnitude $2/\pi$ times the undistorted signal and displaced from it by $3/2$ the pulse length.

Let us next transform the distortion conditions just described into properties of the phase characteristic. Referring to Fig. 22, we see that a displacement of

$$c_1 = \frac{3}{2} \times \text{pulse length} = \frac{\pi}{\omega} = \frac{1}{2f} \tag{129}$$

is equivalent to a variation from a linear phase characteristic in a frequency band of

$$f = \frac{1}{3 \times \text{pulse length}} \tag{130}$$

The amount of variation is determined by the echo size, namely, $2/\pi$ as mentioned above. According to Eq. (84), this means that

$$\frac{J_1(b_1)}{J_0(b_1)} = \frac{2}{\pi} = 0.636 \tag{131}$$

Therefore, according to Fig. 23 this means that

$$b_1 = 1 \qquad \text{(approx)} \tag{132}$$

Equations (130) and (132) thus give us our first criterion, namely: *If the variation from a linear phase characteristic is as much as 1 radian in a frequency range of*

$$\frac{1}{3 \times \text{pulse length}}$$

a complete loss of signal detail may be expected. This criterion corresponds to Eq. (127) as a criterion for the amplitude characteristic. Corresponding to Eq. (126), we shall then somewhat arbitrarily write the second criterion:

If the variation from a linear phase characteristic is no more than ½ radian in a frequency range of

$$\frac{1}{3 \times \text{pulse length}}$$

there will probably be no serious loss of signal detail.

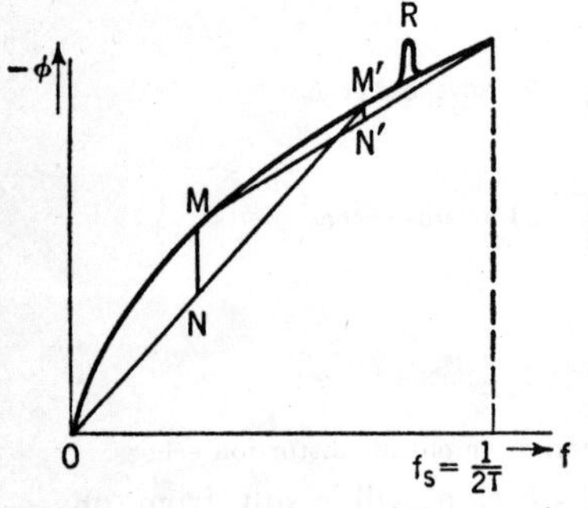

FIG. 30. A phase shift vs. frequency characteristic of a transmission system.

The foregoing criteria can lay no claim to great accuracy, but it is believed that they were obtained from reasonable arguments. They should therefore be of some value in judging the adequacy of a phase characteristic.

As an example, consider the phase characteristic in Fig. 30. The system is expected to pass pulses of length T, so that the bandwidth is made

$$f_s = \frac{1}{2T} \tag{133}$$

according to Eq. (126). According to our second criterion, we then require that the deviation from linearity in ⅔ of the above bandwidth shall not be more than ½ radian. These deviations are shown as MN or $M'N'$ in Fig. 30. If neither of these is more than ½ radian, the phase characteristic is satisfactory for the transmission of details of length T.

The foregoing criteria refer to the frequency bands that contain the major portion of the signal energy. Thus, if there is a large deviation from phase linearity in a very narrow frequency band (illustrated at R in Fig. 30), its effect upon detail can probably be ignored, unless this particular narrow frequency band happens to contain a large percentage of the signal energy. In that case the whole situation would have to be reconsidered.

b. Criteria for Sharp Edges. In Sec. 4.11 we found that while a bandwidth of $3/4T$ gives the best signal-to-noise ratio in a pulse amplifier, an increase in bandwidth to $7/4T$ gives a worth-while improvement in the sharpness of edges, if these edges must be accurately located. Let us now see what stipulation must be made concerning the phase characteristic of the amplifier in this added frequency range so that the additional frequency range shall not be wasted.

The transmitted signal may be expressed as

$$\bar{G}(t) = \frac{1}{2\pi}\int_0^{2\pi\frac{3}{4T}} S(\omega)A(\omega)\epsilon^{j[\omega t+\phi(\omega)+B(\omega)]}\,d\omega + \frac{1}{2\pi}\int_{2\pi\frac{3}{4T}}^{2\pi\frac{7}{4T}} S(\omega)A(\omega)\epsilon^{j[\omega t+\phi(\omega)+B(\omega)]}\,d\omega \tag{134}$$

where

$$G(t) = \frac{1}{2\pi}\int_{-\infty}^{+\infty} S(\omega)\epsilon^{j[\omega t+\phi(\omega)]}\,d\omega \tag{135}$$

is the original signal and

$$A(\omega)\epsilon^{jB(\omega)} \tag{136}$$

is the transmission characteristic of the system.

Applying the principle of stationary phase to Eq. (134), we see that the main[1] part of the energy of the first integral is located at

$$t = \left(-\frac{d\phi}{d\omega} - \frac{dB}{d\omega}\right)_{0<\omega<2\pi\frac{3}{4T}} \tag{137}$$

where the derivatives in Eq. (137) are average values between frequencies 0 and $3/4T$, and the main part of the energy of the second

[1] Most writers on television have assumed that the transmission system introduces a time delay for the frequency components of the signal in a given range of amount B/ω, instead of $dB/d\omega$. This procedure is correct only if the phase shift is linear, which is not the case when there is phase distortion. Such a procedure is analogous to assuming that the phase velocity is equal to the group velocity in wave transmission.

integral is located at

$$t = \left(-\frac{d\phi}{d\omega} - \frac{dB}{d\omega} \right)_{2\pi\frac{3}{4T} < \omega < 2\pi\frac{7}{4T}} \tag{138}$$

where the derivatives are average values between the frequencies $3/4T$ and $7/4T$. If we refer to Fig. 6, we can see the improvement to be expected in the sharpness of edges by the extension of the frequency range if the values of $dB/d\omega$ are constant and equal in both ranges.

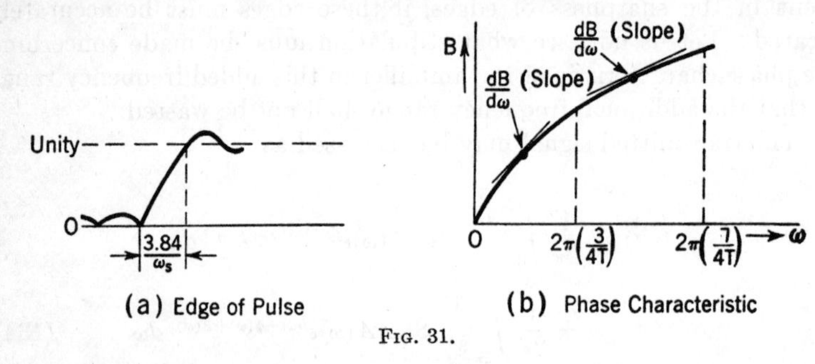

FIG. 31.

For practical purposes, the edge of a pulse rises from zero to unity, as shown in Fig. 31, in a time (see Sec. 4.5)

$$t_r = \text{time of rise} = \frac{3.84}{\omega_s} \tag{139}$$

where $\omega_s/2\pi$ is the cutoff frequency. For the signal of Eq. (137) the time of rise is therefore

$$t_r = \frac{3.84 \times 4T}{6\pi} = 0.81T \tag{140}$$

If the bandwidth is extended to $7/4T$, the time of rise becomes

$$t_{r1} = \frac{3.84 \times 4T}{14\pi} = 0.35T \tag{141}$$

We shall arbitrarily say that the error in the location of an edge is equal to about ¼ the time of rise. Therefore, for the $7/4T$ bandwidth case, the error in the location of an edge is about

$$t_{r1e} = \frac{0.35T}{4} = 0.088T \tag{142}$$

Let us then say that the location of the energy of the second integral in Eq. (134) shall not be displaced from that of the first by more than

$0.088T$. Expressing this mathematically, we write

$$\left(\frac{dB}{d\omega}\right)_{2\pi\frac{3}{4T}<\omega<2\pi\frac{7}{4T}} - \left(\frac{dB}{d\omega}\right)_{0<\omega<2\pi\frac{3}{4T}} \leq 0.088T \qquad (143)$$

as the criterion for maximum allowable difference between the average slopes of the phase characteristics in the two frequency ranges. If the difference in slopes exceeds this value, it would appear that the phase characteristic causes more inaccuracy in the location of edges than the bandwidth limitation.

The criteria in both parts *a* and *b* of this section present more of an approach than they do an answer to the problems under consideration. With these limitations in mind, it is felt that the foregoing discussion shows how the methods of this chapter may be applied to these important practical problems, which it would be difficult to treat by other means.

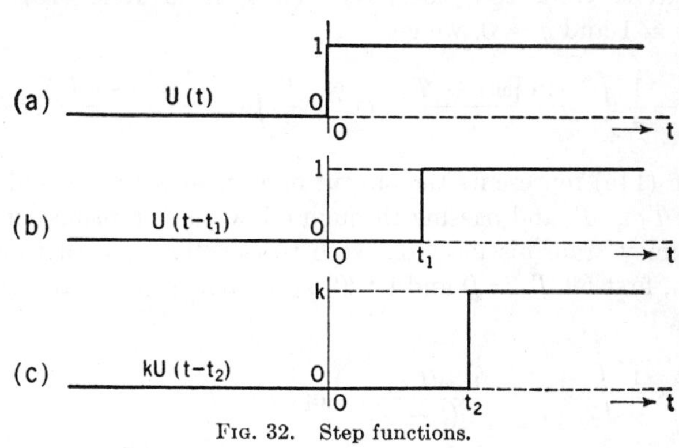

FIG. 32. Step functions.

4.18 Step and Impulse Functions. There is a class of singular functions that is very important in advanced radio theory and that we shall now consider. These singular functions have points of discontinuity, and it is precisely at the points of discontinuity that the most salient characteristics of the functions are located. The importance of these functions arises from the fact that they give a better insight and approximation to certain characteristic radio phenomena than any of the common elementary functions. We shall use them particularly in our study of noise.[1]

[1] These same functions are also very important in the study of transients. See the author's "Transformation Calculus."

a. Step Functions. The *unit step* is a function of an independent variable say t, that has a constant zero value for all negative values of t and a constant value of unity for all positive values of t. At $t = 0$, the function has a discontinuity. The function is shown graphically in Fig. 32*a*. We shall designate it as $U(t)$. A similar function, but with its discontinuity at $t = t_1$, will therefore be $U(t - t_1)$. If the magnitude of the step is different from unity, we need only multiply $U(t)$ by the proper constant to describe it (see Fig. 32*c*).

In order to find the frequency distribution of the unit step, we cannot apply the Fourier integral formulas directly, since

$$\int_{-\infty}^{+\infty} U(t)\, dt = \int_0^{\infty} dt = \infty \tag{144}$$

Nevertheless, the frequency distribution may be found by analyzing a pulse of finite width, as is done in Sec. 4.5, and then letting the width extend from zero to $+\infty$. Thus, from Eqs. (25) to (27), letting $k = 1$ and $g = 0$, we get

$$G_1(t) = -\frac{1}{\pi}\int_0^{\omega_s} \frac{\sin [\omega(t - T_2)]}{\omega}\, d\omega + \frac{1}{\pi}\int_0^{\omega_s} \frac{\sin [\omega(t - T_1)]}{\omega}\, d\omega \tag{145}$$

Equation (145) represents the output of a pulse of unit height extending from T_1 to T_2 and passing through a low-pass transmission system having unity transmission from zero to ω_s. To proceed toward the unit step, first let $T_1 = 0$ and let T_2 approach $+\infty$. Call this $G_2(t)$. Then

$$\begin{aligned} G_2(t) &= -\frac{1}{\pi}\int_0^{\omega_s(t-T_2)} \frac{\sin \omega(t - T_2)}{\omega(t - T_2)}\, d[\omega(t - T_2)] \\ &\qquad + \frac{1}{\pi}\int_0^{\omega_s} \frac{\sin \omega(t - T_1)}{\omega}\, d\omega \\ &= -\frac{1}{\pi}\int_0^{-\infty} \frac{\sin x}{x}\, dx + \frac{1}{\pi}\int_0^{\omega_s} \frac{\sin \omega t}{\omega}\, d\omega \\ &= \frac{1}{2} + \frac{1}{\pi}\int_0^{\omega_s} \frac{\sin \omega t}{\omega}\, d\omega \end{aligned} \tag{146}$$[1]

We next let $\omega_s \to \infty$ and thus obtain the unit step.

$$U(t) = \frac{1}{2} + \frac{1}{\pi}\int_0^{\infty} \frac{\sin \omega t}{\omega}\, d\omega \tag{147}$$

[1] Since
$$\int_0^{\infty} \frac{\sin x}{x}\, dx = \frac{\pi}{2}$$

The integral on the right of Eq. (147) is equal to $\mathrm{Si}\,(+\infty) = \pi/2$ for all positive values of t and to $\mathrm{Si}(-\infty) = -\pi/2$ for all negative values of t. Equation (147) thus agrees with the original definition of the unit step, and our method of derivation is evidence that it really shows the distribution of the frequency components. Equation (147) tells us that the unit step consists of a constant (direct-current) component of magnitude ½ plus a distribution of frequency components of magnitude $1/\pi\omega$. The frequency components are all antisymmetrical with respect to $t = 0$, that is, all the components are sine functions.

The frequency distribution of the energy in the unit step will also be found of interest in later work. This may be found by application of the Fourier integral energy theorem. According to Eq. (100), the energy is distributed among the frequency components in proportion to $[S(\omega)]^2$. For the unit step

$$S(\omega) = \frac{1}{\omega} \tag{148}$$

so that the energy is distributed proportional to $1/\omega^2$. The energy in any frequency band for which $\omega_1 < \omega < \omega_2$ is then proportional to

$$\int_{\omega_1}^{\omega_2} \frac{1}{\omega^2}\,d\omega = \frac{1}{\omega_1} - \frac{1}{\omega_2} \tag{149}$$

The total energy for all frequencies above any frequency $\omega_0/2\pi$ is accordingly proportional to $1/\omega_0$, while the total energy below this frequency is infinite. The energy of the frequency components in a unit step is therefore concentrated at the extremely low frequencies.[1]

b. Ordinary Impulse Functions. We next wish to consider impulse functions and begin with the definition of a unit impulse, which we shall call $\delta(t)$. A *unit impulse* is a function whose value is zero except in an arbitrarily small interval around $t = 0$, where it becomes infinite in such a way that

$$\int_{-a}^{+b} \delta(t)\,dt = 1 \tag{150}$$

In Eq. (150), a and b are any finite positive quantities.

Special types of unit impulse functions may be defined by limiting processes in various ways. For example, we can use

$$\delta(t) = \lim_{\Delta t \to 0} \frac{U\left(t + \dfrac{\Delta t}{2}\right) - U\left(t - \dfrac{\Delta t}{2}\right)}{\Delta t} \tag{151}$$

[1] The total energy in a unit step is infinite, since the unit step is an infinitely long signal.

or

$$\delta(t) = \lim_{\Delta t \to 0} \frac{U(t + \Delta t) - U(t)}{\Delta t} \tag{152}$$

or

$$\delta(t) = \lim_{\Delta t \to 0} \frac{U(t) - U(t - \Delta t)}{\Delta t} \tag{153}$$

or

$$\left.\begin{aligned} \delta(t) &= \lim_{\Delta t \to 0} \frac{\epsilon^{-\frac{t}{\Delta t}}}{\Delta t} \qquad &(\text{when } t > 0) \\ \delta(t) &= 0 \qquad &(\text{when } t < 0) \end{aligned}\right\} \tag{154}$$

These cases are illustrated in Fig. 33*a*, *b*, *c*, and *d*, respectively. The net result of using any of these forms is always the same in practice,

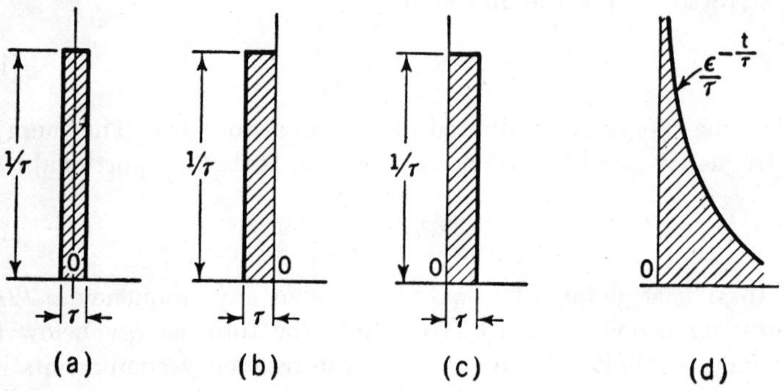

FIG. 33. Various forms which become unit impulse functions as $\tau \to 0$.

so that the particular form should be chosen that is most easily manipulated in the problem at hand. Equation (151), (152), or (153) shows that the unit impulse is formally equivalent to the derivative of the unit step. Furthermore, it is clear that

$$\delta(t - C)$$

expresses a unit impulse at $t = C$; and it may be shown[1] that

$$\int_{-\infty}^{+\infty} g(t)\, \delta(t - C)\, dt = g(C) \tag{155}$$

provided that $g(t)$ is a finite and continuous function of t.

[1] A derivation of Eq. (155) would proceed as follows:

$$\int_{-\infty}^{+\infty} g(t)\, \delta(t - C)\, dt = \int_{C-\epsilon}^{C+\epsilon} g(t)\, \delta(t - C)\, dt = g(C) \int_{C-\epsilon}^{C+\epsilon} \delta(t - C)\, dt = g(C)$$

where ϵ is a very small quantity. If one of the specific forms of $\delta(t)$ [Eqs. (151) to (154)], is chosen, the derivation can easily be made rigorous.

If $P(t)$ is an impulsive function in general (*i.e.*, not necessarily a unit impulse), then

$$\int_{t_1}^{t_2} P(t)\, dt$$

is called the *strength* or *magnitude* of the impulse, where the impulse lies entirely between t_1 and t_2. Accordingly, we can say that a unit impulse is an impulse of unit strength.

The Fourier frequency distribution of a unit impulse can readily be obtained with the aid of Eq. (155). Thus

$$\begin{aligned} F(f) &= \int_{-\infty}^{+\infty} \delta(t) \cos \omega t\, dt - j \int_{-\infty}^{+\infty} \delta(t) \sin \omega t\, dt \\ &= \cos (0) + j \sin (0) = 1 \end{aligned} \tag{156}$$

The Fourier frequency distribution is thus constant and equal to unity for all frequencies in the case of the unit impulse. We may therefore write

$$\delta(t) = \frac{1}{2\pi} \int_{-\infty}^{+\infty} \epsilon^{j\omega t}\, d\omega = \frac{1}{\pi} \int_{0}^{\infty} \cos \omega t\, d\omega \tag{157}$$

Inspection of Eq. (157) shows that all the frequency components are in phase at $t = 0$, which is the reason for the great height of the impulse.

The frequency distribution of the energy in the unit impulse is found by application of the Fourier integral energy theorem as in the case of the unit step. For the unit impulse

$$S(\omega) = 1 \tag{158}$$

so that the energy is uniformly distributed for all frequencies. The energy of a unit impulse in any frequency band is thus proportional to the bandwidth. The total energy for all frequencies below any frequency $\omega_0/2\pi$ is accordingly proportional to ω_0, while the total energy above this frequency is infinite. The energy of the frequency components in a unit impulse is therefore concentrated at the extremely high frequencies. It is worthy of note that although

$$\int_{-\infty}^{+\infty} \delta(t) dt$$

is finite, the energy that it represents and that is proportional to

$$\int_{-\infty}^{+\infty} [\delta(t)]^2\, dt$$

is infinite (but see footnote, page 129).

Step functions and impulse functions never appear in practice except as approximations. Thus the condition in which a quantity changes by a finite amount in an interval so short that a fraction of the interval would be of no practical interest and in which the new value is then retained for the duration of the period of interest of the problem is treated by specifying the quantity as a step function. As a practical example, the closing of a switch connecting a battery to a circuit is analyzed by assuming that a step function of voltage is applied to the circuit. In a similar manner, the condition in which a

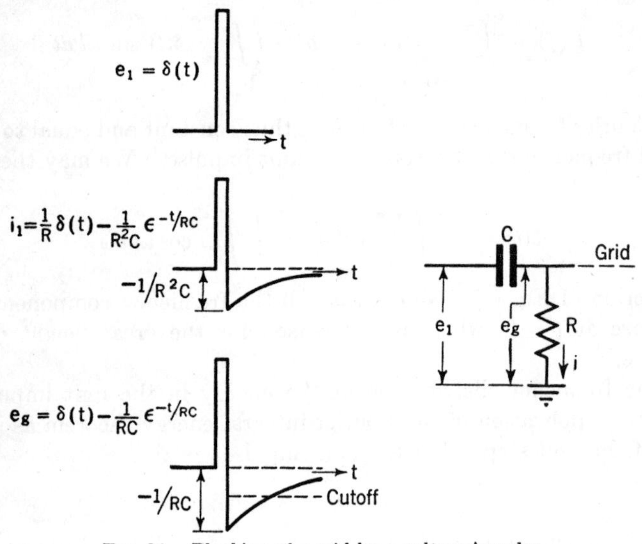

FIG. 34. Blocking of a grid by a voltage impulse.

quantity has so great a value in an interval of negligible duration that a finite change is effected in the state of the system is treated by specifying the quantity as an impulse function. As a practical example, consider a voltage pulse entering the grid circuit of a vacuum tube as shown in Fig. 34. This pulse may be considered an impulse if its duration is negligibly short in comparison with the RC time constant of the circuit and its magnitude is so great that it has an appreciable effect on the circuit despite its short duration. In the case of the impulse in Fig. 34 the ultimate effect is to drive the grid voltage so far negative that the tube is cut off for an appreciable length of time. The actual magnitude and duration of the voltage pulse e_1 are not separately important in this case, but the time integral of e_1 (*i.e.*, the strength of the voltage impulse) determines how far negative the grid voltage goes and how long the tube is cut off. Thus e_1, in this case, is an impulse function.[1]

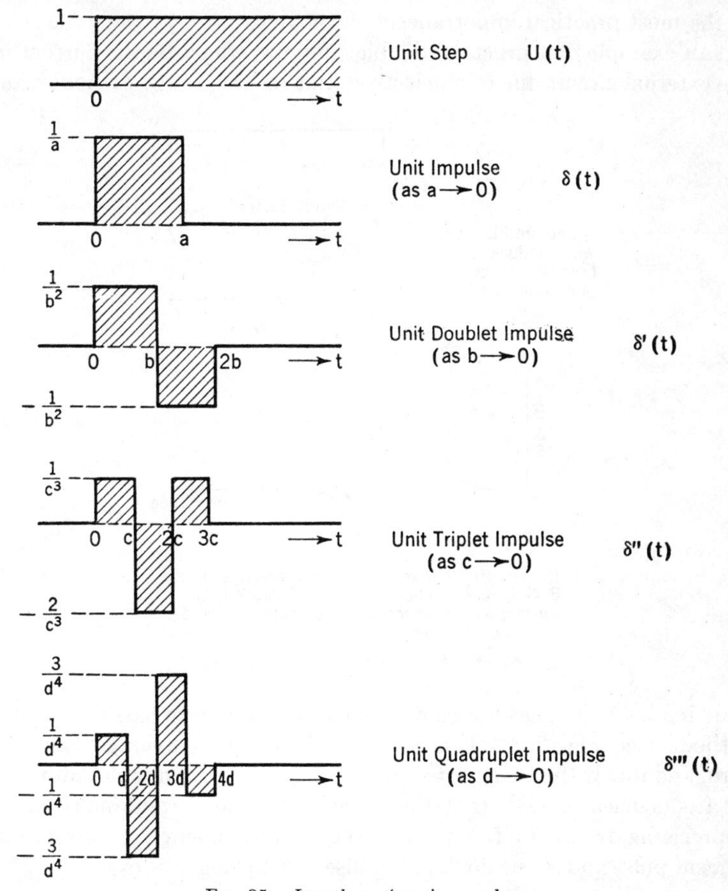

FIG. 35. Impulses of various orders.
Impulses of still higher order are developed in an analogous manner. (Note that the heights of shaded blocks are proportional to the binomial coefficients, *i.e.*, +1, −1 for $\delta'(t)$; +1, −2, +1 for $\delta''(t)$; +1, −3, +3, −1 for $\delta'''(t)$; etc.)

c. Impulses of Higher Order. In addition to step functions and ordinary impulse functions, there are also other singular functions of

[1] It is worth while pointing out that the energy associated with e_1 (or i_1) in any actual case is finite, not infinite as in the ideal case. The reason for this is that the heights and durations of all practical impulses are finite. Therefore, the

the same set that are sometimes of practical importance. The early members of this set of singular functions are shown in Fig. 35. Next to step functions and ordinary impulse functions, doublet impulses are of the most practical importance.

An example of a practical doublet impulse would be the current in the external circuit due to an electron that returns to the cathode after

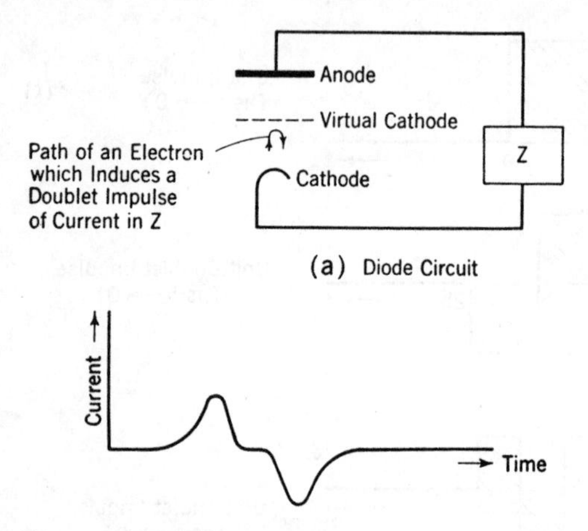

FIG. 36. A practical doublet impulse.

emission because it has not enough emission velocity to pass the virtual cathode (see Fig. 36). This current will have an average value of zero, and its low-frequency spectrum will be that of a doublet impulse. At frequencies so high that the duration of the current pulse is an appreciable fraction of a period, the correspondence between the current pulse and a true doublet impulse will no longer be exact.

---

uniform distribution of frequency components, which is characteristic of impulses, extends only up to some finite frequency and thereafter falls off. The arbitrarily high frequency components that carry the infinite energy of an ideal impulse are thus absent in practice.

From a physical point of view, the fact that the energy of this practical impulse is finite, despite its almost infinitesimal duration, means that, because of its great amplitude, the impulse is able to cause a sizable charge to be accumulated on the condenser in this very short time. The discharge of the condenser then creates a decaying current after the impulse has passed, as shown in Fig. 34.

To find the frequency distribution of the doublet impulse, we write

$$
\begin{aligned}
F(f) &= \int_{-\infty}^{+\infty} G(t)\epsilon^{-j\omega t}\,dt \\
&= \frac{1}{b^2}\left(\int_0^b \epsilon^{-j\omega t}\,dt - \int_b^{2b} \epsilon^{-j\omega t}\,dt\right) \\
&= \frac{j}{b^2\omega}\left(\epsilon^{-j\omega b} - 1 - \epsilon^{-j2\omega b} + \epsilon^{-j\omega b}\right) \qquad (159)
\end{aligned}
$$

As $b \to 0$, we find the value of $F(f)$ by expanding the exponentials in power series and neglecting the higher powered terms.

Thus

$$
\begin{aligned}
F(f) &= \frac{j}{b^2\omega}\left\{\left[1 - j\omega b + \frac{(-j\omega b)^2}{2}\right] - 1 - \left[1 - j2\omega b + \frac{(-j2\omega b)^2}{2}\right]\right. \\
&\qquad\left. + \left[1 - j\omega b + \frac{(-j\omega b)^2}{2}\right]\right\} \\
&= \frac{j}{b^2\omega}(\omega^2 b^2) = j\omega \qquad (160)
\end{aligned}
$$

and

$$
S(\omega) = |F(f)| = \omega \qquad (161)
$$

The frequency distribution of the doublet impulse thus rises linearly with frequency.

Just as in the case of the unit impulse shown in Fig. 33, the impulses of higher order may also be considered as the limiting forms of a number of different sets of functions,[1] as long as their frequency distributions are the proper powers of ω. We may also note that, in a general way, each impulse function may be considered as the time derivative of the impulse of next lower order. We shall use the properties of impulse functions derived in this section in order to obtain important practical results in the chapters on noise.

4.19 Further Discussion of Fourier Pairs. In the discussion preceding the actual tables in the article[2] by Campbell and Foster, the reader will find a description of additional important properties of various Fourier pairs. Furthermore in the author's "Transformation Calculus," we shall find the Laplace transforms there used to be closely

[1] One such set that is different from the set shown in Fig. 35 is given by Campbell and Foster in *Bell Telephone System Mono.* B584, p. 17.

[2] CAMPBELL, G. A., and R. M. FOSTER, Fourier Integrals for Practical Applications, *Bell Telephone System Mono.* B584.

related to Fourier pairs, and the study of one will throw light upon the other. In fact, a table of Laplace transforms can be used as a table of Fourier pairs, and vice versa, provided that certain slight changes are made.

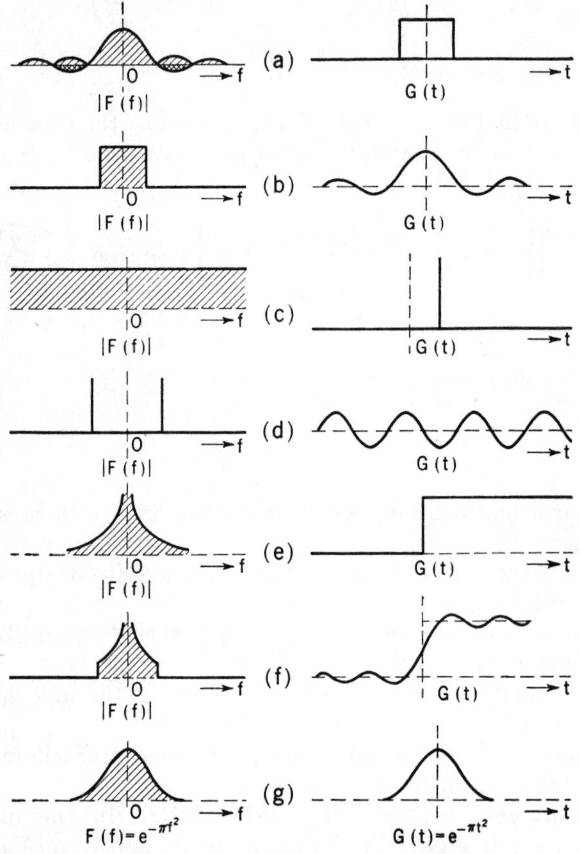

FIG. 37. Curves of some important Fourier transforms.

Before closing our discussion of Fourier integrals, we shall now consider certain general phenomena of wide application.

a. The Effect of Sharp Cutoff. In Sec. 3.4 we found that, if $G(t)$ is a pulse (*i.e.*, a rectangular block), then its frequency distribution $|F(f)|$ is spread out as shown in Fig. 37*a*. On the other hand, if a signal has a frequency-distribution function $F(f)$ that is a rectangular block, then the signal itself is spread out as shown in Fig. 37*b*.[1] We thus see, in these cases, that, if one mate of a Fourier pair has sharp cutoff, the other trails on indefinitely.

In Sec. 4.18 we found that an impulse of infinitesimal duration has a constant frequency distribution with no phase shift for all frequencies. This is shown in Fig. 37*c*. Consequently, if such an impulse went through a transmission system having the frequency characteristic shown in Fig. 37*b*, the output would be the signal $G(t)$ shown in Fig. 37*b*.

Consider next the unit step shown in Fig. 37*e*. If it is subjected to sharp cutoff as shown in Fig. 37*f*, it develops, not only trailing, but also overshoot. These phenomena have already been discussed in Sec. 4.5. All the above-mentioned phenomena are closely related to the phenomena of diffraction in optics and acoustics and to Gibbs's phenomenon in Fourier analysis. It is a well-known diffraction phenomenon that a sharp discontinuity will cause characteristic periodic fluctuations in intensity. In the absence of a sharp discontinuity, these fluctuations are smoothed out.

Now there are certain functions that have the remarkable property of being their own Fourier transforms. These are discussed in the article by Campbell and Foster already mentioned. Probably the simplest of these Fourier pairs is

$$F(f) = \epsilon^{-\pi f^2} \tag{162}$$

$$G(t) = \epsilon^{-\pi t^2} \tag{163}$$

which is shown as Fig. 37*g*. In view of the pairs shown in Fig. 37, especially *a* and *b*, the above pair, (Fig. 37*g*) may be considered as giving the smoothest cutoff.[2] The foregoing general considerations suggest that a frequency characteristic as shown in Fig. 37*g* has less

[1] The derivation is very simple.

$$G(t) = \int_{-f_0}^{+f_0} \epsilon^{j2\pi ft}\,df = \frac{1}{\pi}\left(\frac{\sin \omega_0 t}{t}\right)$$

[2] The above reciprocal pair gives rise to the interesting fact that, if a signal of the form $A\epsilon^{-at^2}$ goes through a system having a frequency characteristic $B\epsilon^{-bf^2}$, the emergent signal will be of the form $C\epsilon^{-ct^2}$. Thus, in a universe in which all signals were of the form $A\epsilon^{-at^2}$ and all systems had frequency characteristics of the form $B\epsilon^{-fb^2}$, all transmission problems could be discussed in terms of a single system of number couples (M,m) in which the first stood for amplitude and the second for exponential multiplier. This is analogous to the universe of linear systems in which sine waves of a given frequency can change only in amplitude and phase. The number couples for the latter, we know, are complex quantities.

tendency to cause trailing oscillations and overshoot than one having sharp cutoff, even for signals other than that shown in Fig. 37*g*.

Wheeler and Loughren[1] have studied means of improving television detail by the use of signals and frequency characteristics that are self-reciprocal. In this same paper will be found an extensive discussion of the effects of sharp cutoff.

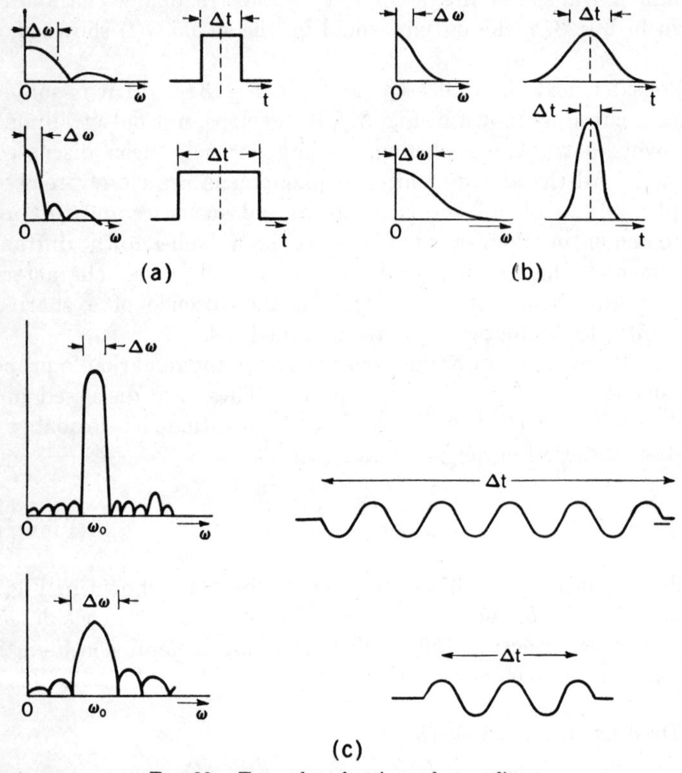

Fig. 38. Examples of reciprocal spreading.

b. Reciprocal Spreading. Another phenomenon closely related to the Fourier transforms shown in Fig. 37 is what may be called *reciprocal spreading*. This is the phenomenon that, *as one member of a Fourier pair becomes narrower, the other spreads out.* The phenomenon is illustrated in Fig. 38. As an immediate consequence of reciprocal spreading, we have the relation that the bandwidth necessary to reproduce a pulse is inversely proportional to the pulse width. As another con-

[1] *Proc. I.R.E.*, May, 1938, p. 540.

sequence, we have that the build-up transient time of a tuned circuit is proportional to the selectivity of the circuit.

In dealing with reciprocal spreading, we use $S(\omega)$, instead of $F(f)$. This avoids the necessity of separate consideration of negative and positive frequencies and of real and imaginary parts of $F(f)$. If we designate the width[1] of the main part of $S(\omega)$ as $\Delta\omega$ and the width of the main part of $G(t)$ as Δt, then for each type of signal we may write

$$\Delta f = \frac{1}{2\pi}\,\Delta\omega \approx \frac{1}{\Delta t} \tag{164}$$

where the symbol $\approx$ in this case means "is proportional to and is of the order of magnitude of . . . ."

If we take the phenomenon of reciprocal spreading into three dimensions, we find that the directivity of an antenna is proportional to the path difference in wavelengths between its extreme rays. For a given frequency this means that the directivity of an antenna is proportional to its diameter. For a given diameter the directivity is proportional to frequency.

Among the applications of *reciprocal spreading* in physics we have the fact that the resolving power of a spectroscope is proportional to the path difference in wavelengths of its extreme rays. Also, the resolving power of a telescope is proportional to the path difference in wavelengths between its extreme rays.

In all the foregoing examples the fundamental principle involved is that, in order to sharpen a characteristic in terms of one variable, it is necessary to increase its breadth in terms of the conjugate variable. This also forms the basis of the *principle of uncertainty* in modern *quantum mechanics* now used in atomic theory. There, the famous relationship of Heisenberg

$$\Delta p\,\Delta q \approx h \tag{165}$$

is used in place of Eq. (164). In Eq. (165) the quantity h is the universal quantum constant, and p and q are any "canonically conjugate" variables.

c. Energy Storage and Selectivity. A phenomenon that is closely related to reciprocal spreading is the relation between energy storage and selectivity. Let us first consider the selectivity of a single tuned *L-R-C* circuit. Let f_0 be its resonant frequency, and let us define its

[1] The exact manner in which $\Delta\omega$ and Δt are defined is optional, so long as they describe the width of the main body of the signal energy.

quality factor Q as

$$Q = \frac{2\pi f_0 L}{R} = \frac{1}{2\pi f_0 CR} \tag{166}$$

In Fig. 39 are shown a series tuned circuit and a parallel tuned circuit of this type.

The curve of the impedance of a tuned circuit as a function of frequency exhibits a sharp peak (or dip), and the frequency at which the peak or dip occurs is called the resonant frequency. As a measure of the selectivity of the impedance, it is customary to define

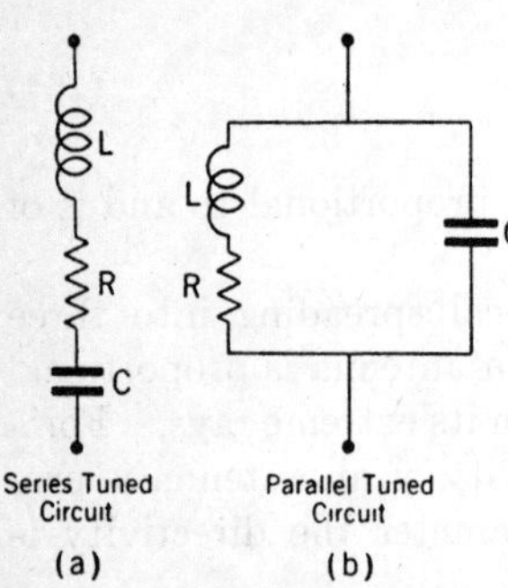

FIG. 39. Elementary types of single-tuned circuits.

$$\text{Selectivity} = \frac{f_0}{f_2 - f_1} \tag{167}$$

where f_0 is the resonant frequency, f_2 is the frequency above resonance at which the impedance differs from its resonant value by a factor of $\sqrt{2}$, and f_1 is the frequency below resonance at which impedance differs from its resonant value by a factor of $\sqrt{2}$.

Let us now calculate the selectivity of the impedance in Fig. 39*a* for a high-Q case. For any frequency,

$$z = R + j\left(\omega L - \frac{1}{\omega C}\right) = R + jX \tag{168}$$

Near resonance, we can expand X about the resonant frequency, in a Taylor series. Thus

$$\begin{aligned} X = \left(\omega L - \frac{1}{\omega C}\right) &= X_0 + \left(\frac{dX}{d\omega}\right)_0 (\omega - \omega_0) + \cdots \\ &= 0 + \left(L + \frac{1}{\omega_0^2 C}\right)(\omega - \omega_0) + \cdots \\ &= \frac{2QR}{\omega_0}(\omega - \omega_0) \text{ (approx)} \end{aligned} \tag{169}$$

or

$$z = R + j2QR\frac{\omega - \omega_0}{\omega_0} \quad \text{(approx)} \tag{170}$$

At resonance

$$z = R \tag{171}$$

z will rise to $\sqrt{2}\,R$ when

$$\left|2Q\,\frac{\omega - \omega_0}{\omega_0}\right| = 1 = \left|2Q\,\frac{f - f_0}{f_0}\right| \tag{172}$$

Equation (172) determines the frequencies f_2 and f_1.

Thus

$$f_2 - f_0 = \frac{f_0}{2Q} = f_0 - f_1 \tag{173}$$

Therefore the selectivity of the series tuned circuit is

$$\frac{f_0}{f_2 - f_1} = Q \tag{174}$$

Since the selectivity of a series tuned circuit has thus been shown to be equal to its quality factor Q, we may, and frequently do, use the same symbol Q for both the selectivity and the quality factor. The reader can show in the exercise below that a similar situation holds for parallel tuned circuits.

We shall next derive an interesting relationship that exists between energy storage and dissipation on the one hand and selectivity on the other. The energy stored in the tuned circuit in Fig. 39a at any instant is

$$\text{Energy stored} = \tfrac{1}{2}(Ce^2 + Li^2) \tag{175}$$

Now this energy flows back and forth between the inductance and capacity, and at those times during a cycle when the magnetic energy in the inductance is a maximum the electrical energy in the condenser is zero.[1] We can therefore find the total stored energy by finding, say, the energy in the inductance at the instant of a current peak. Thus if

$$i = I \sin \omega t \tag{176}$$

then, at the current peak,

$$\sin \omega t = 1 \tag{177}$$

and

$$\text{Stored energy} = \tfrac{1}{2}LI^2 \tag{178}$$

The energy dissipated per cycle in the resistance R of the tuned circuit is

$$\text{Energy dissipated per cycle} = \frac{1}{f}\left(\frac{1}{2}\,RI^2\right) = \frac{2\pi}{\omega}\left(\frac{1}{2}\,RI^2\right) \tag{179}$$

[1] This follows from the 90-deg phase difference between current and voltage in a reactance.

Therefore, *at resonance*,

$$\frac{\text{Stored energy}}{\text{Energy dissipated per cycle}} = \frac{\frac{1}{2}LI^2}{(2\pi/\omega_0)(\frac{1}{2}RI^2)} = \frac{\omega_0 L}{2\pi R} = \frac{Q}{2\pi} \qquad (180)$$

This gives an additional alternative significance to Q. From Eqs. (174) and (180) it follows that for a simple series tuned circuit

$$Q = \text{selectivity} = 2\pi \frac{\text{stored energy}}{\text{energy dissipated per cycle}} \qquad (181)$$

The reader can show in the exercise below that a similar relation holds for a parallel tuned circuit. The same relation also holds for tuned transmission-line sections. The relation between selectivity and energy storage and dissipation is thus apparently quite general; we shall now show that it is closely connected with reciprocal spreading.

When the applied steady-state emf is removed from a tuned circuit, the duration in cycles of the decay transient is a measure of the ratio

$$\frac{\text{Stored energy}}{\text{Energy dissipated per cycle}}$$

It is shown in the author's "Transformation Calculus" that the characteristic transient response of a circuit is the same for all applied emfs. We shall therefore get the same transient by applying a unit impulse of emf to the tuned circuit as is obtained when a steady-state emf is removed. Since the impulse has zero duration, the response is a pure transient except at the instant of application of the impulse. It is shown in Sec. 4.18 that a unit impulse has a uniform amplitude distribution for all frequencies, so that the response of the circuit to a unit impulse, and therefore also the decay transient, has the same frequency distribution as the circuit transmission characteristic. As a consequence of *reciprocal spreading*, the duration of the decay transient is therefore proportional to the circuit selectivity.

Exercise

Near resonance the resistance and reactance of a high-Q parallel tuned circuit may be expressed as

$$r = \frac{RQ^2}{1 + 4Q^2\left(\frac{\omega - \omega_0}{\omega_0}\right)^2}$$

$$x = \frac{2RQ^3 \frac{\omega - \omega_0}{\omega_0}}{1 + 4Q^2\left(\frac{\omega - \omega_0}{\omega_0}\right)^2}$$

Prove that

$$\text{Selectivity} = \frac{f_0}{f_2 - f_1} = Q = 2\pi \frac{\text{stored energy}}{\text{energy dissipated per cycle}}$$

for this case also.

4.20 Conclusion. The Fourier integral, as we have seen, is a tool of great power in analyzing general phenomena and general problems. It actually is not usually readily applicable to the solution of specific circuit problems. For that purpose the methods of differential equations and the more powerful methods of transformation calculus should be used.

In using the Fourier integral we usually deal with idealized systems, *i.e.*, rectangular pulses, sharp cutoff, linear phase shift. Nevertheless, the Fourier integral gives us a remarkably clear picture of what is actually going on in practical systems. In fact, we might almost say that it often answers the important problems and ignores those which are not important. It answers such general problems as how much bandwidth is necessary to handle various types of signal, how much phase shift is permissible, and what general types of distortion may be expected. This is the type of information that is usually desired before designing a specific piece of apparatus, and this is precisely the type of information that Fourier integral analysis is qualified to give.

4.21 Biographical Note. We have already touched upon the researches of Lord Rayleigh in Fourier analysis, including the discovery of the Fourier integral energy theorem and the formula for group velocity. John William Strutt (third Baron Rayleigh, 1842–1919) had a remarkable talent for the application of mathematics to experimental science. He used this talent in all branches of physics, and many of his investigations are basic in radio theory. He put the theory of skin effect on a quantitative basis and derived the formulas that are still used for the depth of penetration of high-frequency current into a conductor. He made the first important investigation in the theory of guided waves some 50 years ago. Although he did not follow up this investigation, it is a tribute to the greatness of his work that this early paper is still considered one of the basic investigations in wave-guide theory.

Lord Rayleigh is probably best known to radio engineers for his work in acoustics. His great textbook "Theory of Sound" is still today, a half century after it was written, the standard work on the subject. Much of the basic theory of sound was worked out by Rayleigh himself. He also devised and performed many classical experiments in acoustics.

Lord Rayleigh's investigations in other branches of physics are no less important. He was the first to put the theory of the resolving power of telescopes and spectroscopes on a quantitative basis. He worked out the theory of the scattering of light. He performed fundamental experiments in the field of thin films, which has since become an important subject owing to the researches of others, notably Langmuir, in the present century. He also founded the branch of mathematical physics known as *dimensional analysis*. In collaboration with Sir William Ramsay, he discovered the inert gases argon, neon, krypton, and xenon.

Perhaps the most remarkable characteristic of Lord Rayleigh's work is its quality of enduring and increasing in importance with the passage of time. This is a great tribute to the soundness of his judgment on what is of fundamental importance as well as to the reliability and correctness of his conclusions.

CHAPTER V

MODULATION

5.0 Introduction. In any useful system of radiobroadcasting or radio communication there must be some way of separating the various signals that are simultaneously present. This is accomplished in practice by letting each signal *modulate* a carrier, and the separation of signals is then accomplished by separation of carriers.[1] The various types of modulation used in practice are the subject matter of this chapter. Our discussion will be limited to modulation theory. For a discussion of apparatus and devices used in modulation and demodulation, the reader is referred to various books on radio engineering.[2]

5.1 Amplitude Modulation. *a. Fundamental Definitions.* The carrier used in most systems of communication is a high-frequency

[1] There are also other reasons for using modulation. For example, the usual type of intelligence (audio, video, or other) transmitted in modern communication systems covers many octaves of frequency. Over such a wide range of frequency, propagation characteristics would vary greatly, so that the transmitting medium would introduce large amounts of uncontrollable frequency discrimination. This can largely be avoided by using a carrier, so that only the relatively narrow frequency range (considered in terms of octaves) of the modulated carrier is involved in transmission. Furthermore, if the energy is to be radiated into space, it is necessary to use a carrier because it is possible to obtain efficient radiation only at high frequencies. It is interesting to note that the human body has solved a corresponding problem in sound radiation in a similar manner. The movements of the muscles of the mouth and oral cavity occur at a rate below 10 per second. However, the human mouth is too small an opening to be an efficient radiator at the wavelength corresponding to 10 cycles/sec, that is, 110 ft. Consequently the vocal cords are used to generate a much higher carrier frequency, which can then be modulated by the other speech-regulating elements in the oral cavity.

[2] For example, Sec. 7 of Terman, "Radio Engineers' Handbook."

An extensive bibliography on frequency modulation and on modulation in general will be found in the textbook "Frequency Modulation" by August Hund; this book itself gives an extensive discussion of a wide variety of topics related to frequency modulation.

No attempt has been made in this or any chapter of the present book to decide questions of priority in the discovery and development of any item, and the references cited should not be interpreted to have such significance. The cited references are almost entirely in American publications, and they are listed for the purpose of telling where additional information can be obtained.

sinusoidal wave of the form

$$A \sin (2\pi F t + \phi) \tag{1}$$

In this wave, A is called the *amplitude*, F is called the *carrier frequency*, and ϕ is called the *phase*. If the information that it is desired to transmit is conveyed by variation of the amplitude of the carrier, the

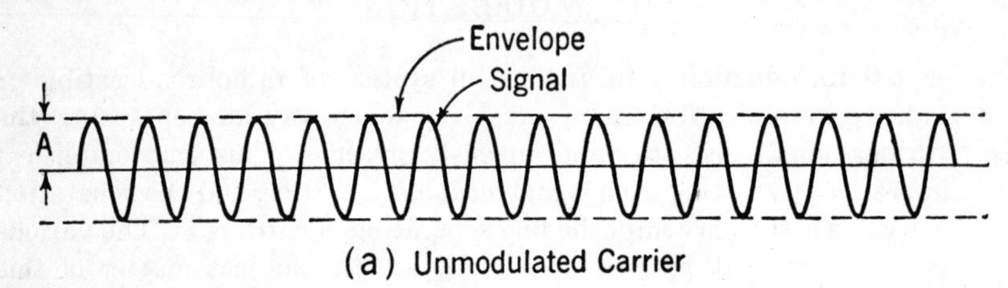

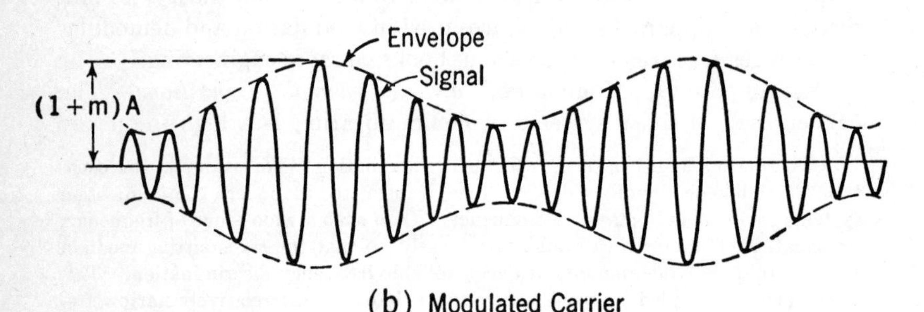

FIG. 1. Illustration of amplitude modulation.

latter is said to be *amplitude-modulated*. Thus, if the carrier is amplitude-modulated by a signal

$$B \cos 2\pi\mu t \tag{2}$$

then the *amplitude-modulated carrier* is of the form

$$a = A(1 + m \cos 2\pi\mu t) \sin (2\pi F t + \phi) \tag{3}$$

where a is the instantaneous value of a variable[1] (such as current or voltage), m is called the *modulation factor* or the *degree of modulation*, and m times 100 per cent is called the *percentage modulation*. The function $B \cos 2\pi\mu t$ is called the *modulation*, *information*, or *intelligence* and μ is called the *modulation frequency*.

[1] Generally speaking, a is considered to be an amplitude (*i.e.*, vector) type of variable (*i.e.*, one to which the principle of superposition applies). Its square is proportional to the instantaneous power in the signal.

In Fig. 1 are shown carriers with and without amplitude modulation. The broken curves in Fig. 1 showing variations of the peak signal amplitude are called *envelopes* of the signal. The shape of the envelope is the same as that of the information which it is desired to transmit.

In the general case the modulation will consist of a general function of time $g(t)$. In such a case the modulated signal will be

$$a = A[1 + mg(t)] \sin (2\pi Ft + \phi) \tag{4}$$

The degree of modulation in this case is defined in Sec. 5.3*b*.

A somewhat different definition is used for percentage modulation in systems, such as television, in which the carrier level is at a maximum with no modulation and modulation can only decrease the carrier level. Such a signal is shown in Fig. 2. In this case, $g(t)$ in Eq. (4) may be considered as including a direct-current (*i.e.*, zero-frequency) component. For the case of Fig. 2 the maximum available carrier level is called 100 per cent modulation, and the percentage modulation in general is defined as the percentage of maximum available carrier level. In the remainder of this chapter, it will usually be clear from the context which definition of percentage modulation is being used.

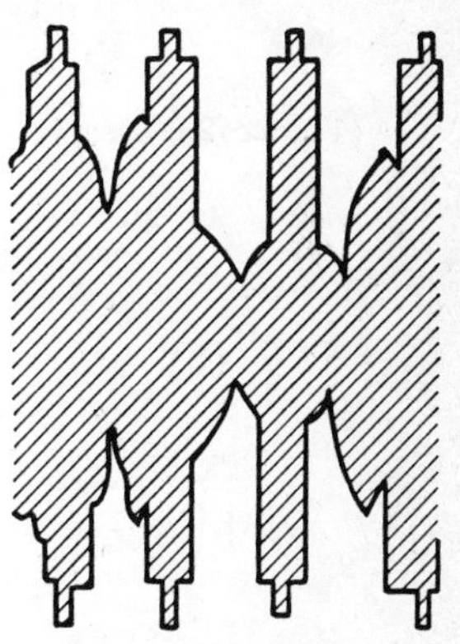

FIG. 2. Television signal. (Variations at carrier frequency shown by shading.)

b. Spectrum and Energy Distribution. If the modulation consists of only a single frequency, then the form of the modulated carrier is given by Eq. (3). This modulated carrier may also be broken down into its frequency components. Thus

$$\begin{aligned} A(1 + m \cos 2\pi\mu t) \sin (2\pi Ft + \phi) \\ &= A \sin (2\pi Ft + \phi) + Am \cos 2\pi\mu t \sin (2\pi Ft + \phi) \quad (5) \\ &= A \sin (2\pi Ft + \phi) + \frac{Am}{2} \sin [2\pi(F + \mu)t + \phi] \\ &\quad + \frac{Am}{2} \sin [2\pi(F - \mu)t + \phi] \quad (6) \end{aligned}$$

according to Eq. 41 of Appendix C. The effect of modulation may therefore be expressed as the addition to the original carrier, $A \sin (2\pi Ft + \phi)$, of a pair of sinusoidal components of amplitude $Am/2$ and differing, respectively, in frequency from the carrier by plus and minus the modulation frequency. These added sinusoidal components due to the modulation are called *sidebands*. In Fig. 3*a* is shown the frequency spectrum of this modulated carrier.

If the carrier is modulated by a general type of signal $g(t)$, then assuming that the system is linear, each frequency component of $g(t)$ gives rise to a pair of side bands. If the frequency composition of $g(t)$

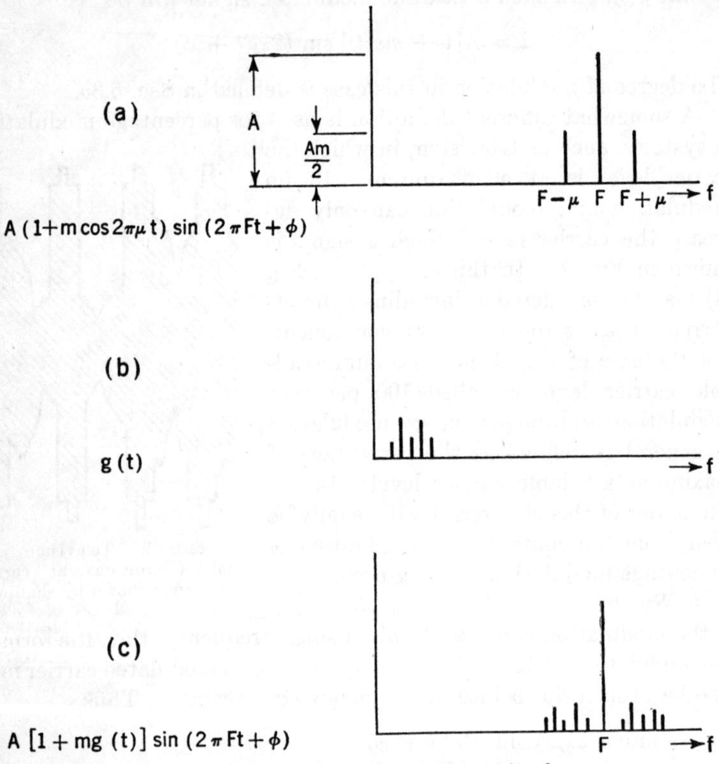

FIG. 3. Frequency spectra of various signals.

is that shown in Fig. 3*b*, then the frequency composition of the signal in which $g(t)$ modulates a carrier is that shown in Fig. 3*c*.

The energy of a signal, as we have often had occasion to note, is proportional to the square of the signal amplitude. From Exercise 5 at the end of Chap. II or by the Fourier integral energy theorem[1] we also know that the energy of a signal is equal to the sum of the energies of its individual frequency components. For example, the energy of

[1] Sec. 4.13.

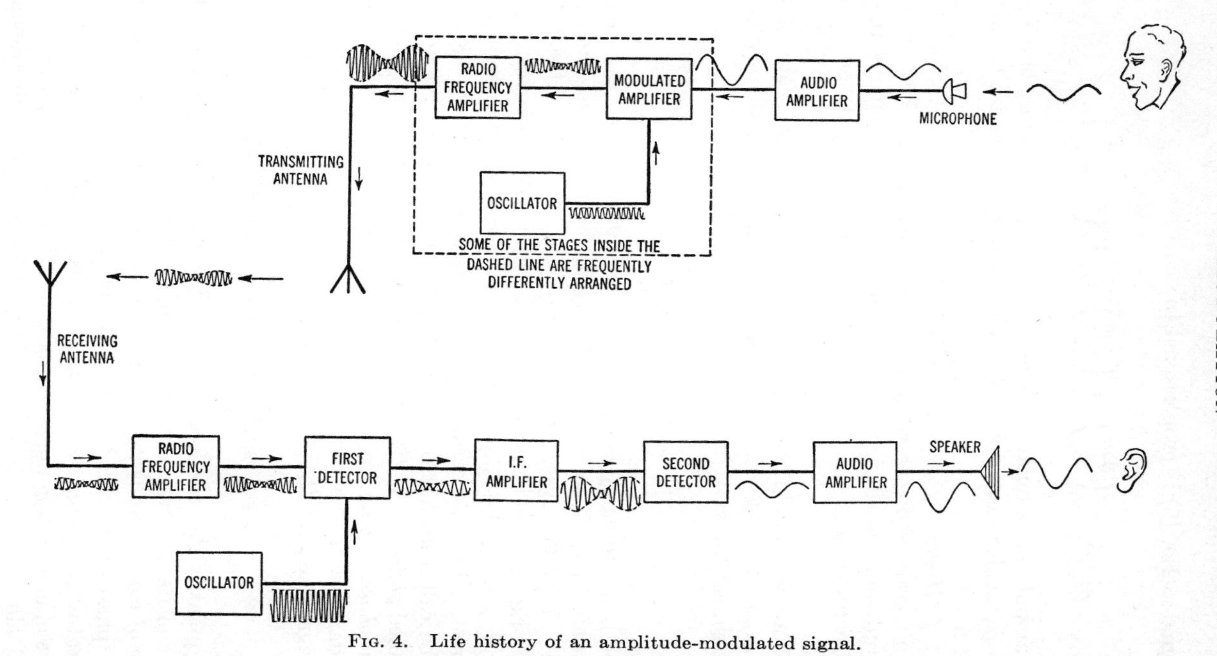

FIG. 4. Life history of an amplitude-modulated signal.

the signal in Eq. (6) is proportional to

$$A^2 + \left(\frac{Am}{2}\right)^2 + \left(\frac{Am}{2}\right)^2 = A^2\left(1 + \frac{m^2}{2}\right) \tag{7}$$

Thus amplitude modulation generally adds to the energy of a signal. In the particular case of Eq. (7) the amount of energy due to modulation is $A^2m^2/2$.

c. Life History of an Amplitude-modulated Signal. In Fig. 4 is a block diagram showing what may be called the life history of an amplitude-modulated signal. This shows the wave shape of the signal at various stages between the origin of the signal and its final utilization.

5.2 Angle Modulation—Frequency and Phase Modulation. *a. Fundamental Definitions.* In the preceding section we pointed out how a sinusoidal wave of the form

$$a = A \sin (2\pi Ft + \phi) \tag{8}$$

can be made to carry information by modulating (*i.e.*, varying) the amplitude factor A, thus giving what is called an amplitude-modulated signal. This, however, is not the only way in which a carrier wave, such as Eq. (8), can be made to carry information. It is, for example, possible to keep the amplitude A constant and vary the argument of the sine function in accordance with the signal to be transmitted. This may be called *angle modulation.* Two simple schemes for doing this are called *phase modulation* and *frequency modulation,* respectively.

In *phase modulation,* the phase ϕ in expression (8) is varied in accordance with the signal. Thus, if the carrier is *phase-modulated* by a signal $\cos 2\pi\mu t$, the *phase-modulated carrier* is of the form

$$a = A \sin [2\pi Ft + (\phi_0 + \Delta\phi \cos 2\pi\mu t)] \tag{9}$$

The quantity $\Delta\phi \cos 2\pi\mu t$ in expression (9) is called the *phase deviation,* and its instantaneous value may be expressed in radians. The *degree of modulation* is usually defined as the ratio of $\Delta\phi$ to the maximum phase deviation that the particular transmitting or receiving apparatus of interest at the moment is capable of handling. The degree of modulation in phase modulation is thus not a property of the signal alone, as it is in amplitude modulation, but is also defined in terms of the properties of the system in which it is used. A graphical representation of a phase-modulated signal is shown in Fig. 5.

In *frequency modulation*, the instantaneous frequency of expression (8) is varied in accordance with the signal. So far, however, we have not defined *instantaneous frequency*—in fact, the phrase sounds almost like a contradiction in terms since it is hard to see how a frequency can be established in an instant. Nevertheless, particularly if the carrier frequency is very high in comparison with the modulation fre-

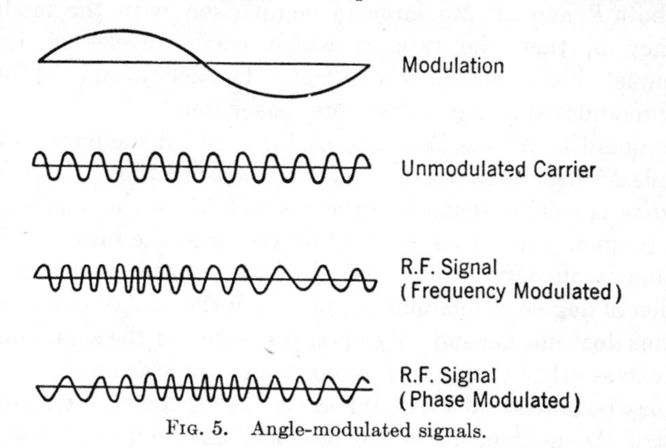

FIG. 5. Angle-modulated signals.

quency, a reasonable and useful definition is possible. This definition is

$$\text{Instantaneous frequency} = \frac{1}{2\pi}\frac{d\theta}{dt} \tag{10}$$

when the frequency-modulated signal is expressed as

$$a = A \sin \theta \tag{11}$$

If $\theta = 2\pi F t$, then

$$\frac{1}{2\pi}\frac{d\theta}{dt} = F \tag{12}$$

so that the definition agrees with the usual one in case F is a constant.

Let us next find the form of a frequency-modulated signal in accordance with the foregoing definition, when the modulation is $\cos 2\pi\mu t$. As a consequence of Eq. (10) we may write

$$\frac{1}{2\pi}\frac{d\theta}{dt} = F + \Delta F \cos 2\pi\mu t \tag{13}$$

in which F and ΔF are constants. Integration of Eq. (13) yields

$$\theta = 2\pi F t + \frac{\Delta F}{\mu} \sin 2\pi\mu t + \theta_0 \tag{14}$$

Thus the *frequency-modulated signal* is

$$a = A \sin \theta = A \sin \left[2\pi F t + \frac{\Delta F}{\mu} \sin 2\pi \mu t + \theta_0 \right] \tag{15}$$

A graphical representation of a frequency-modulated signal is also shown in Fig. 5.

If both F and ΔF are large in comparison with the modulation frequency μ, then the rate at which carrier cycles of Eq. (15) are completed will be $F + \Delta F \cos 2\pi\mu t$. The definition used for a frequency-modulated signal is therefore reasonable.[1]

The quantity $\Delta F \cos 2\pi\mu t$ in Eq. (13) is called the *frequency deviation* while ΔF itself is called the *peak frequency deviation*. The *degree of modulation* is usually defined as the ratio of ΔF to the maximum permitted frequency deviation allowed by law or as the ratio of ΔF to the maximum frequency deviation of which the system is capable. The definition of degree of modulation, just as in the case of phase modulation, thus does not depend only upon properties of the signal itself but also involves other things such as equipment or statutes.[2]

It may be noted that Eqs. (9) and (15) are of the same general form, so that if the modulating signal has only one frequency component there is no important difference between a frequency-modulated and a phase-modulated signal except a difference in percentage of modulation. However, if the modulating signal has components of many frequencies, the frequency-modulated and phase-modulated signals are definitely different, the latter having greater deviations at high modulating frequencies because of the $1/\mu$ factor in Eq. (15). If the modulating signals are audio signals, so that the phase difference between $\cos 2\pi\mu t$ in Eq. (9) and $\sin 2\pi\mu t$ in Eq. (15) is not important,[3] a frequency-modulated system can be changed into a phase-modulated system by preemphasizing the modulating frequency components by

[1] The reader may wonder why

$$A \sin [2\pi(F + \Delta F \cos 2\pi\mu t)t + \theta_0]$$

is not used as the definition of a frequency-modulated signal. If F and ΔF are large in comparison with μ, a good physical picture of the frequency deviation is given by the number of extra carrier cycles completed per unit time, *i.e.*, the number of extra pairs of crossings of the axis. In the above expression, the peak frequency deviation during a modulation frequency cycle would be larger every cycle, which is absurd.

[2] A definition of degree of modulation as $\Delta F/F$ would have absolute significance, but it is usually of no practical value in ordinary frequency modulation.

[3] When there is more than one modulating frequency, these phase differences can change the wave shape of the detected signal.

an amount proportional to their frequency (μ), before modulating the carrier, and correspondingly deemphasizing the high-frequency components after detection. A corresponding change from phase modulation to frequency modulation can also be made.

The abbreviations AM, FM, and PM (or ϕM) are widely used for the lengthy terms amplitude modulation, frequency modulation, and phase modulation, respectively. We shall often use these abbreviations in the present book.

b. Spectra and Energy Distributions. Let us next determine the spectra of frequency-modulated and phase-modulated signals. This is a simple exercise in the manipulation of trigonometric and Bessel functions.

For a frequency-modulated signal, we start from Eq. (15) and obtain[1]

$$\begin{aligned} a &= A \sin \left[2\pi F t + \frac{\Delta F}{\mu} \sin 2\pi\mu t + \theta_0 \right] \\ &= A \left[\sin (2\pi F t + \theta_0) \cos \left(\frac{\Delta F}{\mu} \sin 2\pi\mu t \right) \right. \\ &\qquad \left. + \cos (2\pi F t + \theta_0) \sin \left(\frac{\Delta F}{\mu} \sin 2\pi\mu t \right) \right] \end{aligned} \tag{16}$$

Now, according to Eqs. (3) and (4) of Appendix E,

$$\begin{aligned} \cos \left(\frac{\Delta F}{\mu} \sin 2\pi\mu t \right) = J_0 \left(\frac{\Delta F}{\mu} \right) + 2 \left[J_2 \left(\frac{\Delta F}{\mu} \right) \cos 4\pi\mu t \right. \\ \left. + J_4 \left(\frac{\Delta F}{\mu} \right) \cos 8\pi\mu t + \cdots \right] \end{aligned} \tag{17}$$

and

$$\begin{aligned} \sin \left(\frac{\Delta F}{\mu} \sin 2\pi\mu t \right) = 2 \left[J_1 \left(\frac{\Delta F}{\mu} \right) \sin 2\pi\mu t \right. \\ \left. + J_3 \left(\frac{\Delta F}{\mu} \right) \sin 6\pi\mu t + \cdots \right] \end{aligned} \tag{18}$$

Furthermore,[2]

$$\begin{aligned} &\sin (2\pi F t + \theta_0) \cos 2\pi n\mu t \\ &\qquad = \tfrac{1}{2} \{ \sin [2\pi(F + n\mu)t + \theta_0] + \sin [2\pi(F - n\mu)t + \theta_0] \} \end{aligned} \tag{19}$$

and

$$\begin{aligned} &\cos (2\pi F t + \theta_0) \sin 2\pi n\mu t \\ &\qquad = \tfrac{1}{2} \{ \sin [2\pi(F + n\mu)t + \theta_0] - \sin [2\pi(F - n\mu)t + \theta_0] \} \end{aligned} \tag{20}$$

[1] By Eq. (11) of Appendix C.

[2] By Eq. (41) of Appendix C.

Substituting Eqs. (17) through (20) into (16), we obtain

$$
\begin{aligned}
a &= A \sin \left[2\pi F t + \frac{\Delta F}{\mu} \sin 2\pi \mu t + \theta_0 \right] \\
&= A \left\{ J_0\left(\frac{\Delta F}{\mu}\right) \sin (2\pi F t + \theta_0) \right. \\
&+ J_1\left(\frac{\Delta F}{\mu}\right) \sin [2\pi(F + \mu)t + \theta_0] - J_1\left(\frac{\Delta F}{\mu}\right) \sin [2\pi(F - \mu)t + \theta_0] \\
&+ J_2\left(\frac{\Delta F}{\mu}\right) \sin [2\pi(F + 2\mu)t + \theta_0] + J_2\left(\frac{\Delta F}{\mu}\right) \sin [2\pi(F - 2\mu)t + \theta_0] \\
&+ J_3\left(\frac{\Delta F}{\mu}\right) \sin [2\pi(F + 3\mu)t + \theta_0] - J_3\left(\frac{\Delta F}{\mu}\right) \sin [2\pi(F - 3\mu)t + \theta_0] \\
&+ J_4\left(\frac{\Delta F}{\mu}\right) \sin [2\pi(F + 4\mu)t + \theta_0] + J_4\left(\frac{\Delta F}{\mu}\right) \sin [2\pi(F - 4\mu)t + \theta_0] \\
&\left. + \cdots\cdots\cdots\cdots\cdots\cdots\cdots\cdots \right\} \qquad (21)
\end{aligned}
$$

Equation (21) separates the frequency-modulated wave into its frequency components. We see that the magnitude of the carrier is reduced from unity for the unmodulated wave to a value of $J_0(\Delta F/\mu)$ during modulation. We see also that an infinite number of sidebands are produced which are separated from the carrier in the frequency spectrum by integral multiples of the modulating frequency. However, a glance at Fig. 3 of Appendix E shows that the value of $J_n(k)$ diminishes rapidly when $n > k$. Therefore the sideband amplitudes diminish rapidly outside a region $\pm\Delta F$ removed from the carrier. These characteristics are illustrated in Fig. 6, which shows the spectra of some frequency-modulated signals.

The energy of each sideband is proportional to the square of its Bessel coefficient,[1] and, by Exercise 5 at the end of Chap. II, the total energy is just equal to the sum of the energies of the carrier and individual sidebands. Now since the amplitude of the envelope is unchanged, the average energies of the modulated and unmodulated signals are the same. Frequency modulation thus removes energy from the carrier and puts it in the sidebands. Furthermore, it then

[1] The coefficients $J_n(\Delta F/\mu)$ in Eq. (21) are called *Bessel coefficients* of the FM sidebands.

follows from Exercise 5 at the end of Chap. II and Eq. (21) that

$$\left[J_0\left(\frac{\Delta F}{\mu}\right)\right]^2 + 2\left[J_1\left(\frac{\Delta F}{\mu}\right)\right]^2 + 2\left[J_2\left(\frac{\Delta F}{\mu}\right)\right]^2 + \cdots + 2\left[J_n\left(\frac{\Delta F}{\mu}\right)\right]^2 + \cdots = 1 \quad (22)$$

Equation (22) holds for all values of $\Delta F/\mu$ and is an important relation

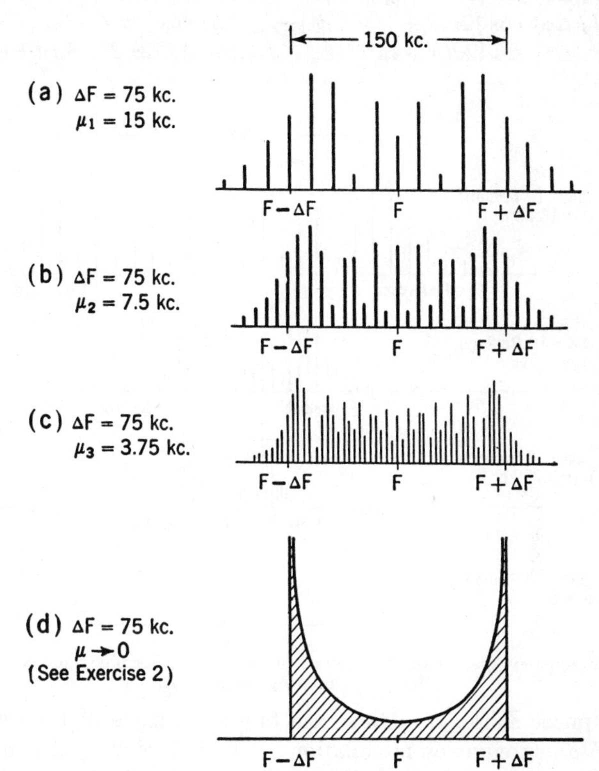

FIG. 6. Frequency spectra of FM signals of the same peak frequency deviation but of different modulating frequencies.

in the theory of Bessel functions. It is interesting that we should be able to derive it with the aid of physical reasoning.

The derivation of the sideband and energy formulas for phase modulation are carried out in an entirely similar manner. Thus we obtain, for a phase-modulated signal,

$$
\begin{aligned}
a &= A \sin(2\pi Ft + \phi_0 + \Delta\phi \cos 2\pi\mu t) \\
&= A \sin(2\pi Ft + \phi_0) \cos(\Delta\phi \cos 2\pi\mu t) \\
&\quad + \cos(2\pi Ft + \phi_0) \sin(\Delta\phi \cos 2\pi\mu t) \\
&= A\{\sin(2\pi Ft + \phi_0)[J_0(\Delta\phi) - 2J_2(\Delta\phi) \cos 4\pi\mu t + 2J_4(\Delta\phi) \cos 8\pi\mu t - \cdots] \\
&\quad + \cos(2\pi Ft + \phi_0)[2J_1(\Delta\phi) \cos 2\pi\mu t - 2J_3(\Delta\phi) \cos 6\pi\mu t + \cdots]\} \\
&= A\{J_0(\Delta\phi) \sin(2\pi Ft + \phi_0) \\
&\quad + J_1(\Delta\phi) \cos[2\pi(F + \mu)t + \phi_0] + J_1(\Delta\phi) \cos[2\pi(F - \mu)t + \phi_0] \\
&\quad - J_2(\Delta\phi) \sin[2\pi(F + 2\mu)t + \phi_0] - J_2(\Delta\phi) \sin[2\pi(F - 2\mu)t + \phi_0] \\
&\quad - J_3(\Delta\phi) \cos[2\pi(F + 3\mu)t + \phi_0] - J_3(\Delta\phi) \cos[2\pi(F - 3\mu)t + \phi_0] \\
&\quad + J_4(\Delta\phi) \sin[2\pi(F + 4\mu)t + \phi_0] + J_4(\Delta\phi) \sin[2\pi(F - 4\mu)t + \phi_0] \\
&\quad + \cdots\cdots\cdots\cdots\cdots\cdots\cdots\cdots\} \qquad (23)^{1}
\end{aligned}
$$

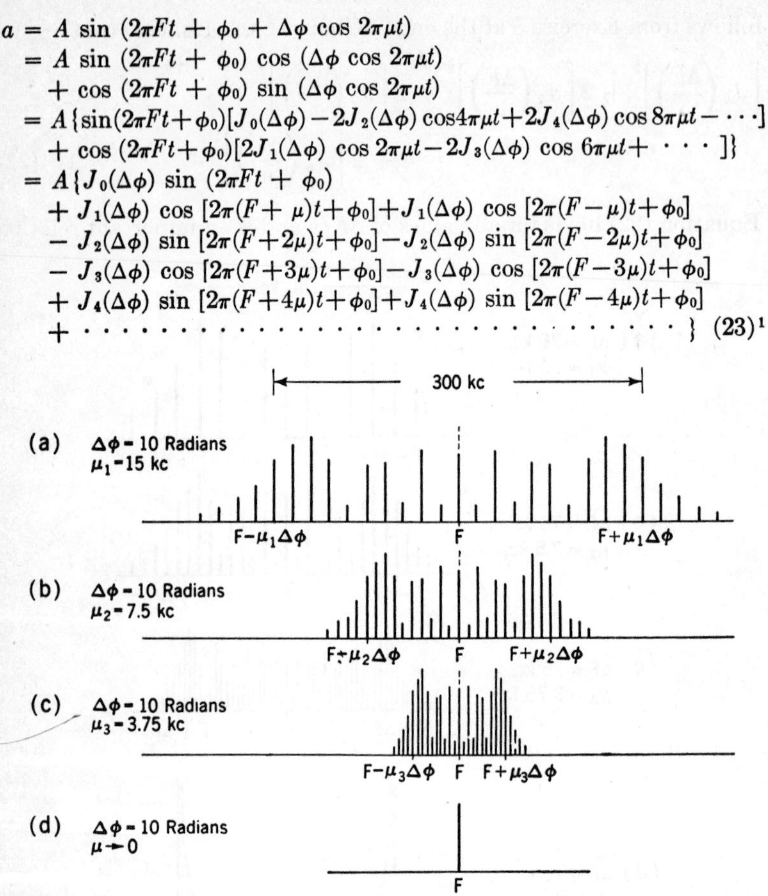

FIG. 7. Frequency spectra of PM signals of the same peak phase deviation but of different modulating frequencies.

The phase shift $\Delta\phi$ in this case takes the place of the deviation ratio $\Delta F/\mu$ in frequency modulation. The values of $J_n(\Delta\phi)$ diminish rapidly when $n > \Delta\phi$, which means that sidebands diminish rapidly in magnitude when they are displaced from the carrier by more than $\mu\,\Delta\phi$. The width of the frequency spectrum in phase modulation is thus proportional to the modulating frequency. This phenomenon is illustrated in Fig. 7, which shows the spectra of some PM signals.

[1] $\Delta F/\mu$ in Eq. (21) and $\Delta\phi$ in Eq. (23) are sometimes called the *modulation index* and are designated by the Greek letter β. $\Delta F/\mu$ in frequency modulation is also frequently called the *deviation ratio.*

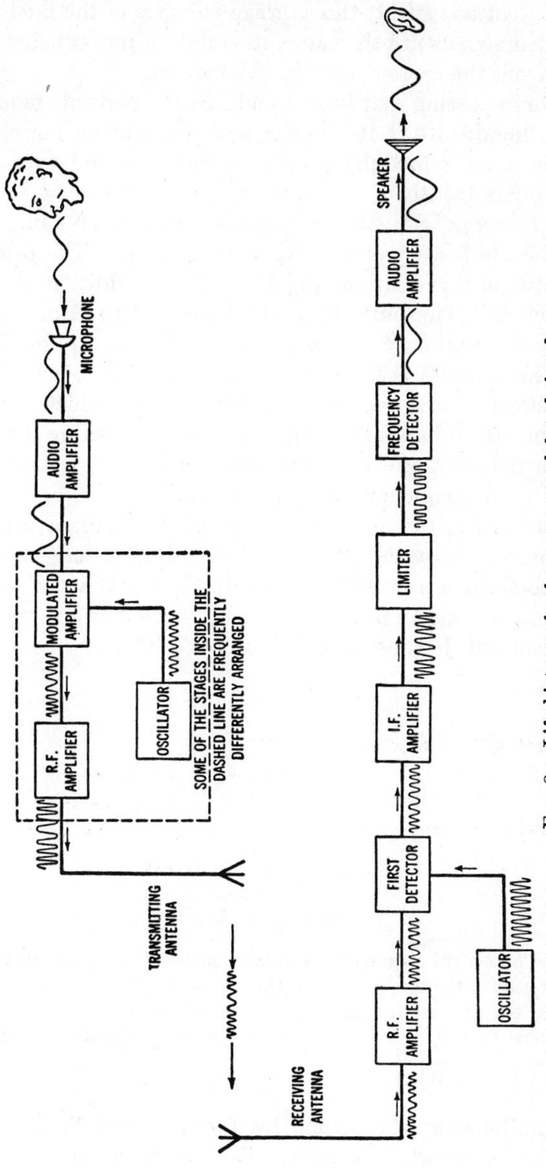

FIG. 8. **Life history of a frequency-modulated signal.**

In PM, just as in FM, the average energies of the modulated and unmodulated signals are the same, modulation just causing a transfer of energy from the carrier into the sidebands.

We note in passing that in FM and PM the percentage modulation affects the bandwidth, but not the peak or average power, while in AM the percentage modulation affects the peak and average power, but not the bandwidth.

c. Life History of FM and PM Signals. In Fig. 8 is a block diagram showing the life history of an FM or PM signal. The principal difference between this diagram and Fig. 4 is the addition of the *limiter* in the receiver. The purpose of the limiter is to strip any residual amplitude modulation from the signal, leaving it a pure FM or PM signal. This enables the system to have the full benefit of certain characteristic advantages of FM and PM systems, which are described later. While the limiter affects the signal levels entering the frequency detector, it does not affect the frequency, since it does not affect the number of radio-frequency cycles per second.

The limiter has the incidental effect of producing avc (automatic volume control) because it fixes the carrier amplitude level. However, it is sometimes necessary to provide additional avc of the rectified voltage type in order to prevent possible overload of the tuned stages, with its resultant detrimental effect on selectivity.

Exercises

1. A frequency-modulated signal

$$a = A \sin \left(2\pi F t + \frac{\Delta F}{\mu} \sin 2\pi \mu t \right)$$

has the following constant values:

$$\begin{aligned} F &= 45{,}000{,}000 \text{ cycles/sec} \\ \Delta F &= 60{,}000 \text{ cycles/sec} \\ \mu &= 6{,}000 \text{ cycles/sec} \end{aligned}$$

Tabulate the numerical magnitudes and frequencies of all sidebands having more than 0.1 per cent of the total energy of the signal.

2. In Fig. 6(*d*), let the frequency of any individual sideband be designated as $F + \Delta f$. Show that the curve of the envelope of sidebands has ordinates proportional to $\left[1 - \left(\frac{\Delta f}{\Delta F}\right)^2\right]^{-1/4}$.

5.3 Simultaneous Modulation by Two or More Frequency Components. *a. Sidebands.* In amplitude modulation, if the modulating signal has two or more frequency components, each of these components causes its own pair of sidebands and there is no apparent interaction between them. Thus,

$$A[1 + m_1 \cos 2\pi\mu_1 t + m_2 \cos (2\pi\mu_2 t + \phi_2)] \sin 2\pi F t$$
$$= A \sin 2\pi F t + \frac{Am_1}{2} \{\sin [2\pi(F + \mu_1)t] + \sin [2\pi(F - \mu_1)t]\}$$
$$+ \frac{Am_2}{2} \{\sin [2\pi(F + \mu_2)t + \phi_2]$$
$$+ \sin [2\pi(F - \mu_2)t - \phi_2]\} \quad (24)^1$$

The situation in FM and PM however, is, not quite so simple. We have already found that in both FM and PM the modulating frequency and all its harmonics cause sidebands. We shall now discover that, when more than one modulating frequency is present in FM or PM, sidebands are caused by all the sum and difference frequencies between the harmonics, as well as by the harmonics themselves. Thus, consider the FM signal

$$A \sin \left[2\pi F t + \frac{\Delta_1 F}{\mu_1} \sin 2\pi\mu_1 t + \frac{\Delta_2 F}{\mu_2} \sin (2\pi\mu_2 t + \phi_2)\right]$$
$$= A \left\{\sin 2\pi F t \cos \left(\frac{\Delta_1 F}{\mu_1} \sin 2\pi\mu_1 t\right) \cos \left[\frac{\Delta_2 F}{\mu_2} \sin (2\pi\mu_2 t + \phi_2)\right]\right.$$
$$+ \cos 2\pi F t \sin \left(\frac{\Delta_1 F}{\mu_1} \sin 2\pi\mu_1 t\right) \cos \left[\frac{\Delta_2 F}{\mu_2} \sin (2\pi\mu_2 t + \phi_2)\right]$$
$$+ \cos 2\pi F t \cos \left(\frac{\Delta_1 F}{\mu_1} \sin 2\pi\mu_1 t\right) \sin \left[\frac{\Delta_2 F}{\mu_2} \sin (2\pi\mu_2 t + \phi_2)\right]$$
$$\left.- \sin 2\pi F t \sin \left(\frac{\Delta_1 F}{\mu_1} \sin 2\pi\mu_1 t\right) \sin \left[\frac{\Delta_2 F}{\mu_2} \sin (2\pi\mu_2 t + \phi_2)\right]\right\} \quad (25)$$

If the factors in the terms of Eq. (25) are now expanded with the aid of Eqs. (17) and (18) and the product terms are combined and separated, it is clear that terms of the form

$$\sin [2\pi(F \pm m\mu_1 \pm n\mu_2)t \pm n\phi_2] \quad (26)$$

for all integral values of m and n will appear in the final result. The actual carrying out of this reduction is too tedious and is not sufficiently important to be set down here in detail.

b. Degree of Modulation. If the modulated signal is of the form

$$a = A[(1 + m_1 \cos (2\pi\mu_1 t + \phi_1) + m_2 \cos (2\pi\mu_2 t + \phi_2) + \cdots$$
$$+ m_p \cos (2\pi\mu_p t + \phi_p)] \sin 2\pi F t \quad (27)$$

[1] For complete generality it is necessary to introduce the phase angle ϕ_2.

then, by Eq. (24) in conjunction with Exercise 5 at the end of Chap. II, the total energy of the signal is proportional to

$$A^2\left(1+\frac{m_1^2}{2}+\frac{m_2^2}{2}+\cdots+\frac{m_p^2}{2}\right) \tag{28}$$

Comparing Eq. (28) with Eq. (7), it is reasonable to define the *effective value of the degree of modulation* as

$$m_{\text{eff}} = \sqrt{m_1^2 + m_2^2 + \cdots + m_p^2} \tag{29}$$

With this definition, m_{eff}^2 is also proportional to the average value of the low-frequency (for instance, audio) energy.

In a like manner, on the basis of the average value of the low-frequency energy, we define the *effective value of the degree of modulation* of an FM signal

$$A \sin\left[2\pi Ft + \frac{\Delta_1 F}{\mu_1}\sin(2\pi\mu_1 t + \phi_1) + \cdots + \frac{\Delta_q F}{\mu_q}\sin(2\pi\mu_q t + \phi_q)\right] \tag{30}$$

as

$$\frac{\sqrt{(\Delta_1 F)^2 + (\Delta_2 F)^2 + \cdots + (\Delta_q F)^2}}{D} \tag{31}$$

where D is the nominal maximum frequency deviation allowed in the system.

The percentage modulation is obtained in any case by multiplying the degree of modulation by 100 per cent.

Exercises

1. Find the percentage modulation of the signal

$$a = A(1 + 0.2 \cos 2\pi\mu_1 t + 0.3 \cos 2\pi\mu_2 t) \sin 2\pi Ft$$

if

$$F = 45{,}000{,}000 \text{ cycles/sec}$$
$$\mu_1 = 5{,}000 \text{ cycles/sec}$$
$$\mu_2 = 3{,}000 \text{ cycles/sec}$$

Answer: 36 per cent.

2. Find the percentage modulation of the signal

$$a = A \sin\left(2\pi Ft + \frac{\Delta_1 F}{\mu_1}\sin 2\pi\mu_1 t + \frac{\Delta_2 F}{\mu_2}\sin 2\pi\mu_2 t\right)$$

$$F = 45{,}000{,}000 \text{ cycles/sec}$$
$$\mu_1 = 5{,}000 \text{ cycles/sec}$$
$$\mu_2 = 3{,}000 \text{ cycles/sec}$$
$$\Delta_1 F = 10{,}000 \text{ cycles/sec}$$
$$\Delta_2 F = 6{,}000 \text{ cycles/sec}$$
$$D = 50{,}000 \text{ cycles/sec}$$

Answer: 23 per cent.

5.4 The Superposition of Harmonic Vibrations. Most of this chapter, dealing as it does with carriers and sidebands, involves the superposition[1] of harmonic vibrations. We shall therefore consider this subject more carefully, starting with some elementary topics, which, in all likelihood, are already familiar to the reader.

a. Superposition of Vibrations of the Same Frequency. In elementary books on kinematics, a simple harmonic vibration $A \cos \omega t$ is described as the motion of the projection on a straight line of a point moving with uniform angular velocity ω on the circumference of a circle of radius A. This is shown in Fig. 9. There P moves around the circle in a counterclockwise direction with constant angular velocity ω, while its projection P' on the line COB moves back and forth about the center O of the circle according to the equation

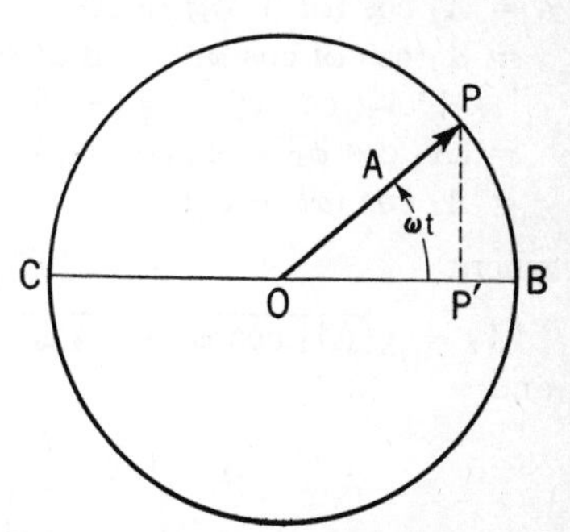

FIG. 9. Development circle of simple harmonic motion.

$$a = OP' = A \cos \omega t \tag{32}$$

In this figure, distances to the right of O are considered positive, while distances to the left of O are considered negative.

According to Eq. (32) the point P coincides with B at time $t = 0$. If the point P does not coincide with B at time $t = 0$ but is at such a point that the angle POB equals ϕ at time $t = 0$, then

$$a = OP' = A \cos (\omega t + \phi) \tag{33}$$

describes the motion of the projection of P on the line COB.

[1] Superposition as used in this book means the simultaneous existence in a linear system and is equivalent to algebraic addition.

Let us next consider the pictorial representation of two superimposed simple harmonic vibrations of the same frequency, *i.e.*,

$$a = A_1 \cos (\omega t + \phi_1) + A_2 \cos (\omega t + \phi_2) \tag{34}$$

In Fig. 10 two circles are drawn corresponding to the two terms on the right side of Eq. (34). Since the angular velocities of both terms are the same ω, the angle between the rotating lines OP_1 and OP_2 remains constant, and is always equal to $\phi_2 - \phi_1$, its value at $t = 0$. Furthermore, the two terms on the right of Eq. (34) can be combined into a single term. Thus

$$\begin{aligned} a &= A_1 \cos (\omega t + \phi_1) + A_2 \cos (\omega t + \phi_2) \\ &= A_1(\cos \omega t \cos \phi_1 - \sin \omega t \sin \phi_1) \\ &\quad + A_2(\cos \omega t \cos \phi_2 - \sin \omega t \sin \phi_2) \\ &= (A_1 \cos \phi_1 + A_2 \cos \phi_2) \cos \omega t - (A_1 \sin \phi_1 + A_2 \sin \phi_2) \sin \omega t \\ &= A_3 \cos (\omega t + \phi_3) \end{aligned} \tag{35}$$

where

$$A_3 = \sqrt{(A_1 \cos \phi_1 + A_2 \cos \phi_2)^2 + (A_1 \sin \phi_1 + A_2 \sin \phi_2)^2} \tag{36}$$

and

$$\phi_3 = \tan^{-1} \left(\frac{A_1 \sin \phi_1 + A_2 \sin \phi_2}{A_1 \cos \phi_1 + A_2 \cos \phi_2} \right) \tag{37}$$

It follows from Eq. (35) that, if two harmonic vibrations of the same frequency are superimposed, the net result is another harmonic vibration of the same frequency. Furthermore, it follows from Eqs. (36) and (37) in conjunction with Fig. 10 that the amplitude and phase of the resultant vibration are obtained by completing the vector parallelogram of OP_1 and OP_2. Thus the projection on COB of the point P_3, rotating in its circle in Fig. 10, represents the superimposed harmonic vibrations.

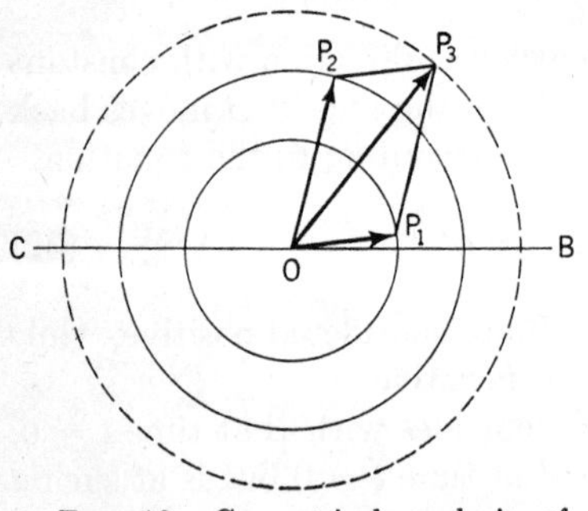

FIG. 10. Geometrical analysis of the superposition of two simple harmonic vibrations of the same frequency.

Since the line P_1P_3 is equal and parallel to OP_2 and P_2P_3 is equal and parallel to OP_1, we may conclude that, in dealing with simple harmonic vibrations of the same frequency, the vibrations may be represented by vectors such as OP_1 and P_1P_3 (or their equivalent OP_2 and P_2P_3) in Fig. 10, and the resultant of two vibrations is obtained by completion of the vector triangle, *i.e.*, the resultant is represented by OP_3. Clearly, this process can be generalized to cover the superposition of any number of vibrations of the same frequency. Thus

$$a = A_1 \cos(\omega t + \phi_1) + A_2 \cos(\omega t + \phi_2) + \cdots + A_n \cos(\omega t + \phi_n) \quad (38)$$

may be obtained by completing the vector polygon in Fig. 11, thus representing the resultant as OP_n. This line of reasoning also shows that superposition of any number of simple harmonic vibrations of the same frequency leads only to another simple harmonic vibration of the same frequency. This is an important result.

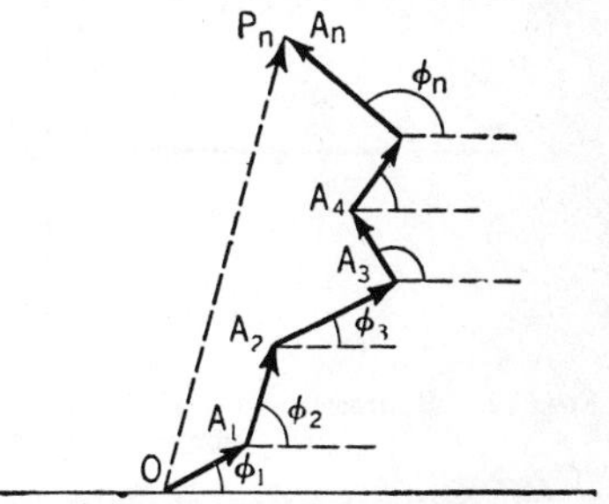

FIG. 11. Vectorial superposition of n simple harmonic vibrations.

All the foregoing results are also consistent with the interpretation of OP in Fig. 9 and all the other vectors representing simple harmonic vibrations in the succeeding figures as rotating vectors in the complex plane, their real components being equal to the simple harmonic vibrations themselves. Thus a vector of length A and initial angle ϕ rotating with uniform angular velocity ω in the complex plane is $A\epsilon^{j(\omega t+\phi)}$; and since

$$A\epsilon^{j(\omega t+\phi)} = A \cos(\omega t + \phi) + jA \sin(\omega t + \phi) \quad (39)$$

the real component of the complex rotating vector is clearly equal to the simple harmonic vibration itself. The superposition results that we have just derived could therefore have been deduced immediately from the properties of complex quantities.

We also should note that a simple harmonic vibration $A \cos(\omega t + \phi)$ may be expressed completely and exactly as the sum of the two conjugate vectors

$$\frac{A}{2}\,\epsilon^{j(\omega t+\phi)} \qquad \text{and} \qquad \frac{A}{2}\,\epsilon^{-j(\omega t+\phi)}$$

which rotate in opposite directions with the absolute angular velocity ω. Thus

$$\frac{A}{2}\epsilon^{j(\omega t+\phi)} + \frac{A}{2}\epsilon^{-j(\omega t+\phi)} = \frac{A}{2}[\cos(\omega t+\phi) + j\sin(\omega t+\phi)] + \frac{A}{2}[\cos(\omega t+\phi) - j\sin(\omega t+\phi)] = A\cos(\omega t+\phi) \quad (40)$$

Equation (40) is depicted in Fig. 12. Since it is an exact representation, it is applicable in all problems dealing with simple harmonic vibrations; in particular, it may be used in dealing with the superposition of these vibrations even when they are not of the same frequency.

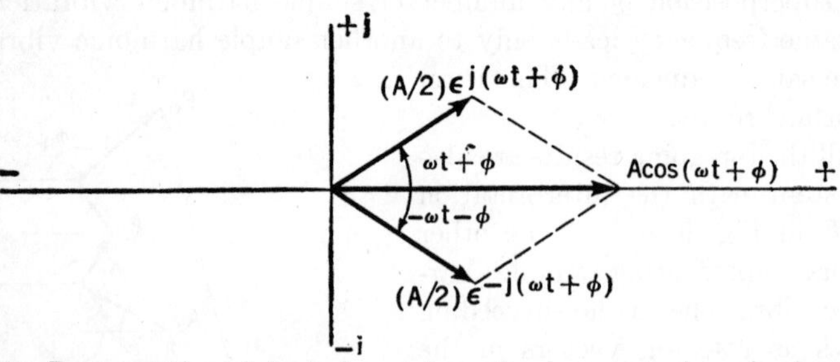

FIG. 12. Representation of simple harmonic motion by means of a pair of rotating conjugate vectors in the complex plane.

b. Superposition of Vibrations of Different Frequencies—Amplitude and Angle Modulation of the Resultant. Let us next consider the superposition of two simple harmonic vibrations of different frequencies, *i.e.*,

$$a = A_1 \cos \omega_1 t + A_2 \cos \omega_2 t \quad (41)$$

Since ω_1 and ω_2 are assumed different, it is unnecessary to include any initial phase angles ϕ_1 and ϕ_2, since both of these can be made to vanish by properly choosing the time when $t = 0$.

Equation (41) can be expressed in a form more descriptive of its behavior. Thus

$$\begin{aligned} a &= A_1 \cos \omega_1 t + A_2 \cos \omega_2 t \\ &= A_1 \cos \omega_1 t + A_2 \cos [\omega_1 t + (\omega_2 - \omega_1)t] \\ &= A_1 \cos \omega_1 t + A_2 \cos \omega_1 t \cos (\omega_2 - \omega_1)t - A_2 \sin \omega_1 t \sin (\omega_2 - \omega_1)t \\ &= [A_1 + A_2 \cos (\omega_2 - \omega_1)t] \cos \omega_1 t - A_2 \sin (\omega_2 - \omega_1)t \sin \omega_1 t \\ &= \sqrt{A_1^2 + 2A_1A_2 \cos (\omega_2 - \omega_1)t + A_2^2} \\ &\qquad \cos \left\{\omega_1 t + \tan^{-1}\left[\frac{A_2 \sin (\omega_2 - \omega_1)t}{A_1 + A_2 \cos (\omega_2 - \omega_1)t}\right]\right\} \end{aligned} \quad (42)$$

The resultant of the two simple harmonic vibrations of different frequencies is thus a single vibration whose amplitude varies up and down with the difference frequency $(\omega_2 - \omega_1)/2\pi$ and whose phase varies back and forth, also at the difference frequency. The components as well as the resultant are depicted in Fig. 13. The variation in amplitude is the well-known phenomenon of beats, and the difference frequency is called the beat frequency. The variation in phase has long been known, but in the past it has not been of such great importance.

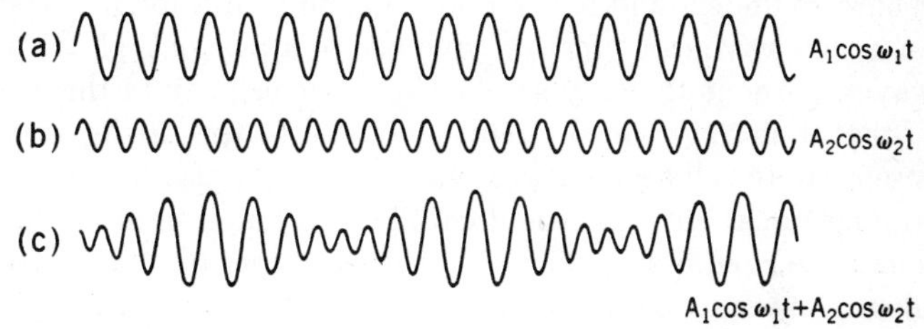

(a) $A_1 \cos \omega_1 t$

(b) $A_2 \cos \omega_2 t$

(c) $A_1 \cos \omega_1 t + A_2 \cos \omega_2 t$

$$A_1 \cos \omega_1 t + A_2 \cos \omega_2 t$$
$$= \sqrt{A_1{}^2 + 2A_1A_2 \cos (\omega_2 - \omega_1)t + A_2{}^2} \cos\left\{\omega_1 t + \tan^{-1}\left[\frac{A_2 \sin (\omega_2 - \omega_1)t}{A_1 + A_2 \cos (\omega_2 - \omega_1)t}\right]\right\}$$

FIG. 13. Superposition of vibrations of different frequencies, showing the phenomenon of the beat frequency.

If A_1 is greater than A_2 and if ω_1 is much greater than $\omega_2 - \omega_1$, then $A_1 \cos \omega_1 t$ may be considered a carrier and $A_2 \cos \omega_2 t$ a sideband. The coefficient

$$\sqrt{A_1^2 + 2A_1A_2 \cos (\omega_2 - \omega_1)t + A_2^2}$$

is then considered the instantaneous amplitude and the time derivative of

$$\omega_1 t + \tan^{-1}\left[\frac{A_2 \sin (\omega_2 - \omega_1)t}{A_1 + A_2 \cos (\omega_2 - \omega_1)t}\right]$$

is considered the instantaneous frequency. Since both these quantities vary at the difference frequency $(\omega_2 - \omega_1)/2\pi$, the resultant of the superposition of two simple harmonic vibrations is both amplitude- and angle-(frequency) modulated at the difference frequency. We found in Sec. 5.1*b* that the addition of just one more simple harmonic component of frequency $\omega_1 - (\omega_2 - \omega_1)$, of amplitude A_2, and of proper phase (*i.e.*, the AM sideband on the other side of the carrier) is sufficient to remove all angle modulation from the resultant. The elimination of amplitude modulation is a more complicated matter, as we found in Sec. 5.2*b*.

This is probably as good a place as any to say a word about the *reality* of sidebands. Certain persons have found it hard to conceive of sidebands as having physical reality. Apparently they consider them as a convenient mathematical fiction, probably something like $\sqrt{-1}$. Such persons usually find no difficulty in ascribing reality to the component vibrations that give rise to beats, since they have seen tuning forks, which separately give pure tones, giving rise to beats when sounded together, or have heard the audio beat note between two high-frequency sine-wave generators. However, they find it hard to understand how a low-frequency variation in the amplitude of a sine wave can "really" give rise to a pair of high-frequency sine waves. About the only simple thing one can say in this connection is that a sharply tuned circuit will tune to the carrier and sidebands separately. The acoustical analogue could also be constructed with tuning forks, but this would entail equal amplitudes of the sidebands and the even more difficult matter of proper phasing. By way of analogy, one may say that sidebands have the same type of reality as the harmonics in the output of a nonlinear amplifier or as the prismatic colors in white light.

c. The Persistence of Period in the Steady State. Another matter that is worth some thought is the *persistence of period in the steady state.* By this is meant essentially the fact that a driving force which is exactly repeated at a constant period of repetition can give rise only to effects of the same period *in the steady state.* By the steady state, we mean the state in which the condition of a system at any time t_1 is exactly repeated at another time t_2 so that it is impossible to tell from the properties of the system whether the time is t_1 or t_2.[1] If this is true, then the identical condition must again be repeated at time

$$t_3 = t_2 + (t_2 - t_1)$$

and again at

$$t_4 = t_3 + (t_2 - t_1)$$

etc. Otherwise the conditions of the system at t_1 and t_2 would not be the same. Furthermore, every other condition of the system, such as shown at T_1 in the simplified diagram, Fig. 14, must also be exactly repeated with the same period, $t_2 - t_1$; otherwise, there would be a noticeable difference between t_1 and t_2.

As a consequence of this type of reasoning, in conjunction with Fourier's theorem, it follows that the response of a system to a sinusoidal driving force can contain no frequency components other than

[1] This is the type of condition reached by a network at time $t = \infty$ when a periodic emf is applied.

harmonics of the frequency of the driving force, in addition to the fundamental and direct-curent components. This is true whether the system is linear or not. The only requirements are that there shall be no other driving force and that the laws of operation of the system shall be always the same.

As another consequence of this type of reasoning, it follows that while the wavelength or velocity of electromagnetic waves may be different in different parts of a transmission-line system in the steady state, depending upon the dielectric, the frequency is everywhere the same.

One phenomenon that may appear to be in disagreement with the foregoing arguments is the Doppler effect. This is the difference in frequency between incident and reflected waves when the point of

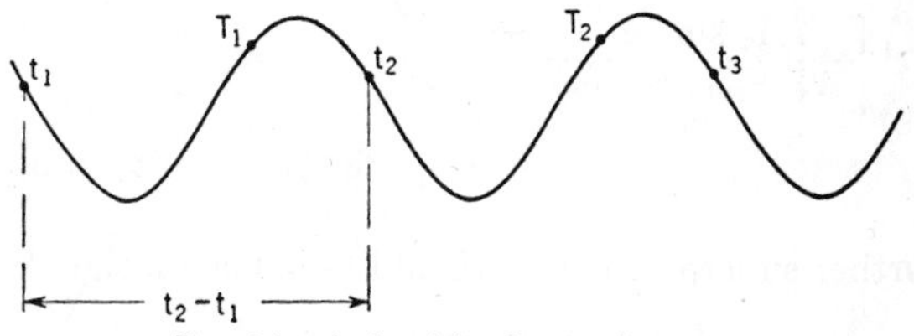

FIG. 14. A signal in the steady state.

reflection is moving. However, in this case the location of the point of reflection changes with time so that the system is no longer the same. Consequently, the foregoing reasoning regarding persistence of period cannot be expected to apply, for a steady state is never reached.

5.5 Comparison of Common-channel Interference in FM and AM. We have now covered enough of the fundamentals of modulation theory so that we can analyze an interesting and important phenomenon, namely, the apparent freedom from common-channel interference enjoyed by FM. We shall analyze common-channel interference in both AM and FM and find to what extent it is reduced in FM.

Common-channel interference is the undesirable effect occurring in radio reception due to the interference between the desired signal and an interfering signal of approximately the same carrier frequency. The modulation produced on an unmodulated desired carrier by the interfering carrier and its sidebands will be used as the measure of common-channel interference. We shall analyze the case in which the interfering signal is small in comparison with the desired signal, since this gives a clear and simple picture of the general phenomenon.[1]

[1] For a more detailed discussion of the FM case, including the effects of circuit components, see H. A. Wheeler, Common-channel Interference between Two

As a first step in this analysis, let us find the form assumed by Eq. (42) for the superposition of two cosine waves of different frequencies, when the amplitude of one is small in comparison with the other. Thus let

$$A_1 \gg A_2 \tag{43}$$

Then, when using Taylor expansions and neglecting terms in A_2/A_1 higher than the first power, the amplitude and angle of Eq. (42) become, respectively,

$$\sqrt{A_1^2 + 2A_1A_2 \cos(\omega_2 - \omega_1)t + A_2^2} = A_1\left[1 + \frac{A_2}{A_1}\cos(\omega_2 - \omega_1)t\right] \quad \text{(approx)} \tag{44}$$[1]

and

$$\omega_1 t + \tan^{-1}\left[\frac{A_2 \sin(\omega_2 - \omega_1)t}{A_1 + A_2\cos(\omega_2 - \omega_1)t}\right] = \omega_1 t + \frac{A_2}{A_1}\sin(\omega_2 - \omega_1)t \quad \text{(approx)} \tag{45}$$

The further superposition of an additional small signal[2]

$$A_3 \cos(\omega_3 t + \phi_3)$$

would make the resultant amplitude

$$A_1\left\{1 + \frac{A_2}{A_1}\cos(\omega_2 - \omega_1)t + \frac{A_3}{A_1}\cos[(\omega_3 - \omega_1)t + \phi_3]\right\} \quad \text{(approx)} \tag{46}$$

and the resultant angle

$$\omega_1 t + \frac{A_2}{A_1}\sin(\omega_2 - \omega_1)t + \frac{A_3}{A_1}\sin[(\omega_3 - \omega_1)t + \phi_3] \quad \text{(approx)} \tag{47}$$

Frequency-modulated Signals, *Proc. I.R.E.*, January, 1942, p. 34, and articles referred to there.

A discussion of the AM case for arbitrary ratios of interference to signal and including modulation of both signals is given by C. B. Aiken, Theory of the Detection of Two Modulated Waves by a Linear Rectifier, *Proc. I.R.E.*, April, 1933, p. 601.

For an interesting illustration of the peculiarities induced in the wave shape in the FM case when the interference is large, see the exercise at the end of this section.

[1] For additional discussion of how a single frequency component $A_2 \cos \omega_2 t$ can be equivalent to two pairs of sidebands, see Secs. 5.6 and 5.7.

[2] When more than two signals are involved, even though they are of different frequencies, a phase angle such as ϕ_3 must be included, for choice of the time $t = 0$ alone will no longer ensure that all signals are in phase.

The effect of further additional small signals can be handled in an analogous manner.

The frequency corresponding to Eq. (47) will be its derivative, namely,

$$\frac{1}{2\pi}\left\{\omega_1 + (\omega_2 - \omega_1)\frac{A_2}{A_1}\cos(\omega_2 - \omega_1)t + (\omega_3 - \omega_1)\frac{A_3}{A_1}\cos[(\omega_3 - \omega_1)t + \phi_3]\right\} \quad (48)$$

In Fig. 15 are shown desired carriers and the carrier and sidebands of an AM and FM interfering signal, respectively. Let us assume that

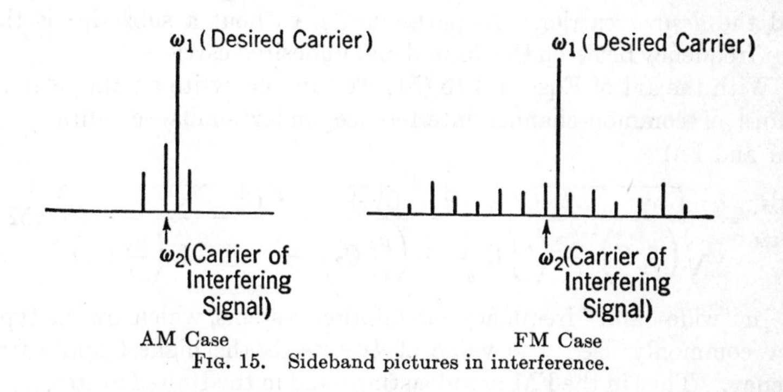

FIG. 15. Sideband pictures in interference.

the two interfering signals (carrier plus sidebands) have equal energies, that the two desired carriers also have equal energies, and that they are much greater than the energies of the interfering signals. We now wish to compare the degree of interference modulation in the FM system with that in the AM system.

Let

$$A \cos \omega t$$

be the expression for the desired carrier in both systems, and let the interfering carrier have an amplitude B and its sidebands have amplitudes $B_1, B_2, \ldots, B_p$ in the AM system, while the interfering carrier in the FM system has an amplitude C and its sidebands have amplitudes $C_1, C_2, \ldots, C_q$. Thus, by the hypothesis of equal energies for the interfering signals,

$$C^2 + C_1^2 + C_2^2 + \cdots + C_q^2 = B^2 + B_1^2 + B_2^2 + \cdots + B_p^2 \quad (49)$$

The degree of modulation of the desired carrier caused by the interference in the AM system is then according to Eq. (29)

$$m_{\mathrm{AM}} = \frac{(B^2 + B_1^2 + B_2^2 + \cdots + B_p^2)^{1/2}}{A} \tag{50}$$

On the other hand, the degree of modulation of the desired carrier caused by the interference in the FM system is, according to Eq. (31),

$$m_{\mathrm{FM}} = \frac{[(\mu C)^2 + (\mu_1 C_1)^2 + (\mu_2 C_2)^2 + \cdots + (\mu_q C_q)^2]^{1/2}}{AD} \tag{51}$$

where D is the nominal maximum frequency deviation allowed in the FM system (corresponding to $m = 1$) and the μ's in Eq. (51) are the difference frequencies between the various frequencies components and the *desired* carrier. In particular, μ without a subscript is the beat frequency between the desired and undesired carriers.

With the aid of Eqs. (49) to (51) we can now write for the relative values of common-channel interference under similar conditions in AM and FM

$$\frac{m_{\mathrm{AM}}}{m_{\mathrm{FM}}} = \sqrt{\frac{C^2 + C_1^2 + C_2^2 + \cdots C_q^2}{\left(\frac{\mu}{D} C\right)^2 + \left(\frac{\mu_1}{D} C_1\right)^2 + \left(\frac{\mu_2}{D} C_2\right)^2 + \cdots + \left(\frac{\mu_q}{D} C_q\right)^2}} \qquad (52)^1$$

In "wide-band" frequency-modulation systems, which are the type now commonly used, the value of D exceeds the highest audio frequency. Thus in the FM broadcasting band in the United States,

$$D = 75 \text{ kc} \tag{53}$$

On the other hand, the audio systems of FM receivers will not pass frequencies above, say, 12 kc. Thus the majority of the terms in the denominator of Eq. (52) are eliminated by the audio system, and only those with relatively small values of μ/D are passed. Consequently, the value of the ratio (52) is always much greater than unity. *Thus FM is inherently less susceptible to common-channel interference than AM.*[2]

[1] This equation assumes that the AM receiver does not respond to frequency modulation in the signal and that the FM receiver does not respond to amplitude modulation in the signal. The first condition is generally unimportant, for, as we shall see, the amount of frequency modulation is small. The second condition is approximately fulfilled if the receiver has a well-balanced detector and a good limiter. Wheeler (Common-channel Interference between Two Frequency-modulated Signals, *Proc. I.R.E.*, January, 1942) discusses the case when the second condition is not fulfilled.

[2] Interference and noise reduction in FM is discussed quantitatively in the next chapter.

A simple physical explanation of the reduced common-channel interference in wide-band FM systems is that the essentially random phase relationship of the sidebands (and carrier) of the interfering signal with the carrier of the desired signal spreads out the beat frequencies between the two signals throughout the entire deviation-frequency range, so that most of the interference is eliminated by the restricted frequency range of the audio system (including the human ear). Furthermore, only those sidebands which are relatively ineffective in causing frequency modulation, *i.e.*, those near the desired carrier, are passed by the audio system, which further reduces the interference. On the other hand, a desired frequency-modulated signal has a specified set of relations between the amplitudes, phases, and frequencies of its sidebands so that they all, including those far removed from the carrier, work together to produce a maximum amount of frequency modulation, and furthermore the frequency modulation that they produce is all in the pass band of the audio system.

In contrast with the FM situation, in AM all the interfering sidebands, including the undesired carrier, are equally efficient in producing interference; and their efficiency exceeds that of the most efficient FM interference-producing sideband by the ratio of the maximum FM deviation frequency to the width of the audio pass band.

Exercise

(Large-magnitude Interference in FM)

If a desired carrier $A \sin 2\pi ft$ and an interfering carrier $B \sin 2\pi gt$ are received simultaneously, show that the exact expression for the frequency modulation of the resultant is

$$\frac{1}{2\pi}\frac{d\phi}{dt} - f = (g - f)\frac{B}{A}\left\{\frac{\cos\,[2\pi(g - f)t] + \dfrac{B}{A}}{1 + \dfrac{2B}{A}\cos\,[2\pi(g - f)t] + \dfrac{B^2}{A^2}}\right\}$$

Plot a curve of $(1/2\pi)\,(d\phi/dt)$ for 1 cycle of the beat frequency $(g - f)$ for $(B/A) = 0.1$, 0.5, 0.9, and 1.0. What is the physical explanation of the sharp spikes that appear as B/A approaches unity?

5.6 Symmetrical and Unsymmetrical Sideband Distributions.[1]

a. Introduction. In the elementary cases of pure amplitude and pure

[1] This section is a development of H. Nyquist, Certain Topics in Telegraph Transmission Theory, *Trans. A.I.E.E.*, April, 1928, p. 617, and H. A. Wheeler, The Solution of Unsymmetrical Sideband Problems with the Aid of the Zero-frequency Carrier, *Proc. I.R.E.*, August, 1941, p. 446.

angle modulation considered in Secs. 5.1 and 5.2 the sidebands were always present in pairs whose frequencies were symmetrically located with respect to the carrier.[1] Thus, if F was the carrier frequency and there was a sideband at $F + \mu$, then there was always a sideband of equal magnitude at $F - \mu$.

We now wish to consider cases in which these simple relationships no longer hold. This condition is sometimes produced intentionally and at other times is due to shortcomings of apparatus or to outside interference. When the condition is produced intentionally, its purpose is economy in frequency bandwidth, or else noise reduction, or both. Thus, while pure modulation produces both upper and lower sidebands, either the upper or the lower set of sidebands alone is actually sufficient to convey the information, even though the lack of the other set will produce distortion. There are consequently many practical situations in which only one set (upper or lower) is transmitted. This practice is described as *single-sideband transmission.*[2] In single-sideband transmission, it is customary not to transmit the carrier but to supply a large carrier locally at the receiver. In this way, the percentage modulation can be kept down, so that there is little distortion despite the fact that only one set of sidebands is used. By using single-sideband transmission, only half the frequency spectrum of ordinary double-sideband transmission is required. Furthermore, we shall see in the next chapter that a worth-while noise reduction can be obtained. In single-sideband transmission, it is sometimes desirable to transmit the carrier at a reduced level and use it to operate the automatic frequency control and automatic volume control at the receiver. When principally, but not exclusively, one set of sidebands is transmitted,[3] the more general terms *selective* or *asymmetric sideband transmission* are used. We shall presently develop simple methods for analyzing the properties of signals in which any type of unsymmetrical distribution of the sidebands occurs.

[1] In frequency modulation, when there is more than one modulating frequency, the sideband distributions need not be symmetrical. This aspect of unsymmetrical sideband distributions, however, will be of only incidental interest in the present section.

[2] For information on practices followed and apparatus used in single-sideband transmission in communication, consult Terman, "Radio Engineers' Handbook" by way of the index and the original papers cited by Terman. For asymmetric sideband transmission in television, see Zworykin and Morton, "Television."

[3] The words "transmitted" and "transmission" in this chapter refer to the over-all transmission system, including both transmitter and receiver, as well as the transmitting medium.

Unintentional cases of unsymmetrical sideband distributions occur in cases in which the transmission system has characteristics that are not symmetrical with respect to the carrier frequency. We shall also show how common-channel interference can be analyzed as a case of an unsymmetrical sideband distribution.

b. Symmetrical and Antisymmetrical Sidebands: Inphase and Quadrature Components.

Definition: If $A \cos (2\pi Ft + \phi)$ *is a carrier wave, then the pair of sidebands*

$$A_1 \cos [2\pi(F + \mu)t + \phi_1] \qquad \text{and} \qquad A_2 \cos [2\pi(F - \mu)t + \phi_2]$$

is said to be symmetrical if

$$A_1 = A_2 \quad \text{and} \quad \phi_1 - \phi = -(\phi_2 - \phi), \quad \text{that is,} \quad \phi_2 = 2\phi - \phi_1$$

The superposition of a carrier and a pair of symmetrical sidebands gives a pure amplitude-modulated signal, since

$$\begin{aligned} &A \cos (2\pi Ft + \phi) + A_1 \cos [2\pi(F + \mu)t + \phi_1] \\ &\qquad\qquad + A_1 \cos [2\pi(F - \mu)t + (2\phi - \phi_1)] \\ &= A \cos (2\pi Ft + \phi) + A_1 \cos [(2\pi Ft + \phi) + (2\pi\mu t + \phi_1 - \phi)] \\ &\qquad\qquad + A_1 \cos [(2\pi Ft + \phi) - (2\pi\mu t + \phi_1 - \phi)] \\ &= A \left[1 + \frac{2A_1}{A} \cos (2\pi\mu t + \phi_1 - \phi)\right] \cos (2\pi Ft + \phi) \\ &= A \left[1 + \frac{2A_1}{A} \cos \left(2\pi\mu t + \frac{\phi_1 - \phi_2}{2}\right)\right] \cos (2\pi Ft + \phi) \end{aligned} \tag{54}$$

Equation (54) is an exact equation for all values of A and A_1.

Definition: If $A \cos (2\pi Ft + \phi)$ *is a carrier wave, then the pair of sidebands*

$$A_1 \cos [2\pi(F + \mu)t + \phi_1] \qquad \text{and} \qquad A_2 \cos [2\pi(F - \mu)t + \phi_2]$$

is said to be antisymmetrical if

$$A_1 = -A_2 \quad \text{and} \quad \phi_1 - \phi = -(\phi_2 - \phi), \quad \text{that is,} \quad \phi_2 = 2\phi - \phi_1$$

We shall now show that the superposition of a carrier and a pair of *small* antisymmetrical sidebands gives rise to an approximately pure angle-modulated signal. As a first step in this direction, let us perform the following expansion:

$$A \cos \left[(2\pi Ft + \phi) + \frac{\Delta F}{\mu} \sin (2\pi\mu t + \theta) \right]$$

$$= A \left\{ \cos (2\pi Ft + \phi) \cos \left[\frac{\Delta F}{\mu} \sin (2\pi\mu t + \theta) \right] - \sin (2\pi Ft + \phi) \sin \left[\frac{\Delta F}{\mu} \sin (2\pi\mu t + \theta) \right] \right\}$$

$$= A \left\{ \cos (2\pi Ft + \phi) \left[J_0 \left(\frac{\Delta F}{\mu} \right) + 2J_2 \left(\frac{\Delta F}{\mu} \right) \cos [2(2\pi\mu t + \theta)] + \cdots \right] - \sin (2\pi Ft + \phi) \left[2J_1 \left(\frac{\Delta F}{\mu} \right) \sin (2\pi\mu t + \theta) + \cdots \right] \right\}$$

$$= A \cos (2\pi Ft + \phi) - A \left(\frac{\Delta F}{\mu} \right) \sin (2\pi\mu t + \theta) \sin (2\pi Ft + \phi) \quad \text{(approx[1])} \quad (55)$$

provided that $\Delta F/\mu$ is small in comparison with unity. Now

$$A \frac{\Delta F}{\mu} \sin (2\pi\mu t + \theta) \sin (2\pi Ft + \phi)$$

$$= \frac{A}{2} \frac{\Delta F}{\mu} \{ \cos [2\pi(F - \mu)t + (\phi - \theta)] - \cos [2\pi(F + \mu)t + (\phi + \theta)] \} \quad (56)$$

by Eq. (42) of Appendix C. Therefore Eq. (55) becomes

$$A \cos \left[(2\pi Ft + \phi) + \frac{\Delta F}{\mu} \sin (2\pi\mu t + \theta) \right]$$

$$= A \cos (2\pi Ft + \phi) + \frac{A}{2} \frac{\Delta F}{\mu} \cos [2\pi(F + \mu)t + (\phi + \theta)] - \frac{A}{2} \frac{\Delta F}{\mu} \cos [2\pi(F - \mu)t + (\phi - \theta)] \quad (57)$$

again provided that $\Delta F/\mu$ is small in comparison with unity.

It follows from Eq. (57) that if A_1 is small in comparison with A, then

[1] This is true when $\Delta F/\mu$ is small because $J_0(x) = 1$, $J_1(x) = x/2$,

$$J_2(x) = 0 = J_3(x) = J_4(x),$$

etc., as a first-order approximation, when x is small. These results follow from Eqs. (12) to (14) of Appendix E.

$$A \cos (2\pi Ft + \phi) + A_1 \cos [2\pi(F + \mu)t + \phi_1] - A_1 \cos [2\pi(F - \mu)t + (2\phi - \phi_1)]$$
$$= A \cos \left\{ (2\pi Ft + \phi) + \frac{2A_1}{A} \sin [2\pi\mu t + (\phi_1 - \phi)] \right\}$$
$$= A \cos \left\{ (2\pi Ft + \phi) + \frac{2A_1}{A} \sin \left[2\pi\mu t + \left(\frac{\phi_1 - \phi_2}{2} \right) \right] \right\} \quad (58)$$

Thus the superposition of a carrier and a pair of small antisymmetrical sidebands gives rise to an approximately pure angle-modulated signal.

Let us next consider the more general case of the superposition of a carrier and a pair of antisymmetrical sidebands, the latter no longer being required to be small. Using the same notation as above, we write

$$A \cos (2\pi Ft + \phi) + A_1 \cos [(2\pi(F + \mu)t + \phi_1] - A_1 \cos [2\pi(F - \mu)t + (2\phi - \phi_1)]$$
$$= A \cos (2\pi Ft + \phi) + A_1 \cos [(2\pi Ft + \phi) + (2\pi\mu t + \phi_1 - \phi)] - A_1 \cos [(2\pi Ft + \phi) - (2\pi\mu t + \phi_1 - \phi)]$$
$$= A \cos (2\pi Ft + \phi) + A_1[\cos (2\pi Ft + \phi) \cos (2\pi\mu t + \phi_1 - \phi) - \sin (2\pi Ft + \phi) \sin (2\pi\mu t + \phi_1 - \phi)] - A_1[\cos (2\pi Ft + \phi) \cos (2\pi\mu t + \phi_1 - \phi) + \sin (2\pi Ft + \phi) \sin (2\pi\mu t + \phi_1 - \phi)]$$
$$= A \cos (2\pi Ft + \phi) - 2A_1 \sin (2\pi\mu t + \phi_1 - \phi) \sin (2\pi Ft + \phi) \quad (59)$$
$$= \sqrt{A^2 + 4A_1^2 \sin^2 (2\pi\mu t + \phi_1 - \phi)} \cos (2\pi Ft + \phi + \psi)$$
$$= A \sqrt{1 + 2\frac{A_1^2}{A^2} - \frac{2A_1^2}{A^2} \cos [2(2\pi\mu t + \phi_1 - \phi)]} \cos (2\pi Ft + \phi + \psi) \quad (60)$$

where

$$\psi = \tan^{-1} \left[2\frac{A_1}{A} \sin (2\pi\mu t + \phi_1 - \phi) \right] \quad (61)$$

Equation (59) tells us that the pair of antisymmetrical sidebands gives rise to a component in quadrature (*i.e.*, 90 deg out of phase) with the original carrier. To find the over-all resultant envelope, we must take the square root of the sum of the squares of the amplitudes of the *inphase* and *quadrature* components as indicated by Eq. (60). We note that the amplitude modulation due to the quadrature component consists entirely of even harmonic distortion.

Since ψ varies with the audio frequency, there is also angle modulation of the carrier, an effect that was absent in the case of symmetrical sidebands as indicated by Eq. (54). In fact, in the case of antisymmetrical sidebands, when A_1 is small in comparison with A, Eqs. (60) and (61) show that the frequency modulation is a first-order effect, while the amplitude modulation is only a second-order effect. This is in harmony with the result already obtained in Eq. (58).

Looking back at Eq. (54), we now note that a pair of symmetrical sidebands gives rise to a component *in phase* with the carrier.

We shall investigate the use and significance of the foregoing results in many of the following pages.

c. Expression of an Arbitrary Unsymmetrical Sideband Distribution as the Sum of Symmetrical and Antisymmetrical Pairs. The practical uses of the results of subsection *b* depend on the fact that any arbitrary unsymmetrical sideband distribution can be expresed as the sum of symmetrical and antisymmetrical pairs.[1] To show this, let us first take a single pair of unsymmetrical sidebands

$$B_1 \cos [2\pi(F + \mu)t + \theta_1] \tag{62}$$

and

$$B_2 \cos [2\pi(F - \mu)t - \theta_2] \tag{63}$$

separated from the carrier

$$A \cos 2\pi Ft \tag{64}$$

by frequencies $+\mu$ and $-\mu$, respectively. No relation whatever is assumed to exist between B_1 and B_2 or between θ_1 and θ_2. In particular, either B_1 or B_2 may be zero. We shall now show that the sum of the two sidebands (62) and (63) can be expressed as the sum of a symmetrical pair of sidebands plus an antisymmetrical pair.

We note first that

$$\begin{aligned} B_1 \cos [2\pi(F + \mu)t + \theta_1] &+ B_2 \cos [2\pi(F - \mu)t - \theta_2] \\ &= B_1[\cos 2\pi Ft \cos (2\pi\mu t + \theta_1) - \sin 2\pi Ft \sin (2\pi\mu t + \theta_1)] \\ &\quad + B_2[\cos 2\pi Ft \cos (2\pi\mu t + \theta_2) + \sin 2\pi Ft \sin (2\pi\mu t + \theta_2)] \\ &= [B_2 \cos (2\pi\mu t + \theta_2) + B_1 \cos (2\pi\mu t + \theta_1)] \cos 2\pi Ft \\ &\quad + [B_2 \sin (2\pi\mu t + \theta_2) - B_1 \sin (2\pi\mu t + \theta_1)] \sin 2\pi Ft \end{aligned} \tag{65}$$

Now the term in $\cos 2\pi Ft$ is the inphase term and is therefore the sum of a pair of symmetrical sidebands, while the term in $\sin 2\pi Ft$ is the quadrature term and is the sum of a pair of antisymmetrical sidebands. In order to find the actual pair of symmetrical sidebands, we let $\phi = 0$, $A_1 = A_s$, and $\phi_1 = \phi_s$ in Eq. (54), so that, after subtracting

[1] This situation is similar to the composition of an arbitrary function as the sum of an even and an odd part.

the carrier, Eq. (54) becomes

$$A_s \cos [2\pi(F + \mu)t + \phi_s] + A_s \cos [2\pi(F - \mu)t - \phi_s] = 2A_s \cos (2\pi\mu t + \phi_s) \cos 2\pi Ft \quad (66)$$

Then, equating coefficients of $\cos 2\pi Ft$ in Eqs. (65) and (66), we have

$$\begin{aligned} 2A_s \cos (2\pi\mu t + \phi_s) &= B_2 \cos (2\pi\mu t + \theta_2) + B_1 \cos (2\pi\mu t + \theta_1) \\ &= B_2(\cos 2\pi\mu t \cos \theta_2 - \sin 2\pi\mu t \sin \theta_2) \\ &\quad + B_1(\cos 2\pi\mu t \cos \theta_1 - \sin 2\pi\mu t \sin \theta_1) \\ &= (B_2 \cos \theta_2 + B_1 \cos \theta_1) \cos 2\pi\mu t - (B_2 \sin \theta_2 + B_1 \sin \theta_1) \sin 2\pi\mu t \\ &= 2A_s(\cos 2\pi\mu t \cos \phi_s - \sin 2\pi\mu t \sin \phi_s) \end{aligned} \quad (67)$$

Equating coefficients of $\cos 2\pi\mu t$ and of $\sin 2\pi\mu t$ on opposite sides of the equation, we have

$$2A_s \cos \phi_s = B_2 \cos \theta_2 + B_1 \cos \theta_1 \quad (68)$$

$$2A_s \sin \phi_s = B_2 \sin \theta_2 + B_1 \sin \theta_1 \quad (69)$$

Therefore

$$\begin{aligned} 2A_s &= \sqrt{(B_2 \cos \theta_2 + B_1 \cos \theta_1)^2 + (B_2 \sin \theta_2 + B_1 \sin \theta_1)^2} \\ &= \sqrt{B_2^2 + B_1^2 + 2B_1B_2 \cos (\theta_2 - \theta_1)} \end{aligned} \quad (70)$$

and

$$\phi_s = \tan^{-1} \left(\frac{B_2 \sin \theta_2 + B_1 \sin \theta_1}{B_2 \cos \theta_2 + B_1 \cos \theta_1} \right) \quad (71)$$

According to these equations, the magnitude A_s and angle ϕ_s of the symmetrical pair of sidebands can be obtained from (B_1, θ_1) and (B_2, θ_2) by vector addition as shown in Fig. 16.

In an entirely similar manner, a comparison of Eqs. (59) and (65) gives

$$2A_a = \sqrt{B_2^2 + B_1^2 - 2B_1B_2 \cos (\theta_2 - \theta_1)} \quad (72)$$

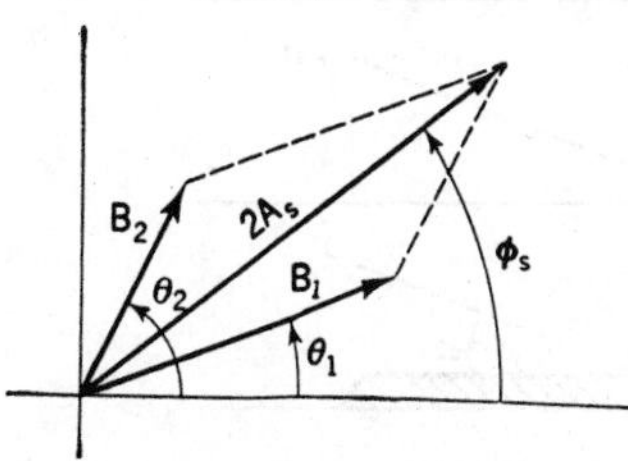

FIG. 16. Vectorial combination of sidebands to obtain symmetrical sideband components.

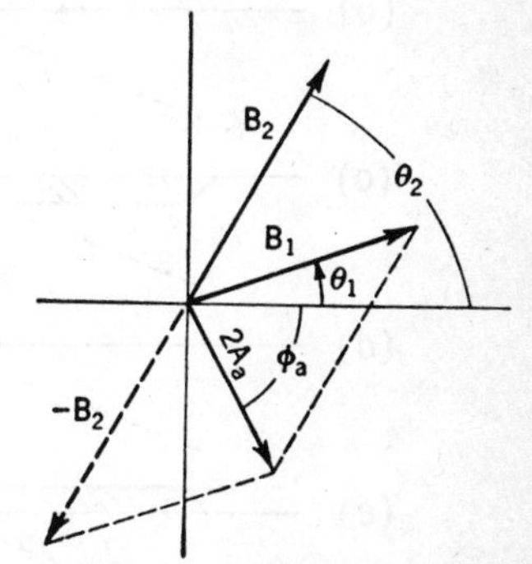

FIG. 17. Vectorial combination of sidebands to obtain antisymmetrical sideband components.

and

$$\phi_a = \tan^{-1}\left(\frac{B_1 \sin \theta_1 - B_2 \sin \theta_2}{B_1 \cos \theta_1 - B_2 \cos \theta_2}\right) \tag{73}$$

for the antisymmetrical pair of sidebands. According to Eqs. (72) and (73), the magnitude A_a and phase ϕ_a of the antisymmetrical pair of sidebands can be obtained from (B_1,θ_1) and (B_2,θ_2) by vector addition as shown in Fig. 17.

As a consequence of the foregoing, we may express the original unsymmetrical pair of sidebands as the sum of a symmetrical and an antisymmetrical pair of sidebands as follows:

$$\begin{aligned} B_1 \cos\,[2\pi(F + \mu)t + \theta_1] &+ B_2 \cos\,[2\pi(F - \mu)t - \theta_2] \\ = A_s \cos\,[2\pi(F + \mu)t + \phi_s] &+ A_s \cos\,[2\pi(F - \mu)t - \phi_s] \\ + A_a \cos\,[2\pi(F + \mu)t + \phi_a] &- A_a \cos\,[2\pi(F - \mu)t - \phi_a] \end{aligned} \tag{74}$$

The values of A_s, ϕ_s, A_a, and ϕ_a are given in Eqs. (70) to (73).

Let us now suppose that we have a distribution of sidebands as shown in Fig. 18a, which, for the sake of generality, is assumed to be a

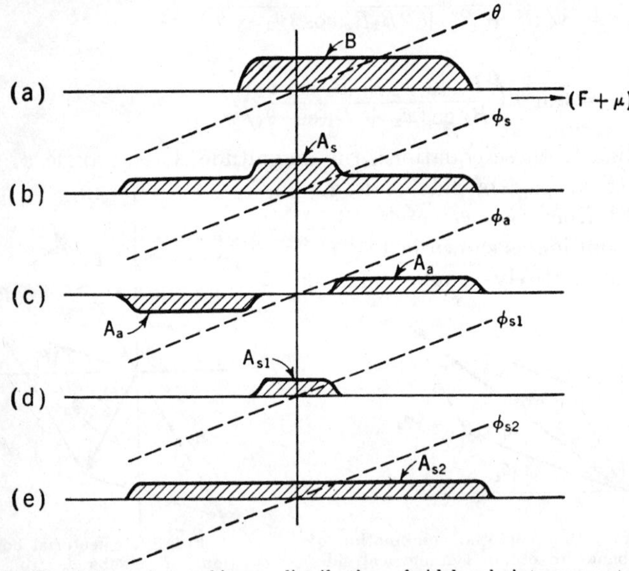

Fig. 18. Resolution of an arbitrary distribution of sidebands into symmetrical and antisymmetrical distributions.

continuous distribution. Equations (70) to (73) still give the values for A_s, ϕ_s, A_a, and ϕ_a for every pair of sidebands displaced $\pm\mu$ from the carrier, where μ is an arbitrary frequency. The curves of A_s, ϕ_s, A_a, and ϕ_a can therefore readily be calculated and plotted. The situation is particularly simple when the phases of the sidebands are a linear function of frequency. In this case

$$\theta_1 = \theta_2 = \theta \tag{75}$$

so that Eqs. (70) to (73) simplify to

$$A_s = \tfrac{1}{2}\sqrt{B_2^2 + B_1^2 + 2B_1B_2} = \tfrac{1}{2}(B_1 + B_2) \tag{76}$$

$$\phi_s = \theta \tag{77}$$

$$A_a = \tfrac{1}{2}\sqrt{B_2^2 + B_1^2 - 2B_1B_2} = \tfrac{1}{2}(B_1 - B_2) \tag{78}$$

$$\phi_a = \theta \tag{79}$$

The symmetrical and antisymmetrical components of such a distribution in Fig. 18*a* are plotted in Figs. 18*b* and *c*. Since the phase shifts for any frequency are here the same for all curves, a mere addition of Figs. 18*b* and *c* gives Fig. 18*a*.

Exercise

Given the carrier

$$500 \cos 2\pi Ft$$

and the two sidebands

$$2 \cos [2\pi(F + 1{,}000)t] \qquad \text{and} \qquad 5 \cos [2\pi(F - 1{,}000)t]$$

Find (*a*) the percentage of amplitude modulation of the composite signal; (*b*) the peak frequency deviation of the composite signal.

d. The Interpretation of Interference as an Unsymmetrical Sideband Distribution. Any type of signal interference can be interpreted as an unsymmetrical sideband distribution for the desired carrier. Thus any particular interference frequency component

$$B \cos [2\pi(F + \alpha)t + \psi] \tag{80}$$

may be interpreted as a pair of symmetrical sidebands plus a pair of antisymmetrical sidebands for the carrier

$$A \cos 2\pi Ft \tag{81}$$

In order to find these sidebands, we can let

$$B_1 = B \tag{82}$$

$$B_2 = 0 \tag{83}$$

and

$$\theta = \psi \tag{84}$$

in Eqs. (76) to (79). Consequently,

$$A_s = \frac{B}{2} \tag{85}$$

$$\phi_s = \psi \tag{86}$$

$$A_a = \frac{B}{2} \tag{87}$$

$$\phi_a = \psi \tag{88}$$

By Eqs. (54), (85), and (86) we know that the symmetrical pair of the above sidebands is equivalent to a component in phase with the carrier and that they cause amplitude modulation with a degree of modulation of amount B/A. On the other hand, by Eqs. (57), (59),

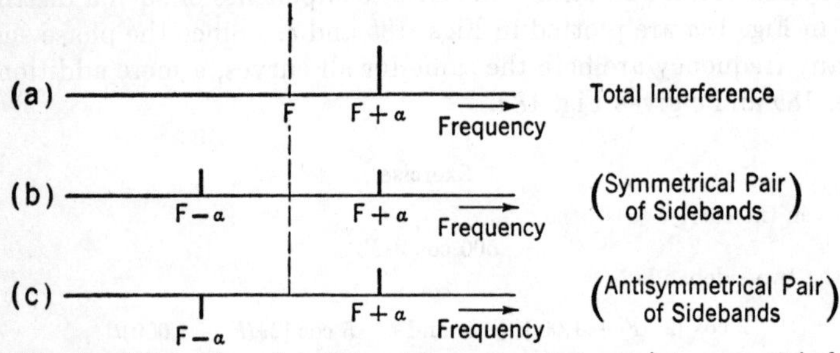

FIG. 19. Resolution of an interfering frequency component into symmetrical and antisymmetrical sidebands.

(87), and (88) we know that the antisymmetrical pair of sidebands is equivalent to a component in quadrature with the carrier and that, if $B \ll A$, they cause frequency modulation of modulation index B/A, *i.e.*, a peak frequency swing of amount $(B/A)\alpha$. These results agree with what we learned when we studied common-channel interference in Sec. 5.5.

The pairs of symmetrical and antisymmetrical sidebands into which the interference signal [Eq. (80)] can be broken down are shown in Fig. 19. The sidebands of frequency $F - \alpha$ in this case are truly a mathematical fiction since there is actually no signal energy at the frequency $F - \alpha$.

This method of looking at interference is very instructive, and readily allows a quick estimate to be made of its effects.

e. Unsymmetrical Sideband Distributions and Television Transmission.[1] We shall now use the methods of this section to simplify prob-

[1] This subject has been discussed in the following papers: POCH, W. J., and D. W. EPSTEIN, Partial Suppression of One Side Band in Television Reception,

lems in the unsymmetrical sideband transmission of television signals. Such problems have already been considered in Secs. 4.8 to

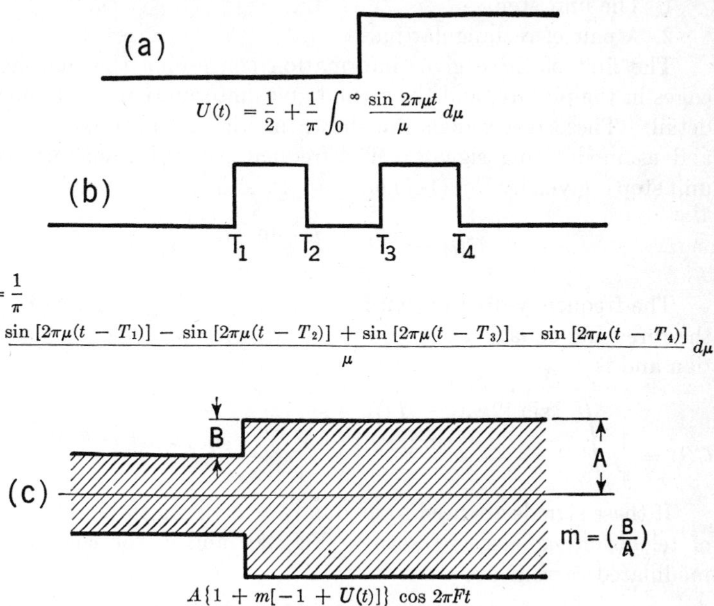

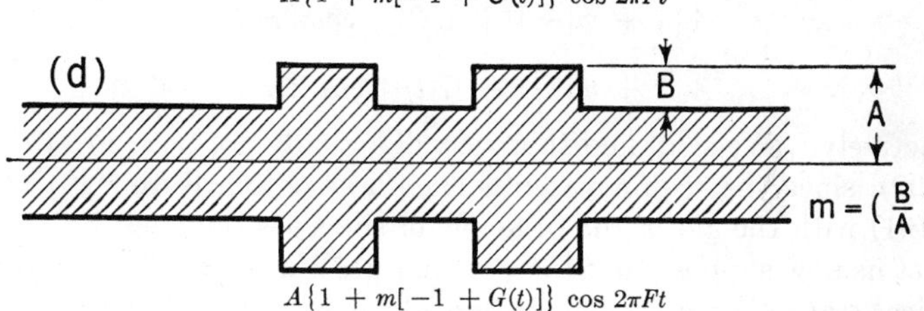

FIG. 20. Television test signals as video and as modulated carriers.

4.10, but we shall now see how the same results can be obtained in a more simple and straightforward manner.

Proc. I.R.E., January, 1937, p. 15; GOLDMAN, S., Television Detail and Selective Side Band Transmission, *Proc. I.R.E.*, November, 1939, p. 725; NYQUIST, H., and K. W. PFLEGER, Effect of the Quadrature Component in Single Sideband Transmission, *Bell System Tech. J.*, January, 1940, p. 63; KELL, R. D., and G. L. FREDENDALL, Selective Sideband Transmission in Television, *R.C.A. Rev.*, April, 1940, p. 425; KALLMANN, H. E., R. E. SPENCER, and C. P. SINGER, Transient Response of Single-sideband Systems, *Proc. I.R.E.*, December, 1940, p. 557. The discussion given here follows most closely that of Nyquist and Pfleger.

As pointed out in Chap. IV, the two best test signals for studying television transmission are probably

1. The unit step
2. A pair of rectangular pulses

The first of these gives information concerning the sharpness of edges in the picture, and the second gives information concerning fine detail. These test signals are shown in Fig. 20, both as pure video and as modulating signals. The frequency-distribution form of the unit step is given by Eq. (147) of Chap. IV and is

$$U(t) = \frac{1}{2} + \frac{1}{\pi}\int_0^\infty \frac{\sin 2\pi\mu t}{\mu}\,d\mu \tag{89}$$

The frequency-distribution form of the pair of pulses follows from the foregoing equation in conjunction with the principle of superposition and is

$$G(t) = \frac{1}{\pi}\int_0^\infty \frac{\begin{array}{c}\sin[2\pi\mu(t - T_1)] - \sin[2\pi\mu(t - T_2)] \\ + \sin[2\pi\mu(t - T_3)] - \sin[2\pi\mu(t - T_4)]\end{array}}{\mu}\,d\mu \tag{90}$$

If these signals are used to modulate a carrier in the special manner of television signals, as shown in Fig. 20*c* and *d*, the corresponding modulated carriers are

$$A\{1 + m[-1 + U(t)]\}\cos 2\pi Ft \tag{91}$$

and

$$A\{1 + m[-1 + G(t)]\}\cos 2\pi Ft \tag{92}$$

respectively. We shall find that we will actually not need Eq. (90) or Eq (92), since the required results can all be obtained from Eqs. (89) and (91) with the aid of the principle of superposition.

Let us now suppose that these signals are sent through two unsymmetrical transmission systems in cascade as shown in Figs. 21*a* and *b*, which represent the characteristics of a television transmitter and receiver, respectively. If

$$y_1(j\omega) = Y_1(\omega)\epsilon^{j\phi_1(\omega)} \tag{93}$$

and

$$y_2(j\omega) = Y_2(\omega)\epsilon^{j\phi_2(\omega)} \tag{94}$$

represent the respective transmission characteristics of the transmitter and receiver, then

$$y_3(j\omega) = Y_3(\omega)\epsilon^{j\phi_3(\omega)} = y_1(j\omega)y_2(j\omega) = Y_1(\omega)Y_2(\omega)\epsilon^{j[\phi_2(\omega)+\phi_1(\omega)]} \tag{95}$$

represents the over-all transmission characteristic. This is shown in Fig. 21*c*.

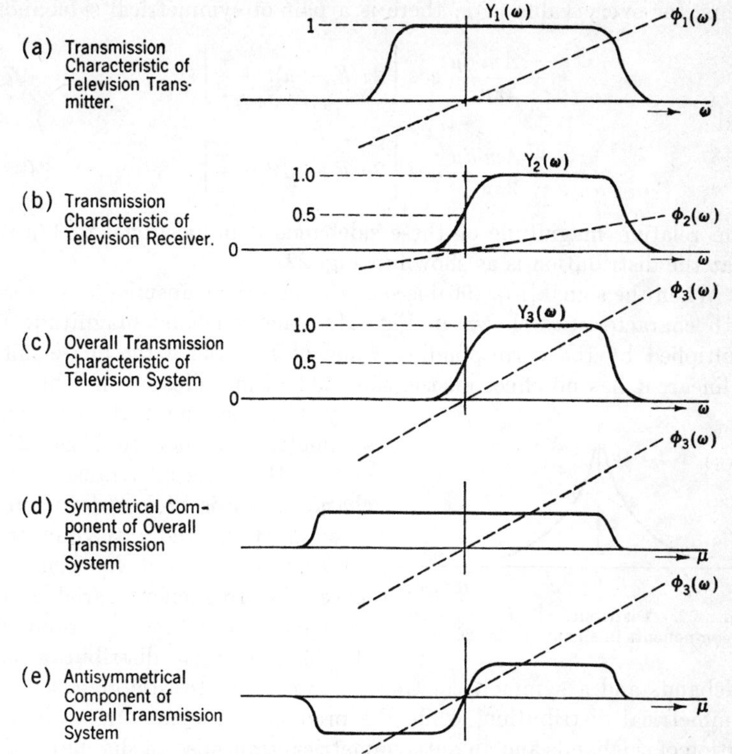

FIG. 21. Resolution of an unsymmetrical television transmission system into symmetrical and antisymmetrical components.

Let us next send the signal of Fig. 20*c* through the transmission system whose characteristics are shown in Fig. 21*c*. The signal in Fig. 20*c* may be written

$$A\,\{1 + m[-1 + U(t)]\}\cos 2\pi Ft$$
$$= A\left[1 + m\left(-1 + \frac{1}{2} + \frac{1}{\pi}\int_0^\infty \frac{\sin 2\pi\mu t}{\mu}\,d\mu\right)\right]\cos 2\pi Ft$$
$$= A\left(1 - \frac{m}{2}\right)\cos 2\pi Ft + \frac{Am}{\pi}\int_0^\infty \frac{\sin 2\pi\mu t}{\mu}(\cos 2\pi Ft)\,d\mu$$
$$= A\left(1 - \frac{m}{2}\right)\cos 2\pi Ft$$
$$-\frac{Am}{2\pi}\int_0^\infty \frac{\cos\left[2\pi(F+\mu)t + \frac{\pi}{2}\right] + \cos\left[2\pi(F-\mu)t - \frac{\pi}{2}\right]}{\mu}\,d\mu \quad (96)$$

Thus, for every value of μ, there is a pair of symmetrical sidebands

$$\frac{-Am\,d\mu}{2\pi\mu}\cos\left[2\pi(F+\mu)t+\frac{\pi}{2}\right] \tag{97}$$

and

$$\frac{-Am\,d\mu}{2\pi\mu}\cos\left[2\pi(F-\mu)t-\frac{\pi}{2}\right] \tag{98}$$

The relative magnitude of these sidebands is proportional to $1/\mu$ so that the distribution is as shown in Fig. 22.

When the signal [Eq. (96)] is sent through the transmission system with characteristics shown in Fig. 21*c*, each sideband magnitude is multiplied by the corresponding value of Y_3. Since the phase shift is linear, it has no effect on the sideband magnitudes or on whether they form symmetrical or antisymmetrical pairs. In Figs. 21*d* and *e* the over-all transmission characteristic is broken down into its symmetrical and antisymmetrical components, and for convenience the frequency variable is changed to μ. Now the product of a symmetrical distribution of sidebands and a symmetrical transmission characteristic gives a new symmetrical distribution, while the product of a symmetrical distribution of sidebands and an antisymmetrical transmission characteristic gives a new antisymmetrical distribution of sidebands. The final signal may thus be written

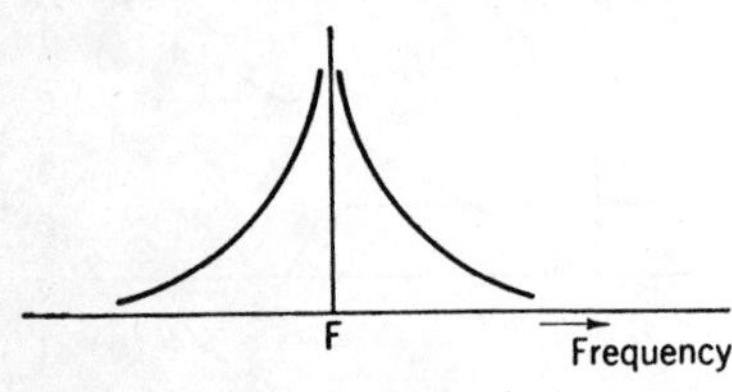

FIG. 22. Distribution of frequency components in signal of Fig. 20(*c*).

$$\begin{aligned}&\frac{A}{2}\left(1-\frac{m}{2}\right)Y_{3F}\cos 2\pi Ft\\&-\frac{Am}{2\pi}\int_0^\infty\frac{Y_{3s}(F+\mu)}{\mu}\left\{\cos\left[2\pi(F+\mu)t+\frac{\pi}{2}+B\mu\right]\right.\\&\qquad\qquad\left.+\cos\left[2\pi(F-\mu)t-\frac{\pi}{2}-B\mu\right]\right\}d\mu\\&-\frac{Am}{2\pi}\int_0^\infty\frac{Y_{3a}(F+\mu)}{\mu}\left\{\cos\left[2\pi(F+\mu)t+\frac{\pi}{2}+B\mu\right]\right.\\&\qquad\qquad\left.-\cos\left[2\pi(F-\mu)t-\frac{\pi}{2}-B\mu\right]\right\}d\mu\end{aligned} \tag{99}$$

where

$$\phi_3(\omega)=B\mu \tag{100}$$

By Eqs. (54) and (59), Eq. (99) may also be written

$$\frac{A}{2}\left(1-\frac{m}{2}\right) Y_{3F} \cos 2\pi Ft$$
$$- \frac{Am}{\pi}\int_0^\infty \frac{Y_{3s}(F+\mu)}{\mu} \cos\left(2\pi\mu t + \frac{\pi}{2} + B\mu\right) d\mu \cos 2\pi Ft$$
$$+ \frac{Am}{\pi}\int_0^\infty \frac{Y_{3a}(F+\mu)}{\mu} \sin\left(2\pi\mu t + \frac{\pi}{2} + B\mu\right) d\mu \sin 2\pi Ft$$
$$= \left[\frac{A}{2}\left(1-\frac{m}{2}\right) Y_{3F} + \frac{Am}{\pi}\int_0^\infty Y_{3s}(F+\mu)\frac{\sin(2\pi\mu t + B\mu)}{\mu} d\mu\right] \cos 2\pi Ft$$
$$+ \left[\frac{Am}{\pi}\int_0^\infty Y_{3a}(F+\mu)\frac{\cos(2\pi\mu t + B\mu)}{\mu} d\mu\right] \sin 2\pi Ft \quad (101)$$

The coefficient of cos $2\pi Ft$, in accordance with our previous terminology, is called the inphase component of the envelope, and the coefficient of sin $2\pi Ft$ is called the quadrature component. The resultant amplitude envelope is the square root of the sum of the squares of the inphase and quadrature components. The inphase and quadrature components of Eq. (101) and their resultant for the case that $m = 1$ and for the values of Y_{3s} and Y_{3a} in Fig. 21 are shown in Fig. 23*a*. The actual calculation of the integrals in Eq. (101) is usually complicated, unless the transmission characteristic is idealized, as is done in Secs. 4.8 and 4.9.

Once the transmitted signal has been calculated for unit-step modulation, the transmitted signals for the other details shown in Figs. 23*b* to *d* can be calculated from Fig. 23*a* by the principle of superposition. It should be remembered that all the inphase components must be added separately and all the quadrature components must be added separately, before taking the square root of the sum of the squares for the final resultant.

The problem of television detail and unsymmetrical sideband transmission has already been discussed in more detail in Chap. IV. The present section, however, has presented a more general outlook upon the subject.

5.7 Vectorial Interpretation of Modulation.[1] In Sec. 5.4*a* and Fig. 12 it is pointed out that a simple harmonic vibration $A \cos(\omega t + \phi)$ may be represented as the pair of rotating complex vectors $(A/2)\epsilon^{j(\omega t+\phi)}$ and $(A/2)\epsilon^{-j(\omega t+\phi)}$ which rotate in opposite directions in the complex

[1] An equivalent discussion of this subject is given by H. A. Wheeler, The Solution of Unsymmetrical Sideband Problems with the Aid of the Zero-frequency Carrier, *Proc. I.R.E.*, August, 1941, p. 446.

plane with angular velocity ω. The carrier and sidebands of an amplitude-modulated carrier may therefore be represented as six complex vectors, three of them rotating clockwise and three rotating

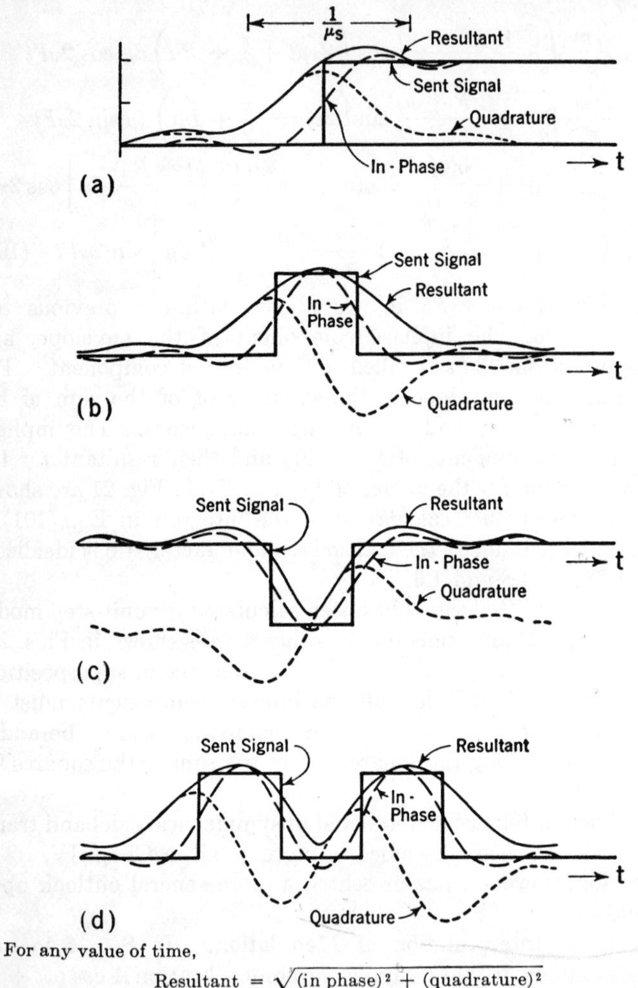

For any value of time,

$$\text{Resultant} = \sqrt{(\text{in phase})^2 + (\text{quadrature})^2}$$

(The time delay between transmitted and received signals is not indicated in this figure.)

FIG. 23. Envelopes of inphase and quadrature components of signals passing through the asymmetrical transmission system of Fig. 21(*c*). (*From Nyquist and Pfleger, Bell System Tech. J., January,* 1940, *reprinted by permission.*)

counterclockwise. The sum of the six vectors is always real and is equal to the instantaneous value of the amplitude-modulated wave. This is shown in Fig. 24.

Since three of the six vectors are conjugate to the other three, one set of three gives all the information about the system, so long as it is kept in mind that the conjugate vectors are also part of the complete picture. We shall therefore conduct our studies in terms of the positive rotating (counterclockwise) set.[1] We also note that the upper-

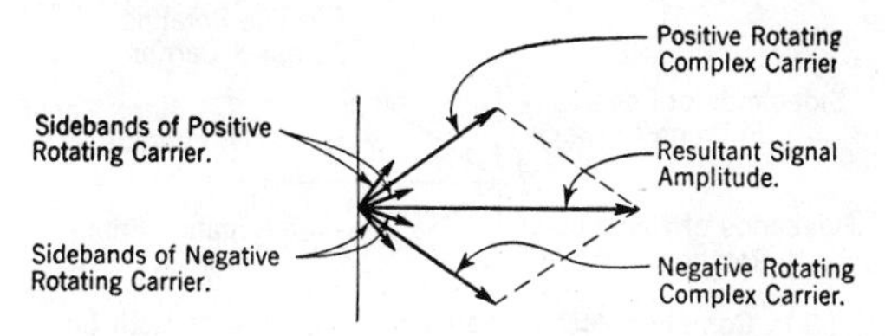

(a) Complete Vector Representation, Showing Both Sets of the Conjugate Vectors

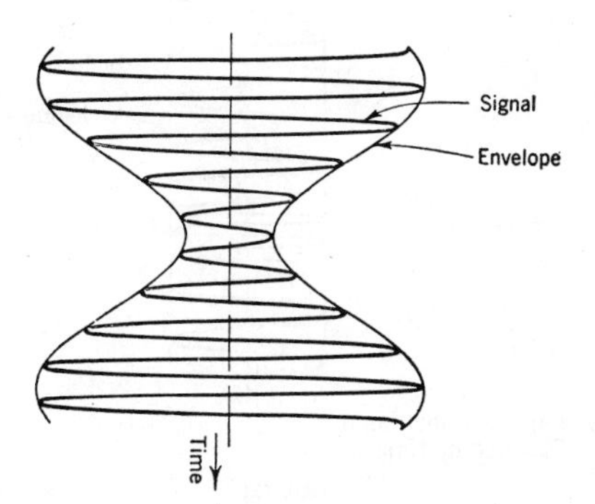

(b) Representation as a Function of Time

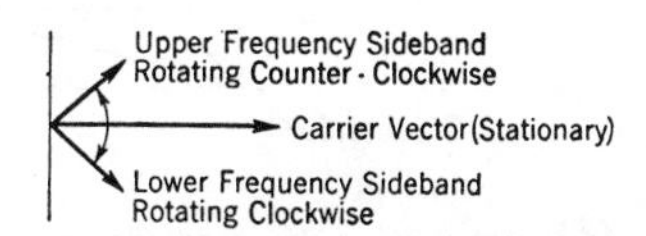

(c) Abbreviated Representation as the Positive Rotating Set

FIG. 24. Representations of an amplitude-modulated signal.

frequency sideband vector is rotating in a positive (counterclockwise) direction about the carrier at the angular velocity of the modulation frequency, and the lower-frequency sideband vector is rotating in a clockwise direction about the carrier with the same angular velocity. In studying sidebands it is sometimes convenient to consider the carrier

[1] For simplicity, we shall often omit the ½ factors when dealing with only one of the two sets of oppositely rotating vectors.

vector as stationary and to study the motion of the sidebands with respect to the carrier.

According to Eq. (54) the upper-frequency sideband vector in AM is always as many radians[1] counterclockwise from the carrier as the lower-frequency sideband vector is radians clockwise from it, as

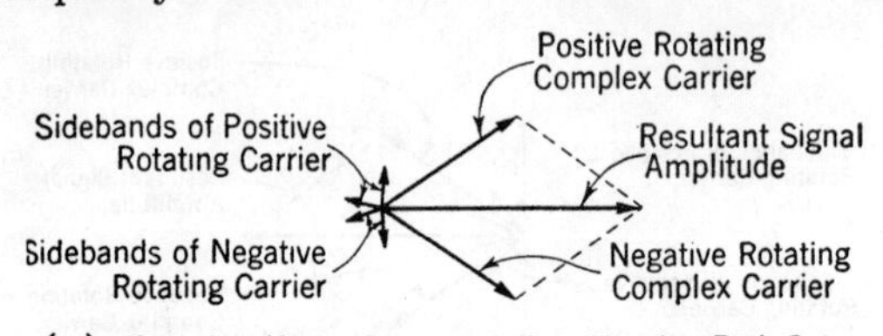

(a) Complete Vector Representation, Showing Both Sets of the Conjugate Vectors

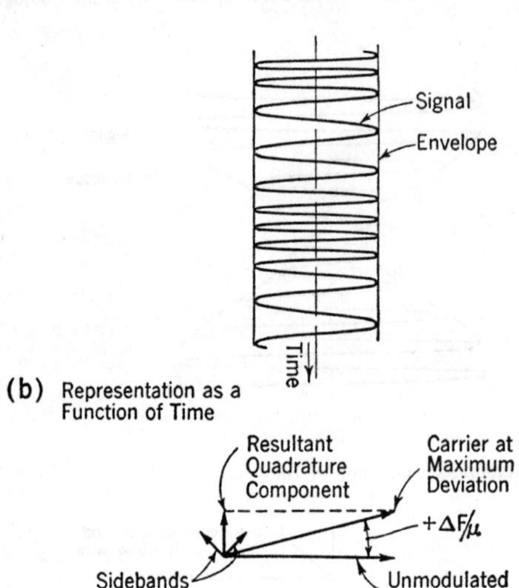

(b) Representation as a Function of Time

(c) Abbreviated Representation as the Positive Rotating Set

FIG. 25. Representations of a frequency-modulated signal.

shown in Fig. 24*c*. In the particular case of Fig. 24*c*, that is, of Eq. (54), the resultant of the two sidebands is thus always in the direction of the carrier (or 180 deg away from it) so that the sidebands cause amplitude modulation of the carrier but no phase (or frequency) modulation. The vector picture thus shows that symmetrical sidebands add an inphase component to the carrier and give pure amplitude modulation.

[1] That is, $2\pi\mu t + \phi_1 - \phi$ radians.

In the case of pure frequency modulation, of small index, the complete rotating-vector representation of Eq. (59), is shown in Fig. 25*a*, and the modulated wave is shown in Fig. 25*b*. The stationary-carrier picture is shown in Fig. 25*c*. Here we see that the resultant of the antisymmetrical sidebands is a component in quadrature with the carrier and causes amplitude modulation only as a second-order effect. However, the phase of the resultant of the carrier plus sidebands shifts from the unmodulated phase to excursions of $\pm\Delta F/\mu$ radians at the rate of the modulation frequency μ. Thus there is frequency modulation. Since the instantaneous frequency is proportional to the time derivative of the phase, the maximum frequency excursion (*i.e.*, FM modulation peak) occurs, not when the phase deviation is a maximum, but rather when the phase is changing most rapidly. This happens to be when the resultant is in phase with the carrier. On the other hand, PM modulation peaks occur at the time of maximum phase deviation.

A case of pure frequency modulation of large index is difficult to illustrate in a diagram. Here a large number of sidebands are necessary, and the resultant is much larger than the carrier. The resultant remains of constant length but rotates about the carrier to the extent of $\Delta F/2\pi\mu$ full rotations away from the carrier phase and back again while the audio goes through one half cycle. During the next half audio cycle the process is repeated, but with reversed angular directions of rotation. The process is not hard to visualize, but it is hard to show in a diagram.

Exercise

Show that phase modulation of small index gives rise to a pair of antisymmetrical sidebands just as FM does.

5.8 Vectorial Discussion of the General Problem of Interference.[1] The vector representation throws new light on the general problem of interference. Let the vector A in Fig. 26 represent the signal, and let B represent the interference, which may be either noise or an undesired signal. The resultant of the two is R. Changes in the length of R represent the total effective amplitude modulation, while the rate of change of the angle ϕ_R is the total effective frequency modulation. In Sec. 5.5 we made an analytical investigation of the problem for the special case in which B was an undesired signal and the ratio B/A was small in comparison with unity. We now wish to consider the more general case of unrestricted values of B/A, and we shall not consider that B is limited to any particular type of signal.

[1] Roder, H., Noise in Frequency Modulation, *Electronics*, May, 1937, p. 22.

It is apparent from Fig. 26 that in a cycle of the difference frequency, the amplitude of the resultant varies between $(A + B)$ and $(A - B)$ so that the amount of the total amplitude modulation rises and falls uniformly with the amplitudes of A and B. At the same time, it is also apparent from Fig. 26 that if $B < A$ then angular variations in B even of thousands of degrees will cause little change in ϕ_R, for the maximum angle between R and A cannot exceed $\sin^{-1}(B/A)$. Therefore, if the modulation of A has a large deviation ratio, such as is characteristic of wide-band frequency modulation, so that A (and therefore R) has several complete revolutions in one audio cycle, the relative effect of B on the over-all frequency modulation will be very small, considerably smaller than in the corresponding case of amplitude modulation.

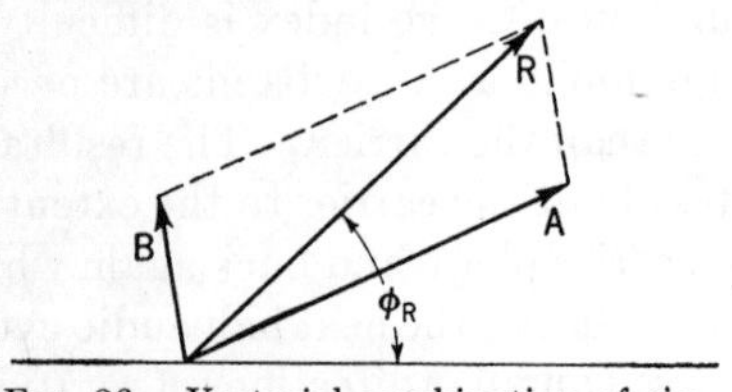

Fig. 26. Vectorial combination of signal and interference.

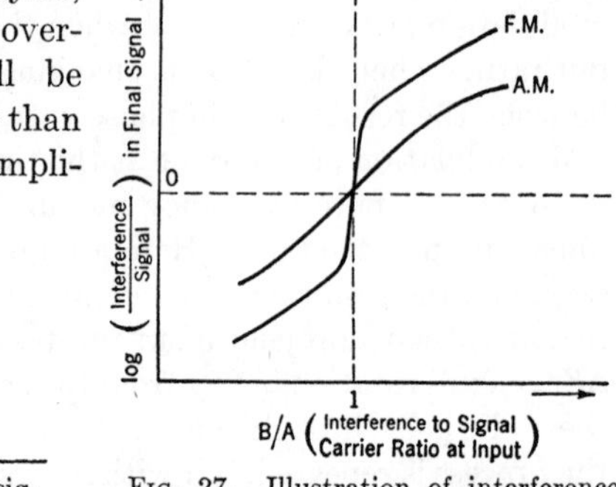

Fig. 27. Illustration of interference reduction in frequency modulation when the incoming signal level exceeds that of the interference.

On the other hand, if B should exceed A, the situation would be exactly reversed and the frequency modulation of A would then have relatively little effect on the total effective frequency modulation of R. The relative importance and the variation of interference are thus quite different in AM and FM. In the former the interference-to-signal ratio varies smoothly with the ratio B/A, while in the latter there is very little interference until the ratio $B/A = 1$ is approached and then the interference rapidly rises to a value that blankets the desired signal. The situation is shown diagrammatically in Fig. 27.

According to the foregoing discussion there is a rather sharp transition between good and poor interference-to-signal ratios in FM. Consequently, in the distribution of FM transmitters around the country, the service areas may be expected to be more clearly defined than is the case with AM. However, even with FM since both the interference and the signal are likely to have some amplitude modulation superimposed upon their frequency modulation, the contours of the transition value of $B/A = 1$ are not as sharply defined as they might be. Nevertheless, the useful service areas are still much more definitely bounded than is the case with AM transmitters.

An analytical and graphical investigation has been made by Roder[1] of FM interference for relatively large values of B/A. His results are in substantial agreement with the foregoing discussion.

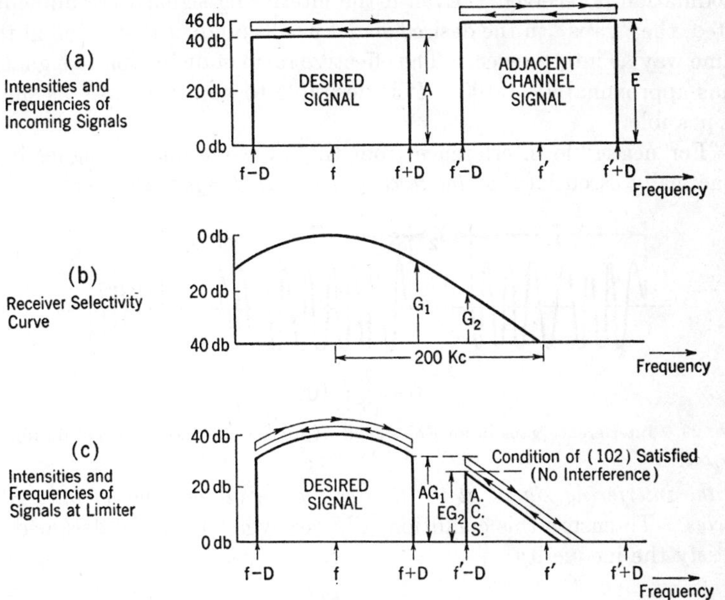

FIG. 28. Effect of selectivity in reducing adjacent-channel interference (FM). (*Goldman, S., Electronics, August,* 1941, *reprinted by permission.*)

5.9 Adjacent-channel Interference in FM.[2] The discussion in the preceding section serves as a good introduction to the problem of adjacent-channel interference in FM. Suppose that we consider the frequency-modulated signals of two adjacent channels as shown in Fig. 28*a*. These signals will be assumed to be pure FM signals, *i.e.*, of constant amplitude but variable frequencies. The numerical values chosen in Fig. 28 are reasonable for present-day FM reception. An assumed selectivity curve of a receiver is shown in Fig. 28*b* and the final signal levels arriving at the limiter are shown in Fig. 28*c*.

[1] RODER, H., Effects of Tuned Circuits upon a Frequency Modulated Signal, *Proc. I.R.E.*, December, 1937, p. 1617.

[2] GOLDMAN, S., F.M. Noise and Interference, *Electronics*, August, 1941, p. 37.

In accordance with our previous discussion, if the desired signal exceeds the interference during all portions of all audio cycles, the interference will cause negligible frequency modulation of the resultant signal arriving at the limiter. However, let us next consider the case in which the interference exceeds the desired signal level at the limiter for an average of n per cent of the time (see Fig. 29). During the time when the interference exceeds the desired signal, the interference modulation is received. Even if the interfering signal were unmodulated, the "gaps" in the desired signal would produce distortion in the same way as interference. The effective ratio of distortion to signal is thus approximately $n/100$. It is desirable to keep this ratio as small as possible.

For negligible interference from the adjacent-channel signal it is practically essential that *the level of the desired signal shall exceed that*

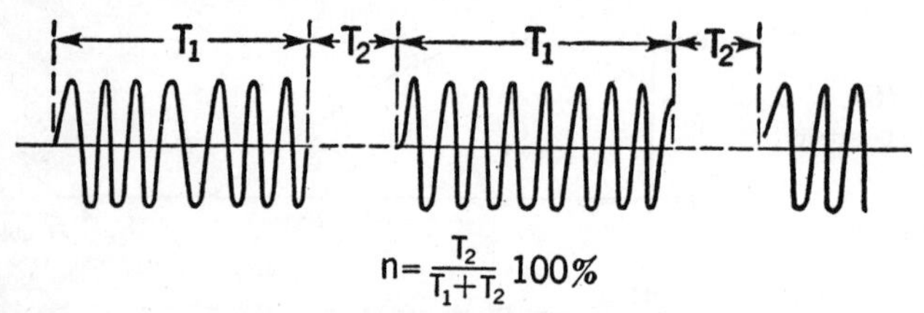

$$n = \frac{T_2}{T_1 + T_2} 100\%$$

FIG. 29. Interference gaps in an FM signal. (Interference exceeds signal during T_2 intervals.)

of the interfering signal at the limiter during all portions of the audio cycles. To ensure this condition, FM receivers should be designed to satisfy the inequality

$$AG_1 > EG_2 \tag{102}$$

where A is the level of the desired signal at the input of the receiver, G_1 is the gain of the receiver at the frequency of maximum deviation of the signal toward the adjacent channel, E is the level of the adjacent-channel interfering signal at the input of the receiver, and G_2 is the gain of the receiver at the frequency of maximum deviation of the adjacent channel toward the signal channel.

According to Eq. (102) there must be enough receiver selectivity in the frequency range between the frequencies of maximum deviation of the signals toward each other to take care of the difference in level of the desired and adjacent-channel signals at the input of the receiver.

When condition (102) is satisfied, the level of the adjacent-channel interference can be calculated as the sum of interference between the various received sidebands of the adjacent-channel signal and desired carrier. The method for such calculations is indicated in the exercises below. The actual calculation is not of sufficient importance to be

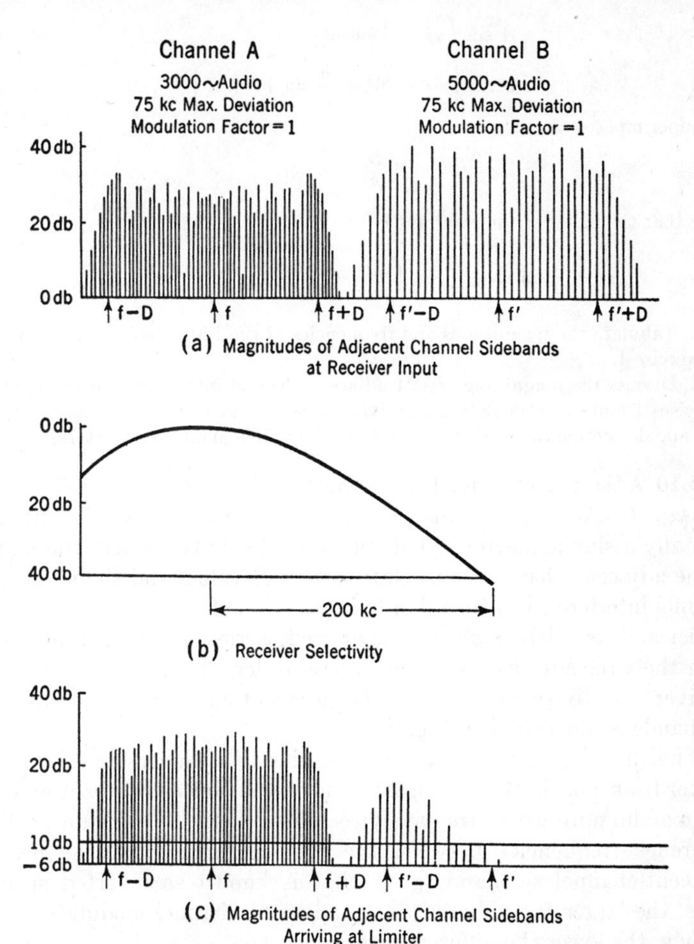

FIG. 30. Sideband picture of the effect of selectivity in reducing adjacent-channel interference (FM). (*Goldman, S., Electronics, August,* 1941, *reprinted by permission.*)

reproduced here, since the interference level is of the order of 60 db below the level of the desired signal when Eq. (102) is satisfied. In Fig. 30 the figures corresponding to Fig. 28 are shown for the individual sidebands.

Exercises

1. If two frequency-modulated signals

$$A \sin \left(\omega t + \frac{a}{\mu} \sin \mu t \right)$$

and

$$B \sin \left[(\omega + \beta)t + \frac{b}{V} \sin Vt + C \right]$$

are superimposed and if

$$\frac{B}{A} \ll 1$$

show that the phase of the resultant is

$$\omega t + \frac{a}{\mu} \sin \mu t + \frac{B}{A} \sin \left(\beta t + C + \frac{b}{V} \sin Vt - \frac{a}{\mu} \sin \mu t \right)$$

2. Tabulate the magnitudes and frequencies of the FM interference sidebands in Exercise 1.

3. Discuss the magnitude of FM adjacent-channel interference in the light of Exercises 1 and 2. Calculate the interference-to-desired-signal ratio in a typical case, and determine the audio frequencies of the principal interference terms.

5.10 Adjacent-channel Interference in AM. *a. Carrier Beat and Monkey Chatter.* Adjacent-channel interference in AM is fundamentally a simple matter. The receiver selectivity reduces the signal in the adjacent channel to a relatively small value, and the adjacent-channel interference is then due to interaction of the adjacent-channel carrier and its sidebands with the desired carrier, all other interaction from the adjacent channel being second-order effects. The action of receiver selectivity in reducing the adjacent-channel carrier and its sidebands is illustrated in Fig. 31.

The difference frequency between the two carriers is called the carrier beat, and in the broadcast band in the United States it gives a 10-kc audio note whose frequency remains practically constant. The difference frequencies between the desired carrier and the nearer adjacent-channel sidebands give what is known as inverted speech since, the larger the value of μ, the adjacent-channel modulation frequency, the lower the difference frequency $\alpha - \mu$.

These difference frequencies vary with the frequencies in the program of the adjacent channel and give completely unintelligible noise, which is usually known by the fanciful name "monkey chatter." The beat notes between the desired carrier and the sidebands on the far side of the adjacent-channel carrier are also included in the term monkey chatter, but their intensity is usually very small and their audio frequency is so high that they are practically eliminated by the audio system of the receiver.

The apparent interference modulation due to the frequency components in the adjacent channel can be written down immediately in view of Sec. 5.6*d* and Eq. 6. Thus, if the amplitude of the desired carrier is A and the amplitude of a particular frequency component in

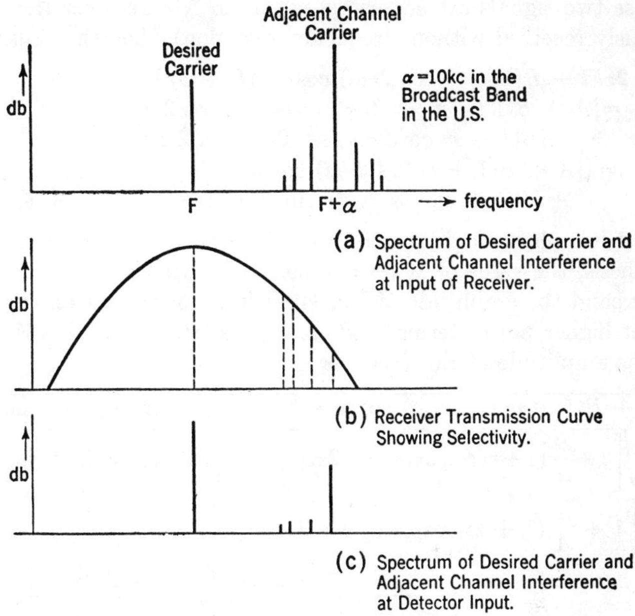

FIG. 31. Sideband pictures of adjacent-channel interference in AM, showing effect of receiver selectivity.

the adjacent channel is C, then this frequency component causes a degree of modulation of the desired carrier of amount

$$\frac{C}{A} \tag{103}$$

b. Masking of a Weak Signal by a Strong One.[1] An interesting phenomenon that occurs in both adjacent-channel interference and common-channel interference in AM receivers is the masking of a weak signal by a strong one. To study this let us suppose we have a

[1] This subject has been exhaustively investigated by C. B. Aiken in Theory of the Detection of Two Modulated Waves by a Linear Rectifier, *Proc. I.R.E.*, April, 1933, p. 601, and the references there quoted.

strong carrier

$$A \cos 2\pi Ft \tag{104}$$

which for simplicity will be considered as unmodulated, and a much weaker modulated carrier

$$B(1 + m \cos 2\pi\mu t) \cos [2\pi(F + \alpha)t] \tag{105}$$

If these two signals are superimposed in an AM receiver (*i.e.*, simultaneously received without frequency selection), then the resultant is

$$\begin{aligned} A \cos 2\pi Ft &+ B(1 + m \cos 2\pi\mu t) \cos [2\pi(F + \alpha)t] \\ &= [A + B(1 + m \cos 2\pi\mu t) \cos 2\pi\alpha t] \cos 2\pi Ft \\ &\qquad - [B(1 + m \cos 2\pi\mu t) \sin 2\pi\alpha t] \sin 2\pi Ft \\ &= \{[A + B(1 + m \cos 2\pi\mu t) \cos 2\pi\alpha t]^2 \\ &\qquad + [B(1 + m \cos 2\pi\mu t) \sin 2\pi\alpha t]^2\}^{1/2} \cos (2\pi Ft + \delta) \end{aligned} \tag{106}$$

where δ is a phase angle that is not of interest in this case. Now, by hypothesis, the value of B is small compared with A. We can therefore expand the amplitude of Eq. (106) in a power series in B/A and neglect higher power terms of B/A. Thus[1] the received AM signal, *i.e.*, the amplitude of Eq. (106), is

$$\begin{aligned} &\sqrt{[A + B(1 + m \cos 2\pi\mu t) \cos 2\pi\alpha t]^2 + [B(1 + m \cos 2\pi\mu t) \sin 2\pi\alpha t]^2} \\ &= A \sqrt{\left[1 + \frac{B}{A} (1 + m \cos 2\pi\mu t) \cos 2\pi\alpha t\right]^2 + \left[\frac{B}{A} (1 + m \cos 2\pi\mu t) \sin 2\pi\alpha t\right]^2} \\ &= A \left[1 + \frac{B}{A} (1 + m \cos 2\pi\mu t) \cos 2\pi\alpha t \right. \\ &\qquad \left. + \frac{B^2}{A^2} \frac{(1 + m \cos 2\pi\mu t)^2 \sin^2 2\pi\alpha t}{2} + \cdots \right] \\ &= A + B \left\{ \cos 2\pi\alpha t + \frac{m}{2} \cos [2\pi(\alpha + \mu)t] + \frac{m}{2} \cos [2\pi(\alpha - \mu)t] \right\} \\ &+ \frac{B^2}{2A} \left\{ \frac{1}{2}\left(1 + \frac{m^2}{2}\right) + m \cos 2\pi\mu t + \frac{m^2}{4} \cos 4\pi\mu t - \frac{1}{2}\left(1 + \frac{m^2}{2}\right) \cos 4\pi\alpha t \right. \\ &\qquad - \frac{m}{2} \cos [2\pi(2\alpha + \mu)t] - \frac{m}{2} \cos [2\pi(2\alpha - \mu)t] \\ &\qquad \left. - \frac{m^2}{8} \cos [4\pi(\alpha + \mu)t] - \frac{m^2}{8} \cos [4\pi(\alpha - \mu)t] \right\} + \cdots \end{aligned} \tag{107}$$

The first-order terms in Eq. (107) are the carrier beat and monkey chatter already considered in subsection *a*. The second-order terms

[1] The reader can easily derive the following Taylor expansion,

$$\sqrt{(1 + ax)^2 + b^2x^2} = 1 + ax + \frac{b^2x^2}{2} + \cdots$$

which is the basis for Eq. (107).

include, among other things, a term in the signal itself, namely,

$$\frac{B^2}{2A} m \cos 2\pi\mu t \tag{108}$$

In the absence of the strong carrier, this term would have been amplitude modulation of amount

$$Bm \cos 2\pi\mu t \tag{109}$$

The strong carrier has thus reduced the signal by a factor

$$\frac{B}{2A} \tag{110}$$

which accordingly is called a *masking factor*.

This masking factor has probably been observed, even if not recognized, by all users of radio receivers. Thus, late at night when a strong local transmitter "leaves the air," an entirely new signal on the same channel or an adjacent channel[1] suddenly appears without retuning the receiver. The only previous indication of the presence of this signal has been a carrier beat (whistle) and some background monkey chatter.[2]

The importance of the masking effect in reducing interference in AM receivers should not be exaggerated, since the larger first-order interference terms are always present. However, if the audio system of the receiver has a rather low frequency cutoff, both carrier beat and monkey chatter may be effectively eliminated from adjacent-channel interference by the audio system itself. In this case, the masking effect will greatly improve the apparent selectivity of the receiver. Part of the importance of masking is also due to the psychological fact that an intelligible interfering signal is more distracting than noise.

Exercise

Assume that receiver selectivity makes one sideband in the adjacent channel twice as large as the other, and investigate whether or not masking is thereby affected.

5.11 Some General Considerations with Respect to Modulation Distortion. There are certain types of distortion, particularly types that vary with tuning, that are a consequence of special sideband

[1] We have neglected the selectivity of the receiver in our discussion. This will have a certain amount of influence on the masking of an adjacent-channel signal because it makes the sidebands unequal.

[2] This phenomenon will occur both with and without avc in the receiver. However, the use of a square-law detector, which gives distortion of the amplitude envelope, tends to eliminate the phenomenon.

distributions. They are thus closely related to modulation theory and will therefore be considered at this point. We shall call them *modulation distortion.*

a. Distortion in Amplitude Modulation. In Sec. 5.6*b* we found that a symmetrical distribution of sidebands gives a component in phase with the carrier and gives only amplitude modulation at the difference frequency between the sidebands and the carrier. A symmetrical transmission system will therefore introduce no new modulation frequency components into an originally symmetrical distribution of sidebands.[1]

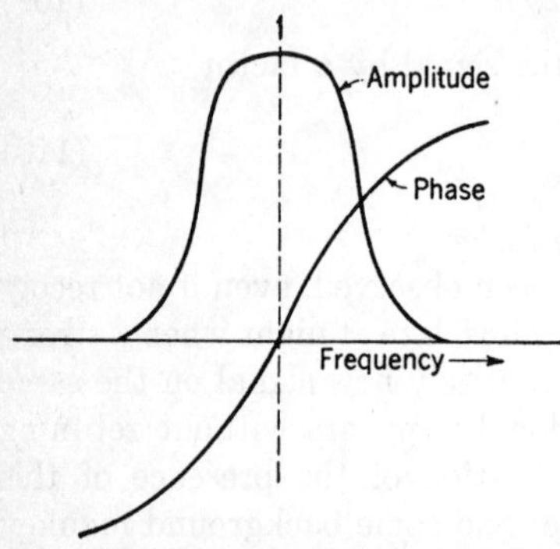

FIG. 32. A symmetrical transmission system.

As an example of a transmission system that leaves an originally symmetrical distribution of sidebands in a symmetrical condition, we have the tuned transmission system in Fig. 32, in which the carrier is tuned to that frequency of the pass band about which the transmission system is symmetrical.

If Fig. 32 represents the transmission characteristic of a receiver and the receiver is tuned so that the carrier is not located at the center of symmetry, then the output will no longer have a symmetrical distribution of sidebands. According to Sec. 5.6*b* and *c* this will introduce a quadrature component in the signal. We shall now show that such a quadrature component gives rise to nonlinear distortion in the envelope.

According to Eqs. (54), (59), and (74) a carrier plus a pair of unsymmetrical sidebands can be expressed as

$$[A + 2A_s \cos (2\pi\mu t + \phi_s)] \cos 2\pi Ft - 2A_a \sin (2\pi\mu t + \phi_a) \sin 2\pi Ft$$
$$= \sqrt{[A + 2A_s \cos (2\pi\mu t + \phi_s)]^2 + [2A_a \sin (2\pi\mu t + \phi_a)]^2} \cos (2\pi Ft + \psi) \quad (111)$$

where

$$\psi = \tan^{-1} \left[\frac{2A_a \sin (2\pi\mu t + \phi_a)}{A + 2A_s \cos (2\pi\mu t + \phi_s)} \right] \quad (112)$$

In this equation

$$A \cos 2\pi Ft$$

is the carrier, and A_s, A_a, ϕ_s, and ϕ_a are the magnitudes and phases of

[1] A transmission system will be defined as symmetrical if its output has a symmetrical distribution of sidebands when the input distribution is symmetrical.

the pairs of symmetrical and antisymmetrical sidebands into which the original pair of unsymmetrical sidebands can be resolved by the method of Sec. 5.6*c*.

Now the amplitude factor

$$\sqrt{[A + 2A_s \cos (2\pi\mu t + \phi_s)]^2 + [2A_a \sin (2\pi\mu t + \phi_a)]^2} \quad (113)$$

although complicated, is clearly periodic in time with a period

$$T = \frac{1}{\mu}$$

since increasing t by any integral multiple of $1/\mu$ leaves the above amplitude factor unchanged. The amplitude factor can therefore be expanded in a Fourier series in the fundamental and harmonics of the frequency μ. Furthermore, harmonics will always be present unless $A_a = 0$. Since A_a will be zero only if the sideband distribution is symmetrical, we conclude that an unsymmetrical transmission system introduces harmonic distortion.

The distortion caused by tuning the carrier away from the center of symmetry of the pass band may properly be called mistuning distortion. If there is more than one modulation frequency present in the signal, there will, of course, be sum and difference tones as well as harmonics in the distortion. A numerical example of the amount of distortion introduced by mistuning in a practical case is given in the exercises below.

Exercises

1. A carrier with 1,000-cycle modulation is sent through a radio receiver with a transmission characteristic as shown in Fig. *B*. If the receiver is mistuned 3 kc, find the per cent second-harmonic distortion and third-harmonic distortion for a 30 per cent modulated signal. Also do the same for a 100 per cent modulated signal. Assume that the phase-shift curve is linear.

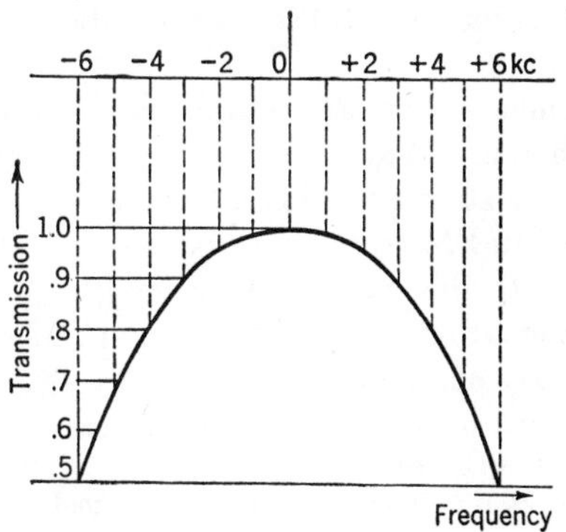

FIG. *B*.

2. Work the same problem with the modulation frequency changed to 2,000 cycles.

b. Distortion in Frequency Modulation. A symmetrical transmission characteristic is not a sufficiently severe requirement for distortion-free transmission in frequency modulation. For distortion-free FM transmission, all the FM sidebands must retain their relative values, and furthermore their relative phase relations must be maintained.[1] Consequently, for no distortion in FM, uniform (*i.e.*, constant) amplitude transmission is required throughout the frequency band in which the FM signal has sidebands of appreciable value, and furthermore the phase shift must be linear. These requirements are very severe, and we shall now investigate what happens when they are not met.

For simplicity, let us consider a hypothetical transmission system in which transient effects are unimportant so that the steady-state curves of Fig. 33*a* can be used for the instantaneous frequency of the signal. Then a modulation signal as shown in Fig. 33*b*, which causes a corresponding deviation of the carrier frequency, will have its instantaneous values of frequency deviation changed to those shown in Fig. 33*c* because of nonlinearity in the phase shift of the transmission system. This would then be the wave shape of the output of the frequency detector, except that the amplitude characteristic in Fig. 33*a* causes a certain amount of flattening of the wave tops and bottoms; this effect is shown in Fig. 33*d*. The ultimate over-all resultant output of the frequency detector is shown in Fig. 33*e*. If the FM receiver has a good limiter, the latter flattens the frequency characteristics (the absence of any transient effects still being assumed) so that all the distortion is then due to curvature of the phase characteristic.

On the basis of the foregoing quasi-steady-state theory, we can make the following tentative observations about distortion in FM systems:

1. The requirements for distortionless transmission in FM systems are more severe than in AM systems. This holds regardless of whether or not a quasi-steady-state situation is assumed.

2. Mistuning of an FM receiver introduces distortion of an amount that rises rapidly with the extent of mistuning.

3. A good limiter will decrease distortion in FM systems because it flattens the frequency characteristic.

[1] (Except for a possible phase shift of each sideband which is proportional to the frequency difference between the sideband and the carrier, the effect of which would be merely to cause a time delay of the whole signal.)

4. In FM receivers with a good limiter, most of the modulation distortion is due to curvature of the phase-shift characteristic.

5. The amount of modulation distortion rises rapidly with the degree of modulation, *i.e.*, with the extent of the frequency deviation.

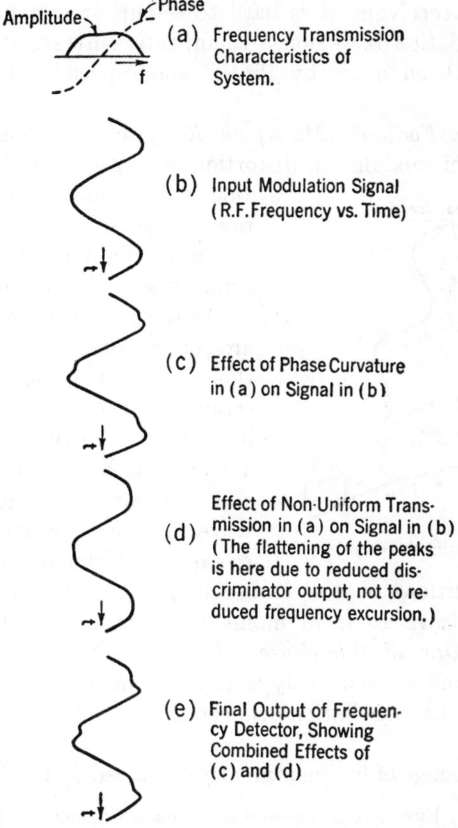

FIG. 33. Effect of amplitude and phase characteristics in producing FM distortion.

6. In a general way, FM distortion due to nonlinearity in the phase-shift characteristic will increase with the number of tuned circuits in the transmission system. The reason for this is that each tuned circuit adds 180 deg to the total phase-shift difference between low and high frequencies, so that nonlinearity will tend to cause larger numerical values of frequency distortion when more tuned circuits are involved.

7. If the amplitude and phase-shift characteristics of the transmission system are symmetrical about the carrier frequency, there will be only odd harmonics in the distortion, since the output (see Figs. 33*c* and *e*) will be mirror-symmetrical.

Since it is usually not practical to measure phase-shift characteristics of FM receivers, it is hard to set up any useful formulas for over-all modulation distortion. Quantitative investigations of FM distortion have been made by Roder[1] and especially Jaffe[2] for single stages.

c. Selective Fading[3] *(Multipath Reception).* Probably the most serious type of modulation distortion occurring in radio communication is that due to multipath reception. The typical case is that which occurs at night at the fringes of the primary service area of a transmitter where the ground wave and sky wave are of about equal intensity. Although the two signals reach the receiver with approximately equal intensities, the sky wave has come by a longer path, as shown in Fig. 34, and therefore lags behind the ground wave in phase. Furthermore, owing to variations from moment to moment in local conditions at the ionosphere, the length of path of the sky wave also varies from moment to moment. There is thus a rapid fluctuation of the phase difference between the ground and sky waves, and consequently a rapid change back and forth from reinforcement to cancellation between them. This condition is known as *fading*.

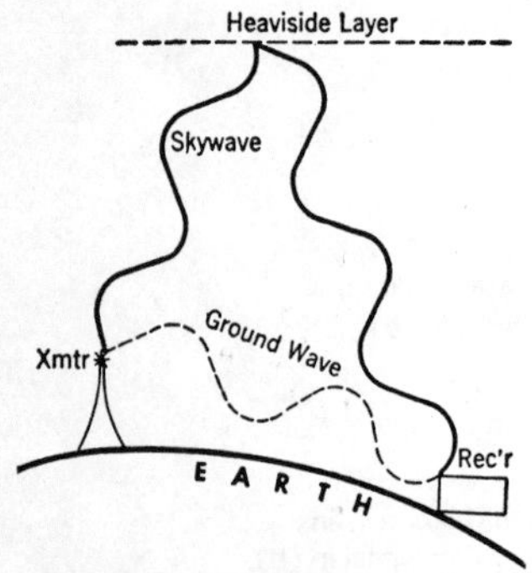

FIG. 34. Multipath reception.

The seriousness of fading is greatly enhanced by the fact that fading

[1] RODER, H., Effects of a Tuned Circuit on a Frequency Modulated Signal, *Proc. I.R.E.*, December, 1937, p. 1617.

[2] JAFFE, D. L., A Theoretical and Experimental Investigation of Tuned-circuit Distortion in Frequency-modulation Systems, *Proc. I.R.E.*, May, 1945, p. 318.

[3] BOWN, R., DE L. K. MARTIN, and R. K. POTTER, Some Studies in Radio Broadcast Transmission, *Proc. I.R.E.*, February, 1926, p. 57; POTTER, R. K., Transmission Characteristics of a Short Wave Telephone Circuit, *Proc. I.R.E.* April, 1930, p. 581; CROSBY, M. G., Frequency Modulation Propagation Characteristics, *Proc. I.R.E.*, June, 1936, p. 898; CROSBY, M. G., Observations of Frequency Modulation Propagation on 26 Megacycles, *Proc. I.R.E.*, July, 1941, p. 398.

conditions are different for the carrier and the various sidebands.[1] The phenomenon is therefore more completely described as *selective fading*. In mild cases of selective fading there is asymmetry in the sideband distributions, which, as we have seen, causes a certain amount of distortion. In severe cases in AM the carrier may fade so much more than some sidebands that the index of modulation rises above unity, which results in so much distortion as to make the signal completely unintelligible (see Fig. 35). In severe cases of selective fading in FM the resultant distortion is also bad, but the explanation cannot be given so simply. It is still a matter of controversy whether AM or FM is more sensitive to selective fading.

[1] The reason for fading conditions varying with frequency is easily explained. The analytical form of a traveling wave is

$$A \cos \left(\omega t - \frac{2\pi x}{\lambda} + \phi_0\right) \qquad (a)$$

This may also be written

$$A \cos \left(2\pi f t - \frac{2\pi x f}{V} + \phi_0\right) \qquad (b)$$

where t is time, x is the distance traveled, f is frequency, V is wave velocity, and ϕ_0 is an initial phase. The phase difference between the ground and sky waves is therefore

$$\text{Phase diff.} = \Delta\phi = \frac{2\pi\,\Delta x}{V} f \qquad (c)$$

where Δx is the difference in length of travel path. In a typical case, if

$$\begin{aligned} f &= 10^6 \text{ cycles/sec} \\ V &= 3 \times 10^5 \text{ km/sec} \\ \Delta x &= 100 \text{ km} \end{aligned}$$

then

$$\Delta\phi = \frac{2\pi 100}{3 \times 10^5} \times 10^6 = \frac{2{,}000\pi}{3} \text{ radians} \qquad (d)$$

which is an enormous phase difference. Let us now see how this phase difference varies with frequency. Taking differentials of Eq. (*c*), we have

$$d\,\Delta\phi = \frac{2\pi\,\Delta x}{V}\,df \qquad (e)$$

$$d\,\Delta\phi = \frac{2\pi 100}{3 \times 10^5}\,df \qquad (f)$$

in the above case. If $df = 1{,}500$ cycles, then $d\,\Delta\phi = \pi$, so that a frequency difference of 1,500 cycles is all that is required for a complete reversal from wave addition to wave cancellation. In this case, the fading conditions are therefore highly selective with respect to frequency. It may also be noted that the value of $d\,\Delta\phi$ depends only on the frequency difference df, not on the absolute carrier frequency f.

It is rather curious that the interference-reduction properties of FM lose part of their effectiveness in combating selective fading, but an elementary analysis will show why. The interference-reducing properties of FM depend for the most part on two facts, as shown in Sec. 5.5.

1. The interference sidebands are ordinarily so related in amplitude, frequency, and phase with respect to the *desired* carrier that they are inefficient in producing frequency modulation as compared with the sidebands of the desired signal.

2. The frequency modulation produced by the most effective sidebands of the interference is of too high an audio frequency to pass through the audio system of the receiver.

Neither of these properties is as effective in combating distortion due to selective fading, since the interference carries the same intel-

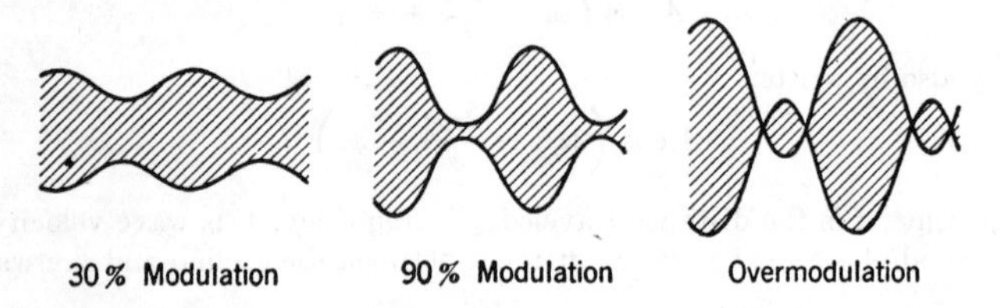

FIG. 35. Origin of envelope distortion in AM due to overmodulation.

ligence as the desired signal and can therefore act directly against its sidebands.

The foregoing statement has assumed that the path difference between the desired and interfering waves is sufficiently small so that the two may be considered coherent. If the path difference is so large that the waves cannot be considered coherent and, in particular, if the instantaneous modulation has had time to change, then the foregoing discussion no longer applies and the regular interference- reducing effects of FM will come into play. Let us now apply these considerations to see whether the use of frequency modulation of the picture carrier would tend to reduce the "ghosts" due to multipath reception in television, as compared with the present condition in which the picture carrier is amplitude-modulated. In this problem the effective instantaneous intelligence of the two signals is different, so that the interference cannot act directly against the sidebands of the desired signal.[1] The interference-reducing effect of FM therefore

[1] The fundamental difference between the television and the audio cases is that the modulation frequency of the direct signal remains the same in the time

should come into play, and the signal of smaller intensity will just act like interference. Consequently, the effect of "ghosts" will be greatly diminished if FM video is used.

5.12 Subcarriers and Pulse Modulation. In certain types of communication, a double tuning process is used. In this case, a wide frequency channel has a main carrier, which is simultaneously modulated by several secondary modulated carriers. The latter are called subcarriers. Tuning to the individual subcarriers can be accomplished either at the original radio frequency or else at some lower frequency where sharper tuning is available after frequency conversion of the

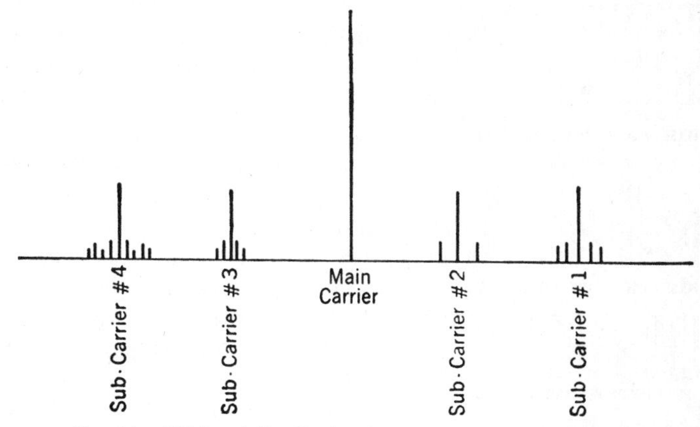

FIG. 36. Sideband distribution in a signal having subcarriers.

original signal. The spectrum of a signal with several subcarriers is shown in Fig. 36. This type of operation allows several signals to be transmitted simultaneously by a single transmitter and allows the high-frequency spectrum to be more completely utilized, despite relatively large frequency drifts of the main carrier. There are also other advantages for special purposes.

In the example shown in Fig. 36 both the main and subcarriers are amplitude-modulated. While it is usually necessary to amplitude-modulate the main carrier, in order to prevent the overlapping of subchannels, it might be perfectly practical to frequency- or phase-modulate the subcarriers.

---

interval between the arrival of the direct signal and the echo in the audio case, but not in the television case. Furthermore, in the audio case we are interested only in the *nonlinear* distortion, which is generally a second-order effect from an energy point of view.

A variation of the subcarrier technique that is of particular value at extremely high frequencies[1] is *pulse modulation.* Generally speaking, a pulse-modulated signal is one in which the energy is grouped into certain chosen intervals (pulses) and absent from other intervals, so as to increase the ratio of peak to average power. The modulation in such a signal is carried by change in location, amplitude, number, duration, or shape of the pulses in response to the intelligence being transmitted.

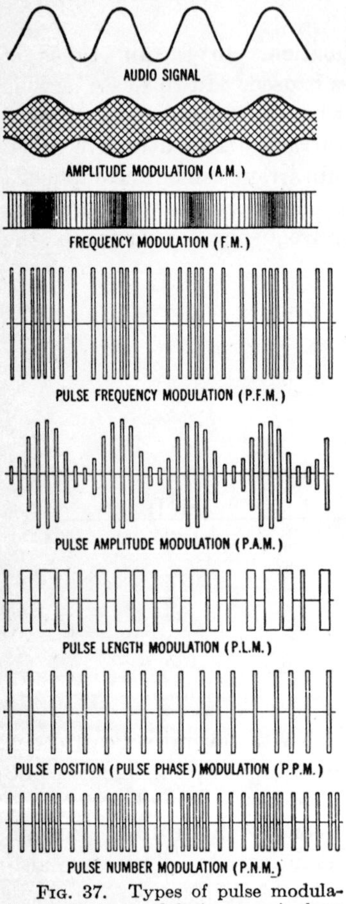

AUDIO SIGNAL

AMPLITUDE MODULATION (A.M.)

FREQUENCY MODULATION (F.M.)

PULSE FREQUENCY MODULATION (P.F.M.)

PULSE AMPLITUDE MODULATION (P.A.M.)

PULSE LENGTH MODULATION (P.L.M.)

PULSE POSITION (PULSE PHASE) MODULATION (P.P.M.)

PULSE NUMBER MODULATION (P.N.M.)

FIG. 37. Types of pulse modulation. (Pulse-modulation terminology has not yet been standardized.)

Several types of pulse-modulated signals are shown in Fig. 37. The outlined areas in these figures indicate the presence of a high-frequency carrier. It is shown in the next chapter that these types of modulation may have valuable noise-reducing properties. By way of illustration, block diagrams of a PFM transmitter and receiver are shown in Fig. 38. It has been suggested that pulse modulation of the synchronizing pulses should be used for the audio of television programs. The subject of pulse modulation is currently very active, both in theory and practice.

5.13 General. As stated at the outset of this chapter, carriers and modulation are necessary for the separation of signals that exist simultaneously. Frequency separation of modulated carriers by means of tuning is by far the most widely

[1] One reason why pulse modulation is particularly appropriate for extremely high frequencies is that the characteristically high peak voltages of pulse modulation give better transmitter oscillator efficiencies at these frequencies. Furthermore, oscillators are subject to large frequency drift at these frequencies, which would disturb ordinary frequency modulation, and also the oscillators do not respond smoothly to amplitude modulation.

used method of separation, although the discussion in the preceding section shows that other types of separation are possible. The discussion could have been continued to show that separation can be achieved by means of individual pulse lengths or pulse locations. In general, it may be said that the number of possible types of modulation and of carrier separation are almost limitless, although few are of practical importance.

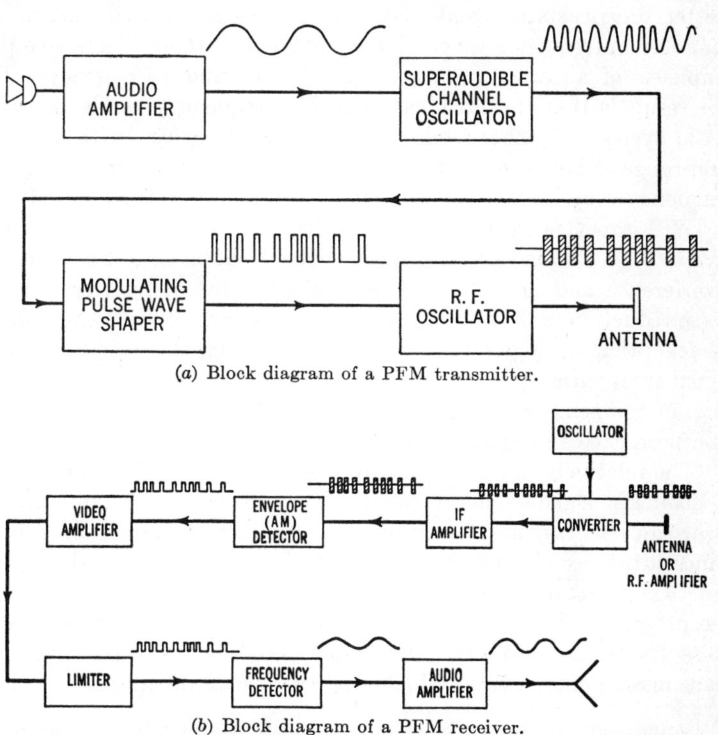

(*a*) Block diagram of a PFM transmitter.

(*b*) Block diagram of a PFM receiver.

FIG. 38. A PFM transmission system (showing wave shapes at various points).

For many years, amplitude modulation was almost the only type of modulation used. When the sideband analysis of amplitude modulation was first made and it was shown that amplitude modulation requires a bandwidth of twice the audio frequency, narrow-band frequency modulation was proposed as a means of decreasing bandwidth requirements. However, when it was shown that even narrow-band frequency modulation requires more bandwidth than amplitude modulation, interest in frequency modulation lagged. Many years later, the subject of frequency modulation became of interest again when Prof. Armstrong[1] showed that wide-band frequency modulation is an effective means of noise reduction, a subject that we shall discuss in detail in the next chapter. Since then, frequency modulation has been a subject of lively interest.

The present American system of FM broadcasting is actually a hybrid of frequency modulation and phase modulation. The transmitter broadcasts a signal that is frequency modulated, but in the modulation-frequency range above 2,000 cycles there is selective pre-emphasis of an amount proportional to the audio frequency. The net result is that the broadcast signal is frequency-modulated below 1,000 cycles and phase-modulated above 2,000 cycles, with a transition range in between. At the receiver there is an inverse amount of frequency compensation, so that the over-all system is equalized.

With this type of frequency compensation the receiver is less sensitive to high modulation frequencies, which are the largest elements in interference and noise. A considerable amount of interference and noise reduction is thus obtained, as will be shown in the next chapter. The fact that the high modulation frequency components in the desired signal are invariably of low energy content makes it practical to use this type of compensation without exceeding the limit of frequency deviation permitted in the transmitter.

The relatively low levels of interference and noise in the reception of good FM signals make it practical to increase the dynamic range[2] in broadcast programs. Furthermore, the larger available frequency bandwidths per channel in the present FM broadcast band make it practical to retain even the highest audio modulation frequencies in the program. For these reasons, including the low interference and noise levels, the FM broadcast band has been singled out for the transmission of particularly high-quality musical programs.

[1] ARMSTRONG, E. H., Method of Reducing Disturbances in Radio Signaling by a System of Frequency Modulation, *Proc. I.R.E.*, May, 1936, p. 689.

[2] *Dynamic range* is the ratio of maximum to minimum per cent modulation in a signal. This is probably most informative when expressed in decibels. Reduction of the interference and noise levels increases the available dynamic range since it makes possible smaller useful minimum percentages of modulation. In the absence of interference and noise there is no theoretical limit to the minimum possible percentage of modulation in any type of modulation, so that the dynamic range is also unlimited.

CHAPTER VI

NOISE I: GENERAL AND PRACTICAL DISCUSSION AND THE SOLUTION OF NOISE PROBLEMS

6.0 Introduction. One of the fundamental topics in radio engineering is the subject of noise. The transmission of a signal is of no value if the signal is drowned out by noise, and, in the case of signals transmitted for entertainment purposes, the entertainment value declines sharply as the relative amount of noise rises. Noise thus sets a limit upon the useful operating range of radio equipment, whether this limit is a matter of service range in miles, dynamic range in decibels, or range of practically any kind.

Certain types of noise are of an eliminable character, such as noise due to faulty contacts, vibrations of equipment, or even the neighbor's electric razor. While the elimination of such noise is not necessarily an easy matter, it is possible, at least theoretically, to remove it altogether. The study of the nature and methods of elimination of noise of the foregoing types is outside the scope of this book. However, we shall learn how to deal with a different type of noise, which is more important and fundamental and which can never be wholly eliminated, even theoretically. This is the noise which is due to the atomic nature of matter and electricity and which may be described by the general term *fluctuation noise.* This includes thermal noise, shot noise, magnetic fluctuation noise, and other such phenomena. We shall learn how to calculate the amount of such noise and how to design equipment so that as little of it as possible appears to interfere with desired signals.

The part of this book devoted to the subject of noise is divided into four chapters. In the first chapter, topics of general interest in connection with noise are discussed, and methods for the solution of noise problems are given, by use of formulas derived in the following chapters. In this first chapter, practically all the information and formulas are given that are needed to handle most problems and questions that arise in connection with noise in circuit design. The first chapter is of a relatively elementary nature. The other three chapters on noise are devoted to the development of fundamental noise theory and the derivation of noise formulas. These chapters are of a more advanced and mathematical nature.

6.1 General Characteristics of Random Noise. The fundamental type of noise present in radio equipment due to the atomicity of matter and electricity is remarkable in that it is completely without regularity in its detailed properties. It is consequently called *random noise.* However, its average energy is usually definite and determinable, and so is the average frequency distribution of its energy, *i.e.*, its so-called *power spectrum.* On the other hand, the phases of the frequency components are distributed completely at random. These matters are discussed in detail in Sec. 7.14.

In this book we shall use the term *quadratic content* for the time integral of the square of the amplitude. The quadratic content of noise is thus proportional to the average noise power or noise energy. Probably the most important wave-shape property of random noise is that, *if two independent random-noise signals are superimposed, the quadratic content of the combined signal is equal to the sum of the quadratic contents of the individual signals.* In other words, noise powers are additive. This property is proved in Sec. 7.14g and is used in many problems later in the present chapter. It may also be shown (see Sec. 7.14c and e) that the amplitude of random noise has what, in probability theory, is called a *normal distribution.* By this is meant that the amplitude I at any particular time cannot be predicted exactly but that the likelihood, or *probability*, of its having a value between I and $I + dI$ is equal to

$$\frac{1}{\sigma_I \sqrt{2\pi}} \epsilon^{\frac{-I^2}{2\sigma_I^2}} dI \tag{1}$$

where

$$\sigma_I = \sqrt{\text{mean square value of } I} = \sqrt{\overline{I^2}} \tag{2}$$

Thus all values of I are possible, but the likelihood of any particular value is determined by Eq. (1).

The properties of random noise expressed as a function of frequency are analogous to its properties when expressed as a function of time. Thus while the average frequency distribution of the energy of noise is a smooth curve, if we consider the noise during any specific interval of time, such as a particular oscillogram of random noise, a diagram of the frequency distribution of its energy would show the same fine-grained fluctuation as the original amplitude vs. time curve which constituted the oscillogram.

A detailed discussion of the properties of random noise is given in Sec. 7.14.

6.2 Types of Noise. *a. Introduction.* Noise in radio equipment may arise through almost countless causes. In addition to thermal noise, shot noise, and magnetic fluctuation noise, to which reference has already been made, practically every type of radio equipment introduces its own characteristic types of noise. These noises are usually assigned descriptive names such as "scratch," "hiss," "howl," "flutter," "wow," "hum," and "motorboating" by the men who work with them. In addition, there are natural noises, such as atmospherics (sometimes called "static"), and also atomic and quasi-atomic noises not yet mentioned.

The analysis in Chap. VII shows that noise which arises as the resultant of a large number of individual, but not necessarily identical, overlapping disturbances which occur without any specifiable regularity will have the general character of random noise. On the other hand, noise that exhibits definite regularities has more of the character of signal interference. To illustrate the difference between the two, consider the difference in the way in which their wave shapes vary with the bandwidth in the transmission system. In the case of random noise, if the bandwidth is increased, the general character of the signal remains the same, showing only an increase in average height and a finer structure. The effect of increased bandwidth is thus something like an accordion compression of the noise wave. On the other hand, the effect of increased bandwidth on the wave form of signal interference is to bring out the detail of the wave form. The effect of increased bandwidth in this case is similar to bringing the wave shape of the signal interference into sharper focus.

In the case of random noise due to a large number of impulsive-type disturbances of irregular occurrence, such as the noise due to film scratches on the sound track of a sound-on-film recording, the diminutive contact breakdowns in a noisy resistor, or the fluctuations in electron emission in a vacuum tube, it is shown in the next chapter that the noise will have a uniform frequency distribution of its energy in the low-frequency range. Neglecting the frequency characteristics of the transmission system, this uniform frequency distribution will continue up to frequencies at which the elementary disturbances can no longer be considered to be of an impulsive type. This frequency limit will occur at high audio frequencies for film-scratch noise, but will not occur up to far beyond a thousand megacycles for thermal noise.

In the remainder of this section we shall discuss some of the properties of the more common types of noise that occur in radio systems.

b. Flicker Effect.[1] Superimposed upon the shot noise, there is, in vacuum tubes, another source of noise that at low audio and subaudible frequencies becomes large enough to exceed the shot effect by several orders of magnitude. This second source of noise was named the *flicker effect* by Schottky, who, following Johnson, considered it as due to a kind of flickering of the electron emission from the cathode. As a general theory of flicker effect, we give the following quotation from J. B. Johnson.

> The electron emission at any time depends upon the condition of the cathode surface, and the surface is probably in a continual process of change due to such causes as evaporation, diffusion, chemical action, structural rearrangements, and gas-ion bombardment. These changes would go on at different rates in different parts of the surface, and would cover areas very large compared with that involved in the emission of one electron. The changes involving the greater area or larger amplitude might be expected to require a longer time, while changes so small as to affect only a few electrons would lose their significance in the general statistical emission. The general effect of these changes would be a variation in the total space current superimposed upon the fluctuations of the Schottky effect, having little influence at the high frequencies and an increasing effect as the natural frequency of the measuring circuit becomes lower.

Unlike shot effect, flicker effect can be reduced continually by proper processing of the cathode, so that it is not considered an ultimate source of noise like shot effect or thermal noise. Because of flicker effect, tubes for very low frequency applications, such as use in an electrocardiograph, frequently have their cathodes specially processed to reduce flicker effect.

c. Contact and Breakdown Noise.[2] Another general category of random noise may be described as *contact* and *breakdown noise*. This is noise due to the breakdown of insulation or the loss of contact in minute paths in the components of equipment. This noise includes the excessive noise that occurs in certain types of commercial resistors, the noise that occurs in a condenser microphone having a high direct-current voltage between closely spaced plates, the so-called *wall-charge noise* in vacuum tubes, and other types of noise due to intermittent conduc-

[1] For further information, see Moullin, "Spontaneous Fluctuations of Voltage," Chap. VI, where references to the original literature may also be found.

[2] MOULLIN, "Spontaneous Fluctuations of Voltage," pp. 209–215.

tion. This noise can all be avoided, although the necessary steps to be taken are not always easy. Wall-charge noise in vacuum tubes is reduced by coating the walls with a semiconductor (Aquadag). Condenser-microphone noise is reduced by cleaning the space between the condenser plates. The reduction of resistor noise is a more involved and complicated matter, which we cannot enter into here. Generally speaking, the amount of noise of any of the contact and breakdown types rises rapidly with the current or voltage present.

d. Dirt Noise and Grain-size Noise. *Dirt noise* and *grain-size noise* are due to minute irregularities in the equipment's structure, either innate in the specific material used or developed in the material during handling. The background noise of a phonograph or a sound-on-film recording is of this type.

e. Incidental Noise of Atomic Origin in Vacuum Tubes.[1] In addition to the shot noise that occurs in vacuum tubes, there are also other smaller sources of tube noise of atomic origin. Generally speaking, they can be eliminated by changing the operating conditions of the tube. This noise includes noise due to secondary emission, to collision ionization, and even to fluctuations in the emission of positive ions.

f. Atmospherics, Interstellar Interference, etc.[2] An important type of noise, especially in warm weather and warm climates, is the noise of atmospheric origin picked up by a receiving antenna and colloquially called "static" in the United States. Much of this noise originates in thunderstorms, in discharges between clouds, and in similar ways. Atmospherics have somewhat of the general character of random noise but their intensity is spasmodic. Measurements showing the variation in intensity of atmospherics with frequency[3] and with the time of the day in the northeastern United States are given in Figs. 1 and 2, due to R. K. Potter. Above 50 mc, practically all atmospherics are local, for there is usually no reflection from the Heaviside layer.

[1] MOULLIN, "Spontaneous Fluctuations of Voltage," Chap. VI; THOMPSON and NORTH, *R.C.A. Rev.*, January, 1941, p. 252.

[2] POTTER, R. K., *Proc. I.R.E.*, September, 1932, p. 1512; JANSKY, K. G., *Proc. I.R.E.*, December, 1939, p. 763; CHAKRAVARTI, GHOSH, and GHOSH, *Proc. I.R.E.*, December, 1939, p. 780.

[3] The following quotation from Terman is of interest in this connection: "The field strength of static appears on the average to be approximately inversely proportional to frequency. This indicates that the electrical discharge that generates the radio wave representing the static interference is a pulse having relatively long duration, and there is experimental evidence to bear this out."

Another natural source of noise that originates outside the radio equipment is interstellar interference.[1] This is quasi-random noise whose direction of arrival is such that it appears to originate in the heavens in the general region of the Milky Way.

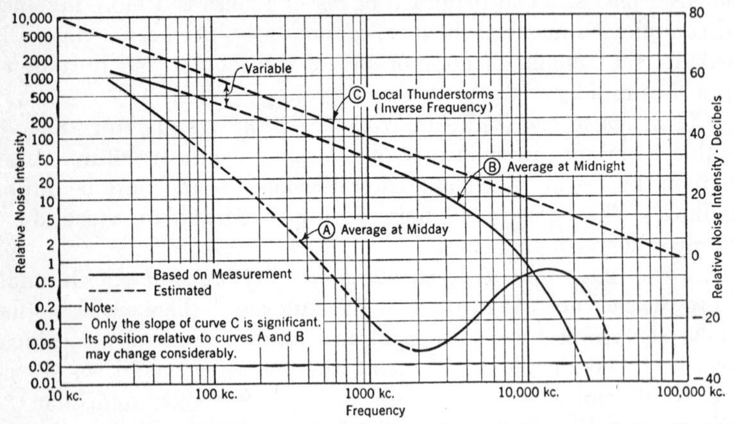

FIG. 1. Reliable variation of radio noise intensity with frequency for northeastern United States as measured on simple vertical antenna. (*From Potter, R. K., Proc. I.R.E., September*, 1932, *reprinted by permission.*)

g. Nonrandom Noise. So far we have considered only random noise. However, there is also noise in radio equipment that is not of a random nature and that has characteristic wave shapes of its own. This includes "hum," *i.e.*, the power-line frequency and its various harmonics, which get into the equipment in one way or another. Then there is "wow," due to some irregularity that is periodic at the frequency of rotation of some mechanical equipment, such as a phonograph turntable. "Microphonics" are noises due to mechanical vibrations of the radio equipment, chiefly electrodes of the vacuum tubes. "Howl" and "motorboating" are due to over-all feedback and oscillation of the system. Howl usually involves feedback caused by the final sound output, whereas motorboating is generally feedback through the power supply. All these types of noise are of an eliminable nature if proper precautions are taken. In addition to the foregoing, there is interference that comes into a receiver from the outside, by way of the antenna. This may be undesired broadcast signals, or it may be nonbroadcast interference such as automobile ignition noise.

One special characteristic of ignition noise and noise of similar origin is that it is of an impulsive type. If these impulses are of random

[1] JANSKY, K. G., *Proc. I.R.E.*, October, 1935, p. 1158.

occurrence and are so closely spaced that the individual wave shapes are not separated by the radio equipment, then the noise has the wave shape and characteristics of random noise. However, if the individual impulses are separated, as is usually the case, then

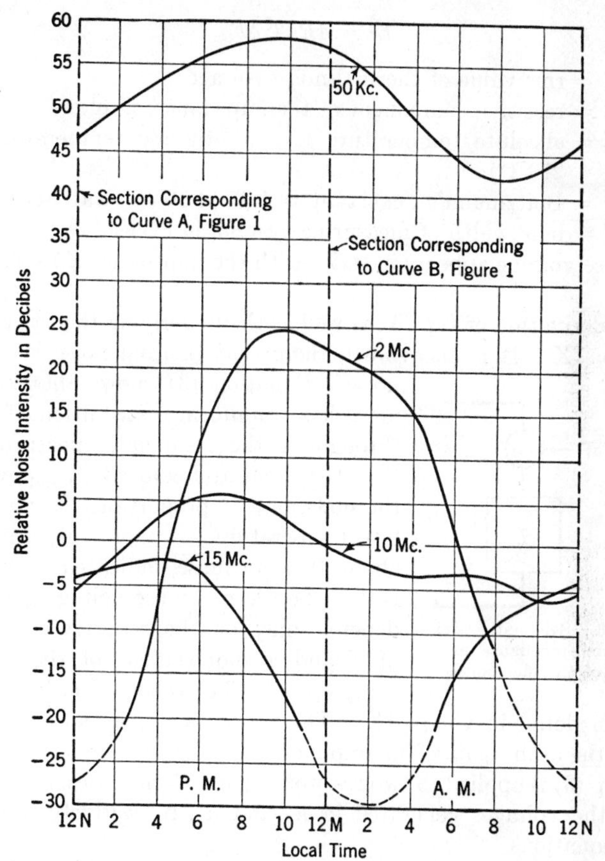

FIG. 2. Average diurnal variation of atmospheric noise, representative of several frequencies. (*From Potter, R. K., Proc. I.R.E., September, 1932, reprinted by permission.*)

the interference no longer has the wave shape of random noise. In particular, it then has an amplitude which is directly proportional to the bandwidth of the transmission system, instead of being proportional to the square root of the bandwidth, as is the case with random noise.

6.3 Thermal Noise. *a. The Fundamental Formula.* In 1928, J. B. Johnson showed that the minute currents caused by the thermal motion of the conduction electrons in a resistor can be detected as noise in a high-gain amplifier. He called this *thermal noise.* At the same time, H. Nyquist was able to show on the basis of the statistical theory of thermodynamics that the thermal-noise voltage generated in an impedance Z is given by the equation

$$\overline{E^2} = 4RkT\,\Delta F \qquad (3)^{1}$$

where E = rms value of thermal-noise voltage
R = resistive component of the impedance, in ohms
T = absolute temperature (*i.e.*, centigrade temperature plus 273.1°)
k = Boltzmann's constant = 1.37×10^{-23} watt-second/deg
ΔF = bandwidth of measuring system, in cycles/sec

This noise voltage appears in series with the impedance Z as shown in Fig. 3.

The derivation of Eq. (3) as well as the underlying theory, is given in Chap. IX. It is also shown there that thermal noise is random noise. Equation (3) shows that thermal noise has a uniform distribution of power throughout the frequency spectrum[2] and that the quadratic content (*i.e.*, power) of thermal noise is proportional to the absolute temperature. A more surprising fact about thermal noise, indicated by Eq. (3), is that the thermal-noise voltage generated depends only on the resistive component of Z and is independent of the reactive component. The reasons for this are discussed in detail in Chap. IX. The existence of thermal noise sets a limit to the usable gain of an amplifier.

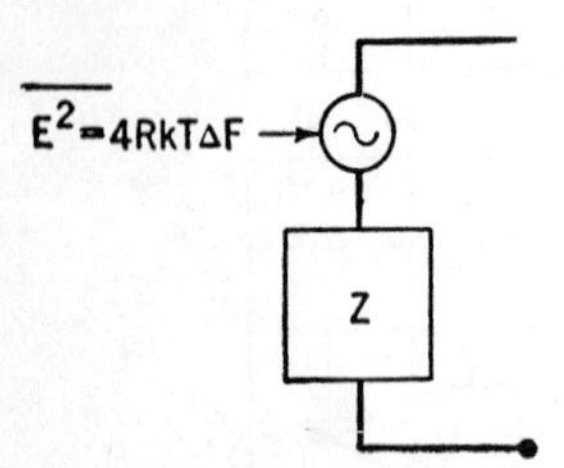

FIG. 3. Schematic diagram of an impedance as a generator of thermal noise.

If Eq. (3) is applied to two resistors R_1 and R_2, in series, as shown in Fig. 4, the voltages generated in R_1 and R_2, respectively, are given by the equations

$$\overline{E_1^2} = 4R_1kT\,\Delta F \qquad (3a)$$

and

$$\overline{E_2^2} = 4R_2kT\,\Delta F \qquad (3b)$$

Since E_1 and E_2 are both random noise, their combined effect, accord-

[1] We shall ordinarily use the averaging bar across E^2 since the value of E in short intervals may fluctuate. However, this is not mandatory as long as it is understood that E is an rms value.

[2] This holds up to frequencies of the order of a million megacycles.

ing to Sec. 6.1, is equivalent to that of a single voltage whose quadratic content is equal to the sum of the quadratic contents of E_1 and E_2. Thus

$$\overline{E^2} = \overline{E_1^2} + \overline{E_2^2} = 4(R_1 + R_2)kT\,\Delta F \tag{3c}$$

This is precisely the voltage we would have obtained by applying Eq. (3) to the series combination of R_1 and R_2. Thus Eq. (3) is consistent with the property of the addition of quadratic contents for random noise.

b. A First Example. Let us now calculate the thermal-noise voltage in a simple case. Consider the resistive input circuit of an audio amplifier shown in Fig. 5. Let us calculate the effective thermal-noise voltage appearing in the grid circuit. By the *effective* thermal-noise voltage we mean that portion of it which lies within the frequency band passed by the amplifier. Let us assume, for simplicity, that the amplifier has uniform transmission from zero to 5 kc and has no transmission outside this band. Let us also assume that $R = 10{,}000$ ohms and that its temperature is 20°C (that is, 293° abs). Let us further assume that the effect of the input capacitance of the tube is negligible in the pass band of the amplifier. Then by Eq. (3) the thermal-noise voltage on the grid of the first tube is

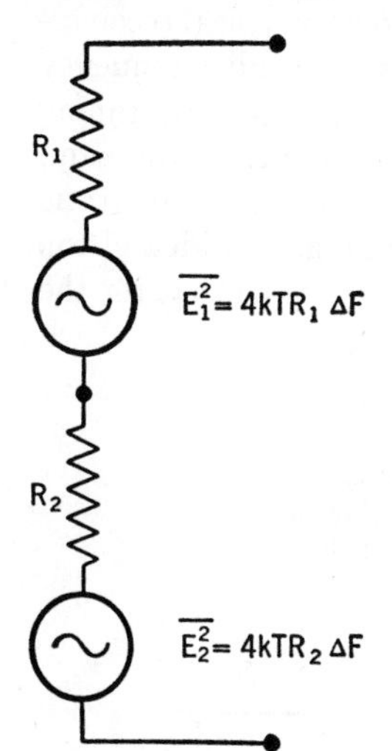

FIG. 4. Diagrammatic representation of two resistors in series, each generating thermal noise.

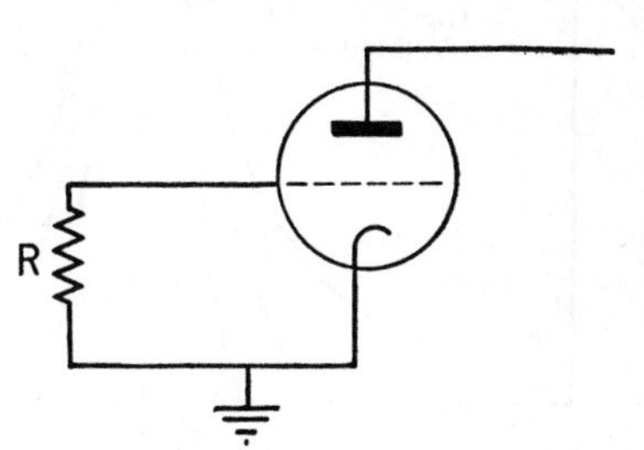

FIG. 5. Input circuit of an audio amplifier.

$$\begin{aligned} E_{\text{rms}} &= \sqrt{4RkT\,\Delta F} \\ &= \sqrt{4 \times 10{,}000 \times 1.37 \times 10^{-23} \times 293 \times 5{,}000} \\ &= 0.9 \times 10^{-6} \text{ volt} \end{aligned} \tag{4}$$

In order to obtain a high-quality signal from the amplifier, it is consequently necessary that the input signal shall exceed the noise voltage given by Eq. (4) by a large factor.

c. A Second Example. Let us next calculate the thermal-noise voltage appearing on the grid of the tube shown in Fig. 6. This can be obtained directly from Eq. (3), using the resistive component of the grid-to-ground impedance. Substituting this value into Eq. (3) of the present chapter, we have plotted the thermal-noise grid-voltage square in Fig. 7. In the same figure is also shown a typical receiver-gain vs. frequency (radio-frequency plus intermediate-frequency) tuning curve. By multiplying the thermal noise by the square of the gain, we obtain a curve showing how the thermal-noise sideband quadratic content varies with frequency at the detector. To get an idea of the order of magnitude of the thermal-noise voltage, we note that for the

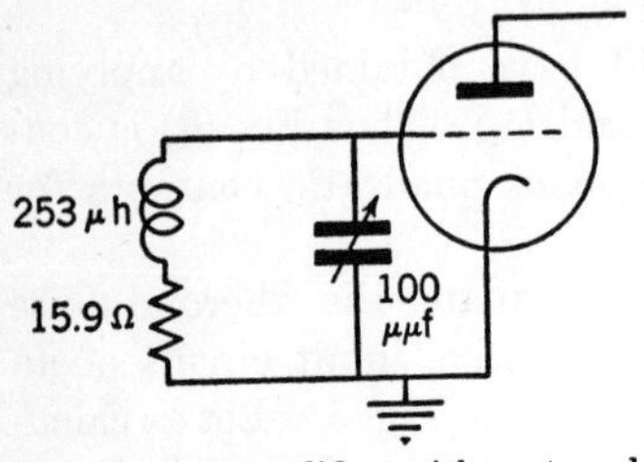

Fig. 6. An amplifier with a tuned grid circuit.

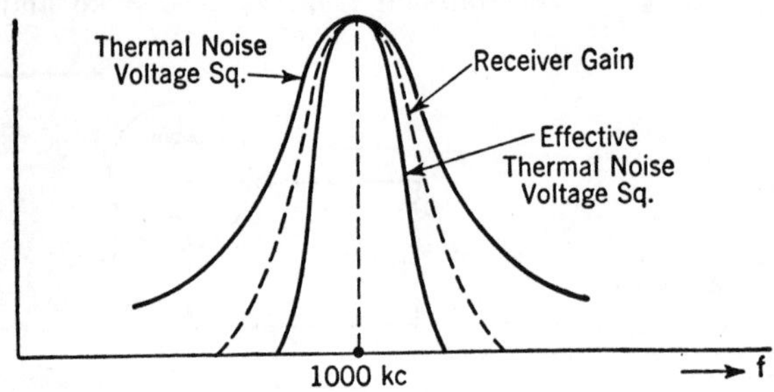

Fig. 7. Effect of amplifier selectivity on the frequency distribution of thermal noise in its output.

circuit of Fig. 6 the resistive component of the impedance at resonance is

$$\frac{(2\pi \times 10^6 \times 253 \times 10^{-6})^2}{15.9} = 159{,}000 \text{ ohms} \tag{5}$$

Consequently, at the top of the resonance curve (*i.e.*, at 1,000 kc) the thermal-noise voltage is

$$\sqrt{4 \times 159{,}000 \times 1.37 \times 10^{-23} \times 293 \times 1{,}000} = 1.6 \times 10^{-6} \text{ volt/ kc}^{1/2} \tag{6}$$

It should be remembered that, since thermal noise is random noise, its amplitude is proportional to the square root of the bandwidth and is not directly proportional to the bandwidth itself.

The reader may wonder whether the same value of thermal-noise voltage on the grid would be obtained by considering the 15.9-ohm resistor in Fig. 6 as the source of the thermal-noise voltage. The answer must, of course, be yes, since otherwise Eq. (3) would give contradictory answers. In Chap. IX it is proved that such answers will always be the same when Eq. (3) is used, but as a matter of interest we shall now give a numerical verification for the particular case of Fig. 6. The thermal-noise voltage squared generated in the 15.9-ohm resistor will be

$$\begin{aligned} E &= \sqrt{4 \times 15.9 \times 1.37 \times 10^{-23} \times 293 \times 1{,}000} \\ &= 0.016 \times 10^{-6} \text{ volt/kc}^{1/2} \end{aligned} \tag{7}$$

The thermal-noise current flowing in the circuit at resonance will be

$$I = \frac{E}{R} = \frac{0.016 \times 10^{-6}}{15.9} = 1.006 \times 10^{-9} \text{ ampere/kc}^{1/2} \tag{8}$$

The thermal-noise voltage on the grid will be the voltage drop that this current creates across the condenser. This will be

$$\frac{I}{\omega C} = \frac{1.006 \times 10^{-9}}{2\pi \times 10^{6} \times 100 \times 10^{-12}} = 1.6 \times 10^{-6} \text{ volt/kc}^{1/2} \tag{9}$$

in agreement with Eq. (6). It is therefore apparently immaterial whether we consider the thermal-noise voltage as generated in the resistive component of the impedance or whether we go back to the ultimate resistive elements themselves as the source. Equation (3) will give the same answer in either case. The electron theory, discussed in Chap. IX, indicates, however, that the resistive elements are the real source of thermal noise.

d. Amplitude and Frequency Modulation of a Carrier Due to Random Noise. We next shall determine what amount of amplitude and frequency modulation of the carrier of the incoming signal is caused by random noise. For simplicity, we shall assume that the carrier of the incoming signal is large in comparison with the random noise. Then according to Sec. 5.6*c* the random noise can be resolved into symmetrical and antisymmetrical sidebands of the carrier. If the carrier is large, the symmetrical sidebands will then cause amplitude modulation, while the antisymmetrical sidebands will cause frequency modulation.

According to Eqs. (29), (66), and (70) of Chap. V, if A is the carrier amplitude, B_{a1} is the noise-sideband amplitude a cycles above the carrier, and B_{a2} is the noise-sideband amplitude a cycles below the carrier, then the degree of amplitude modulation m_A due to random noise is

$$m_A = \frac{1}{A}\sqrt{\sum_a [B_{a1}^2 + B_{a2}^2 + 2B_{a1}B_{a2}\cos(\theta_{a2} - \theta_{a1})]}$$

$$= \frac{1}{A}\sqrt{\sum_a (B_{a1}^2 + B_{a2}^2)}$$

$$= \sqrt{\frac{\text{quadratic content of noise}}{\text{quadratic content of carrier}}} \qquad (10)$$

The cross-product terms reduce to

$$\sum_a 2B_{a1}B_{a2}\cos(\theta_{a2} - \theta_{a1}) = 0 \qquad (11)$$

since the average value of $\cos(\theta_{a2} - \theta_{a1})$ is zero in any range of values of a, because of the randomness of phase of noise sidebands. Correspondingly, Eqs. (31), (58), and (72) of Chap. V show that the effective degree of frequency modulation of the carrier by the random noise is

$$m_F = \frac{1}{AD}\sqrt{\sum_a a^2[B_{a1}^2 + B_{a2}^2 - 2B_{a1}B_{a2}\cos(\theta_{a2} - \theta_{a1})]}$$

$$= \frac{1}{AD}\sqrt{\sum_a a^2(B_{a1}^2 + B_{a2}^2)} \qquad (12)$$

In the special case of Fig. 7, if the carrier is at the tuning frequency of 1,000 kc and if N^2 is the ordinate variable of the effective thermal-noise voltage square vs. kilocycle curve, then

$$m_A^2A^2 = \int 2N^2\,df \qquad (13)$$

and

$$m_F^2A^2 = \frac{1}{D^2}\int 2a^2N^2\,df \qquad (14)$$

where the factor 2 is required because N is an rms value. Equations (13) and (14) show the degree of noise modulation of the carrier as it enters the detector.[1]

e. The Superposition of Thermal-no se Voltages—Alternative Methods of Calculation. Let us next consider a case in which we have two

[1] In this connection the reader will also find Sec. 6.8*c* of interest.

thermal-noise voltages in series, such as are shown in Fig. 8, and let us suppose that we wish to calculate the thermal-noise voltage across C_1, this voltage being designated e_g. We can determine this voltage in three different ways, all of which are instructive and all of which must lead to the same answer. Accordingly we shall carry out this determination by three different methods, the last of which will be a superposition method.

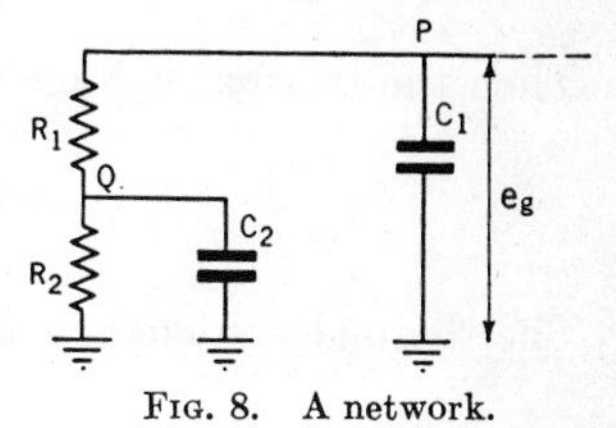

FIG. 8. A network.

1. Let us first determine the total impedance from the point P to ground. If the resistive component of this impedance is multiplied by $4kT\ \Delta F$, the resultant product must give the square of the desired thermal-noise voltage. Let the impedance from P to ground be called Z_p, and let the impedance of R_2 and C_2 in parallel be called Z_2. Then

$$Z_2 = \frac{R_2/j\omega C_2}{R_2 + (1/j\omega C_2)} = \frac{R_2}{1 + R_2^2\omega^2 C_2^2} - j\frac{R_2^2\omega C_2}{1 + R_2^2\omega^2 C_2^2} \tag{15}$$

and

$$Z_p = \frac{\left[\left(R_1 + \dfrac{R_2}{1 + R_2^2\omega^2 C_2^2}\right) - j\dfrac{R_2^2\omega C_2}{1 + R_2^2\omega^2 C_2^2}\right]\dfrac{1}{j\omega C_1}}{\left[\left(R_1 + \dfrac{R_2}{1 + R_2^2\omega^2 C_2^2}\right) - j\dfrac{R_2^2\omega C_2}{1 + R_2^2\omega^2 C_2^2}\right] + \dfrac{1}{j\omega C_1}}$$

$$= \frac{R_1 + \dfrac{R_2}{1 + R_2^2\omega^2 C_2^2}}{\left(1 + \dfrac{R_2^2\omega^2 C_1 C_2}{1 + R_2^2\omega^2 C_2^2}\right)^2 + \omega^2 C_1^2\left(R_1 + \dfrac{R_2}{1 + R_2^2\omega^2 C_2^2}\right)^2}$$

$$-j\left[\frac{\omega C_1\left(R_1 + \dfrac{R_2}{1 + R_2^2\omega^2 C_2^2}\right)^2 + \dfrac{R_2^2\omega C_2}{1 + R_2^2\omega^2 C_2^2}\left(1 + \dfrac{R_2^2\omega^2 C_1 C_2}{1 + R_2^2\omega^2 C_2^2}\right)}{\left(1 + \dfrac{R_2^2\omega^2 C_1 C_2}{1 + R_2^2\omega^2 C_2^2}\right)^2 + \omega^2 C_1^2\left(R_1 + \dfrac{R_2}{1 + R_2^2\omega^2 C_2^2}\right)^2}\right] \tag{16}$$

The square of the thermal-noise voltage across C_1 is then $4kT\ \Delta F$ times the resistive component of Z_p. Thus

$$\overline{e_g^2} = \frac{4kT\ \Delta F\left(R_1 + \dfrac{R_2}{1 + R_2^2\omega^2 C_2^2}\right)}{\left(1 + \dfrac{R_2^2\omega^2 C_1 C_2}{1 + R_2^2\omega^2 C_2^2}\right)^2 + \omega^2 C_1^2\left(R_1 + \dfrac{R_2}{1 + R_2^2\omega^2 C_2^2}\right)^2} \tag{17}$$

2. We next determine the thermal voltage across C_1 by finding the thermal voltage developed in the impedance Z_1, shown in Fig. 9,

and then seeing what voltage this develops across C_1 when it is put in series with Z_1. With the aid of Eq. (15) we have

$$Z_1 = R_1 + Z_2 = \left(R_1 + \frac{R_2}{1 + R_2^2\omega^2C_2^2}\right) - j\frac{R_2^2\omega C_2}{1 + R_2^2\omega^2C_2^2} \tag{18}$$

Then the thermal voltage e_1 developed in Z_1 is given by the equation

$$\overline{e_1^2} = 4kT\,\Delta F\left(R_1 + \frac{R_2}{1 + R_2^2\omega^2C_2^2}\right) \tag{19}$$

The thermal voltage across C_1 in Fig. 8 is therefore

$$\overline{e_g^2} = \overline{e_1^2}\left|\frac{\dfrac{1}{j\omega C_1}}{Z_1 + \dfrac{1}{j\omega C_1}}\right|^2 = \frac{4kT\,\Delta F\left(R_1 + \dfrac{R_2}{1 + R_2^2\omega^2C_2^2}\right)}{\left(1 + \dfrac{R_2^2\omega^2C_1C_2}{1 + R_2^2\omega^2C_2^2}\right)^2 + \omega^2C_1^2\left(R_1 + \dfrac{R_2}{1 + R_2^2\omega^2C_2^2}\right)^2} \tag{20}$$

This value of e_g^2 agrees with that already found in Eq. (17).

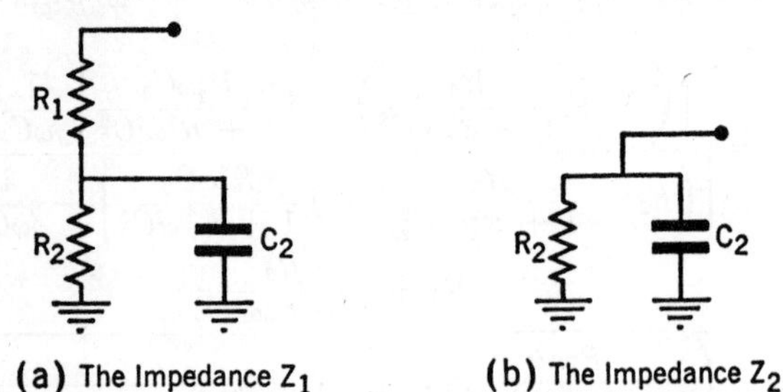

FIG. 9. Terminology for parts of the network in Fig. 8.

3. Finally, we shall determine the thermal-noise voltage across C_1 by the superposition of the thermal voltages that the equivalent generators in R_1 and Z_2 separately develop across C_1.

The equivalent generator in R_1 develops a thermal-noise voltage squared $4R_1kT\,\Delta F$, of which

$$4R_1kT\,\Delta F\left|\frac{1/j\omega C_1}{Z_1 + (1/j\omega C_1)}\right|^2 = \overline{e_{R1}^2} \tag{21}$$

appears across C_1. In Eq. (21), e_{R1} is the thermal-noise voltage generated in R_1 that appears across C_1.

The equivalent generator in Z_2 develops a thermal-noise voltage squared

$$4\frac{R_2}{1 + R_2^2\omega^2C_2^2}kT\,\Delta F \tag{22}$$

of which

$$4 \frac{R_2}{1 + R_2^2\omega^2C_2^2} kT\,\Delta F \left| \frac{1/j\omega C_1}{Z_1 + (1/j\omega C_1)} \right|^2 = \overline{e_{Z2}^2} \tag{23}$$

appears across C_1. In Eq. (23), e_{Z2} is the thermal-noise voltage generated in Z_2 that appears across C_1.

The total thermal-noise voltage appearing across C_1 is obtained by superposition of the thermal voltages across C_1 due to R_1 and Z_2

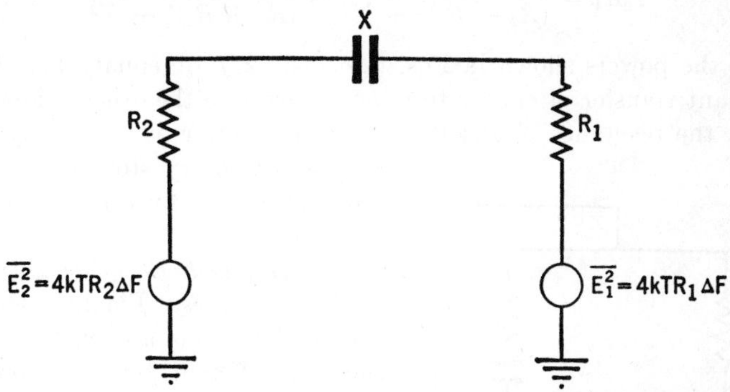

FIG. 10. Diagram showing a circuit in which two resistors are generating thermal-noise voltage.

separately. Since these are both random noise, the superimposed quadratic content is obtained, according to Sec. 6.1, by addition of the separate quadratic contents. Thus

$$\overline{e_g^2} = \overline{e_{R1}^2} + \overline{e_{Z2}^2} = \frac{4kT\,\Delta F\left(R_1 + \dfrac{R_2}{1 + R_2^2\omega^2C_2^2}\right)}{\left(1 + \dfrac{R_2^2\omega^2C_1C_2}{1 + R_2^2\omega^2C_2^2}\right)^2 + \omega^2C_1^2\left(R_1 + \dfrac{R_2}{1 + R_2^2\omega^2C_2^2}\right)^2} \tag{24}$$

This value of $\overline{e_g^2}$ agrees with that already obtained in Eqs. (20) and (17), as was to be expected.

f. No Power Transfer from Resistor to Resistor at the Same Temperature. We shall now show that, if two resistors are at the same temperature, there is no resultant transfer of power from one to the other due to thermal-noise voltages. Consider the circuit in Fig. 10, showing resistors R_1 and R_2. For generality, a reactance X is also shown. Let I_1 be the current due to the thermal-noise voltage in R_1, and let I_2 be the current due to the thermal-noise voltage in R_2. Then

$$I_1 = \frac{E_1}{\sqrt{(R_1 + R_2)^2 + X^2}} \qquad \text{and} \qquad I_2 = \frac{E_2}{\sqrt{(R_1 + R_2)^2 + X^2}} \tag{25}$$

The power absorbed in R_2 due to the thermal-noise voltage in R_1 will then be

$$\overline{I_1^2}R_2 = \frac{\overline{E_1^2}R_2}{(R_1 + R_2)^2 + X^2} = \frac{4kT\,\Delta F R_1 R_2}{(R_1 + R_2)^2 + X^2} \tag{26}$$

At the same time, the power absorbed in R_1 due to the thermal-noise voltage in R_2 will be

$$\overline{I_2^2}R_1 = \frac{\overline{E_2^2}R_1}{(R_1 + R_2)^2 + X^2} = \frac{4kT\,\Delta F R_2 R_1}{(R_1 + R_2)^2 + X^2} \tag{27}$$

Since the powers shown in Eqs. (26) and (27) are equal, there is no resultant transfer of energy from one resistor to the other. Furthermore, the reactance X absorbs no average power but acts only as a place of temporary storage of energy of any frequency for certain portions of a cycle.

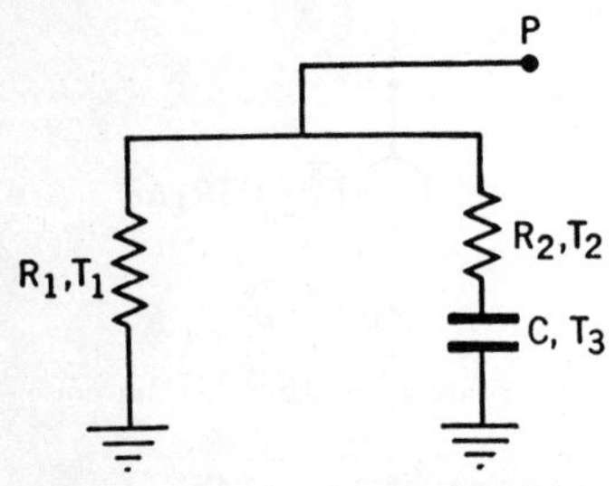

FIG. 11. A circuit in which there are elements at different temperatures.

g. Circuit with Elements at Different Temperatures. Finally, let us consider the case of a circuit with elements at different temperatures, as shown in Fig. 11. In this case, each resistive element just generates its expected thermal-noise voltage for its own temperature, and as in the constant-temperature case these voltages determine the current that flows. Thus, in the case of Fig. 11, if the thermal-noise voltage from P to ground is called E, while that portion of it due to R_1 is called E_1 and that portion of it due to R_2 is called E_2, then

$$\overline{E_1^2} = 4kT_1R_1\,\Delta F\,\frac{R_2^2 + (1/\omega^2C^2)}{(R_1 + R_2)^2 + (1/\omega^2C^2)} \tag{28}$$

$$\overline{E_2^2} = 4kT_2R_2\,\Delta F\,\frac{R_1^2}{(R_1 + R_2)^2 + (1/\omega^2C^2)} \tag{29}$$

and

$$\overline{E^2} = \overline{E_1^2} + \overline{E_2^2} = 4k\,\Delta F\,\frac{R_1T_1\left(R_2^2 + \dfrac{1}{\omega^2C^2}\right) + R_2T_2R_1^2}{(R_1 + R_2)^2 + \dfrac{1}{\omega^2C^2}} \tag{30}$$

As a check on Eq. (30), we note that if

$$T_1 = T_2 = T$$

and if the capacitor is short-circuited, *i.e.*, if

$$C = \infty$$

then Eq. (30) becomes

$$\overline{E^2} = 4k\,\Delta F\,\frac{TR_1R_2}{R_1 + R_2} \tag{31}$$

which is the thermal-noise voltage to be expected of the two resistors in parallel.

When T_1 and T_2 are different, there is a net power transfer between the resistors. For simplicity, let us take the case of Fig. 12. Here the power transferred from R_1 to R_2 is

$$\overline{I_1^2}R_2 = \frac{\overline{E_1^2}R_2}{(R_1 + R_2)^2} = \frac{4kT_1R_1R_2\,\Delta F}{(R_1 + R_2)^2} \tag{32}$$

At the same time, the power transferred from R_2 to R_1 is

$$\overline{I_2^2}R_1 = \frac{\overline{E_2^2}R_1}{(R_1 + R_2)^2} = \frac{4kT_2R_2R_1\,\Delta F}{(R_1 + R_2)^2} \tag{33}$$

If $T_2 > T_1$, there is a net power transfer from R_2 to R_1 of

$$(\overline{I_2^2}R_1 - \overline{I_1^2}R_2) = \frac{4kR_2R_1\,\Delta F}{(R_1 + R_2)^2}\,(T_2 - T_1) \tag{34}$$

Despite the apparent simplicity of Eq. (34), it is difficult to interpret in a practical way whether or not the energy flow between R_2 and R_1 due to thermal-noise voltage is a large fraction of the total energy transfer due to thermal conductivity. The reason for the difficulty is that the inherent inductance and capacity of any physical resistors affect the value of ΔF to be used. In a general way, however, it may be said that, except in highly artificial cases, the energy transfer due to thermal-noise voltages represents only an inconsequential fraction of the total energy transfer due to thermal conductivity.

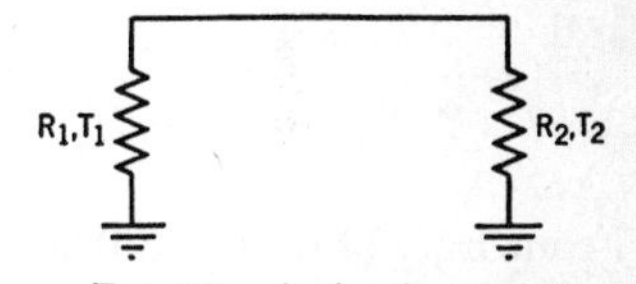

FIG. 12. A circuit consisting of two resistors at different temperatures.

6.4 The Equivalence of Current- and Voltage-generator Representations. In Fig. 3 and Eq. (3) it is shown how the generation of thermal noise in an impedance may be represented and calculated as a voltage generator in series with the impedance. We shall now show that there is an equivalent current-generator representation which will in all cases give exactly the same results as the voltage-generator representation.

In Fig. 13*a* is shown a voltage-generator representation of thermal noise in accordance with Nyquist's formula discussed in Sec. 6.3*a*. Here the thermal noise originating in a general impedance Z_1 creates a

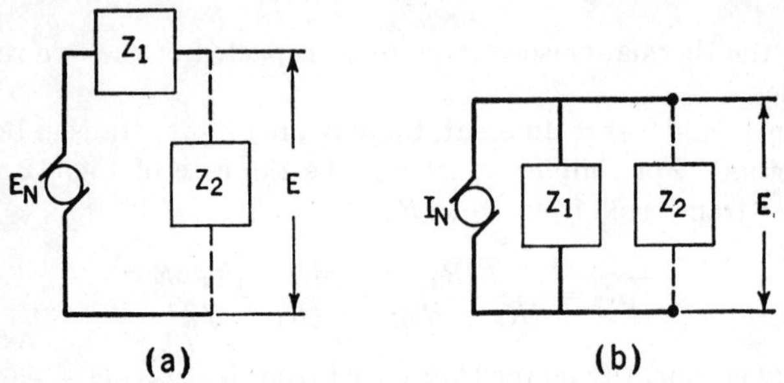

FIG. 13. Equivalent voltage- and current-generator representations.

thermal-noise voltage E across a general external impedance Z_2. Let us see if we can find a value of I_N in the current-generator representation in Fig. 13*b* that will give exactly the same voltage E across Z_2 and will thus be exactly equivalent to Fig. 13*a*.

In the first place, from elementary circuit theory, we require for complete equivalence

$$E = \frac{Z_2}{Z_1 + Z_2} E_N \tag{35}$$

and

$$E = \frac{Z_1 Z_2}{Z_1 + Z_2} I_N \tag{36}$$

From Eqs. (35) and (36) it follows that

$$I_N = \frac{E_N}{Z_1} \qquad \text{so that} \qquad \overline{I_N^2} = \frac{\overline{E_N^2}}{|Z_1|^2} \tag{37}$$

This is the fundamental equation relating equivalent current- and voltage-generator representations.

By Eq. (3),

$$\overline{E_N^2} = 4kTR_1\,\Delta F \tag{38}$$

where R_1 is the resistive component of Z_1. Consequently, from Eqs. (37) and (38)

$$\overline{I_N^2} = \frac{\overline{E_N^2}}{|Z_1|^2} = \frac{4kTR_1\,\Delta F}{|Z_1|^2} = 4kTG_1\,\Delta F \tag{39}$$

where

$$G_1 = \frac{R_1}{|Z_1|^2} \tag{40}$$[1]

is the conductance of Z_1.

Since I_N given by Eq. (39) will always give the same external effects in the current-generator representation of Fig. 13*b*, as E_N given by Eq. (3) will give in the voltage-generator representation of Fig. 13*a*, Eq. (39) may be considered as completely equivalent to Eq. (3). When we discuss shot effect in the next section, we shall start with a current generator and use Eq. (37) to find the equivalent voltage generator.

6.5 Shot Effect. *a. Introduction.* In 1918, W. Schottky pointed out that, since the electric current emitted from a hot cathode consists of the combined effect of a large number of independently emitted electrons, the emission current is never steady but exhibits minute fluctuations due to the finite charge of an electron in combination with its random emission. Part of these emission-current fluctuations also become plate-current fluctuations. In a high-gain amplifier, such plate-current fluctuations of the early tubes produce noise in the final output. Tube-current fluctuations thus will limit the useful gain of an amplifier, just as thermal noise does. In fact, tube-current fluctuations and thermal noise are the two principal causes of the unavoidable noise in a high-gain amplifier.

The fluctuation noise created by the electrons in the tube current reminded Schottky of the noise caused by a hail of shot striking a target. He therefore named the phenomenon *shot effect*, a name which has been retained in the literature for tube noise due to the "grain size" (*i.e.*, finite electronic charge) of the emission current.

The theory of shot effect is discussed at length in Chap. VIII. In this chapter we shall describe the results obtained in Chap. VIII and use them in the solution of practical problems.

b. Shot Effect in the Temperature-limited Case. The theory of shot effect is simplest when the tube in question is operated in the temperature-limited state, *i.e.*, when the plate voltage is so high that all the emission current gets to the plate. In this case, it is shown in Chap. VIII that, if I_N is the rms value of the fluctuating component of the plate current, then

$$\overline{I_N^2} = 2\kappa I \, \Delta F \tag{41}$$

[1] $$\frac{1}{Z_1} = \frac{1}{R_1 + jX_1} = \frac{R_1 - jX_1}{R_1^2 + X_1^2} = \frac{R_1}{|Z_1|^2} - j\frac{X_1}{|Z_1|^2} = G_1 + jS_1$$

Thus $G_1 = R_1/|Z_1|^2$ is the real component of $1/Z_1$.

where κ is the electronic charge ($= 1.60 \times 10^{-19}$ coulomb); I is the average value (*i.e.*, direct-current component) of plate current, in amperes; ΔF is the bandwidth, in cycles; and I_N is given in amperes.

Equation (41) holds for diodes or negative-grid triodes in temperature-limited operation or for any tubes for which the entire emission current goes to one collector electrode,[1] since fundamentally Eq. (41) gives the fluctuation component of the emission current. Equation (41) holds up to frequencies for which transit times are important. When transit times become important, the effective value of κ must be revised.

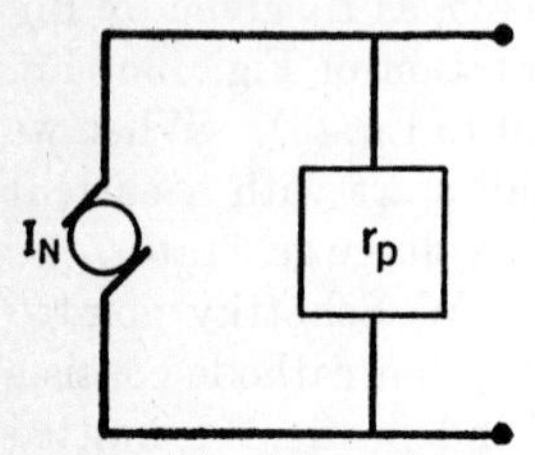

FIG. 14. Schematic diagram showing the shunting effect of plate impedance on the generation of noise current.

The temperature-limited case, although simple in theory, is not very important in practice because vacuum tubes cannot be used as amplifiers in temperature-limited operation.

c. The Current-generator Representation and the Shunting Effect of Plate Impedance. We shall next see what currents are produced external to the tube by shot effect and also examine the effect of the plate impedance. In Chap. VIII it is shown that, for calculating the results of shot effect, a tube may be considered a current generator, as shown in Fig. 14. The plate impedance r_p of the tube acts as a shunt on the current generator. In the temperature-limited case, I_N is given by Eq. (41). In the more important space-charge-controlled cases, the formulas for I_N are given in the following pages. These formulas give the external current provided that the electrodes are grounded for alternating current. When the electrodes are not grounded, the shunting effect of the internal impedance must be included in accordance with Fig. 14.

d. Operation in the Space-charge-controlled Region. Most tubes are used in the *space-charge-controlled* region of operation, in which the entire emission current does not go to the plate, but rather the amount of plate current is a function of plate voltage. In Chap. VIII a discussion is given of how the space-charge cloud of electrons which exists in this case operates to eliminate a large amount of the shot fluctua-

[1] A photoelectric tube is a good example of this type. In a phototube, the emission of photoelectrons exhibits the same type of statistical fluctuations as the emission of electrons from a hot cathode. If all the emitted photoelectrons go to the collector anode, which is usually the case, the fluctuations of the phototube current I will be given by Eq. (41).

tions from the plate current, so that the shot effect in *space-charge-controlled* operation is considerably less than the value given by Eq. (41). The shot effect is then given by the modified equation

$$\overline{I_N^2} = \Gamma^2 2\kappa I \,\Delta F \tag{42}$$

where Γ^2 is a positive constant less than unity, which may be called a space-charge noise-reduction factor.

The actual form of Γ^2 tends to be quite complicated. It may, however, be shown that other more usable formulas than Eq. (42) can be derived for space-charge reduced shot effect which hold for most practical ranges of operation. These formulas are

$$\overline{I_N^2} = 0.644\; 4kT_c g \,\Delta F \tag{43}$$

for diodes and

$$\overline{I_N^2} = \frac{0.644}{\sigma}\, 4kT_c g_m \,\Delta F \tag{44}$$

for negative-grid triodes. In Eqs. (43) and (44), T_c is the absolute temperature of the cathode, usually about 1000° for oxide-coated cathodes, and k is Boltzmann's constant. In Eq. (43), g is the plate conductance of the diode, whereas g_m in Eq. (44) is the transconductance of the triode. The quantity σ in Eq. (44) is a tube parameter, which usually lies between 0.5 and 1.0. Equations (43) and (44) bear a striking resemblance to Eq. (39) for thermal noise. Except in limiting cases, however, the resemblance is more formal than intrinsic.

The current-generator representation of Fig. 14, including the shunting effect of plate impedance, holds for space-charge-controlled operation as well as for the temperature-limited case. In the case of a triode, the true plate impedance $\delta e_p/\delta i_p$ is used in Fig. 14, and not a reciprocal of the transconductance, as might be suggested by Eq. (44).

e. Transformation to Equivalent Input Resistance Values. The principal sources of background noise of local origin in radio equipment are, as previously stated, thermal noise and shot noise. It would therefore be convenient to express them in comparable units. It so happens that this can be done quite conveniently for triodes and other amplifying tubes by expressing the plate-current fluctuations of shot noise as equivalent grid-voltage fluctuations. These grid-voltage fluctuations may then be expressed as the thermal-noise voltage fluctuations of an equivalent grid resistor. Thus since

$$i_p = g_m e_g \tag{45}$$

according to the definition of g_m, if i_p and e_g are the variational components of plate current and grid voltage, respectively, Eq. (44) may be transformed to

$$\overline{E_N^2} = \frac{\overline{I_N^2}}{g_m^2} = \frac{0.644}{\sigma g_m} 4kT_c \,\Delta F \tag{46}$$

where E_N represents the noise voltage of the equivalent grid resistor. Comparing Eq. (46) with Eq. (3), we see that the size of the equivalent grid resistor is

$$R_{eq} = \frac{0.644}{\sigma} \frac{T_c}{T} \frac{1}{g_m} \tag{47}$$[1]

where T is the temperature chosen for the equivalent grid resistor.

Equation (47) holds for the same range of operation as Eq. (44), which is the normal range of operation of most amplifying tubes. To get an idea of the size of R_{eq}, let us use $T = 20°\text{C} = 293°$ abs, $T_c = 1000°$ abs, and $\sigma = 0.75$ as typical values. Then corresponding to values of g_m of 1,000, 5,000, and 10,000, we obtain from Eq. (47) the respective values of R_{eq} as 2,940 and 588 and 294 ohms, respectively. The value of R_{eq}, since it is proportional to the quadratic content of shot noise, can be added directly to the resistive component of the grid impedance in order to calculate the combined shot plus thermal noise. A glance at the above values of R_{eq} indicates that the resistive component of the actual grid impedance greatly exceeds R_{eq} in the usual broadcast receiver,[2] but, in the case of a microwave receiver, R_{eq} is likely to be predominant. Numerical examples of the calculation of total receiver noise are given in Sec. 6.7, and a table of the noise characteristics of specific tubes is also given on page 234.

Since the noise magnitude indicated by Eq. (47) is referred to the grid circuit and is equivalent to input noise, it can be used as a measure of the effect of the tube on the *signal-to-noise ratio*. The equation thus tells us that, if shot noise is the predominant noise, the signal-to-noise ratio improves directly as $\sqrt{g_m}$.

f. Shot Effect in Multicollector Tubes. There is a general tendency for triodes to be quieter than tetrodes and pentodes. In the case of

[1] We could, of course, similarly transform the thermal noise of the grid resistance into plate-current fluctuations and obtain

$$\overline{I_{GN}^2} = g_m^2 4kTR_G \,\Delta F$$

where I_{GN} is the fluctuating plate current due to the resistive component R_G of the grid impedance. This equation however, is not frequently used.

[2] If the first tube in the receiver is a converter, this is likely not to be true any more. See Sec. 6.7*a*.

tetrodes, it was at first thought that the excess noise might be introduced by secondary emission from the screen grid. While there is no doubt an effect of this kind, it is only part of the story, for the same type of excess noise is also present in pentodes, where the suppressor grid should eliminate secondary emission. D. O. North has developed a comprehensive and quantitative theory showing how excess noise is due to the division of the tube current between the collector electrodes, whereby the noise-reduction effects of space charge are decreased. This theory is presented in Sec. 8.7 of the present book.

The general results of North's theory are contained in two equations,

$$\overline{I_{Nq}^2} = \Gamma_q^2 2\kappa I_q \,\Delta F \tag{48}$$

and

$$\Gamma_q^2 = 1 - \frac{I_q}{I_t}(1 - \Gamma^2) \tag{49}$$

where I_q = space current to the qth electrode

I_t = total space current to all electrodes

Γ^2 = space-charge noise-reduction factor of the total space current as defined in Eq. (42)

I_{Nq} = fluctuating component of the space current to the qth electrode

κ = electronic charge, in coulombs

ΔF = bandwidth, in cycles/sec

All currents in the above equations are measured in amperes. Equations (48) and (49) apply to tubes of the type in which the space-current streams to the different electrodes are essentially superimposed, as shown in Fig. 15*a*. However, they cannot be expected to apply to tubes with aligned grids of the beam type, and they will definitely not apply to tubes such as are shown in Fig. 15*b*, in which the space-current streams to the different electrodes are not superimposed.

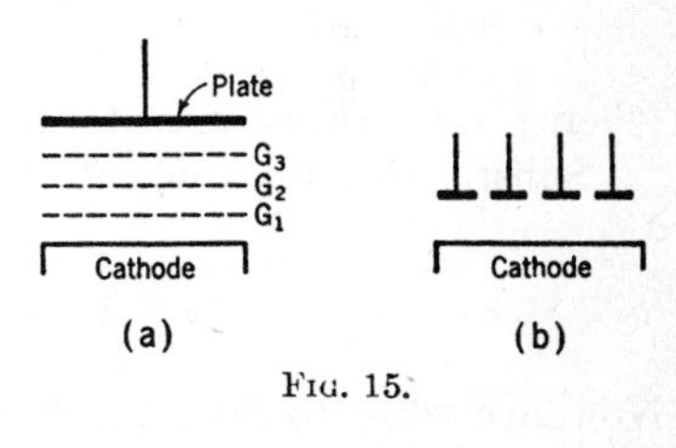

FIG. 15.

Let us apply the above equations to the most important practical case, namely, that of a pentode. Let us write

I_b = plate current

I_{c2} = screen current

$\overline{i_{g2}^2}$ = quadratic content of fluctuating component of screen current

$\overline{i_p^2}$ = quadratic content of fluctuating component of plate current

$I_a = I_b + I_{c2}$ = total space current of tube
$\overline{i_a^2}$ = quadratic content of fluctuating component of total space current

Then, it follows from Eqs. (48) and (49) that

$$\overline{i_{g2}^2} = \frac{\Gamma^2 I_{c2} + I_b}{I_a} I_{c2} 2\kappa\, \Delta F \tag{50}$$

$$\overline{i_p^2} = \frac{\Gamma^2 I_b + I_{c2}}{I_a} I_b 2\kappa\, \Delta F \tag{51}$$

Furthermore by Eq. (42)

$$\overline{i_a^2} = \Gamma^2(I_a 2\kappa\, \Delta F) \tag{52}$$

Generally speaking, it is $\overline{i_p^2}$ that appears in the output and is therefore of most importance. Consequently, let us transform $\overline{i_p^2}$ into equivalent grid noise. Since

$$e_g = \frac{i_p}{g_m} \tag{53}$$

where g_m is the transconductance of the pentode, we may rewrite Eq. (51) as

$$\overline{e_g^2} = \frac{\overline{i_p^2}}{g_m^2} = \frac{\Gamma^2 I_b + I_{c2}}{g_m^2 I_a} I_b 2\kappa\, \Delta F \tag{54}$$

If the tube were operated as a triode, it is usually found, and will therefore be assumed for our purposes, that

$$g_t = \frac{I_a}{I_b} g_m \tag{55}$$

where g_t is the transconductance of the tube operated as a triode.

Substituting Eq. (55) into Eq. (54), we obtain

$$\overline{e_g^2} = \left(1 + \frac{I_{c2}}{I_b \Gamma^2}\right) \frac{\Gamma^2 I_a 2\kappa\, \Delta F}{g_t^2} \tag{56}$$

Now, according to Eq. (42), the equivalent grid noise of the tube operated as a triode is given by

$$\overline{e_t^2} = \frac{\Gamma^2 I_a 2\kappa\, \Delta F}{g_t^2} \tag{57}$$

where $\overline{e_t^2}$ is the average quadratic content of the equivalent grid noise voltage when the tube is operated as a triode. Therefore

$$\overline{e_g^2} = \left(1 + \frac{I_{c2}}{I_b \Gamma^2}\right) \overline{e_t^2} \tag{58}$$

Eq. (58) shows that pentode noise exceeds triode noise in the ratio

$$1 + \frac{I_{c2}}{I_b \Gamma^2} \tag{59}$$

To obtain this ratio in a more practical form we find the value of Γ^2 from Eqs. (42) and (44), namely,

$$\Gamma^2 = \frac{0.644}{\sigma} \frac{4kT_c}{2\kappa I_a} g_t \tag{60}$$

Consequently, with the use of Eq. (55), we obtain

$$\frac{I_{c2}}{I_b \Gamma^2} = \frac{I_{c2}}{g_m} \frac{1}{T_c} \frac{\sigma}{0.644} \frac{\kappa}{2k} = 8.7\sigma \frac{I_{c2}}{g_m} \frac{1{,}000}{T_c} \tag{61}$$

Substituting this value into Eq. (58), we obtain

$$\overline{e_g^2} = \left(1 + 8.7\sigma \frac{I_{c2}}{g_m} \frac{1{,}000}{T_c}\right) \overline{e_t^2} \tag{62}$$

If we write R_{eq} (pentode) for the equivalent grid noise resistance of the tube operated as a pentode and R_{eq} (triode) for the equivalent grid noise resistance of the tube operated as a triode, then

$$R_{eq} \text{ (pentode)} = \frac{\overline{e_g^2}}{4kT\,\Delta F} \tag{63}$$

$$R_{eq} \text{ (triode)} = \frac{\overline{e_t^2}}{4kT\,\Delta F} \tag{64}$$

Therefore, from Eq. (62)

$$R_{eq} \text{ (pentode)} = \left(1 + 8.7\sigma \frac{I_{c2}}{g_m} \frac{1{,}000}{T_c}\right) R_{eq} \text{ (triode)} \tag{65}$$

The value of R_{eq} (triode) is given by Eq. (47) as

$$R_{eq} \text{ (triode)} = \frac{0.644}{\sigma} \frac{T_c}{T} \frac{1}{g_t} \tag{66}$$

Let us now apply these formulas to the case of a pentode for which

$$T_c = 1000^\circ \qquad g_m = 1{,}200 \text{ micromhos}$$
$$I_{c2} = 0.0005 \text{ amp} \qquad g_t = 1{,}500 \text{ micromhos}$$
$$\sigma = 0.83$$

and let T be taken as 293° (that is, 20°C). Then

$$R_{eq} \text{ (triode)} = \frac{0.644}{0.83} \frac{1{,}000}{293} \frac{1}{0.0015} = 1{,}770 \text{ ohms} \tag{67}$$

$$R_{eq} \text{ (pentode)} = \left[1 + 8.7(0.83)\frac{0.0005}{0.0012}\right] 1{,}770 = 7{,}100 \text{ ohms} \quad (68)$$

It is clear that the tube is much noisier in pentode operation.

g. Shot Effect in Converters.[1] We shall next study fluctuation noise in converters. Let us first consider a triode mixer. The plate noise at the intermediate frequency is given by Eq. (44) as

$$\overline{I_N^2} = \frac{0.644}{\sigma} 4kT_c\overline{g_m}\,\Delta F \quad (69)$$

where $\overline{g_m}$ is the average value, over the conditions during an oscillator cycle, of the transconductance of the tube considered as a triode amplifier. If this value is translated into equivalent grid noise at the radio frequency, we have

$$\overline{e_{gt}^2} = \frac{1}{g_c^2}\left(\frac{0.644}{\sigma} 4kT_c\overline{g_m}\,\Delta F\right) \quad (70)$$

where g_c is the conversion conductance. Therefore the equivalent grid noise resistance of a triode mixer is

$$R_{eq} \text{ (triode mixer)} = \frac{\overline{e_{gt}^2}}{4kT\,\Delta F} = \frac{0.644}{\sigma}\frac{T_c}{T}\frac{\overline{g_m}}{g_c^2} \quad (71)$$

For pentode mixers the use of Eq. (65) will then give

$$R_{eq} \text{ (pentode mixer)} = \left(1 + 8.7\frac{I_{c2}}{g_m}\frac{1{,}000}{T_c}\right)\frac{0.644}{\sigma}\frac{T_c}{T}\frac{\overline{g_m}}{g_c^2} \quad (72)$$

Since the operating transconductance of a triode or pentode is three to four times its conversion conductance and since even the average transconductance over an oscillator cycle is greater than the conversion conductance, it follows that any given tube will be considerably noisier as a mixer than as an amplifier. This is one reason why it is usually desirable to have a stage of radio-frequency amplification ahead of the converter in a receiver.

Multigrid converters and mixers are the noisiest of all. In this case, currents to electrodes other than the plate are so large that there is not very much space-charge reduction of shot effect in the plate current, and Eq. (49) becomes approximately

$$\Gamma_q^2 = 1 - \frac{I_q}{I_t} \quad (73)$$

[1] HEROLD, E. W., *R.C.A. Rev.*, January, 1940, p. 324, and *Proc. I.R.E.*, February, 1942, p. 84.

where q refers to the plate. With this value of Γ_q^2, Eq. (48) becomes

$$\overline{I_{Np}^2} = \frac{I_t - I_p}{I_t} 2\kappa I_p \, \Delta F \tag{74}$$

The equivalent grid noise resistance is then

$$R_{eq} \text{ (multigrid converter)} = \frac{\overline{I_{Np}^2}}{g_c^2 4kT \, \Delta F}$$
$$= \frac{2\kappa}{4kT} \frac{I_t - I_p}{g_c^2 I_t} I_p = 19.6 \frac{I_t - I_p}{g_c^2 I_t} I_p \tag{75}$$

for $T = 293°$. The value of g_c in a multigrid converter or mixer is usually smaller than in a triode or pentode mixer, which further increases the noise. In addition, some noise is also introduced into the system on the oscillator electrodes, but this noise is probably small unless there is an appreciable impedance from these electrodes to ground at the signal frequency.

According to Eqs. (71), (72), and (75) the optimum operating condition of a converter or mixer from a noise standpoint is generally that for which the conversion conductance g_c is a maximum.

h. Equivalent Grid Noise-resistance Formulas.[1] At this point we shall summarize our results for the noise produced in various types of tubes by giving simple practical formulas for the equivalent grid noise resistance. We shall first list these formulas and then show that they are practical approximations for formulas previously derived.

For triode amplifiers,

$$R_{eq} = \frac{2.5}{g_m} \tag{76}$$

For pentode amplifiers,

$$R_{eq} = \frac{I_b}{I_b + I_{c2}} \left(\frac{2.5}{g_m} + \frac{20 I_{c2}}{g_m^2} \right) \tag{77}$$

For triode mixers,

$$R_{eq} = \frac{2.5 \overline{g_m}}{g_c^2} \tag{78}$$

which can usually be further simplified to

$$R_{eq} = \frac{4}{g_c} \tag{79}$$

[1] HARRIS, W. A., *R.C.A. Rev.*, April, 1941, and July, 1941, has given the formulas listed in this subsection.

For pentode mixers,

$$R_{eq} = \frac{I_b}{I_b + I_{c2}}\left(\frac{2.5\overline{g_m}}{g_c^2} + \frac{20I_{c2}}{g_c^2}\right) \tag{80}$$

which can usually be further simplified to

$$R_{eq} = \frac{I_b}{I_b + I_{c2}}\left(\frac{4}{g_c} + \frac{20I_{c2}}{g_c^2}\right) \tag{81}$$

For multigrid converters and mixers,

$$R_{eq} = \frac{20I_b(I_a - I_b)}{I_a g_c^2} \tag{82}$$

In the foregoing formulas,

R_{eq} = equivalent grid noise resistance, in ohms
g_m = transconductance, in mhos
I_b = average plate current, in amperes
I_{c2} = average screen current, in amperes
$\overline{g_m}$ = average value, in mhos, of transconductance of tube considered as an amplifier, the transconductance being averaged over the voltage conditions existing during an oscillator cycle
g_c = conversion conductance, in mhos
I_a = total space current of tube in amperes (*i.e.*, sum of currents from cathode to all other electrodes)

Equations (76) to (82) are not exact, but they are practical approximations. Equation (76) is obtained from Eq. (47) by letting

$$\sigma = 0.88$$
$$T_c = 1000° \text{ abs}$$
$$T = 293° \text{ abs} = 20°\text{C}$$

Equation (77) is obtained from Eqs. (65), (66), and (76) by letting

$$g_m = \tfrac{4}{5}g_t$$

and

$$I_b = 4I_{c2}$$

in addition to the values of σ, T_c, and T already listed. With these values, the multiplier of I_{c2} in Eq. (77) is actually 19.2 rather than 20. However, since the values of σ, T_c, etc., chosen above are not exact in any case, it is just as well, and very probably just as accurate, to use the simpler multiplier 20.

Equation (78) is obtained from Eq. (71) by using the values of σ, T_c, and T already used above. Equation (79) is then obtained from

Eq. (78) by using the approximation

$$\overline{g_m} = 1.6g_c$$

Equation (80) is obtained from Eq. (72) by the same methods as those used in the derivation of Eq. (77). Equation (81) is then obtained from Eq. (80) by using the above approximation for $\overline{g_m}$.

Equation (82) is an approximation to Eq. (75) with certain changes in notation. A glance at Table I shows that multigrid converters and mixers are quite noisy.

In Table I (taken from Harris) is a list of the calculated values of R_{eq} for many practical tubes. Some comparisons with measured values are also given. This table and the foregoing formulas will be used in Sec. 6.7 in the solution of practical problems.

6.6 Magnetic Fluctuation Noise. Another type of fluctuation noise that may appear in amplifiers is magnetic fluctuation noise, sometimes called Barkhausen effect. It has certain mathematical and physical similarities to shot effect. When a piece of iron is being magnetized, the fact that it is not a uniform and continuous magnetic material but rather consists of minute magnetic grains which can be lined up in the direction of the field causes the magnetization to take place in discrete steps, which gives rise to fluctuation noise.

The most important practical example of Barkhausen effect is the case of a modern radio receiver of the type having a loop antenna and an iron-core power transformer. In such a receiver the iron of the power transformer is magnetized and demagnetized at the power frequency (60 cyles/sec in the United States). The magnetic fluctuation noise generated in the iron core during the magnetization cycles is picked up by the loop antenna; and if the coupling between the loop and the power transformer is not kept very low, this noise may limit the sensitivity of the receiver. To reduce the coupling, it may be necessary to use extra shielding on the transformer and to turn it in such a direction that its stray lines do not thread the loop. The mathematical theory of magnetic fluctuation noise is developed in Sec. 8.9.

6.7 Receiver Noise. As a practical application of the foregoing theory we shall calculate the noise in a radio receiver in a few typical cases and discuss certain important matters related to receiver noise.

a. First Tube a Converter.[1] Let us first consider the case shown in Fig. 16, in which the first tube in the receiver is a 6SA7 converter.

[1] Examples *a* and *b* are closely patterned after similar examples in the article by Harris (*R.C.A. Rev.*, April and July, 1941).

TABLE I.—TUBE NOISE VALUES*

Type	Application	Voltages			Currents			Transconductance, micromhos	Noise-equivalent resistance		Noise-equivalent input voltage,‖ microvolts
		Plate volts	Screen volts	Bias volts	Plate ma	Screen ma	Cathode ma		Calculated ohms	Measured ohms	
6SK7	Pentode amplifier	250	100	−3	9.2	2.4	11.6	2,000	10,500	9,400–11,500	0.94
6SJ7	Pentode amplifier	250	100	−3	3	0.8	3.8	1,650	5,800	5,800	0.70
6SG7	Pentode amplifier	250	125	−1	11.8	4.4	16.2	4,700	3,300	....	0.53
6AC7/1852	Pentode amplifier	300	150	−2	10	2.5	12.5	9,000	720	600–700	0.25
956	Pentode amplifier	250	100	−3	5.5	1.8	7.3	1,800	9,400	....	0.90
IT4	Pentode amplifier	90	45	0	2.0	0.65	2.65	750	20,000	....	1.3
6SA7	Frequency converter	250	100	0	3.4	8.0	11.9	450§	240,000	210,000	4.5
6K8	Frequency converter	250	100	−3	2.5	6.0	8.5‡	350§	290,000	....	4.9
1R5	Frequency converter	90	45	0	0.8	1.8	2.75	250§	170,000	....	3.8
6L7	Pentagrid mixer	250	100	−3	2.4	7.1	9.5	375§	255,000	210,000	4.6
6J5	Triode amplifier	250	...	−8	9.0	...	.....	2,600	960	1,250	0.28
955	Triode amplifier	180	...	−5	4.5	...	.....	2,000	1,250	....	0.32
6AC7/1852	Triode amplifier	150	150	−2	....	...	12.5	11,200	220	200	0.14
6AC7/1852	Pentode mixer	300	150	−1†	5.2	1.3	6.5	3,400§	2,750	3,000	0.48
6SG7	Pentode mixer	250	125	−1†	3.0	1.1	4.1	1,180§	13,000	....	1.0
956	Pentode mixer	250	100	−1†	2.3	0.8	3.1	650§	33,000	....	1.7
6J5	Triode mixer	100	...	−1†	2.1	...	.....	620§	6,500	....	0.74
6AC7/1852	Triode mixer	150	150	−1†	....	...	6.5	4,200§	950	....	0.28
955	Triode mixer	150	...	−1†	2.8	...	.....	660§	6,100	....	0.72

* Taken from W. A. Harris, *R.C.A. Rev.*, April and July, 1941.
† At peak of oscillator cycle.
‡ Hexode section only. Triode section takes its current from a separate part of the cathode.
§ Conversion transconductance value.
‖ For effective bandwidth of 5,000 cycles.

According to Table I this tube has an equivalent grid noise resistance of 240,000 ohms. Let us assume that the grid-to-ground impedance of the grid circuit has an average resistive component of 150,000 ohms in the pass band. Now since shot noise and thermal noise are both random noise, their quadratic contents are additive when they are

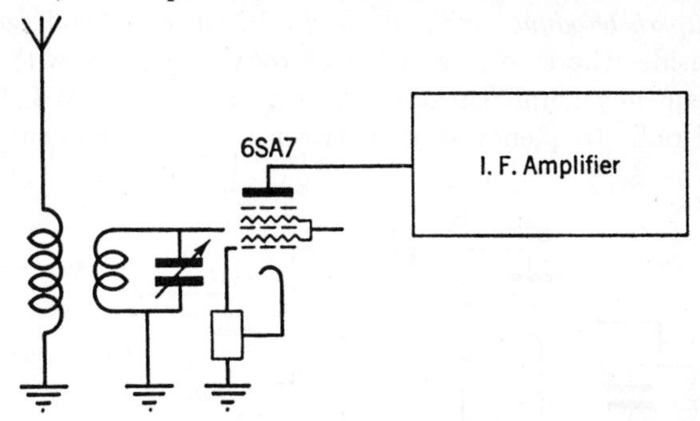

FIG. 16. Input circuit of a radio receiver with a converter tube in the first stage.

superimposed, according to Sec. 6.1. Therefore their equivalent noise-resistance values are additive. The total equivalent noise resistance of the stage in Fig. 16 might then be expected to be

$$240{,}000 + 150{,}000 = 390{,}000 \text{ ohms} \tag{83}$$

However, this is incomplete, for noise at the image[1] frequency will also pass through the intermediate-frequency amplifier. A glance at the frequency characteristics of a parallel tuned circuit[2] will show, nevertheless, that the *resistive component* of the grid impedance will be negligible at the image frequency. Thus Eq. (83) gives a good approximation to the equivalent noise input resistance of the stage in Fig. 16. Translated into microvolts, Eq. (83) says that the receiver noise in this case (for an effective bandwidth of, say, 6kc) is equivalent to

$$\begin{aligned}\sqrt{4kTR\,\Delta F} &= \sqrt{4 \times 1.37 \times 10^{-23} \times 293 \times 390{,}000 \times 6{,}000} \text{ volts} \\ &= 6.1 \text{ microvolts}\end{aligned} \tag{84}$$

of noise on the grid of the converter.

In the foregoing example we have assumed that the resistive component of the grid impedance could be considered at the temperature

[1] The image frequency of a superheterodyne receiver is the frequency located on the opposite side of the oscillator frequency from the desired carrier and displaced from the oscillator frequency by an amount equal to the intermediate frequency.

[2] TERMAN, "Radio Engineers' Handbook," p. 145.

of the receiver. This amounts to assuming that the radiation resistance of the antenna does not reflect into the grid impedance an appreciable percentage of the latter's resistive component. For ordinary broadcast receivers this is usually true. A more detailed discussion of the situation when this is not true will be given in a later example.

b. Superheterodyne with a Radio-frequency Amplifier. Let us next consider the case of a superheterodyne receiver with a stage of radio-frequency amplification as shown in Fig. 17. We shall use an untuned radio-frequency stage between the radio-frequency amplifier

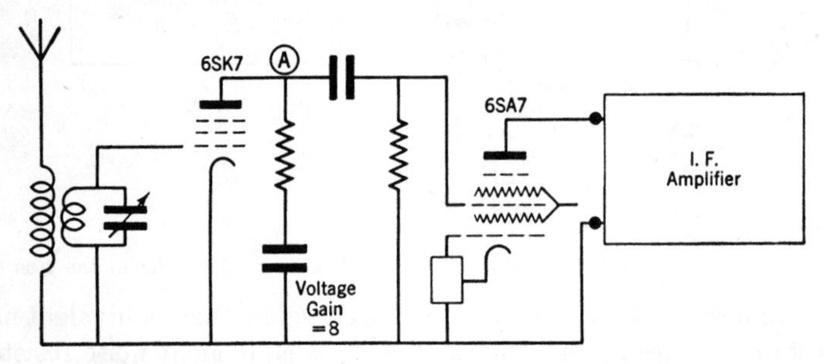

FIG. 17. Input circuit of a superheterodyne receiver having a radio-frequency amplifier stage.

and the converter, not because this is supposed to be desirable in practice, but because it will allow us to illustrate certain points in noise calculation.

In the case illustrated in Fig. 17 the noise generated in both the radio-frequency and converter stages must be taken into account. In order to transform all the noise to a comparable basis, we shall express it all in terms of an equivalent noise resistance at the grid of the radio-frequency stage. Thus, for example, the converter tube noise, which is listed in the table as having an equivalent grid noise resistance of 240,000 ohms, becomes

$$\frac{240{,}000}{64} = 3{,}750 \text{ ohms} \tag{85}$$

when referred to the radio-frequency grid, it being assumed that the power gain of the radio-frequency stage is 64 (*i.e.*, a voltage gain of 8). The resistive component of the grid impedance of the converter stage is, say, 3,000 ohms. When referred to the radio-frequency grid, this becomes

$$\frac{3{,}000}{64} = 47 \text{ ohms} \tag{86}$$

which is negligible.

The tube noise of the radio-frequency tube is listed as 10,500 ohms, referred to its own grid. However, this represents only the noise that the tube generates at the radio frequency. We shall now show that several additions must be made to this value, for the radio-frequency tube also generates noise at several other frequencies, which gets through the receiver. To be specific, let us suppose that the radio frequency is 1,000 kc and the intermediate frequency 455 kc. Then the image frequency is 1,910 kc (assuming that the oscillator is at 1,455 kc). Now the shot current at point A in Fig. 17 has components

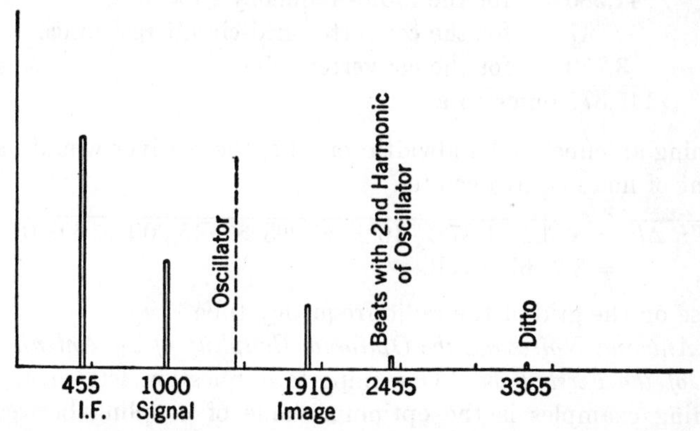

FIG. 18. Relative noise power outputs at various frequencies due to the shot noise introduced into the receiver by the 6SK7 in Fig. 17. (*From W. A. Harris. RCA Review, July,* 1941.)

of all frequencies, so that all frequencies for which a signal introduced at A gives an output will contribute to the noise. The relative contributions to the noise for various frequencies at A are shown in Fig. 18. This shows the relative power sensitivity of the receiver for a constant-current signal generator substituted for the radio-frequency tube at A. According to Fig. 18, we see that the equivalent grid resistances due to noise at other frequencies than the radio frequency are

$$\left.\begin{array}{rlr} 2.2 \times 10{,}500 = & 23{,}100 \text{ ohms} & (\text{for } 455 \text{ kc}) \\ 0.6 \times 10{,}500 = & 6{,}300 \text{ ohms} & (\text{for } 1{,}910 \text{ kc}) \\ 0.1 \times 10{,}500 = & 1{,}050 \text{ ohms} & (\text{for } 2{,}455 \text{ kc}) \\ 0.06 \times 10{,}500 = & 630 \text{ ohms} & (\text{for } 3{,}365 \text{ kc}) \end{array}\right\} \quad (87)[1]$$

[1] The noise components in Fig. 18 at frequencies other than the signal frequency are largely eliminated if there is a circuit tuned to the signal frequency between the point A and the grid of the converter.

The total equivalent grid noise resistance of the radio-frequency tube is therefore

$$10{,}500 + 23{,}100 + 6{,}300 + 1{,}050 + 630 = 41{,}580 \text{ ohms} \qquad (88)$$

The grid-circuit resistance of the radio-frequency tube is, say, 100,000 ohms at the radio frequency and is negligible at the other frequencies. Then the total equivalent noise resistance referred to the grid of the radio-frequency stage is

100,000	for the radio-frequency grid-circuit resistance
41,580	for the radio-frequency tube
47	for the converter grid-circuit resistance
3,750	for the converter tube
145,377	ohms total

Assuming an effective bandwidth[1] of 6 kc, the receiver would have an amount of noise equivalent to

$$\sqrt{4kTR\,\Delta F} = \sqrt{4 \times 1.37 \times 10^{-23} \times 293 \times 145{,}000 \times 6{,}000} \text{ volts}$$
$$= 3.7 \text{ microvolts} \qquad (89)$$

of noise on the grid of the radio-frequency tube.

c. Antenna Noise and the Optimum Coupling of an Antenna to the Input of the First Tube. One important question left open in the preceding examples is the optimum value of coupling between the antenna and the grid circuit. This depends greatly upon the amount of antenna noise. Now the noise of an antenna is partly due to ohmic resistance in the antenna circuit and partly due to noise absorbed by the antenna from space. The ohmic-resistance noise can be handled ike any other thermal noise, but the noise absorbed from space deserves special consideration.

The noise absorbed from space includes atmospherics, man-made noise and interference generated in the vicinity of the antenna, and the thermal noise of radiation resistance.[2] We can add the quadratic contents of the various components of this noise and obtain a total

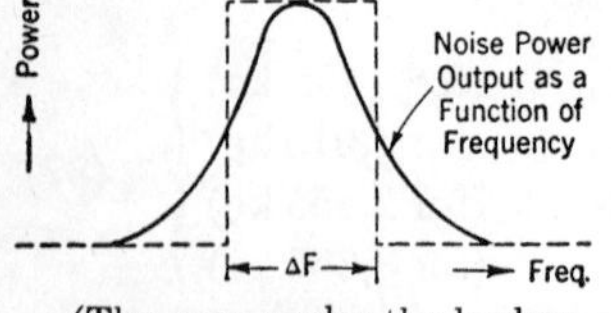

(The area under the broken-line rectangle is equal to that under the solid curve.)

[1] The effective bandwidth that should be used is the effective bandwidth of the receiver for a signal at the radio-frequency grid. This does not include the selectivity of the radio-frequency grid circuit and the receiver input circuit. The meaning of "effective bandwidth" is the bandwidth of a sharp cutoff system that would give rise to the same amount of noise as the actual system [see Sec. 6.9*d*(3)].

[2] The thermal noise of radiation resistance is discussed in Sec. 9.8.

antenna-absorbed noise voltage squared e_A^2. Then, if R_A is the radiation resistance of the antenna, we can write

$$\frac{e_A^2}{4kR_A\,\Delta F} = T_A \tag{90}$$

and thus obtain what may be called the effective noise temperature T_A of the radiation resistance of the antenna. The value of T_A is above room temperature in probably all practical installations, but it is much higher in some locations than in others. With the aid of this fictitious temperature, which is really only a description of the noisiness of the receiver location, we shall now continue with our discussion of the coupling problem.

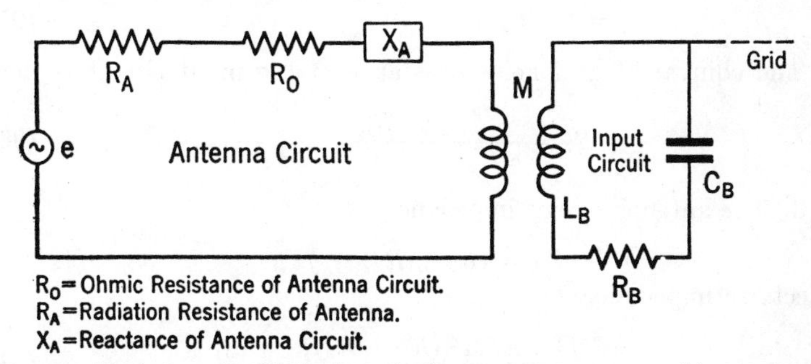

FIG. 19. Equivalent simplified schematic diagram of an antenna and input circuit.

Consider a simplified antenna and input circuit such as that shown in Fig. 19. There will be four[1] sources of noise in this circuit, which we may list as follows:

1. Tube noise
2. Thermal noise in the input circuit
3. Thermal noise (ohmic) in the antenna circuit
4. Antenna noise

Let us now see how each of these can be expressed as an equivalent noise resistance between grid and ground of the first tube.

1. The tube noise is already expressed as an equivalent grid noise resistance in Table I or a similar table. Let us call this R_1.

2. The thermal noise of the input circuit is that due to R_B. This causes a series voltage in the input circuit given by

$$e_B^2 = 4kTR_B\,\Delta F \tag{91}$$

[1] In parts *a* and *b* of this section, we, in effect, assumed that antenna-circuit noise was negligible.

This in turn causes a current

$$i_2^2 = \frac{e_B^2}{|Z_B + (\omega^2M^2/Z_A)|^2} = \frac{4kTR_B\,\Delta F}{|Z_B + (\omega^2M^2/Z_A)|^2} \tag{92}$$

where

$$Z_B = R_B + j\left(\omega L_B - \frac{1}{\omega C_B}\right) \tag{93}$$

and

$$Z_A = (R_0 + R_A) + jX_A \tag{94}$$

The grid voltage due to i_2 is given by

$$\begin{aligned} e_2^2 &= \frac{i_2^2}{\omega^2C_B^2} = \frac{4kTR_B\,\Delta F}{\omega^2C_B^2|Z_B + (\omega^2M^2/Z_A)|^2} \\ &= 4kTR_2\,\Delta F \end{aligned} \tag{95}$$

The equivalent grid noise resistance of the input circuit is then

$$R_2 = \frac{R_B}{\omega^2C_B^2|Z_B + (\omega^2M^2/Z_A)|^2} \tag{96}$$

3. The antenna-circuit impedance

$$Z_A = (R_0 + R_A) + jX_A$$

reflects an impedance

$$\frac{\omega^2M^2}{Z_A} = \frac{\omega^2M^2[(R_0 + R_A) - jX_A]}{(R_0 + R_A)^2 + X_A^2} \tag{97}$$

into the input circuit. This has a resistive component

$$\frac{\omega^2M^2(R_0 + R_A)}{(R_0 + R_A)^2 + X_A^2} \tag{98}$$

of which

$$\frac{\omega^2M^2R_0}{(R_0 + R_A)^2 + X_A^2} \tag{99}$$

has the equivalent temperature T of R_0 and

$$\frac{\omega^2M^2R_A}{(R_0 + R_A)^2 + X_A^2} \tag{100}$$

has the equivalent temperature T_A of R_A. Thus, if we substitute Eq. (99) for R_B in Eq. (96), we obtain R_3, the equivalent grid noise resistance of the ohmic resistance of the antenna circuit. Accordingly,

$$R_3 = \frac{\omega^2M^2R_0}{[(R_0 + R_A)^2 + X_A^2]|Z_B + (\omega^2M^2/Z_A)|^2\omega^2C_B^2} \tag{101}$$

4. The equivalent grid noise resistance of the absorbed antenna noise is next obtained by substituting Eq. (100) for R_B in Eq. (96) and multiplying by T_A/T to take care of the difference in effective temperature. Thus

$$R_4 = \frac{\omega^2 M^2 R_A (T_A/T)}{[(R_0 + R_A)^2 + X_A^2]|Z_B + (\omega^2 M^2/Z_A)|^2 \omega^2 C_B^2} \tag{102}$$

The total noise voltage squared on the grid is consequently $e_N^2 = 4kT\,\Delta F(R_1 + R_2 + R_3 + R_4)$

$$= \frac{4kT\,\Delta F}{|Z_A Z_B + \omega^2 M^2|^2} \left\{ R_1 |Z_A Z_B + \omega^2 M^2|^2 + \frac{R_B |Z_A|^2}{\omega^2 C_B^2} + \frac{\omega^2 M^2 R_0 |Z_A|^2}{[(R_0 + R_A)^2 + X_A^2]\omega^2 C_B^2} + \frac{\omega^2 M^2 R_A T_A |Z_A|^2}{T[(R_0 + R_A)^2 + X_A^2]\omega^2 C_B^2} \right\} \tag{103}$$

To compare with this, the signal voltage on the grid obtained by solving the network of Fig. 19 is given by

$$e_s^2 = \frac{\omega^2 M^2 e^2}{\omega^2 C_B^2 |Z_A Z_B + \omega^2 M^2|^2} \tag{104}$$

The signal-to-noise power ratio is then obtained by dividing Eq. (104) by Eq. (103). This is

$$\frac{e_s^2}{e_N^2} = \frac{\omega^2 M^2 e^2}{4kT\,\Delta F \left\{ \omega^2 C_B^2 R_1 |Z_A Z_B + \omega^2 M^2|^2 + R_B Z_A{}^2 + \frac{\omega^2 M^2 R_0 |Z_A|^2}{(R_0 + R_A)^2 + X_A^2} + \frac{\omega^2 M^2 R_A T_A |Z_A|^2}{T[(R_0 + R_A)^2 + X_A^2]} \right\}} \tag{105}$$

The largest (*i.e.*, optimum) signal-to-noise ratio is obtained by making Eq. (105) a maximum. This can be done in any particular case by actually maximizing the expression (105) if the temperature T_A is known. However, we can draw some general conclusions from Eq. (105) without the labor of maximizing it.

a. If most of the noise originates in the antenna circuit or is picked up by the antenna (*i.e.*, $R_3 + R_4 \gg R_1 + R_2$), the signal-to-noise ratio is independent of the mutual inductance M as long as M is large enough so that the foregoing inequality holds.

b. If most of the noise originates in the input circuit (*i.e.*, $R_2 \gg R_1 + R_3 + R_4$), the signal-to-noise ratio continues to improve as the mutual inductance M is increased.

c. If most of the noise originates in the tube

$$(i.e.,\ R_1 \gg R_2 + R_3 + R_4),$$

then Eq. (105) will have a maximum for the value of M for which

$$\frac{M^2}{|Z_A Z_B + \omega^2 M^2|^2}$$

has a maximum. If the value of M thus obtained is physically realizable, then the maximum signal-to-noise ratio will be obtained by using this value of M.

d. If antenna noise is negligible but both tube noise and input-circuit noise are important, then Eq. (105) will have a distinct maximum for a value of M that can be obtained by maximizing

$$\frac{M^2}{R_1|Z_A Z_B + \omega^2 M^2|^2 + R_B|Z_A|^2} \tag{106}$$

If the value of M thus obtained is physically realizable, it will give the best signal-to-noise ratio.

Two additional observations are also in order. In the first place, if the denominator of Eq. (105) varies widely in the pass band ΔF, then, instead of multiplying the quantity in braces by ΔF, it becomes necessary to integrate it with respect to F over the range ΔF. In the second place, it is shown in Sec. 6.10 that, when the input conductance of the tube becomes important, a correction must be made for its effective temperature.

6.8 The Measurement and Output Characteristics of Noise and Noise plus Signal. *a. General.* The peculiar and unpredictable wave-shape properties of noise make it difficult to interpret the measurements of noise as obtained from the usual measuring systems. It is, of course, possible to measure the energy (*i.e.*, the quadratic content) of a noise signal with a thermal meter and thus determine the rms value of the noise signal. There are, however, other things we should like to know about noise measurements. These matters are dealt with in detail in Sec. 7.17 to 7.19, and in the present section we shall give the results there derived and developed. Besides the question of measurement, the question of resultant output in the combination of noise and signal is also of great importance. This matter will also be treated in the present section. The background noise in a radio or television program is a familiar phenomenon, and it will be of interest to deal with it on a quantitative basis.

A good idea of the combination of signal and noise is given in Fig. 20, which shows an oscilloscope representation of the superposition of noise on a pulse-type signal. If this represents a television signal, the noise will cause a grainy, fine structure in the background of the picture. As the signal becomes smaller, it gradually becomes lost in the background of noise. It will be noted that both height and duration (*i.e.*, power × time = energy) of the signal are important in making it perceptible through the noise.

We mention in passing that it is shown in Chap. VII that, while random noise will change its general wave shape with changes in the frequency characteristics of the transmission system, it will still retain the properties of random noise. This is important, for, as a consequence, the various formulas of (*b*), (*c*), and (*d*) of this section will be independent of the frequency distribution of the noise power.

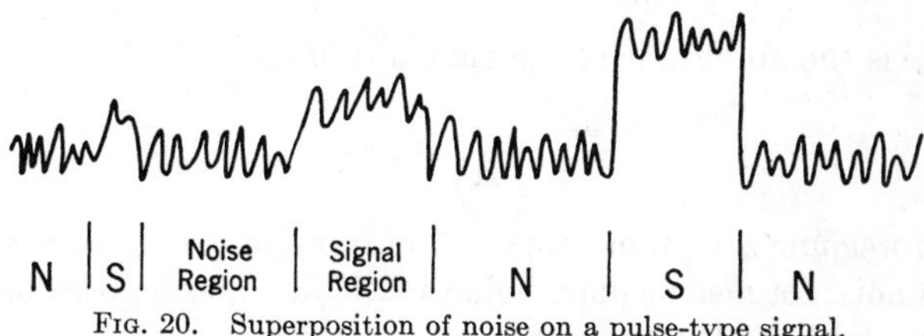

FIG. 20. Superposition of noise on a pulse-type signal.

The output signal, consisting of noise plus desired signal, in Fig. 20, is usually the envelope of a radio-frequency signal having the carrier frequency of the desired signal. The tuning of the receiver, which transmits only a narrow band of frequencies in the neighborhood of the carrier of the desired signal, selects from the total noise generated only a portion of it, which is approximately periodic at the tuning frequency rate and which has an envelope whose frequency components have a frequency range about equal to the bandwidth of the receiver. The envelope of this signal is what appears in the regions marked N in Fig. 20.

b. The Envelope of Noise and of Noise plus a Carrier. If e_N is a random-noise amplitude function such as the radio-frequency noise function whose envelope is shown in the N regions of Fig. 20, then the value of e_N at any instant cannot be predicted ahead of time since it is a random function. All that is known about such a function is the probability of its having a particular value. Thus, according to Eq. (1), we do know that the probability of e_N lying between a particular value e_N and $e_N + de_N$ is

$$P(e_N)de_N = \frac{A}{\sqrt{\pi}} \epsilon^{-A^2 e_N^2}\, de_N \tag{107}$$

where

$$A^2 = \frac{1}{2\overline{e_N^2}} = \frac{1}{2 \times \text{mean square value of } e_N} \tag{108}$$

According to Eq. (108), A is a measure of the average noise level. If A is known, the probability of e_N lying in any particular narrow range is given by Eq. (107). One method of determining A, as already mentioned, is by measuring e_N with a thermal meter. Other methods will be given below.

If the probability distribution of the values of e_N is given by Eq. (107) and if the frequency components of e_N are limited to a relatively narrow high-frequency channel, it is shown in Sec. 7.17 that the probability distribution of the envelope of e_N is

$$P(R_N)dR_N = 2A^2R_N\epsilon^{-A^2R_N^2}\,dR_N \tag{109}$$

where R_N is the amplitude of the envelope of e_N, and

$$\overline{R_N^2} = \frac{1}{A^2} = 2\overline{e_N^2} \tag{110}$$

The foregoing equations apply to pure noise. However, suppose that this noise, of mean square value $1/2A^2$, is superimposed on a carrier $K \cos 2\pi Ft$, so that the combined signal is

$$e_N + K \cos 2\pi Ft \qquad (111)[1]$$

Let R be the envelope of Eq. (111). Then it is also shown in Sec. 7.17 that the envelope of the combined signal has a probability distribution

$$P(R)dR = 2A^2R\epsilon^{-A^2(R^2+K^2)}I_0(2A^2KR)dR \qquad (112)[2]$$

Equation (112) tells, better than anything else can, what will be seen in the plot of a signal, such as Fig. 20. In Fig. 21, Eq. (112) is shown graphically for various values of the ratio $\sqrt{2}AK$. This shows the probability $P(R)$ of the amplitude R depending upon the values of the carrier strength K and the rms value of noise $1/A\sqrt{2}$. An exact description of the wave shape in Fig. 20 cannot be given. However, we do know that the frequency distribution of the noise power determines the "fineness of grain" of the noise wave shape.

At one time, it was quite common to discuss the "crest factor" of noise. The crest factor was defined as the ratio of the amplitude of the highest peaks to the rms value of the amplitude. Experimental

[1] The product

$$AK = \frac{\text{rms carrier}}{\text{rms noise}}$$

is usually the quantity of interest when a carrier is present.

[2] I_0 is the modified Bessel function of the first kind of zero order, which is discussed in Appendix E.

values between 3.4 and 4.5 were obtained for this ratio. If we look at Eq. (112), we see that there will be peaks of practically infinite value if the observer is only willing to wait for them. However, the form of the pure noise curve ($\sqrt{2}AK = 0$) in Fig. 21 shows that values between 3.4 and 4.5 are what may be expected in practical intervals of observation for the crest factor.[1]

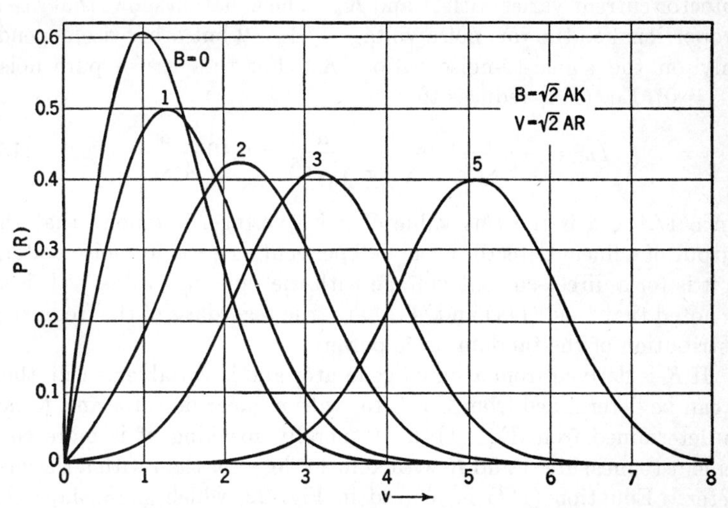

FIG. 21. Probability distribution of the envelope when random noise is superimposed upon a carrier. (V is the ratio of envelope amplitude to rms noise, while AK is the ratio of rms carrier to rms noise.) (*From S. O. Rice, Bell System Tech. J., January,* 1945.)

c. Rectified Output and Low-frequency Output in Linear Detection. Let a noise plus carrier signal of the form of Eq. (111) be applied to a linear detector having the characteristic

$$\left.\begin{aligned} I &= 0 \qquad \text{(when } V < 0) \\ &= \alpha V \qquad \text{(when } V > 0) \end{aligned}\right\} \tag{113}$$

where I is the detector current and V is the applied voltage. Then it is shown in Sec. 7.18 that the direct-current component of the detector current is

[1] RICE, S. O., *Bell System Tech. J.*, January, 1945, has also derived a formula for the probability distribution of the amplitudes of the wave maxima and has plotted it on p. 85 of his article. This is somewhat different from the probability distribution of the instantaneous values of the amplitudes given by Eq. (112). However, Eq. (112) actually gives a better idea of how long one must expect to wait before observing an amplitude of a given large value.

$$I_{DC} = \frac{\alpha}{2A\sqrt{\pi}} \epsilon^{-\frac{A^2K^2}{2}} \left[(1 + A^2K^2) I_0 \left(\frac{A^2K^2}{2} \right) + A^2K^2 I_1 \left(\frac{A^2K^2}{2} \right) \right] \quad (114)$$ [1]

Equation (114) shows how the direct-current component of the detector current varies with A and K. The equation shows that I_{DC} is proportional to the rms noise voltage $1/A\sqrt{2}$ but otherwise depends only on the signal-to-noise ratio AK. For the case of pure noise ($K = 0$), Eq. (114) reduces to

$$I_{DC} = \frac{\alpha}{2A\sqrt{\pi}} = \frac{1}{\sqrt{2\pi}} \frac{\alpha}{A\sqrt{2}} = 0.40 \frac{\alpha}{A\sqrt{2}} \quad (115)$$

Since $1/A\sqrt{2}$ is the rms value of noise voltage, it follows that the output of a linear detector is only 40 per cent as great for noise voltage as it is for a direct-current voltage with the same rms value.[2] It is to be noted that Eqs. (114) and (115) are true regardless of the frequency distribution of the random noise power.

If K is derived from a signal generator and is variable at will, then A can be determined from Eq. (115) with a linear detector and K can be determined from Eq. (114). Generally speaking, it is more convenient to measure A and K with a linear detector than with a thermal meter. Equation (114) is plotted in Fig. 22, which shows how the direct-current output rises with increase in the carrier-signal level.

Another matter of great interest is the magnitude of the detector output (audio, video, or other) in the case of linear detection. Suppose we let I_{AC} stand for the detector current from which the radio-frequency and the direct-current components have been removed. It is shown in Sec. 7.18 that the average quadratic content (power) of I_{AC} is

$$\overline{I_{AC}^2} = \frac{\alpha^2}{A^2\pi^2}(1 + A^2K^2) - \frac{\alpha^2}{4A^2\pi} \epsilon^{-A^2K^2} \left[(1 + A^2K^2) I_0 \left(\frac{A^2K^2}{2} \right) + A^2K^2 I_1 \left(\frac{A^2K^2}{2} \right) \right]^2 \quad (116)$$ [3]

[1] I_0 is the modified Bessel function of the first kind of zero order, and I_1 is the modified Bessel function of the first kind of the first order. Both are discussed in Appendix E.

[2] By way of comparison, it may be noted that the output of a linear detector for an applied sinusoidal voltage is $(\sqrt{2}/\pi) = 0.45$ times its output for direct-current voltage with the same rms value.

[3] The value of $\overline{I_{AC}^2}$ in Eqs. (116) to (118) includes all the frequency components (excepting the direct current) in the rectified envelope. It is therefore

For the case of pure noise ($K = 0$) Eq. (116) reduces to

$$\overline{I_{AC}^2} = \frac{\alpha^2}{4\pi^2 A^2}(4 - \pi) \tag{117}$$

On the other hand, for large K, Eq. (116) reduces to

$$\overline{I_{AC}^2} = \frac{\alpha^2}{2\pi^2 A^2} \tag{118}$$

Thus, for large K, the output-signal level is independent of K but depends only on the radio-frequency noise. This situation will, of

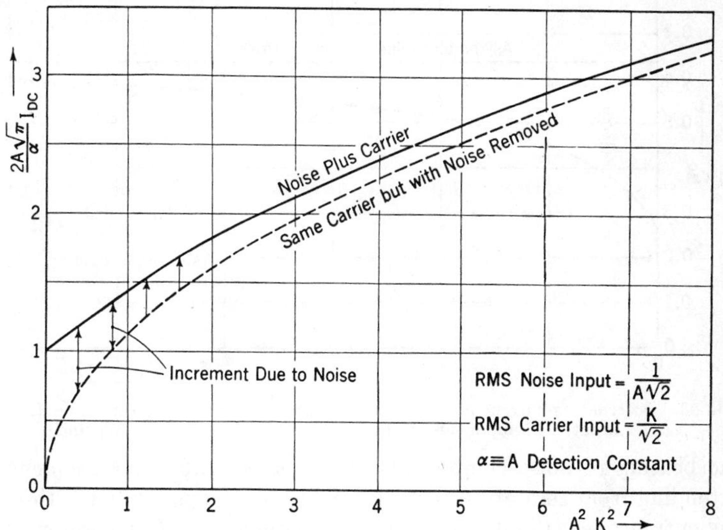

FIG. 22. Direct-current output of a linear detector with a random noise plus carrier input.

course, change if the signal carrier is modulated, as discussed below. Equation (116) is shown graphically in Fig. 23.

The ratio of Eq. (118) to Eq. (117) gives the increase in apparent noise that is always observed in a radio receiver when a carrier is tuned in. This ratio is

$$\frac{\alpha^2/2\pi^2A^2}{(\alpha^2/4\pi^2A^2)(4 - \pi)} = \frac{2}{4 - \pi} = 2.33 \tag{119}$$

The ratio given in Eq. (119) is actually the minimum value that can be observed for the ratio of noise with and without a carrier. In

essential in using these equations that the measuring system should not attenuate any frequencies of consequence in the rectified envelope.

actual receivers, two characteristics tend to increase this ratio, often manyfold. One of these characteristics is the frequency characteristic of the low-frequency amplifier. Thus, if the carrier is located at the center of the pass band of the noise and the carrier is of large amplitude, the low-frequency noise output is pretty well confined to a band extending from zero frequency to a frequency of one-half the width of the radio-frequency noise pass band. The reason for this is that the low-frequency noise in this case arises from beating of the carrier with the separate noise components. However, when the carrier is absent,

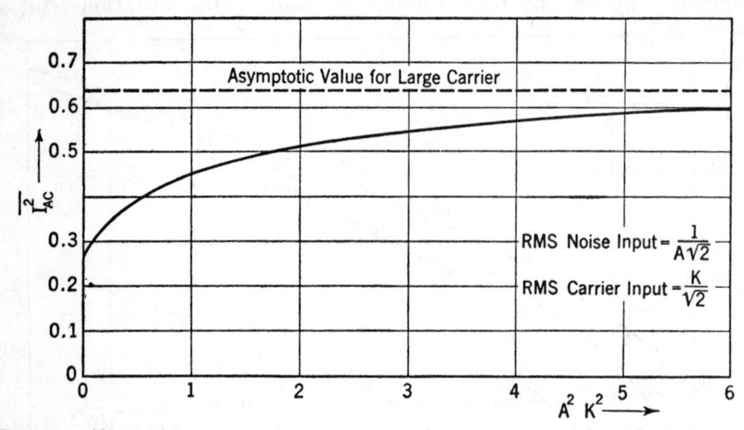

FIG. 23. Alternating-current power output of a linear detector with random noise plus carrier input. (Components in the carrier frequency range are not included.)

the beating of noise components gives rise to important frequencies extending from zero up to the entire width of the pass band, although the output does fall off at these higher frequencies. Furthermore, the asymmetrical noise sidebands, which practically give rise only to frequency modulation when a large carrier is present, will, in the absence of a carrier, also give rise to harmonics of the noise beat frequencies, thus still further extending the low-frequency range. Consequently, unless the low-frequency amplifier has a very wide pass band, it will act to increase the ratio given in Eq. (119).[1]

The other characteristic of a receiver that tends to increase the ratio in Eq. (119) is nonlinearity of the detector at low amplitudes. This will make the detector relatively insensitive at the low amplitudes that may occur when noise alone is present, thus often causing a manyfold increase in the ratio given by Eq. (119). For this same reason it

[1] The asymmetrical sideband effect will be very marked in television systems of present-day standards.

is important that large signal levels be present when Eq. (114) is used to evaluate noise measured with a diode meter.

If the carrier $K \cos 2\pi Ft$ is modulated, so that the radio-frequency signal is

$$K(1 + m \cos 2\pi\mu t) \cos 2\pi Ft \tag{120}$$

then standard linear-detector theory tells us that the alternating-current-signal power output is

$$\overline{I_{ACS}^2} = \frac{\alpha^2 m^2 K^2}{2\pi^2} \tag{121}$$

Comparing this with Eq. (118), we see that, for low noise conditions, the signal-to-noise power ratio is

$$\frac{\overline{I_{ACS}^2}}{\overline{I_{ACN}^2}} = \frac{\alpha^2 m^2 K^2/2\pi^2}{\alpha^2/2\pi^2 A^2} = m^2 A^2 K^2 \tag{122}$$

Thus the apparent degree of noise amplitude modulation is $1/AK$ (see also Exercise 3 below).

Exercises

1. Show that according to the definition in Sec. 5.3*b*

Effective value of degree of amplitude modulation

$$= \sqrt{2 \frac{\text{average power of symmetrical sidebands}}{\text{average power of unmodulated carrier}}}$$

This equation is applicable in all cases in which the antisymmetrical sidebands are small.

2. Show that according to the definition in Sec. 5.3*b*, when there is only one pair of antisymmetrical sidebands and the degree of modulation is small,

Effective value of degree of frequency modulation

$$= \frac{\mu}{D} \sqrt{2 \frac{\text{average power of antisymmetrical sidebands}}{\text{average power of unmodulated carrier}}}$$

3. Show that according to Eq. (122), when the degree of noise modulation is small,

Effective value of degree of noise amplitude modulation

$$= \sqrt{\frac{\text{average power of noise}}{\text{average power of carrier}}}$$

Comparison of this result with that of Exercise 1 and noting of the disappearance of the factor of 2 show that there is an equal division of energy between the symmetrical and the antisymmetrical sidebands in the noise. This is fundamentally a consequence of the random phases of the noise sidebands.

4. Suppose that the output of the intermediate-frequency amplifier of a receiver is fed into a linear detector and that the internal noise of the receiver causes a direct-current component of 1 ma in the output of the detector. Next, suppose that an unmodulated carrier is added to the noise. What is the direct-current output reading when (a) the average carrier power is equal to the average noise power; (b) the average carrier power is equal to twice the noise power? Figure 22 may be used in finding the answer.

Answer: (a) 1.44 ma., (b) 1.82 ma.

d. Quadratic Transmission System, Particularly a Square-law Detector. Next suppose that we are dealing with a quadratic transmission system having a response characteristic

$$I = \alpha V^2 + \beta V + \gamma \tag{123}$$

where I is the output of the system, V is the applied voltage, and α, β, and γ are constants of the system.

The foregoing system may be a vacuum tube operated on a nonlinear portion of its characteristic, or it may be a square-law detector. For such a system it is shown in Sec. 7.19 that the rectified output is

$$I_{DC} = \frac{\alpha}{2A^2}(1 + A^2K^2) + \gamma \tag{124}$$

Since γ is a constant, it can usually be balanced out of the reading or removed from it by subtraction, so that Eq. (124) becomes

$$I'_{DC} = \frac{\alpha}{2A^2}(1 + A^2K^2) \tag{125}$$

For pure noise, $K = 0$, so that Eq. (125) becomes

$$I'_{DC} = \frac{\alpha}{2A^2} \tag{126}$$

In this case, the direct current then measures the mean square value of noise.

Let us next consider the low-frequency output for the quadratic detector with the characteristic given in Eq. (123). For this case, it is shown in Sec. 7.19 that

$$\overline{I_{AC}^2} = \frac{\alpha^2}{4A^4}(1 + 2A^2K^2) \tag{127}$$

For this case, we see that the noise output rises continuously with increasing values of K. As in the case of the linear detector, the pure noise terms have a wider frequency spectrum than the original frequency band, so that narrowing the pass band of the low-frequency amplifier will discriminate against noise.

6.9 Noise Ratings and Noise Figures. *a. Introduction.* In order to be able to discuss noise in a simple and intelligent manner, it is desirable to have concise quantitative descriptions of the noise properties of the things we are talking about. We shall briefly discuss the quantitative noise ratings of

1. Signals
2. Receivers or amplifiers
3. Complete receiving installations
4. Complete transmission systems

b. The Noise Rating of Signals. The noise rating of a signal is usually described in terms of the signal-to-noise ratio (S/N ratio). This measure has not been well standardized so that the S/N ratio may refer to

$$\frac{\text{Rms signal voltage}}{\text{Rms noise voltage}} \tag{128}$$

or

$$\frac{\text{Peak signal voltage}}{\text{Peak noise voltage}} \tag{129}$$

or

$$\frac{\text{Average signal power}}{\text{Average noise power}} \tag{130}$$

or various other ratios. It is therefore desirable to tell precisely what is meant in speaking of a signal-to-noise ratio in any particular case. Probably the most commonly used S/N ratio is the ratio of rms voltages.

Another method of rating the noise content of a signal is to give the number of decibels by which the signal exceeds the noise. Thus

$$10 \log_{10} \frac{\text{average signal power}}{\text{average noise power}} = \text{db level of signal above noise} \tag{131}$$

Equation (131) gives a rather good rating of the noisiness of an audio signal.

In many important cases, as in a discussion of the noise properties of FM and pulse-modulation systems, the foregoing definitions are quite inadequate, and it is necessary to describe noise properties in detail. Furthermore, in an FM or a pulse-modulation receiver, the same signal will have S/N ratios in the intermediate frequency and in the audio that are almost completely unrelated, regardless of definition. Consequently, the S/N ratio cannot be considered a complete measure of the noise properties of a signal, since a more detailed story will often be required.

c. The Equivalent Noise Sideband Input. Prior to the war, a widely used measure for the noisiness of radio receivers was the *equiv-*

alent noise sideband input (ENSI). This measure has the practical advantage that it is easy to determine experimentally. There are important objections to it, however, especially in the case of short-wave receivers in which the receiver is designed for use with a specific type of antenna. Nevertheless, the ENSI is likely to continue in use as a standard for broadcast receivers, since it is a good practical measure for that purpose.

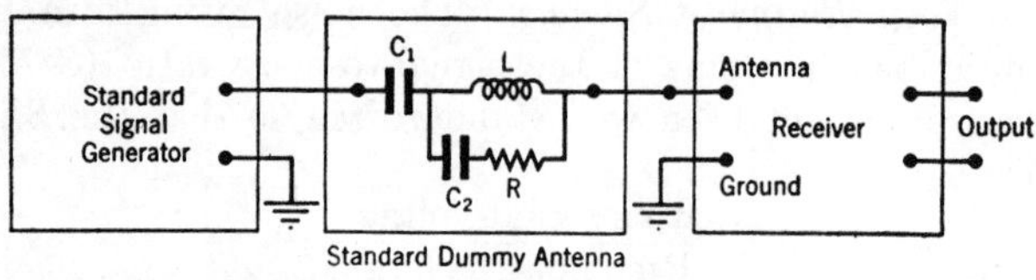

FIG. 24. Arrangement of equipment in measuring the equivalent noise sideband input.

To measure[1] the ENSI, a receiver is connected as shown in Fig. 24. The ENSI is then defined as

$$\text{ENSI} = mE_S \sqrt{\frac{P'_N}{P'_S}} \tag{132}$$

where P'_N = rms noise power output when signal input is reduced to zero

P'_S = rms signal power output when signal is applied

$$(P'_S \gg P'_N)$$

E_S = signal carrier (rms of unmodulated carrier) input voltage

m = degree of modulation of signal carrier

By definition, the modulation frequency is 400 cycles, and the degree of modulation of the carrier by both noise and signal is kept relatively small. The standard signal generator should be of very low or very high impedance, so that it is as completely mismatched as is practical from the dummy antenna and receiver and thus will not transfer appreciable noise power into the receiver. As defined above, the ENSI measures the rms value of the noise input voltage, it being assumed that the receiver is operated without distortion. On this same assumption, the ENSI is independent of the exact value of the input voltage, of the sensitivity of the receiver, and of the volume-control setting. It is a direct measure (referred to the level of the receiver input) of the noise generated in the dummy antenna and the receiver, if it is assumed that no appreciable noise is transferred to the receiver from the signal generator.

[1] I.R.E. Standards on Radio Receivers (1938).

The ENSI is a good practical measure for the noise rating of broadcast receivers. However, it is not flexible enough to rate fairly a receiver that has been designed specifically for use with a nonstandard antenna. For this purpose, in recent years, a more fundamental rating has been defined. This is the *noise figure*, which we shall define and discuss after presenting a few preliminary definitions.

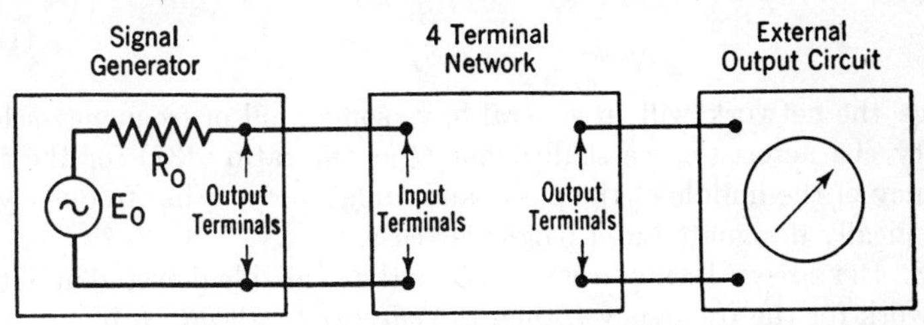

FIG. 25. Equipment for measuring noise figure.

d. Some Preliminary Definitions. 1. AVAILABLE SIGNAL POWER. If a signal generator is connected to a network as shown in Fig. 25 and if the resistive component of the internal output impedance of the generator is R_0 (ohms) and the emf that it generates is E_0 (volts), then the maximum power that the generator can deliver is

$$\frac{E_0^2}{4R_0} \tag{133}$$

This is the power that is delivered under the conditions of matched impedances, *i.e.*, when

$$R_1 = R_0 \qquad \text{and} \qquad X_1 = -X_0 \tag{134}$$

where R_1 = resistive component of network input impedance
X_1 = reactive component of network input impedance
X_0 = reactive component of internal output impedance of the generator

We shall call the maximum power that can be removed from the generator (for a given setting of its controls) the available signal power and designate it by the symbol S_g. Thus

$$S_g = \frac{E_0^2}{4R_0} \tag{135}$$

2. AVAILABLE POWER GAIN. The output terminals of the four-terminal network in Fig. 25 may be considered as a source of power in exactly the same way as the signal generator. Thus if the internal impedance of the output circuit of the network is R and the signal

voltage generated in the output circuit is E, then the available signal power in the output circuit is

$$S = \frac{E^2}{4R} \tag{136}$$

We shall now define the *available power gain* (designated as G) of the network as

$$G = \frac{S}{S_g} \tag{137}$$

Since the network will in general have some kind of frequency-selectivity characteristic, we shall define G as the ratio (137) for the frequency of the middle of the pass band, unless some other frequency is specifically designated in a particular case.

3. Effective Bandwidth. If G_f is the available power gain of the network for the frequency f, then the *effective bandwidth* B of the network is defined as

$$B = \frac{1}{G} \int G_f \, df \tag{138}$$

4. Available Noise Power. An ideal signal generator, from a noise point of view, will generate no noise other than the thermal noise of its internal resistive component R_0. Thus the available noise power in the frequency interval df from an ideal signal generator will be

$$\frac{E_n^2}{4R_0} = \frac{4kTR_0 \, df}{4R_0} = kT \, df \tag{139}$$

If the network in Fig. 25 were a lossless transformer or a filter made of pure reactive components, the internal resistive component of its output circuit, R, would then merely be the reflected impedance due to R_0 of the signal generator. Since the network would have no noise sources of its own, the available output noise power would be merely that due to the thermal noise of R_0 transformed to the impedance level of R, but still of magnitude

$$kT \, df$$

If the network had power gain but generated no noise of its own, the entire available output noise power for all frequencies would then, in view of Eq. (138), be

$$kTBG \tag{140}$$

Since Eq. (140) gives the available output noise power of an ideal network that generates no noise of its own, we define

$$N_g = kTB \tag{141}$$

as the *ideal available input noise power* of a network having the same gain characteristic as the ideal network.

If a signal generator is not ideal from a noise point of view, it will make available more noise than the amount indicated by Eqs. (139) and (140). Generally speaking, the network in Fig. 25 will act as a nonideal signal generator. We shall designate its available output noise power as N.

e. The Noise Figure of a Network.[1] With the aid of the foregoing definitions, we shall now introduce the *noise figure* of a network as a measure of its noise-generation properties. We define the *noise figure* F of a network as the ratio

$$F = \frac{\text{available input signal power/ideal available input noise power}}{\text{available output signal power/available output noise power}}$$

$$= \frac{S_g/kTB}{S/N} = \frac{N}{GkTB} \qquad (142)^2$$

The noise figure of a network is thus the ratio of the actual available output noise power to the available output noise power of an ideal network having the same gain characteristic. Therefore the noise figure of an ideal network that generates no noise itself is $F = 1$; and, correspondingly, the part of the noise figure of any network due to internally generated noise is $F - 1$.

In order to complete the definition of the noise figure we must specify the temperature T of the ideal signal generator. For convenience in calculation, we shall follow Friis and specify

$$T = 290° \text{ abs} = 17°\text{C} = 63°\text{F} \qquad (143)$$

With this specification of T, we have

$$kT = 4 \times 10^{-21} \text{ watt/cycle} \qquad (144)$$

After some discussion of the measurement and combination qualities of noise figures, we shall return to a consideration of the merits and demerits of the noise figure as a measure of the noise quality of a network.

[1] The use of the noise figure of a network originated with H. T. Friis, *Proc. I.R.E.*, July, 1944, p. 419. Much of Sec. 6.9 follows closely the development in Friis's paper.

[2] The noise figure is frequently transformed into decibels, to give the decibels of noise above that of an ideal receiver. However, when noise powers are added, it is confusing to use decibels. Thus they should be used only to express over-all receiver noise performance. They should not be used in intermediate calculations.

f. The Measurement of Noise Figure. The measurement of noise figure is usually performed with connections as shown in Fig. 25. According to the definition the output impedance of the generator should be made to match the input impedance of the network over the entire frequency range of interest, so that the network receives the entire available power of signal and noise. Usually, however, this condition is relaxed in practice since impedance matching conditions are the same for both signal and noise, and matching is usually obtained only at the midband frequency and sometimes not at all. Owing to the difference in frequency distribution of signal and noise, this will introduce some error. Similar considerations apply to the output of the network.

If the output of the signal generator is adjusted so that the final output of noise plus signal is double that due to noise alone, then

$$S = N \tag{145}$$

Since, we also have

$$S = GS_g \tag{146}$$

it follows from Eq. (142) that

$$F = \frac{S_g}{kTB} = \frac{E_0^2}{4R_0kTB} = \frac{E_0'^2}{R_0'kTB} \tag{147}$$

where kT is assigned the value given in Eq. (144) and

E_0' = terminal voltage of signal generator
= $E_0/2$ when impedances are matched

R_0' = input resistance of network = R_0(when impedances are matched)

The use of the last form of Eq. (147) is permissible only if the reactance of the output circuit of the signal generator is equal in magnitude and opposite in sign to the reactance of the input circuit of the network, *i.e.*, if the circuit reactance is tuned out.

Equation (147) is the standard equation for use in measuring noise figure. The technique of determining E_0, R_0, and B or E_0', R_0', and B at very high frequencies, although quite important, is outside the scope of this book. A random-noise generator is frequently used as the signal generator, for such a generator is easily adjusted and calibrated at low power levels, and it is then easy to measure the combined noise-plus-signal output. There is then also no question about whether the second detector treats signal and noise differently. A discussion of random-noise generators justifies our brief attention.

g. Noise Generators. One of the simplest and most practical types of noise generators is the temperature-limited diode. Its noise power output can be calculated very accurately with the aid of Eq. (41) in the frequency range below that in which transit time is important and above the range in which flicker effect is of consequence. By using high anode voltages and close electrode spacing the operating frequency range can be extended to quite high frequencies. At still higher frequencies the output can be calibrated with a thermal meter or a rectifier.

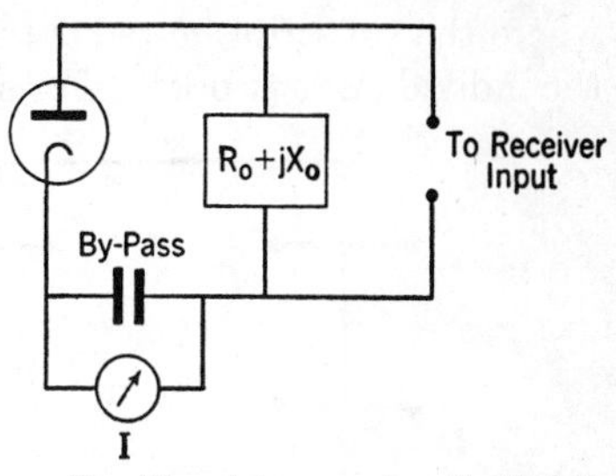

FIG. 26. A temperature-limited diode connected as a random-noise generator. (R_0 and X_0 are varied to match the receiver input.)

According to Eq. (41) the noise output current of a temperature-limited diode is

$$\overline{I_N^2} = 2\kappa I \,\Delta F \qquad (148)$$

where κ is the electronic charge $= 1.60 \times 10^{-19}$ coulomb; I is the average anode current, in amperes; ΔF is the bandwidth, in cycles per seconds; and I_N is given in amperes.

By connecting the diode as shown in Fig. 26 it follows from Sec. 6.4 that the diode will act as a noise voltage generator of voltage

$$E_N = \sqrt{(R_0^2 + X_0^2)2\kappa I \,\Delta F} \qquad (149)$$

and having an output impedance $R_0 + jX_0$. The internal alternating-current impedance of the diode is to be included in calculating the effective value of R_0 and X_0 in accordance with Sec. 6.5*c*. The resistive component of the internal impedance of a temperature-limited diode is usually so large that it can be neglected, but the shunt capacity is important. When noise figures are measured, X_0 should be adjusted to a value which tunes out the input reactance of the network being measured. Then the noise generator may be considered to generate a voltage $R_0 \sqrt{2\kappa I \,\Delta F}$, and to have an internal series impedance R_0, and to operate into a resistive input. These are the most convenient conditions for the measurement of noise figures. The output of the noise generator can readily be varied by adjusting the cathode heating current and thus changing I. The temperature-limited diode is a very convenient noise generator for the broadcast and medium-high-frequency ranges. At the highest frequencies, specially designed noise generators of more complicated types must be used.

h. Noise Figures for Two or More Networks in Cascade. Let us suppose that we have two networks in cascade, as shown in Fig. 27, and that we wish to know the noise figure of the combination in terms of the noise figures of the individual networks. To find this, let us first consider the combination as a single network. Then, according to Eq. (142), the available noise output N_{ab} is

$$N_{ab} = F_{ab}G_{ab}kTB_{ab} \tag{150}$$

where the subscript ab refers to the combination, and a and b refer to the individual networks. For simplicity, let us assume that the band-

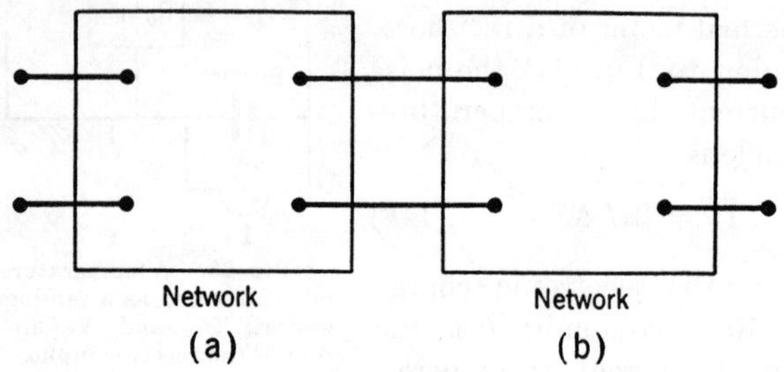

FIG. 27. Combination of two networks in cascade.

widths of the two networks are identical and equal to the bandwidth of the combination. Thus

$$B_{ab} = B_a = B_b = B \tag{151}$$

From Fig. 27 it is also clear that

$$G_{ab} = G_aG_b \tag{152}$$

and, applying Eq. (142) to the single network a, we also have

$$N_a = F_aG_akTB \tag{153}$$

Now this noise would cause a noise output from b of

$$G_bN_a = F_aG_bG_akTB \tag{154}$$

if there were no noise generated in the network b itself. Furthermore, according to Sec. 6.9e, the noise output of b due to noise generated within it is

$$(F_b - 1)G_bkTB \tag{155}$$

The total noise output of b is then the sum of Eqs. (154) and (155). Accordingly,

$$\begin{aligned} N_{ab} &= (F_b - 1)G_bkTB + F_aG_aG_bkTB \\ &= \left(F_a + \frac{F_b - 1}{G_a}\right)G_aG_bkTB = \left(F_a + \frac{F_b - 1}{G_a}\right)G_{ab}kTB \end{aligned} \tag{156}$$

Comparing Eq. (156) with Eq. (150), we have

$$F_{ab} = F_a + \frac{F_b - 1}{G_a} \tag{157}$$

This gives the noise figure of the combination of the two networks in cascade in terms of the noise figures of the individual networks and the gain of the earlier one. The derivation of Eq. (157) involved the assumption of equal bandwidths for the two networks. If this assumption is not justified, the formula for F_{ab} will be more complicated.

Formula (157) can readily be generalized for more than two networks in cascade. Thus, if the three networks a, b, and c are in cascade, we have

$$F_{abc} = F_{ab} + \frac{F_c - 1}{G_{ab}} = F_a + \frac{F_b - 1}{G_a} + \frac{F_c - 1}{G_a G_b} \tag{158}$$

If the gains of the individual networks are appreciably greater than unity, only the noise figures of the earlier ones will be important.

The discussion in Sec. 6.7*c* of the effect of coupling between the antenna and input circuits on the signal-to-noise ratio shows that the best noise figure for a combination of two networks[1] is not necessarily obtained when the impedances of the networks are matched. The methods of Sec. 6.7*c* can be used as a guide in analyzing any particular case of interest.

i. The Measurement of Noise Figures with Networks in Cascade. When two networks are in cascade, as shown in Fig. 27, if the gain of the earlier network is low, it may be necessary to determine its noise figure by indirect means. This may happen, for example, if the network a is the radio-frequency stage of an ultra-high-frequency amplifier. In this case, if F_b and F_{ab} can be determined by the standard means of measuring noise figure and if the gain G_a of the network a can be determined by inserting and removing the network a, then F_a can be determined by substitution in Eq. (157).

A second method of measurement of F_a and F_{ab} is based upon what is known as the Y figure of a divided network. Suppose that the input of the network b is connected to a passive impedance[2] having the value of the output impedance of the network a. Then the noise output of the network b is

$$N_b = F_b G_b k T B_b \tag{159}$$

[1] The two networks in that case were the antenna circuit and the rest of the receiver.

[2] A passive impedance is one that generates no emf other than its normal thermal noise.

Let us now define Y by the equation

$$Y = \frac{N_{ab}}{N_b} \tag{160}$$

From Eqs. (150), (159), and (160) it then follows that

$$F_{ab} = \frac{F_b Y}{G_a} \frac{B_b}{B_{ab}} \tag{161}$$

If we continue with the previously made simplifying assumption of the equality of bandwidths, then Eq. (161) becomes

$$F_{ab} = \frac{F_b Y}{G_a} \tag{162}$$

Substituting Eq. (162) into Eq. (157), we obtain

$$F_a = \frac{F_b(Y - 1) + 1}{G_a} \tag{163}$$

Equations (162) and (163) are often convenient formulas for determining F_a and F_{ab}. It is frequently easier to measure F_b, Y, and G_a directly than it is to measure F_a or F_{ab}.

j. The Noise Figure as a Measure of Noise Quality. The noise figure of a network, particularly a receiver, has come into widespread use in recent years as a fundamental measure of noise quality. We now wish to pause briefly to consider the merits and demerits of the noise figure for this purpose.

The outstanding merit of the noise figure is that it directly compares (or should compare) the actual noise obtained with that which would be obtained if the network were ideal from a noise standpoint. This is an absolute measure of quality and immediately tells whether it is possible and worth while to try to improve the noise characteristics. A second advantage of the noise figure is that it applies to four-terminal networks in general and is not limited to receivers. Finally, the noise-figure method has the convenient property that it has simple means for combining the noise figures of networks in cascade.

Against these advantages, there are certain disadvantages whose importance should be weighed. The fundamental disadvantage of the noise-figure definition is that it assumes that the actual selectivity (gain vs. frequency) curve of the network is also the optimum possible for best signal-to-noise ratio in the output. In Chap. IV, we discussed the effects of the width of the pass band on the signal-to-noise ratio for the elementary case of uniform transmission in the pass band, and we found that there is an optimum value. According to the noise-figure definition a network is not penalized for an improper selectivity characteristic, even though this may cause serious deterioration of its noise quality. To separate the noise and selectivity characteristics, it has been suggested that noise figure shall be defined for each narrow frequency band df by the ratio

$$F = \frac{dN}{G_f kT\, df} \tag{164}$$

This "differential noise figure" may then be plotted as a function of frequency to show the noise characteristics of the network. While this has considerable value, the real quantity of interest is the ratio of the actual total noise to the amount that it could be under the best possible noise conditions. In other words, a properly defined total noise figure F is what is really desired, and this includes a determination of how near the selectivity characteristic of the receiver is to what it should be for best signal-to-noise ratio.

Another important point is the matter of noise in the intermediate-frequency and image channels of a receiver. If a receiver responds to input noise in the intermediate-frequency and image channels, it should be penalized for so doing. To take care of this question, we can limit the integral in Eq. (138) to the signal-frequency channel. Then any gain that the complete receiver has in the intermediate-frequency and image channels will not contribute to the bandwidth B, which is used in Eq. (142) in determining the noise figure. If this change is made in the definition of B, the noise figure cannot be criticized for not taking intermediate-frequency and image-channel noise into account.

k. The "Absolute Sensitivity," or "Field-strength Sensitivity," of a Receiving Installation.[1] We have now discussed the noise ratings of signals and of receivers or networks. Let us next turn to the noise rating of a complete receiving installation. In rating a receiving installation the question of interest is how large a field strength is required of the incoming signal in order that the signal should override the noise. In order to be specific, North has rated receiving installations on the basis of the field strength required to give a signal output equal to the noise output. He has called the numerical value of this field strength the *absolute sensitivity* of a receiving installation. As a somewhat more descriptive name, we shall call it the *field-strength sensitivity*.

[1] NORTH, D. O., The Absolute Sensitivity of Radio Receivers," *R.C.A. Rev.*, January, 1942.

In Fig. 28 is a schematic diagram of a receiving installation. If R_a is the resistive component of the antenna impedance, then the available signal power that the receiver can get from the antenna is

$$\frac{(Eh)^2}{R_a} \tag{165}$$

where E is the field strength of the incoming field and h is the effective height of the antenna. At the same time, the total available noise power is

$$4k(T_A R_A + TR)B \tag{166}$$

where T_A = effective temperature of radiation resistance [defined in Eq. (90)]
B = bandwidth
R_A = radiation resistance of antenna
R = ohmic component of antenna resistance

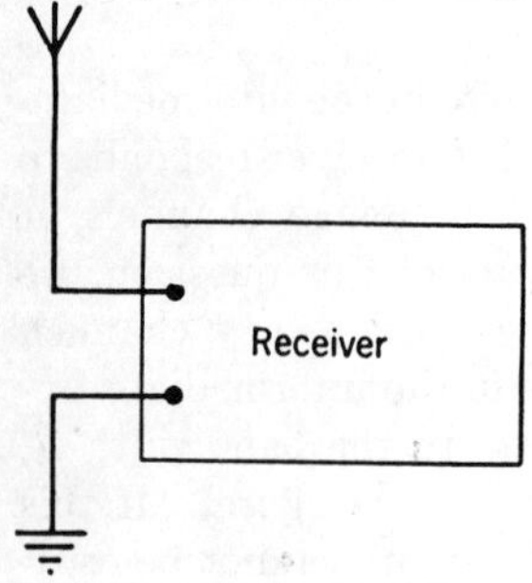

FIG. 28. Schematic diagram of a receiving installation.

so that

$$R_A + R = R_a \tag{167}$$

The signal power output of the receiver will be

$$\frac{(Eh)^2}{R_A + R} cG \tag{168}$$

where G is the power gain of the receiver and c is the ratio of the actual signal power into the receiver divided by the available signal power. At the same time, the noise power output of the receiver is

$$4kTRBcG + 4kT_A R_A BcG + 4kT(R_A + R)(F - 1)BcG \tag{169}$$

where the last term in Eq. (169 is due to noise generated within the receiver. The constant c in Eq. (169) may be assumed equal to c in Eq. (168) for a reasonably well-designed installation.

According to the definition given above the field-strength sensitivity is that value of E for which Eqs. (168) and (169) are equal. If we call the field-strength sensitivity E_S, then

$$E_S^2 = \frac{4k(R_A + R)B}{h^2} [TR + T_A R_A + T(R_A + R)(F - 1)] \tag{170}$$

The effective height h depends upon the polarization and direction of arrival of the incoming wave. North[1] has shown that the effective

[1] NORTH, D. D., The Absolute Sensitivity of Radio Receivers, *R.C.A. Rev.*, January, 1942.

height can be expressed in terms of the wavelength λ, the power directivity of the antenna, $D^2(\alpha,\beta,\phi)$, and the radiation resistance R_A. In particular,

$$h^2(\alpha,\beta,\phi) = \frac{\lambda^2}{2\pi}\frac{R_A}{120\pi}D^2(\alpha,\beta,\phi) \tag{171}$$[1]

where α and β are angular coordinates defining the direction of arrival of the incoming wave and ϕ defines its direction of polarization. Substituting Eq. (171) into Eq. (170), we have

$$E_S^2 = \frac{4k(R_A + R)B}{\left(\frac{\lambda^2}{2\pi}\right)\left(\frac{R_A}{120\pi}\right)D^2(\alpha,\beta,\phi)}[TR + T_AR_A + T(R_A + R)(F-1)] \tag{172}$$

This is a general formula for field-strength sensitivity. If R is negligible, it reduces to

$$E_S^2 = \frac{960\pi^2kTB}{\lambda^2D^2(\alpha,\beta,\phi)}\left(F + \frac{T_A}{T} - 1\right) \tag{173}$$

where, by previous convention, we have chosen $T = 290°$. The quantity $F + T_A/T - 1$ has been called the *operating noise factor* by North. Equation (173) shows the effect on the field-strength sensitivity of the wavelength, antenna directivity, receiver noise, and the incoming noise field. However, the practical value of the equation is limited by the difficulties in determining $D^2(\alpha,\beta,\phi)$ and T_A. But these difficulties are by no means insuperable; and since the field-strength sensitivity is the real quantity of interest in rating receiving installations, determinations of E_S may come into more common use.

The quantity T_A, the effective temperature of radiation resistance, is of great practical importance. This quantity depends upon the directional receiving pattern of the antenna as installed and upon the wavelength. In the broadcast band, owing to atmospherics, T_A is much higher than the standard temperature ($T = 290°$). At frequencies above 50 mc, T_A continues to be higher than the standard temperature in urban localities in the daytime owing to diathermy noise and in all localities in certain directions of reception at all times owing to interstellar interference. However, it appears that at extremely high frequencies, with an antenna directed to eliminate interstellar interference as far as possible, values of T_A below the standard temperature might be obtainable.

[1] $D^2(\alpha,\beta,\phi)$ is normalized so that its average value for all possible values of α, β, and ϕ is unity.

l. The Noise Rating of Transmission Systems. Before closing the subject of noise rating, a few words should be said about the noise ratings of transmission systems, including both transmitter and receiver. One quantity of interest here is the power required to obtain a certain operating range in miles. Another matter of interest is the so-called "noise-reducing" properties obtainable with the system after a certain signal-to-noise threshold is exceeded. The noise-reducing properties of FM and pulse modulation are considered in later sections. All that need be said here is that, as far as operating range as determined by the ability to get information through above unavoidable random noise is concerned, it appears that no system can do better for a given average power than ordinary amplitude modulation. In fact, the way in which all systems seem to find this an insuperable limit suggests that we are here operating with something like a law of nature, of the type of the second law of thermodynamics, but here applied to information vs. fluctuation noise. A somewhat different situation exists in noise-reduction schemes for signals already above the noise threshold, in which the amount of noise reduction obtainable depends upon the bandwidth and upon special characteristics of the type of modulation.[1]

Exercises

1. Show that, if all the internal noise generated in an amplifier is due to the noise generated in the resistive component of the grid circut of its first tube, then the noise figure of the amplifier is $F = 2$.

2. Show that, if the input leads of an amplifier go directly to grid and ground of the first tube, and if the first tube has a high gain and has a negligible equivalent grid noise resistance, then the noise figure of the amplifier is $F = 1$. All the noise in this case comes in with the signal. None is generated in the amplifier itself.

3. If the input circuit of an amplifier has a resistive component R_0 between grid and ground, and if the first tube has an equivalent grid noise resistance R_{eq} show that

$$F = 2\left(1 + 2\frac{R_{eq}}{R_0}\right)$$

provided that no appreciable noise is generated in the amplifier after the first tube.

4. In the circuit of Fig. 16, assume that the input circuit is critically coupled when the antenna is connected and that there is no resistance in the antenna circuit primary except the radiation resistance of the antenna. Assume that the grid-to-

[1] In a paper written after the present book was in process of publication, the author has analyzed more fully the problems discussed in this paragraph from the point of view of general information theory. This paper, entitled Some Fundamental Considerations Concerning Noise Reduction and Range in Radar and Communication, will be published in *Proc. I.R.E.*

ground resistance of the input tube, when the antenna is connected, is 150,000 ohms and that the R_{eq} of the tube is 240,000 ohms. Show that

$$F = 2\left(1 + \frac{240,000}{150,000}\right) = 5.2$$

5. In the circuit of Fig. 17, assume that the input circuit is critically coupled when the antenna is connected and that there is no resistance in the antenna circuit primary except the radiation resistance of the antenna. For the numerical values given in Sec. 6.7*b*, show that

$$F = 2\left(\frac{145,377}{100,000}\right) = 2.9$$

6.10 Noise at Frequencies for Which Input Conductance Is Appreciable. *a. Introduction.* The theory of the shot effect at frequencies so high that transit time is no longer negligible is discussed in some detail in Sec. 8.8. Here we shall only outline the results and show their practical application. Theory predicts that for the temperature-limited diode the shot noise should gradually fall off with frequency as the transit time becomes appreciable. On the other hand, for the space-charge-limited diode, theory predicts that the shot noise will rise with frequency as transit angles become appreciable, because the noise-reduction effects of space charge deteriorate. For the more important case of the negative-grid triode operated in the space-charge-controlled region, in addition to the rise in shot noise that occurs for the corresponding diode, there is also additional shot noise due to noise induced in the grid circuit by the plate-current fluctuations as they pass the grid. It so happens that, at the same frequencies for which this grid-induced shot effect becomes important, the triode also starts to show input conductance. In Sec. 8.8 it is pointed out that the size of the grid-current fluctuations due to grid-induced shot effect are given by the formula

$$\overline{i_g^2} = 1.43(4kT_c g_g\,\Delta F) \tag{174}$$

where g_g is the input conductance of the tube and T_c is its cathode temperature. It thus appears that the input conductance of the tube may be considered as a source of thermal noise. However, its effective temperature ($1.43T_c$) is about five times as high as room temperature, so that, correspondingly, the noise power that it generates is five times as great. We may therefore conclude that, owing to transit times, the shot effect in tubes rises with frequency and, furthermore, that it is considerably worse for tubes with grids than it is for diodes.

b. The Conversion Conductance of a Linear Rectifier. At this point, we shall digress for a moment to calculate the conversion conductance of a linear rectifier. Suppose that we have a linear rectifier having the current-voltage characteristic

$$\left.\begin{aligned} i &= ge \qquad (\text{when } e > 0) \\ &= 0 \qquad (\text{when } e < 0) \end{aligned}\right\} \tag{175}$$

where i is current, e is voltage, and g is a constant. Such a rectifier might be either a diode or a crystal operated at high signal levels. Next suppose that we apply to the rectifier a voltage

$$e = A \cos \omega t + B \cos [(\omega + \alpha)t] \tag{176}$$

where $A \cos \omega t$ is the large signal coming from the local oscillator of a superheterodyne receiver and $B \cos [(\omega + \alpha)t]$ is the relatively small

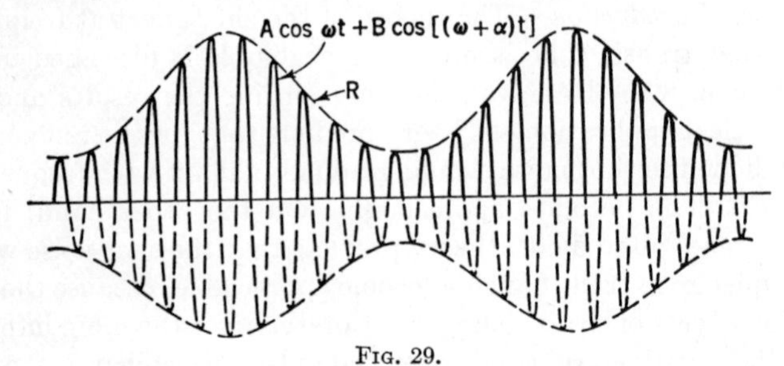

FIG. 29.

incoming signal. The voltage e is shown in Fig. 29, and so is its envelope. If we let R stand for the envelope of e, then, according to Eqs. (42) and (44) of Chap. V if $B/A \ll 1$,

$$R = A + B \cos \alpha t \tag{177}$$

If the output of the linear rectifier to which the voltage e is applied has the high frequencies ω and $\omega + \alpha$, etc., filtered out of it and if $\omega \gg \alpha$, it is clear from Fig. 29 that the remaining output i_1 will be approximately

$$i_1 = \frac{gR}{\pi} = \frac{gA}{\pi} + \frac{gB}{\pi} \cos \alpha t \tag{178}$$

since the average value of a half sine wave is $1/\pi$ times its peak value, *i.e.*,

$$\frac{1}{2\pi} \int_0^{\pi} R_0 \sin \omega t \, d(\omega t) = \frac{2R_0}{2\pi} = \frac{R_0}{\pi} \tag{179}$$

Since α is the intermediate frequency of the signal corresponding to Eq. (176), it follows from Eqs. (176) and (178) that the conversion conductance of a linear rectifier is

$$g_c = \frac{g}{\pi} \tag{180}$$

c. Ultra-high-frequency Converters. In the light of the foregoing development, we now shall briefly discuss ultra-high-frequency converters from the standpoint of noisiness. Since converters are one of the principal sources of noise, if not the principal source, at the highest frequencies, this subject is of special importance.

In Sec. 6.5*h* it is pointed out that triode mixers are less noisy than pentode or other types of multigrid mixers or converters. Consequently, the triode is to be preferred over the other types of converters discussed in Secs. 6.5*g* and *h*. However, at ultra-high frequencies, the grid-induced shot noise present in a triode suggests that a diode, since it does not have such noise, may be a less noisy converter. In Eq. (71) it is shown that the equivalent grid noise resistance of a triode mixer at low frequencies is

$$R_{eq} \text{ (triode)} = \frac{0.644}{\sigma} \frac{T_c}{T} \frac{\overline{g_m}}{g_c^2} \tag{181}$$

When transit times become appreciable, we must add to this the equivalent resistance of the grid-induced shot noise according to (174) and obtain

$$R'_{eq} \text{ (triode)} = \frac{0.644}{\sigma} \frac{T_c}{T} \frac{\overline{g_m}}{g_c^2} + 1.43 \frac{T_c}{T} \frac{1}{g_g} \tag{182}$$[1]

R_{eq} would be still further increased if we took into account the fact that space-charge noise-reduction effects have started to get out of phase.

To compare with (182), we have for a diode rectifier, according to Eqs. (43) and (180),

$$\begin{aligned} R_{eq} \text{ (diode)} &= 0.644 \frac{T_c}{T} \frac{g}{g_c} \frac{1}{g} \\ &= 0.644 \frac{T_c}{T} \frac{1}{g_c} = 0.644 \frac{T_c}{T} \frac{\pi}{g} \end{aligned} \tag{183}$$

For a crystal rectifier, we have, according to Eq. (180)

$$R_{eq} \text{ (crystal)} = \frac{1}{g_c} = \frac{\pi}{g} \tag{184}$$[2]

[1] The last term in Eq. (182) may give the erroneous impression that the larger the value of g_g, the less noisy the triode mixer. Actually, the term $1.43T_c/Tg_g$ represents an equivalent grid noise resistance only if g_g is much larger than the external grid-circuit admittance. When this is not the case, the external grid circuit by-passes a major portion of the grid-induced shot noise.

[2] Crystal noise generally exceeds that due to the crystal's resistance and temperature alone, so that there is apparently some "contact" noise present.

From Eqs. (182) to (184) we may conclude that, of the three cases studied, least noise is generated in the converter when a crystal is used and most noise is generated in the converter when a triode is used. These conclusions are contingent upon the practical obtainable values of the various conductances involved and upon whether or not it is practical to develop the impedances in the antenna and input circuits required to match the input impedance of the converter, or, more accurately, to develop the impedances required for optimum mismatch to obtain minimum noise. It should also be pointed out that the higher conversion gain of a triode, especially at lower frequencies, makes it less likely that later tubes in the receiver will generate appreciable noise when a triode converter is used. Consequently, one cannot make a dogmatic statement about what type of converter is best in any particular case without studying the situation in detail.

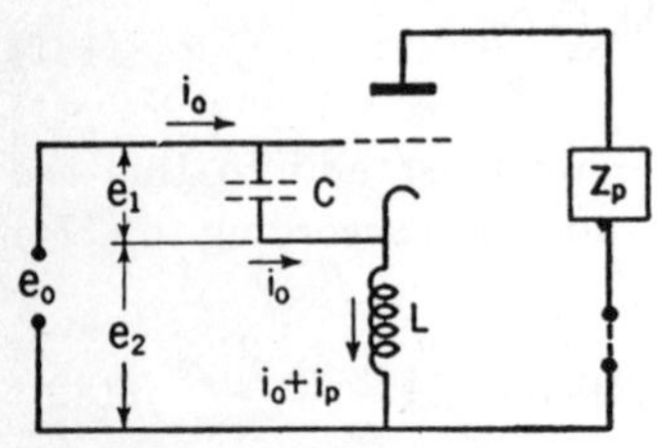

FIG. 30. Input circuit of a tube having cathode lead inductance.

d. Input Loading Due to Cathode Lead Inductance.[1] Earlier in this section, we mentioned the fact that a triode develops input conductance owing to transit time, and we pointed out that this input conductance may be considered a source of noise. We shall now discuss another important cause of input conductance at ultra-high frequencies, namely, cathode lead inductance, and investigate its effect upon noise.

In Fig. 30 is a schematic diagram of the input circuit of a tube showing the grid-to-cathode capacity C and the cathode lead inductance L. We shall now show that feedback across L gives rise to input conductance.

Let e_0 = grid-to-ground (input) voltage
e_1 = grid-to-cathode voltage
e_2 = voltage across L
i_0 = input current
i_p = plate current

Then

$$e_0 = e_1 + e_2 = -\frac{ji_0}{\omega C} + j(i_0 + i_p)\omega L \tag{185}$$

Now

$$i_p = \frac{\mu e_1}{r_p + Z_p} = \frac{-j\mu i_0}{\omega C(r_p + Z_p)} \tag{186}$$

[1] A more complete discussion of this and related subjects is given by Strutt and VanDerZiel, *Proc. I.R.E.*, August, 1938, p. 1011.

where r_p = plate impedance of tube

Z_p = load impedance of tube, and $r_p + Z_p \gg \omega L$

Substituting Eq. (186) into Eq. (185) we have

$$e_0 = -ji_0 \left[\frac{1}{\omega C} - \omega L + j \frac{\mu\omega L}{\omega C(r_p + Z_p)} \right] \tag{187}$$

The apparent input impedance is then

$$\frac{e_0}{i_0} = \frac{\mu\omega L}{\omega C(r_p + Z_p)} - \frac{j}{\omega C} + j\omega L \tag{188}$$

Let us assume that

$$\omega L \ll \frac{1}{\omega C} \quad \text{and} \quad \frac{\mu\omega L}{\omega C(r_p + Z_p)} \ll \frac{1}{\omega C}$$

which is generally true in practice, and transform the apparent series resistance in Eq. (188), $\mu\omega L/\omega C(r_p + Z_p)$, into an equivalent parallel resistance. Using the method of Fig. 31, we obtain

$$\text{Effective parallel input resistance} = \frac{(1/\omega C)^2}{\mu\omega L/\omega C(r_p + Z_p)} = \frac{r_p + Z_p}{\mu\omega^2 LC} \tag{189}$$

This may also be expressed as an equivalent parallel input conductance

$$g_L = \frac{\mu\omega^2 LC}{r_p + Z_p} \tag{190}$$

Equation (190) or (189) gives the input loading due to cathode lead inductance.

Comparison of Eq. (190) with Eq. (51) of Chap. VIII shows that both the input loading due to cathode inductance and the input loading due to transit time increase with the square of the frequency. The situation with respect to noise, however, is different. The increased noise due to cathode loading is the increased noise due to feedback of the shot fluctuations of the plate current across L. However, this same feedback causes a regeneration of the signal of essentially the same amount. Since the feedback voltage across L is in quadrature with both the grid voltage and the plate current, the feedback signal and feedback noise are both combined with the original values on an addition-of-power

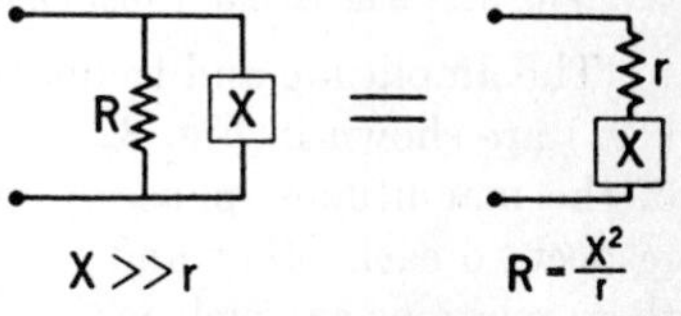

FIG. 31. Transformation of a high parallel resistance into a low series resistance.

basis. *Consequently, the signal-to-noise ratio is essentially unaffected by feedback in the cathode lead inductance.*

Methods of neutralizing the loading effects due to both transit time and cathode lead inductance may be found elsewhere.[1] However, such neutralization does not remove the grid-induced shot noise.

6.11 Noise Reduction in Frequency Modulation. *a. Introduction.* In Secs. 5.5 and 5.8 we discussed the reduction in common-channel interference obtained by using wide-band frequency modulation rather than amplitude modulation. A closely related phenomenon is the reduction of noise obtained by using FM. Before discussing this subject quantitatively, we shall consider a physical picture of what occurs.

In wide-band frequency modulation of a carrier the carrier frequency is varied by relatively large amounts in response to a signal. To be specific, consider the simple FM signal

$$a = A \sin\left(2\pi F t + \frac{\Delta F}{\mu} \sin 2\pi\mu t\right) \tag{191}$$

In Eq. (191) a is the instantaneous value of the amplitude of the FM signal, A is its peak value, t is time, F is the carrier frequency, μ is the modulation frequency, and ΔF is the peak value of the deviation of the carrier frequency from its unmodulated value F. If ΔF is much greater than μ, the signal is said to have wide-band frequency modulation.

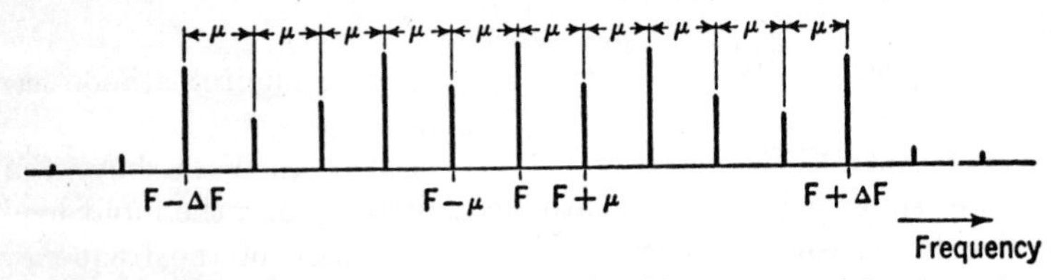

FIG. 32. Sideband distribution in a wide-band frequency-modulated signal.

The amplitude and frequency distribution of the sidebands of Eq. (191) are shown in Fig. 32. A detailed investigation of the relations of the magnitudes, phases,[2] and frequencies of these sidebands with respect to each other and with respect to the carrier will show that these relations are such as to be very effective in causing a large deviation ΔF of the carrier frequency at the rate of the modulation frequency μ. If the magnitudes and phases of the sidebands were distributed at random, the frequency deviation obtained at the rate of the modula-

[1] TERMAN, "Radio Engineers' Handbook," pp. 472–473.

[2] The phases are given in Sec. 5.2.

tion frequency μ would be very much reduced. Here we have the first reason for the noise-reducing properties of FM, since noise consists in a random distribution of sidebands.

When a carrier $A_1 \cos \omega_1 t$ and a single sideband $A_2 \cos \omega_2 t$ are superimposed, the frequency deviation of the carrier caused by the sideband, according to Eq. (48) of Chap. V, is proportional to $\omega_2 - \omega_1$ and the modulating frequency is $(1/2\pi)(\omega_2 - \omega_1)$. Consequently, if a random distribution of noise sidebands is superimposed on a carrier, those sidebands which are most effective in causing frequency deviation of the carrier will cause high modulation frequencies. In wide-band frequency modulation, as, for example, in the FM broadcasting system in use in the United States, most of these modulation-frequency components are of too high an audio frequency to pass through the audio amplifier of the FM receiver. Consequently, they cause no noise. Thus only those noise sidebands which are near the carrier frequency and are therefore relatively ineffective in producing frequency modulation will generally cause noise in an FM receiver. This is in decided contrast with the signal, which has effective sidebands far removed from the carrier and all of whose sidebands act together to swing the carrier frequency at the rate of the signal modulation frequency. Here we have the second reason for the noise-reducing properties of FM.

The discussion of the foregoing two reasons for FM noise reduction requires that the signal level shall exceed the noise, preferably by a good margin of safety. If the noise amplitude exceeds the signal, then (see Sec. 5.8) the noise supplies the effective carrier and the magnitudes, frequencies, and phases of the signal sidebands are no longer correct for causing efficient swinging of the effective carrier frequency. Thus, when the noise level exceeds the signal, the foregoing noise-reducing properties of FM are lost.

It will be noted that we have so far said nothing about the limiter or the balanced discriminator of the FM receiver, which are widely believed by the public to be the cause of FM noise reduction. These are very valuable in an FM receiver, but the function of the limiter is to strip the signal of amplitude modulation, while the balanced discriminator makes pure amplitude modulation ineffective in causing output. With the aid of these devices, the receiver is left sensitive only to frequency modulation, so that the previously mentioned FM noise-reduction properties can take effect without being masked by any amplitude-modulation disturbances. Both the limiter and balanced discriminator are usually necessary in practice, since neither is perfect in operation. The limiter is good with respect to random noise, but its time constant might cause it to miss the early parts of sharp impulses. The latter are largely eliminated from the output by a well-balanced discriminator.

b. The Reduction of Random Noise.[1] The degree of frequency modulation and of amplitude modulation by random noise of a specified amount on a carrier of given size has already been found in Eqs. (13) and (14):

$$m_A = \frac{1}{A} \sqrt{\int 2N^2 \, da} \tag{192}$$

and

$$m_F = \frac{1}{A \, \Delta F} \sqrt{\int 2a^2 N^2 \, da} \tag{193}$$

These equations were derived for the standard case in which the carrier is at the center of the pass band. In the above equations

m_A = degree of amplitude modulation by the noise
m_F = degree of frequency modulation by the noise
ΔF = maximum deviation frequency permitted in FM system
N = rms value of noise in the frequency interval da
a = frequency difference of a given frequency F from the carrier F_0, that is, $a = F - F_0$,

In the case of any particular receivers the integrals in the above equations are integrated over the pass bands of the receivers. If we make the simplifying assumption that the receivers have uniform gain in the pass band so that N, if it is due to shot and thermal noise, is a constant, then the above equations become

$$m_A = \frac{1}{A} \sqrt{\int_{-\frac{1}{2}B_A}^{+\frac{1}{2}B_A} 2N^2 \, da} = \frac{N}{A} \sqrt{2B_A} \tag{194}$$

$$m_F = \frac{1}{A \, \Delta F} \sqrt{\int_{-\frac{1}{2}B_F}^{+\frac{1}{2}B_F} 2N^2 a^2 \, da} = \frac{N}{A} \frac{B_F}{2 \, \Delta F} \frac{\sqrt{2B_F}}{\sqrt{3}} \tag{195}$$

when the pass band of the AM receiver has a width of B_A and the pass band of the FM receiver has a width of B_F.

Now let F_a be the width of the audio pass band of the AM receiver. Normally, we shall then have

$$F_a = \tfrac{1}{2} B_A \tag{196}$$

[1] For a thorough study, including the case when limiting is incomplete, see Carson and Fry, *Bell System Tech. J.*, October, 1937.

The effective noise-to-signal ratio at the output of the receiver, referred to a 100 per cent modulated signal, will then be

$$n_A = \frac{2N}{A} \sqrt{F_a} \tag{197}$$

Let us assume that the FM receiver has the same audio pass band F_a as the AM receiver. Since, as previously pointed out, the audio frequency of the noise will be equal to the frequency difference between the original radio-frequency noise and the carrier, only that noise in Eq. (195) due to components in the range $\pm F_a$ from the carrier will pass through the audio amplifier. Therefore, the effective noise-to-signal ratio at the output of the FM receiver, referred to a 100 per cent modulated signal, will be

$$n_F = \frac{1}{A\,\Delta F} \sqrt{\int_{-F_a}^{+F_a} 2N^2 a^2 \, da} = \frac{2N}{A} \frac{F_a}{\Delta F} \frac{\sqrt{F_a}}{\sqrt{3}} \tag{198}$$

Comparing Eq. (197) with Eq. (198), we obtain for the noise reduction due to FM as compared with AM

$$\text{Noise-voltage-reduction factor} = R = \frac{n_A}{n_F} = \sqrt{3}\,\frac{\Delta F}{F_a} \tag{199}$$

A pictorial idea of the noise reduction[1] of FM is shown in Fig. 33. In the American system of FM broadcasting (see Sec. 5.13) there is an accentuation of high audio frequencies at the transmitter and a compensating reduction of highs at the receiver. Figure 33*c* shows how this compensation still further decreases the noise in an FM receiver. The corresponding change in Eq. (199) is readily shown to be approximately

$$R' = \sqrt{3}\,\frac{\Delta F}{2{,}000} \tag{200}$$

where R' is the noise-voltage-reduction factor of a compensated FM system.

c. The Reduction of Impulse Noise. Let us next consider the way in which FM reduces impulse noise. In Sec. 6.2*a* and *g* it was pointed out that noise of an impulsive type, such as automobile ignition noise, will show increasingly fine detail as the bandwidth of reception is increased, provided that the bandwidth is sufficient to separate the individual impulses. We found in Chap. IV that impulses have a uniform distribution of frequency components throughout the fre-

[1] The shaded areas in Fig. 33 do not have quantitative significance since the abscissas are drawn on a power basis and the ordinates on a voltage basis.

quency spectrum and that these components are all in phase. Consequently, the peak amplitudes of received impulses are proportional to the bandwidth of reception. Furthermore, because of the relations between bandwidth and detail worked out in Chap. IV, the durations of impulses are inversely proportional to the bandwidth of reception. As applied to the reduction of impulse noise in FM reception, the most

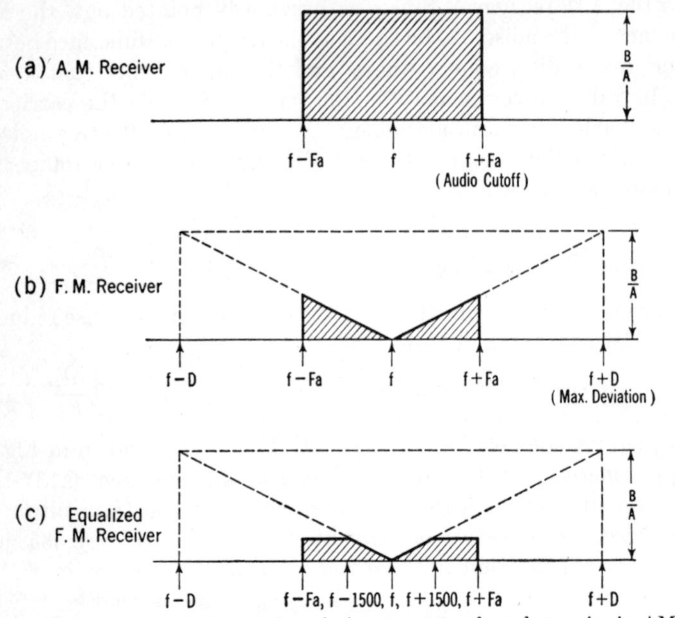

FIG. 33. Pictorial presentation of the relative amounts of random noise in AM and FM reception. ($\Delta F = D$.)

important of the foregoing characteristics is the fact that the amplitude of impulse noise is proportional to the bandwidth. In this respect it differs from random noise, whose amplitude is proportional to the square root of the bandwidth.

We shall now examine the problem analytically and show that an impulse will generally cause both frequency and amplitude modulation of the carrier and that the FM and AM modulating signals will be of a similar nature. Suppose that we have a carrier $A \cos 2\pi Ft$ and an impulse of strength S occurring at time $t = t_1$. Then, according to Sec. 4.18, this may be expressed as

$$\begin{aligned} a &= A \cos 2\pi Ft + S\delta(t - t_1) \\ &= A \cos 2\pi Ft + \frac{S}{\pi} \int_0^\infty \cos\,[\omega(t - t_1)]\, d\omega \end{aligned} \tag{201}$$

If this signal is passed through the receiver having a pass band from $F - (B/2)$ to $F + (B/2)$, it becomes

$$a_1 = A \cos 2\pi Ft + \frac{S}{\pi} \int_{2\pi\left(F-\frac{B}{2}\right)}^{2\pi\left(F+\frac{B}{2}\right)} \cos \omega(t - t_1)\, d\omega$$

$$= A \cos 2\pi Ft + \frac{S}{\pi} \int_{\mu=-\frac{B}{2}}^{\mu=+\frac{B}{2}} \cos [2\pi(F + \mu)t - 2\pi(F + \mu)t_1]\, d\mu \tag{202}$$

The phase angles $2\pi(F + \mu)t_1$ of the sidebands in Eq. (202) are not symmetrical with respect to the carrier because of the presence of F, unless $t_1 = 0$. Therefore, according to Sec. 5.6, they will cause frequency modulation as well as amplitude modulation. Using the method and notation of Sec. 5.6*c*, we can readily determine the amount of amplitude and of frequency modulation. We shall assume that the impulse noise in Eq. (202) is small with respect to the carrier so that the simple analysis for small sidebands will apply. Thus, in the notation of Sec. 5.6*c*,

$$\theta_1 = -2\pi(F + \mu)t_1 \tag{203}$$
$$\theta_2 = +2\pi(F - \mu)t_1 \tag{204}$$
$$B_1 = B_2 = \frac{S}{\pi} \tag{205}$$
$$A = A \tag{206}$$

Substituting in Eqs. (70) and (71) of Chap. V, we have

$$2A_S = \frac{S}{\pi} \sqrt{(1 + \cos 4\pi Ft_1)} = \frac{\sqrt{2}}{\pi} S \cos 2\pi Ft_1 \tag{207}$$

$$\tan \phi_S = \frac{\sin [2\pi(F - \mu)t_1] + \sin [-2\pi(F + \mu)t_1]}{\cos [2\pi(F - \mu)t_1] + \cos [-2\pi(F + \mu)t_1]} = -\tan 2\pi\mu t_1 \tag{208}$$

or

$$\phi_S = -2\pi\mu t_1 \tag{209}$$

Thus the symmetrical sidebands are of amplitude

$$\frac{1}{\pi\sqrt{2}} S \cos 2\pi Ft_1$$

and have a phase shift proportional to frequency. According to Eq. (66) of Chap. V, the AM signal is then

$$a_{AM} = \int_0^{\frac{B}{2}} \frac{\sqrt{2}S}{\pi} \cos 2\pi Ft_1 \cos [2\pi\mu(t - t_1)]\, d\mu$$

$$= \frac{\sqrt{2}S \cos 2\pi Ft_1}{\pi 2\pi(t - t_1)} \sin \left[2\pi \frac{B}{2}(t - t_1)\right] \tag{210}$$

The peak value of Eq. (210) occurs at $t = t_1$, for which

$$a_{AM}\ (\max) = \frac{\sqrt{2}S(B/2)}{\pi} \cos 2\pi F t_1 \tag{211}$$

The form of Eq. (210) is shown in Fig. 34. The peak degree of modulation is

$$\frac{a_{AM}\ (\max)}{A} = \frac{\sqrt{2}S(B/2)}{\pi A} \cos 2\pi F t_1 \tag{212}$$

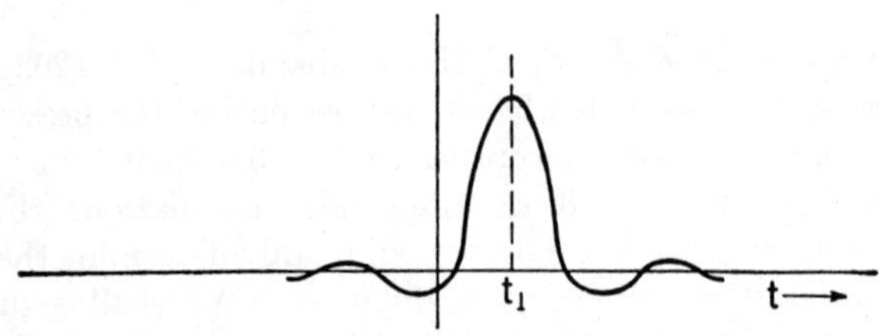

FIG. 34. Amplitude modulation of a carrier due to an impulse at $t = t_1$ (carrier at center of pass band of transmission system).

Next, to find the FM signal, we substitute in Eqs. (72) and (73) of Chap. V, to obtain

$$2A_a = \frac{S}{\pi}\sqrt{1 - \cos 4\pi F t_1} = \frac{\sqrt{2}}{\pi} S \sin 2\pi F t_1 \tag{213}$$

and

$$\tan \phi_a = \frac{\sin\,[-2\pi(F + \mu)t_1] - \sin\,[2\pi(F - \mu)t_1]}{\cos\,[-2\pi(F + \mu)t_1] - \cos\,[2\pi(F - \mu)t_1]} = \cot\,(2\pi\mu t_1) \tag{214}$$

or

$$\phi_a = \frac{\pi}{2} - 2\pi\mu t_1 \tag{215}$$

Thus the antisymmetrical sidebands cause a carrier phase, according to Eqs. (57) and (74) of Chap. V, of

$$2\pi F t + \int_0^{\frac{B}{2}} \frac{\sqrt{2}S}{\pi A} \sin 2\pi F t_1 \sin\left[2\pi\mu(t - t_1) + \frac{\pi}{2}\right] d\mu \tag{216}$$

The instantaneous frequency is $1/2\pi$ times the time derivative of Eq. (216) and is accordingly

$$f = F + \int_0^{\frac{B}{2}} \frac{\sqrt{2}S\mu}{\pi A} \sin 2\pi F t_1 \cos\left[2\pi\mu(t - t_1) + \frac{\pi}{2}\right] d\mu$$

$$= F - \int_0^{\frac{B}{2}} \frac{\sqrt{2}S\mu}{\pi A} \sin 2\pi F t_1 \sin\,[2\pi\mu(t - t_1)]\, d\mu$$

$$= F - \frac{\sqrt{2S} \sin 2\pi F t_1}{\pi A[2\pi(t - t_1)]^2}$$

$$\left\{-2\pi \frac{B}{2}(t - t_1) \cos \left[2\pi \frac{B}{2}(t - t_1)\right] + \sin \left[2\pi \frac{B}{2}(t - t_1)\right]\right\}$$

$$= F - \frac{\sqrt{2S}(B/2)^2 \sin 2\pi F t_1}{\pi A}\left(-\frac{\cos x}{x} + \frac{\sin x}{x^2}\right) \tag{217}$$

where

$$x = 2\pi \frac{B}{2}(t - t_1) \tag{218}$$

The frequency deviation is thus

$$\frac{-\sqrt{2S}\left(\frac{B}{2}\right)^2 \sin 2\pi F t_1}{\pi A}\left(-\frac{\cos x}{x} + \frac{\sin x}{x^2}\right) \tag{219}$$

The form of Eq. (219) is shown in Fig. 35. The peak frequency devia-

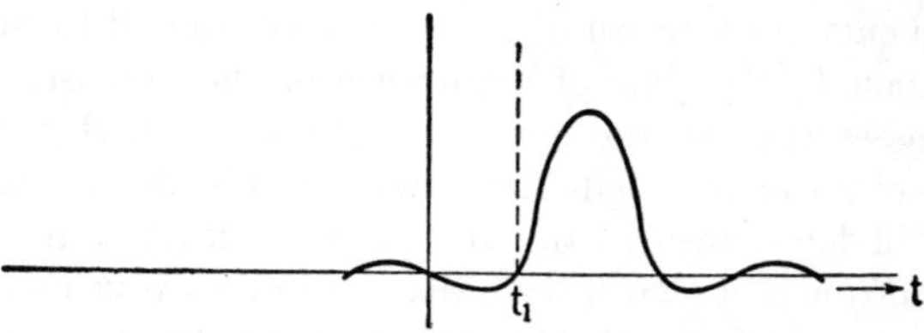

Fig. 35. Frequency modulation of a carrier due to an impulse at $t = t_1$ (carrier at center of pass band of transmission system).

tion occurs when $x = 1.265$, for which value

$$-\frac{\cos x}{x} + \frac{\sin x}{x^2} = 0.357 \tag{220}$$

Thus the maximum frequency deviation is

$$\Delta f_{FM} = \frac{0.357\sqrt{2S}\left(\frac{B}{2}\right)^2 \sin 2\pi F t_1}{\pi A} \tag{221}$$

The peak degree of frequency modulation is then

$$\frac{\Delta f_{FM}}{\Delta F} = \frac{0.357\sqrt{2S}\left(\frac{B}{2}\right)^2 \sin 2\pi F t_1}{\pi A \, \Delta F} \tag{222}$$

Since only those frequencies which get through the audio system will be heard, we must substitute F_a (the width of the audio pass band) for $B/2$ from Eq. (217) on, to get the true audio output. Substituting F_a for $B/2$ in Eq. (222), we obtain for the peak output (referred to a

100 per cent modulated signal)

$$\frac{0.357\sqrt{2}S(F_a)^2 \sin 2\pi F t_1}{\pi A \, \Delta F} \tag{223}$$

For the AM receiver, $B/2$ is equal to F_a so that Eq. (212) becomes

$$\frac{\sqrt{2}SF_a}{\pi A} \cos 2\pi F t_1 \tag{224}$$

To find the noise-voltage-reduction factor of FM for impulse noise, we then divide Eq. (224) by Eq. (223) and obtain

$$R_{\text{impulse}} = \frac{\cot 2\pi F t_1}{0.357} \frac{\Delta F}{F_a} \tag{225}$$

Equation (225) for impulse noise is rather difficult to interpret, because of the factor cot $2\pi F t_1$. This factor expresses the fact that the answer to the question of how much amplitude modulation and how much frequency modulation of the carrier are caused by the impulse depends upon t_1, the time of occurrence of the impulse. After the impulse passes through the amplifier of bandwidth B, it becomes a wave train of the approximate frequency F, but its phase relation to the carrier is still determined by t_1. If we ignore this phase-relation effect, since sin $2\pi F t_1$ and cos $2\pi F t_1$ have the same average value for random values of t_1, we obtain for the remaining noise-voltage-reduction factor

$$\frac{1}{0.357} \frac{\Delta F}{F_a} = 2.8 \frac{\Delta F}{F_a} \tag{226}$$

This may be compared with the corresponding value for random noise given by Eq. (199), and we see that the noise reduction in both cases is proportional to $\Delta F/F_a$.

The practical importance of Eqs. (225) and (226) depends upon whether or not practical impulse noise is similar either to a series of ideal impulses or whether it at least gives wave trains after passing through an amplifier of bandwidth B that are similar to those produced by ideal impulses. There is experimental evidence that there is actually considerable similarity. In any case, the theoretical noise-reduction properties of FM for random noise and impulse noise are quite similar, so that the factor $\Delta F/F_a$ at least may be expected to hold for practical impulse noise.

The foregoing analysis applies to impulse noise that is smaller than the signal carrier as it reaches the frequency detector. For impulse noise that is larger than the carrier, the wide bandwidth of the amplifier ahead of the limiter keeps the impulses short, so that not too much FM quadratic content is left in them after they pass through the limiter. Thus the limiter in wide-band FM tends to reduce impulse noise even if it exceeds the carrier strength. As previously mentioned, both the limiter and the balanced discriminator are relied upon to remove residual amplitude modulation due to impulse noise in an FM receiver.

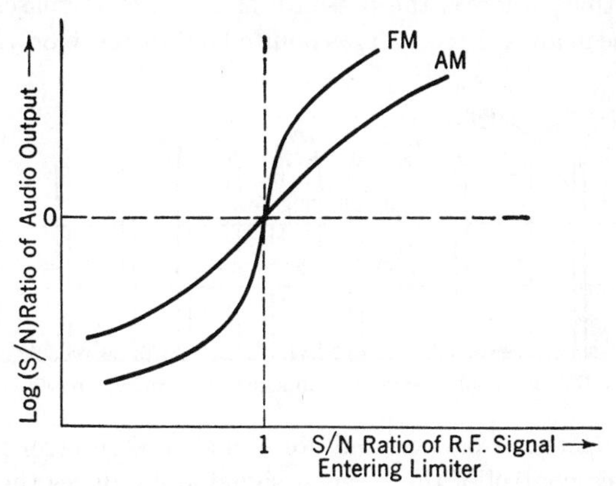

FIG. 36.—Illustration of the improvement threshold (quieting threshold) in FM.

d. Improvement Thresholds and FM Quieting. The noise-reducing properties of FM systems, especially with regard to random noise, require that the signal level shall exceed the noise level. When the noise exceeds the signal, the situation becomes reversed and the noise tends to wipe out the signal. The corresponding phenomenon for interference is illustrated in Fig. 27 of Chap. V; the same figure will serve as well to illustrate noise reduction and is reproduced here as Fig. 36. For a given receiving installation, having a specified amount of noise, there is consequently a sharp threshold value of FM input signal above which the output signal is relatively free of noise and below which the output signal is practically all noise. This threshold is often referred to as an *improvement threshold.*

The receiver noise level for random noise at the input to the limiter is proportional to the square root of the high-frequency bandwidth; and since the bandwidth is approximately equal to twice the peak deviation frequency ΔF, the noise level at the limiter is proportional to $\sqrt{\Delta F}$. On the other hand, the FM noise reduction for random noise is $\sqrt{3}\,\Delta F/F_a$.[1] Consequently, the larger the value of ΔF, the greater the signal required to reach the improvement threshold; on the other

[1] $20 \log_{10} (\sqrt{3}\,\Delta F/F_a)$ is sometimes called the *decibel quieting effect* of an FM system.

hand, the greater the noise reduction once the improvement threshold is reached. Therefore, the optimum value of the maximum frequency deviation ΔF in an FM system is a compromise between the service range in miles required and the decibel quieting effect of FM desired.[1]

Before leaving the general subject of FM quieting, it should be mentioned that, whereas the presence of a carrier increases the background noise in an AM receiver, as pointed out in Sec. 6.8*c*, the presence

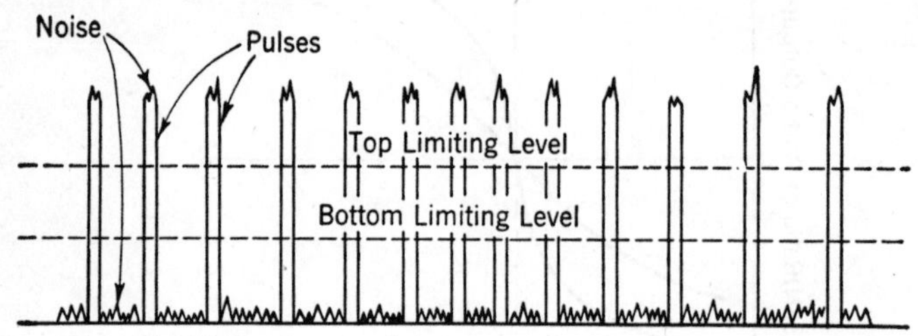

FIG. 37. Pulse-phase-modulation signal with superimposed noise.

of a carrier decreases background noise in an FM receiver because the carrier[2] takes control of the receiver signal and reduces the frequency deviation due to noise to a small value. Consequently, FM receivers are notably quiet during pauses in a program. This phenomenon is not actually different from ordinary FM quieting already discussed, but its effect is especially notable during the passages in a program when there is no signal modulation.

e. Noise Reduction in Pulse-modulation Systems.[3] Various pulse-modulation systems discussed in Sec. 5.12 also have noise-reducing properties. Consider the pulse-phase-modulation signal[4] in Fig. 37, in which a background of superimposed random noise is also shown. In this case, the desired signal, say audio, modulates the pulse phase. The pulses themselves occur at a superaudible rate, say 50,000 per second, and their length is perhaps 1 or 2 μsec. These pulses in turn modulate the radio-frequency carrier. The two dotted lines in Fig. 37 represent the levels of operation of top and bottom limiters, so that

[1] This subject is ably and extensively discussed by M. G. Crosby, The Service Range of Frequency Modulation, *R.C.A. Rev.*, January, 1940, p. 349. Crosby and V. D. Landon are responsible for much of the analysis of the noise reduction by FM systems.

[2] This requires that the carrier shall exceed the noise level, as explained in Sec. 5.8.

[3] Only random noise will here be considered.

[4] This signal has also had the radio frequency removed.

only the signal between the two dotted lines reaches the final pulse-phase detector. Offhand, it might appear that the noise has been completely eliminated, but we shall see on closer investigation that that is not the case.

In Fig. 38 is shown a single pulse from Fig. 37. It will be noted that its sides do not rise and fall vertically but have a finite slope limited by the bandwidth of the system. The dotted sloping lines represent the original signal pulse, and the solid lines represent the pulse with the noise superimposed. The distances N and N' represent the noise amplitudes during the pulse rise and fall, respectively.

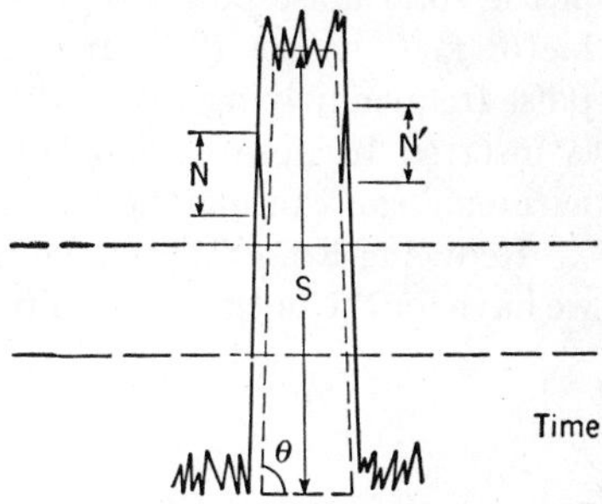

FIG. 38. Expanded view of a single pulse from Fig. 37.

If the pulse-phase detector operates by location of the leading edge of the pulse, the noise in Fig. 38 will cause a change Δt in the location of the pulse where

$$\Delta t = N \cot \theta \tag{227}$$

If $1/T = f_p$ is the unmodulated pulse rate, then the pulse-phase shift due to the noise is

$$\phi'_N = 2\pi \frac{\Delta t}{T} = 2\pi \frac{N}{T} \cot \theta = 2\pi f_p N \cot \theta \tag{228}$$

Furthermore,

$$\tan \theta = \frac{S}{\text{time of rise}} = 2f_c S \qquad \text{(approx)} \tag{229}$$

where f_c is the bandwidth of the frequency components in the pulse (see Sec. 4.7). Substituting Eq. (229) in Eq. (228), we have

$$\phi'_N = \frac{\pi f_p}{f_c} \frac{N}{S} \tag{230}$$

This is the pulse-phase shift caused by noise.

Not all this noise, however, gets through the audio amplifier. If F_a is the bandwidth of the audio amplifier, then only noise components lying within $+F_a$ of the pulse frequency or its harmonics will cause noise that will get through the audio amplifier. Thus, if the noise has components up to the frequency f_B (corresponding to a bandwidth $2f_B$ for the intermediate-frequency amplifier of the receiver), then only a factor

$$2\frac{f_B}{f_p}\frac{F_a}{f_B} = 2\frac{F_a}{f_p} \tag{231}$$

of the total noise power represents effective audio noise power. The factor f_B/f_p in Eq. (231) represents the number of harmonics of the pulse frequency lying within the receiver's bandwidth, and the factor 2 is inserted because components on either side of a pulse-frequency harmonic can cause audio noise.

Reducing Eq. (231) to a voltage basis and inserting it in Eq. (230), we have for the pulse-phase shift caused by *effective* audio noise

$$\phi_N = \sqrt{\frac{2F_a}{f_p}}\frac{\pi f_p}{f_c}\frac{N}{S} \tag{232}$$

If $\Delta\phi$ represents the maximum pulse-phase shift available in the system, then

$$m_N = \frac{\phi_N}{\Delta\phi} = \frac{1}{\Delta\phi}\sqrt{\frac{2F_a}{f_p}}\frac{\pi f_p}{f_c}\frac{N}{S} \tag{233}$$

represents the degree of effective audio noise modulation. We thus see that despite the top and bottom limiters in Figs. 37 and 38 there still is a definite amount of random noise in a pulse-phase-modulation receiver.

Next let us determine the noise-reduction factor of a pulse-phase-modulation system. Other things being similar, the input noise powers in an AM and a PPM receiver stand in the same ratio as their bandwidths. Therefore, if N' represents the AM receiver noise voltage and N represents that of the PPM receiver

$$\frac{N'}{N} = \sqrt{\frac{F_a}{f_B}} \tag{234}$$

where the bandwidth of the AM receiver is $2F_a$. At the same time, owing to the fact that all the PPM signal power is concentrated into the pulses, the ratio of AM and PPM power levels, for the same average power, is

$$\frac{S'}{S} = \sqrt{\frac{a}{T}} = \sqrt{af_p} \tag{235}$$

where a is the pulse length and $T = 1/f_p$ is the time between pulse centers. Combining Eqs. (234) and (235), we have

$$\frac{N'}{S'} = \frac{N}{S}\sqrt{\frac{F_a}{f_B af_p}} \tag{236}$$

Since the degree of effective audio noise modulation in the AM receiver is N'/S', we have for the noise-voltage-reduction factor of PPM, according to Eqs. (233) and (236),

$$R_{\text{PPM}} = \sqrt{\frac{F_a}{f_B a f_p}} \Delta\phi \sqrt{\frac{f_p}{2F_a}} \frac{f_c}{\pi f_p}$$
$$= \frac{\Delta\phi}{\pi\sqrt{2}} \frac{1}{\sqrt{a f_B}} \frac{f_c}{f_p} \qquad (237)[1]$$

Since

$$f_B = f_c = \frac{1}{a} \qquad \text{(approx)} \qquad (238)$$

in a well-designed PPM receiver, Eq. (237) reduces to

$$R'_{\text{PPM}} = \frac{\Delta\phi}{\pi\sqrt{2}} \frac{f_c}{f_p} = \frac{\Delta\phi}{\pi\sqrt{2}} \left(\frac{1}{a f_p}\right) \qquad (239)$$

If we next let

$$\Delta\phi = \pi \qquad (240)$$

which is a reasonable value, we obtain

$$R''_{\text{PPM}} = \frac{1}{\sqrt{2}} \frac{1}{a f_p} = \frac{1}{\sqrt{2}} \frac{T}{a} \qquad (241)$$

The noise reduction is thus inversely proportional to the fraction of the total time that the pulses are on.

The foregoing discussion of noise reduction in pulse-phase modulation illustrates the general methods to be used in calculating the noise reduction in any type of pulse modulation. The reader can calculate the noise reduction of any other type of pulse modulation shown in Sec. 5.12 by similar means.

f. Some General Facts about Improvement Thresholds. In subsection *d* above we noted the existence of an improvement threshold in the case of an FM receiver. It should be realized that the presence of an improvement threshold is not limited to FM systems but is a characteristic of all modulation detectors whose operation depends upon the amplitude, phase, and frequency relations between a transmitted carrier and one or more sets of sidebands. This includes practically all modulation systems in use today except single-sideband amplitude modulation, in which the carrier is supplied at the receiver.

In the case of pulse-phase modulation discussed above, the improvement threshold occurs when the signal pulses are twice as high as the

[1] This result was independently derived by H.O. Peterson.

peak noise fluctuations that are likely to occur during the reception of a message. At this level it is possible to use top and bottom limiters to remove all noise except that which occurs during the time of rise and fall of the pulses. If the signal falls below the improvement-threshold level, the reception of noise between pulses causes a sudden great increase in the noise output, usually so great that it will blanket the desired signal.

In the case of FM, when the signal exceeds the noise entering the detector, the frequency modulation of the signal by the noise is relatively small, as has already been explained. If, however, the noise exceeds the signal, then it is the noise which controls the phase of the signal-plus-noise combination, and the various sidebands of the desired signal are no longer coherent in phase with the effective carrier and can no longer operate effectively in unison to give large amounts of frequency modulation. The transition level between larger signal and larger noise is the improvement threshold in frequency modulation.

In the case of double-sideband amplitude modulation, there is also an improvement threshold. Below this threshold, the noise is large enough so that the carrier is modulated more than 100 per cent most of the time by the noise sidebands. This eliminates most of the desired signal or transforms it into distortion. Above the threshold the upper and lower sets of sidebands of the desired signal, because of their phase relation with respect to each other and with respect to the effective carrier, have double efficiency in causing amplitude modulation.

In all three cases when the signal-to-noise ratio exceeded the improvement threshold, the detector was able to use the coherence of the signal carrier and its sidebands to give the desired signal a magnified response with respect to the noise. Below the improvement threshold, the detector loses its ability to distinguish the coherent sidebands, because it loses its standard of coherence. This standard is the location of the pulses in pulse-phase modulation; it is the frequency and phase of the desired carrier in frequency modulation, and it is the frequency and phase of the desired carrier in amplitude modulation.

The maximum operating range of any communication system is determined by the location at which the signal falls below the improvement threshold. When this occurs, even in ordinary (double-sideband) amplitude modulation, there is a relatively sudden large rise of the noise level which effectively blankets the signal. A realization of this fact is important in the design of communication systems. For example, in the design of an amplitude-modulated communication or radar receiver, if the signal-to-noise ratio is much higher than the improvement threshold, the bandwidth of the receiver prior to the second detector can be increased manyfold in order not to lose the signal in case there is frequency drift of either the transmitter or the receiver oscillator. There will be no loss in signal-to-noise ratio in the final output, despite the increased predetection noise caused by the increased bandwidth, so long as the bandwidth is again narrowed to its optimum value by the audio (or video) amplifier. The situation, however, is quite different in case the signal-to-noise ratio is near the improvement threshold. In that case, widening of the predetection bandwidth to the extent that the signal-to-noise ratio falls into the range[1] of the improvement threshold will cause a rise in noise which cannot be erased by narrowing the bandwidth of the audio (or video) amplifier. For this reason, if maximum range is desired, the predetection bandwidth should not be increased beyond its normal value of twice the modulation frequency range except insofar as is absolutely necessary because of frequency drift.

Finally, it may also be noted that, if by some ingenious means, we can maintain the coherence standard of the detector beyond its normal operating range, the useful range of transmission may be increased. The synchronization of a radar display by the transmitted pulses is an example of this type. Any method of transmitting additional properly phased carrier to an AM receiver to enhance that normally received with the modulated signal carrier would serve a similar purpose.

[1] The improvement threshold has a narrow range of about 3 or 6 db, depending on the type of modulation. The coherence standard is gradually lost as the input signal-to-noise ratio falls to the bottom of this level.

CHAPTER VII

NOISE II: BASIC MATHEMATICAL PHENOMENA

7.0 Introduction.[1] The basis for noise theory is to be found in a group of curious mathematical phenomena mostly concerned with fluctuations and random distributions in the theory of probability. This fascinating subject will now be briefly introduced and those parts of it which we shall require will be developed. This work will then serve as a foundation for the mathematical theory of random noise that is developed in the remainder of the chapter and for the theory of shot noise and thermal noise developed in the following chapters.

7.1 Permutations and Combinations—Binomial Coefficients. Suppose we have the letters a,b,c, and d written on four slips of paper, and let us further suppose that these four slips of paper are folded up and placed in a hat. Let us suppose that these slips of paper are used to let chance decide some issue. Accordingly, the letters may, for example, represent the names of dancing partners, or they may represent parts of a Thanksgiving turkey to be assigned to their holders, or any of countless other items. Now if three persons in a specified order draw letters from the hat, the following different situations may occur as indicated by different letter arrangements!

TABLE I

abc	acb	bac	bca	cab	cba
abd	adb	bad	bda	dab	dba
acd	adc	cad	cda	dac	dca
bcd	bdc	cbd	cdb	dbc	dcb

The 24 different possible situations indicated by Table I are called 24 different *permutations* of the four letters a,b,c, and d taken three at a time. If we ignore different arrangements of the same letters but consider only what letters are involved, then there are only four different possible situations shown in Table I and these are the four shown, for example, in the first column. We describe this situation by saying that there are four different *combinations* of four letters

[1] For an excellent source of additional information on the subject matter of the early parts of this chapter, see T. C. Fry, "Probability and Its Engineering Uses," D. Van Nostrand Company, Inc., New York, 1928.

taken three at a time. In the foregoing example, these combinations tell which dancing partners are chosen or which parts of the turkey are eaten, but they do not tell who got them.

Let us use the symbol P_n^m to stand for the number of different possible permutations of m things taken n at a time. Then a little thought will show that

$$\begin{aligned} P_n^m &= m(m-1)(m-2) \cdots (m-n+1) \\ &= \frac{m!}{(m-n)!} \end{aligned} \qquad (1)^1$$

To show this, we point out that for the first letter there are m choices but for the second only $m - 1$, since the first has already been removed; for the third only $m - 2$ choices; and so on. For the particular case of Table I, Eq. (1) tells us that

$$P_3^4 = \frac{4!}{1!} = 24 \qquad (2)$$

which agrees with what we have found.

As a special case of Eq. (1), we have

$$P_m^m = m! \qquad (3)$$

which means that m things can be arranged in $m!$ different orders. For example, the letters abc can be arranged in the orders

abc, acb, bac, bca, cab, cba

This is

$$3! = 6$$

different orders, in agreement with Eq. (3).

Let us next use the symbol C_n^m to stand for the number of different possible combinations of m things taken n at a time. Then, clearly,

$$C_n^m = \frac{P_n^m}{P_n^n} = \frac{m!}{n!(m-n)!} = \frac{m(m-1) \cdots (m-n+1)}{n!} \qquad (4)$$

Again, in the particular case of Table I, we have

$$C_3^4 = \frac{4!}{3!1!} = \frac{24}{6} = 4 \qquad (5)$$

which also agrees with what we have already found. The reader will shortly be given a chance to test his proficiency in dealing with permu-

[1] The sign ! stands for the factorial, that is, $n! = 1 \times 2 \times 3 \times \cdots \times (n-1) \times n$. It should also be remembered that, by special definition, $0! = 1$.

tations and combinations by working a number of exercises dealing with games of chance.

The quantities C_n^m are also known as *binomial coefficients,* since they are the coefficients of a binomial expansion. Thus

$$(a + x)^m = C_0^m a^m + C_1^m a^{m-1}x + C_2^m a^{m-2}x^2 + \cdots + C_m^m x^m \qquad (6)$$

To show that the coefficients in the expansion (6) agree with the definition of C_n^m in Eq. (4), the reader need only expand $(a + x)^m$ in a Taylor series.

7.2 Probability. As a woman goes to the delivery room of a hospital to have a child, her husband is asked the question: What is the probability that the child will be a girl? His answer is: It is as likely to be a girl as not to be a girl. For the state of the husband's knowledge, his answer is correct. However, since the child is already fully developed, the question of whether it is a boy or a girl is in fact settled: the uncertainty is in the mind of the father. In many scientific problems dealing with probability a similar situation occurs. The actual facts may be settled, but owing to incomplete data, probability theory must be used to deal with a situation.

As far as the father is concerned, the question of whether this particular child is a boy or a girl is a matter of considerable consequence, since it will affect the pattern of his family life. However, as far as society is concerned, the question of whether this particular child is a boy or girl is of little consequence. On the other hand, the question of the numerical probability that a child born will be a girl—which will consequently determine the approximate ratio of men to women in the world—is a matter of the greatest consequence to society. Thus, for example, the social, economic, and political life of the country would be greatly affected if the ratio of men to women departed markedly from its normal approximate value of 1 to 1.

In the foregoing example the father was interested in a particular event, while society was interested in averages. A somewhat parallel situation exists in the theory of random noise. There we deal with the Fourier components of a noise signal. Each component can be dealt with by the laws of electric-circuit theory. However, our practical interest is in the noise signal, which is the superposition of a very large number of these components. It will be our task in the present chapter to develop the mathematical technique for dealing with phenomena which are the result of the superposition of many individual components of random occurrence, each of which can be dealt with by known laws when it exists by itself.

Another aspect of probability theory, and one of great scientific importance, is the matter of *fluctuations*. Thus, while there is essentially the same likelihood that a child to be born will be a boy as it is that it will be a girl, it is common knowledge that a family with six children will not necessarily have three boys and three girls. For instance, the family may have five boys and one girl. Such a deviation from the average is called a fluctuation, and it will be one of our tasks in this chapter to develop the probability laws of fluctuation. We shall find that they are at the very heart of noise theory.

7.3 The Mathematical Development of Probability Theory. In order to develop a mathematical theory of probability, it is necessary to assign numerical magnitudes to probabilities. In the quantitative theory, it is customary to assign a unit value of probability to an event that is certain to occur. Thus, if a coin is tossed, we say that the probability that it will be a head is 0.5 and the probability that it will be a tail is 0.5, while the probability that it will be either a head or a tail is unity. The foregoing also illustrates another feature of the scale, or measure, of probabilities, namely, that, *if two probabilities are mutually exclusive, the probability that either one or the other will occur is equal to the sum of their separate probabilities.*

When we say that the probability that a coin about to be tossed will be a head is 0.5, what we mean mathematically is that, in an arbitrarily large number of independent trials of tossing the coin, 0.5 represents the fraction of the total number of trials which will yield heads. Furthermore, if the matter is controlled purely by probability considerations, it is also true that the probability of obtaining heads is unaffected by what has happened in preceding trials. Thus, the fact that even the 10 preceding trials yielded heads does not affect the 0.5 probability of obtaining heads in the next trial.[1] It may appear to the reader that there is some logical inconsistency in the foregoing; but this is resolved by the fact that, as we shall see, the probability of any perceptible percentage fluctuation from the average approaches zero when the number of trials is made sufficiently large.[2] A situation that is controlled by true probability is called a *random process.* More specifically, *a random process is a process in which the probability of obtaining a particular result in any trial is independent of the results obtained in any other trials.*

[1] However, in practice, it might lead to the suspicion that the probability in the preceding trials was not really 0.5, since the a priori probability of obtaining 10 consecutive heads on a 0.5 probability is only 1/1,024, as we shall see.

[2] For example, see Eq. (64) and Sec. 7.7.

Another important law or axiom of probability theory is that the probability of the simultaneous occurrence of n events is the product of the n individual probabilities of the n events. Thus, if the probability of the occurrence of a head in the tossing of a coin is 0.5, the probability of obtaining two heads in the tossing of two coins is

$$0.5 \times 0.5 = 0.25 \tag{7}$$

On the other hand, the probability of obtaining one head and one tail in tossing two coins is greater than 0.25 since one head and one tail can be obtained in two different ways. Thus, if the first coin tossed is a head and the second a tail, one head and one tail will be obtained, while, if the first coin tossed is a tail and the second a head, the same result of one head and one tail will also be obtained. Now these two possibilities are mutually exclusive (*i.e.*, if one occurs, the other cannot), so that the probability that either one or the other will occur is the sum of their separate probabilities. Consequently, we have

Probability of obtaining one head and one tail in the tossing of two coins

= probability that first is a head and second is a tail + probability that first is a tail and second a head

$$= (0.5 \times 0.5) + (0.5 \times 0.5) = 0.25 + 0.25 = 0.50 \tag{8}$$

The probability of obtaining one head and one tail in the tossing of two coins is therefore 0.50.

With the aid of the foregoing simple rules of probability theory just illustrated,[1] we shall now derive the probability distribution laws that will serve as the basis of noise theory.

7.4 The Bernoulli Distribution Law. *a. Derivation.* We shall use the symbol $P_m(n)$ to stand for the probability that an event will occur exactly n times in m independent trials. We shall now show that, if the probability of the event occurring in any particular trial is p, then

$$P_m(n) = C_n^m p^n(1-p)^{m-n} = \frac{m!}{n!(m-n)!} p^n(1-p)^{m-n} \tag{9}$$

Equation (9) is called the Bernoulli distribution formula.

To prove this formula, we note that the result of n occurrences in m independent trials requires n occurrences (each having a probability p) and $m - n$ "not occurrences" (each having a probability $1 - p$).

[1] Concerning the logical basis for these rules, see T. C. Fry, "Probability and Its Engineering Uses," D. Van Nostrand Company, Inc., New York, 1928.

If we distinguish between the m independent trials by, for example, assigning different letters to each, then the probability of a particular group of n occurrences in m trials is

$$p^n(1 - p)^{m-n}$$

Now there are C_n^m different ways of obtaining n occurrences in m trials, since there are C_n^m different combinations of m things taken n at a time. Consequently,

$$P_m(n) = C_n^m p^n(1 - p)^{m-n} \tag{10}$$

which is what we set out to demonstrate.

As an example, let us calculate the probability of obtaining three heads in five tosses of a coin, using Eq. (10). In this case

$$p = 0.5 \tag{11}$$

$$1 - p = 0.5 \tag{12}$$

$$n = 3 \tag{13}$$

$$m = 5 \tag{14}$$

$$C_n^m = C_3^5 = \frac{5!}{3!2!} = \frac{120}{6 \times 2} = 10 \tag{15}$$

$$P_m(n) = 10(\tfrac{1}{2})^3(\tfrac{1}{2})^2 = \tfrac{10}{32} \tag{16}$$

To illustrate this result in tabular form, let us designate the trials as a, b, c, d, and e; a being the first, b the second, and so on. The possible ways of obtaining three heads are then having heads in the trials

TABLE II

abc
abd
abe
acd
ace
ade
bcd
bce
bde
cde

The probability of obtaining three heads in any particular one of these arrangements is

$$(0.5)^3(1 - 0.5)^2 = \tfrac{1}{32} \tag{17}$$

Consequently, the probability of obtaining three heads in five trials is $\tfrac{10}{32}$.

Exercises

1. Show that the probability of obtaining (*a*) one head in five trials is $5/32$; (*b*) two heads in five trials is $10/32$; (*c*) four heads in five trials is $5/32$; (*d*) five heads in five trials is $1/32$; (*e*) zero heads in five trials is $1/32$.

2. Show that the probability of obtaining either zero, one, two, three, four, or five heads in five trials is unity.

3. *a.* What is the probability of obtaining a sum of 7 when two dice are thrown? *Answer:*

$$6 \times (1/6)^2 = 6/36 = 1/6$$

b. What is the probability of obtaining a sum of 2 when two dice are thrown? *Answer:*

$$1 \times (1/6)^2 = 1/36$$

b. The Average Value of a Bernoulli Distribution. Let us next find the average value of the Bernoulli distribution [Eq. (9)]. As an introduction, we shall calculate the average number of heads that would be obtained in five tosses of a coin if the process were repeated a large number of times. According to the preceding discussion and the exercises, the probability of obtaining zero heads is $1/32$, one head is $5/32$, two heads is $10/32$, three heads is $10/32$, four heads is $5/32$, and five heads is $1/32$. The average number of heads obtained will therefore be

$$(0 \times 1/32) + (1 \times 5/32) + (2 \times 10/32) + (3 \times 10/32) + (4 \times 5/32) + (5 \times 1/32) = 80/32 = 2\tfrac{1}{2} \quad (18)$$

This, of course, is precisely what we should have expected, since, by hypothesis, heads are just as likely to occur as tails.

We shall next calculate the average value of a Bernoulli distribution in general. If $\bar{n}$ stands for the average value of n, we have

$$\bar{n} = \sum_{n=1}^{n=m} nP_m(n) = \sum_{n=1}^{n=m} nC_n^m p^n(1-p)^{m-n} \quad (19)$$

The value of $\bar{n}$ can be obtained by a rather neat trick. Let p and q be any two constants, and let u be a variable. Then, by the binomial theorem [Eq. (6)],

$$(q + pu)^m = C_0^m q^m + C_1^m q^{m-1}pu + C_2^m q^{m-2}(pu)^2 + \cdots + C_m^m (pu)^m \quad (20)$$

and, by differentiation of Eq. (20),

$$\frac{d}{du}(q + pu)^m = C_1^m q^{m-1}p + C_2^m q^{m-2}2p(pu) + \cdots + C_m^m mp(pu)^{m-1} \quad (21)$$

According to the regular formula of differentiation, we also know that

$$\frac{d}{du}(q + pu)^m = mp(q + pu)^{m-1} \tag{22}$$

Therefore, it follows from Eqs. (21) and (22) that

$$C_1^m q^{m-1}p + C_2^m q^{m-2}2p(pu) + \cdots + C_m^m mp(pu)^{m-1} = mp(q + pu)^{m-1} \tag{23}$$

Equation (23) is true for all values of p, q, and u. For our purposes, let us now set

$$q = 1 - p \tag{24}$$
$$u = 1 \tag{25}$$

Then Eq. (23) becomes

$$C_1^m(1 - p)^{m-1}p + C_2^m(1 - p)^{m-2}2p^2 + \cdots + C_m^m mp^m = mp \tag{26}$$

Comparing Eq. (26) with Eq. (19), we see that we have obtained the required value of $\bar{n}$. Thus

$$\bar{n} = mp \tag{27}$$

This is an important formula. We might almost have considered that it followed directly from the definition of p, but it is well to have an independent derivation. The latter shows that the Bernoulli formula (9) does not lead to contraditions.

Exercise

Show that

$$\sum_{n=0}^{n=m} P_m(n) = 1$$

for a Bernoulli distribution. This is as it should be, since the value of n must clearly lie in the range $0 \leq n \leq m$.

7.5 The Poisson Distribution. *a. Derivation.* If the probability p of the occurrence of an event is very small but the number of independent trials, m, is very large and if $m \gg n$, then the Bernoulli distribution formula (9) can be simplified considerably. The simpler form is called a Poisson distribution, and we shall now proceed to derive it.

According to Eq. (9),

$$P_m(n) = \frac{m!}{n!(m - n)!} p^n(1 - p)^{m-n} \tag{28}$$

Now, by Eq. (27)

$$p = \frac{\bar{n}}{m} \tag{29}$$

Furthermore, by definition of the factorial

$$\frac{m!}{(m-n)!} = m(m-1)(m-2) \cdots (m-n+1) \tag{30}$$

Thus (28) may be rewritten

$$\begin{aligned} P_m(n) &= \frac{m(m-1)(m-2) \cdots (m-n+1)}{n!} \left(\frac{\bar{n}}{m}\right)^n \left(1 - \frac{\bar{n}}{m}\right)^{m-n} \\ &= \left(1 - \frac{1}{m}\right)\left(1 - \frac{2}{m}\right) \cdots \left(1 - \frac{n-1}{m}\right)\left(1 - \frac{\bar{n}}{m}\right)^{-n} \\ &\qquad \left(1 - \frac{\bar{n}}{m}\right)^m \frac{(\bar{n})^n}{n!} \end{aligned} \tag{31}$$

If we assume that $m \gg n$ and m is very large,

$$\left(1 - \frac{1}{m}\right)\left(1 - \frac{2}{m}\right) \cdots \left(1 - \frac{n-1}{m}\right) = 1 \quad \text{(approx)} \tag{32}$$

$$\left(1 - \frac{\bar{n}}{m}\right)^{-n} = 1 \quad \text{(approx)} \tag{33}$$

$$\left(1 - \frac{\bar{n}}{m}\right)^m = \epsilon^{-\bar{n}} \qquad (34)^1$$

Therefore Eq. (31) becomes

$$P_m(n) = \epsilon^{-\bar{n}} \frac{(\bar{n})^n}{n!} \tag{35}$$

Equation (35) is called the Poisson distribution formula. It is much simpler and more practical for our purposes than the Bernoulli formula [Eq. (9)], since it involves only n and $\bar{n}$, which are usually available, at least theoretically, and does not involve m and p, which are usually not available in our problems. It must, of course, be remembered that the Poisson distribution requires that m be large and that it be much larger than n, and furthermore p is required to be small. It should also be realized that, for either Eq. (35) or (9) to hold, p must be a constant.

b. A First Example of a Poisson Distribution—Tossing Pennies. As an introductory example of a Poisson distribution, let us consider successive trials of tossing five pennies at a time. Let us calculate the probability of obtaining six sets of all five heads in 100 trials.

[1] We have not previously used the relation (34), but the reader can easily show that when m is very large, the binomial expansion of the left side of Eq. (34) is equal to the Taylor expansion of the right side.

In this case,

$$m = 100 \tag{36}$$

$$n = 6 \tag{37}$$

and

$$\bar{n} = mp = 100 \times \tfrac{1}{32} = 3.12 \tag{38}$$

since we know that the probability of obtaining five heads out of five is

$$p = (\tfrac{1}{2})^5 = \tfrac{1}{32} \tag{39}$$

Substituting these values into Eq. (35), we obtain

$$P_{100}(6) = \frac{\epsilon^{-3.12}(3.12)^6}{6!} = 0.0566 \tag{40}$$

The probability of obtaining five heads out of five, six times in 100 trials, is thus 0.0566.

The probability of obtaining five heads out of five, 7 times in 100 trials, can now also readily be calculated. It is

$$P_{100}(7) = \frac{\epsilon^{-3.12}(3.12)^7}{7!} = 0.0252 \tag{41}$$

Similar probabilities can be calculated in a like manner. It is easy to see that $P_{100}(n)$ is a maximum in this case when $n = 3$.

c. A Second Example of a Poisson Distribution—Thermionic Emission. As a second example of a Poisson distribution, let us consider the emission of electrons from a hot cathode. Let us consider the temperature-limited case, *i.e.*, the case in which all emitted electrons flow to the anode. Let us suppose that the total emission current is 0.1 amp.

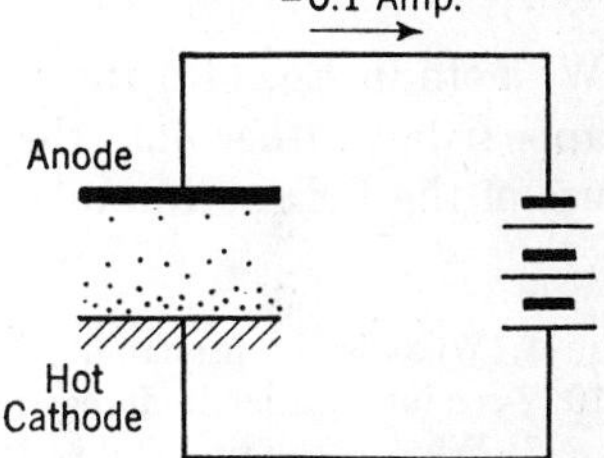

FIG. 1. Flow of electrons in a case of thermionic emission.

Since the charge on an electron is 1.59×10^{-19} coulomb, this means that there are

$$\frac{0.1}{1.59 \times 10^{-19}} = 6.3 \times 10^{17} \text{ electrons} \tag{42}$$

emitted by the cathode per second.

So long as we consider intervals of time of the order of seconds, the number of electrons emitted in successive intervals is approximately constant. We shall see why this is so when we study Gaussian distributions in the next section. However, let us now consider intervals of time of the order of 10^{-20} sec. In such an interval there is a certain probability p that an electron will be emitted (and incidentally a negligible probability that more than one electron will be emitted). We shall assume it to be a law of nature that an electron is just as likely to be emitted in one of these 10^{-20}-sec intervals as another.[1] Thus we are really just assuming that p is a constant. It is also small in comparison with unity. Let us now calculate the probability that, say, six electrons will be emitted in a longer interval of 10^{-17} sec. This longer interval consists of 1,000 of the shorter intervals. We can consider each of the shorter intervals as one trial in the use of Poisson's formula, and the probability of the emission of an electron in this trial is p. Since each trial has equal probability, we can as well as not, in considering 1,000 trials, consider them to be consecutive and thus make up one of the long intervals. Consequently, we have

$$m = 1{,}000 \tag{43}$$

and, according to Eq. (42)

$$\bar{n} = 6.3 \tag{44}$$

for use in Poisson's formula (35). Thus the probability of the emission of just six electrons in a 10^{-17}-sec interval is

$$P_{(1,000)}(6) = \epsilon^{-6.3} \frac{(6.3)^6}{6!} = 0.160 \tag{45}$$

We note in Eq. (45) that the actual values of m and p do not really appear but rather only the values of n and $\bar{n}$. This is typical of the use of the Poisson formula.

Exercises

1. What is the probability that there are exactly four electrons emitted in a 10^{-17}-sec interval in the foregoing example?

2. What is the probability that there are exactly eight electrons emitted in a 10^{-17}-sec interval in the foregoing example?

7.6 The Gaussian Distribution. When the value of n becomes very large, as it does in most cases that will be of interest to us, the calculation of $n!$ and $(\bar{n})^n$ in the Poisson formula becomes unwieldly. For such cases, we shall now show that the Poisson formula reduces to the renowned formula of Gauss.

According to the Poisson formula (35),

$$P_m(n) = \epsilon^{-\bar{n}} \frac{(\bar{n})^n}{n!} \tag{46}$$

[1] This condition of equal probabilities for all intervals is also described as *random emission* of the electrons.

Then

$$\log_\epsilon [P_m(n)] = -\bar{n} + n \log \bar{n} - \log (n!) \tag{47}$$

Now, by Stirling's approximation,[1]

$$\log (n!) = (n + \tfrac{1}{2}) \log n - n + \tfrac{1}{2} \log 2\pi \tag{48}$$

when n is very large. Therefore,

$$\log [P_m(n)] = -\bar{n} + n \log \bar{n} - (n + \tfrac{1}{2}) \log n + n - \tfrac{1}{2} \log 2\pi \tag{49}$$

If we now let

$$D = n - \bar{n} \tag{50}$$

then Eq. (49) becomes

$$\begin{aligned} \log [P_m(n)] &= -\left(n + \frac{1}{2}\right) \log n + \left(n + \frac{1}{2}\right) \log \bar{n} - \frac{1}{2} \log \bar{n} \\ &\qquad - \frac{1}{2} \log 2\pi + (n - \bar{n}) \\ &= -\left(\bar{n} + D + \frac{1}{2}\right) \log \left(1 + \frac{D}{\bar{n}}\right) + D - \frac{1}{2} \log 2\pi\bar{n} \end{aligned} \tag{51}$$

In the region of interest $|D/\bar{n}| \ll 1$, so that we can expand $\log [1 + (D/\bar{n})]$ in a power series and disregard higher power terms. Thus

$$\log \left(1 + \frac{D}{\bar{n}}\right) = \frac{D}{\bar{n}} - \frac{D^2}{2\bar{n}^2} \qquad \text{(approx)} \tag{52}$$

Substituting this value into Eq. (51), we obtain

$$\begin{aligned} \log [P_m(n)] &= -\left(\bar{n} + D + \frac{1}{2}\right)\left(\frac{D}{\bar{n}} - \frac{D^2}{2\bar{n}^2}\right) + D - \frac{1}{2} \log 2\pi\bar{n} \\ &= -\frac{D^2}{2\bar{n}} + \frac{D^3}{2\bar{n}^2} - \frac{1}{2}\frac{D}{\bar{n}} + \frac{D^2}{4\bar{n}^2} - \frac{1}{2} \log 2\pi\bar{n} \end{aligned} \tag{53}$$

If now we assume

$$D \gg 1 \tag{54}$$

in addition to the previously made assumption

$$\left|\frac{D}{\bar{n}}\right| \ll 1 \tag{55}$$

then Eq. (53) reduces to

$$\log [P_m(n)] = -\frac{D^2}{2\bar{n}} - \frac{1}{2} \log 2\pi\bar{n} \tag{56}$$

[1] See WILSON, "Advanced Calculus," p. 386.

It follows from Eq. (56) that

$$P_m(n) = \frac{1}{\sqrt{2\pi\bar{n}}} \epsilon^{-\frac{D^2}{2\bar{n}}} = \frac{1}{\sqrt{2\pi\bar{n}}} \epsilon^{-\frac{(n-\bar{n})^2}{2\bar{n}}} \tag{57}$$

This is the Gaussian distribution formula. It is the formula that applies and is most convenient for use when all the numbers involved are very large.

Equation (57) is sharply peaked at the value $n = \bar{n}$. To show this, let us introduce the variable

$$y = \left(\frac{D}{\bar{n}}\right) \tag{58}$$

so that y represents the fractional deviation from the average value $\bar{n}$. Then Eq. (57) may be written as

$$P_m(n) = \frac{1}{\sqrt{2\pi\bar{n}}} \epsilon^{-\frac{\bar{n}}{2}y^2} \tag{59}$$

If $\bar{n}$ is a very large number, as has already been required by Eqs. (54) and (55), then $P_m(n)$ is very small except in the neighborhood of $y = 0$, that is, the neighborhood of $n = \bar{n}$. $P_m(n)$ is therefore sharply peaked at $n = \bar{n}$.

If we let

$$k = \frac{1}{\sqrt{2\bar{n}}} \tag{60}$$

we can see that the right side of Eq. (57) becomes the well-known Gaussian error function.

As an example of the application of the Gaussian distribution formula, let us consider the case of the thermionic emission of electrons already considered in Sec. 7.5*c*, but let us consider intervals of 10^{-9} second duration. Thus

$$m = 10^{11} \tag{61}$$

meaning that there are 10^{11} intervals of duration 10^{-20} sec in one of the new intervals. Furthermore, by Eq. (42),

$$\bar{n} = 6.3 \times 10^{17} \times 10^{-9} = 6.3 \times 10^{8} \text{ electrons} \tag{62}$$

Then by Eq. (57) the probability that there are exactly 6.3×10^8 electrons emitted in any particular 10^{-9}-sec interval is

$$P_m(\bar{n}) = \frac{1}{\sqrt{2\pi\bar{n}}} \tag{63}$$

This probability is, of course, small, since it is unlikely that there will be exactly $\bar{n}$ electrons emitted in any particular 10^{-9}-sec interval. However, the probability of a deviation of, say, 1 per cent from $\bar{n}$ is breathtakingly much smaller. Thus

$$P_m(1.01\bar{n}) = \frac{1}{\sqrt{2\pi\bar{n}}}\epsilon^{-\frac{\bar{n}}{2}(0.01)^2} = \frac{1}{\sqrt{2\pi\bar{n}}}\epsilon^{-31,500} = \frac{10^{-13,700}}{\sqrt{2\pi\bar{n}}} \tag{64}$$

It is thus clear that, when the numbers involved are large, the probability of a large percentage deviation from the average in a random distribution is slight indeed. Nevertheless, it should be pointed out that it is the deviations, as we shall see, that give rise to such phenomena as shot effect.

7.7 Discussion of the Distribution Formulas. *a. Cause of the Sharp Peak.* There is probably nothing in all human experience that even approaches in the smallness of its numerical magnitude the small probabilities of sizable percentage fluctuations from the average in the random distributions of large numbers of units. We are therefore led to inquire further into the cause and meaning of this remarkable behavior.

Let us first investigate why the Gaussian distribution is so sharply peaked. To get at the root of this, let us consider the Bernoulli distribution (9), of which the Gaussian distribution is a special case. This tells us that

$$P_m(n) = \frac{m!}{n!(m-n)!}p^n(1-p)^{m-n} \tag{65}$$

Here $P_m(n)$ is, as before, the probability that an event will occur exactly n times in m independent trials. If n is changed to $n+1$, then, according to Eq. (65), $P_m(n)$ is increased by the ratio

$$R = \frac{m-n}{n+1}\frac{p}{1-p} \tag{66}$$

Now, according to Eq. (66), R always decreases as n increases. Consequently $P_m(n)$ will have a maximum[1] for

$$R = \frac{m-n}{n+1}\frac{p}{1-p} = 1 \tag{67}$$

In the case of a Gaussian distribution, $m \gg n$ while $n \gg 1$ and $p \ll 1$, so that Eq. (67) reduces to

$$R = \frac{mp}{n} = 1 \qquad \text{(approx)} \tag{68}$$

as the condition for maximum $P_m(n)$.

[1] If R were greater than 1, $P_m(n)$ would be increasing with n, while, if R were less than 1, $P_m(n)$ would be decreasing with n. Since R decreases with n, the maximum value of $P_m(n)$ occurs when $R = 1$.

Equation(68) in conjunction with Eq. (27) shows that the maximum of $P_m(n)$ occurs when

$$n = mp = \bar{n} \tag{69}$$

To show why the peak is so sharp, we note that, as soon as the ratio R differs appreciably from unity, each unit change of n causes an appreciable decrease in $P_m(n)$. Therefore, if $\bar{n}$ is an extremely large number (such as 6.3×10^8 in the example of Sec. 7.6), a small percentage change in n still means a change of n by a very large number of units (that is, 6.3×10^6 in the example). The resulting change in the value of $P_m(n)$ according to Eqs. (68) and (27) is therefore of the order of magnitude of

$$(1.005)^{6,300,000} \sim 10^{13,700} \qquad (70)^1$$

This is the reason for the sharp peak in $P_m(n)$.

b. Elementary Significance of $P_m(n)$. Now that we have found that $P_m(n)$ has such remarkable properties, let us consider once more what $P_m(n)$ really means. To do this, let us consider the electron-emission problem of Sec. 7.6 but consider a length of time consisting only of five of the short 10^{-20}-sec intervals discussed in Sec. 6.5*c*. Thus $m = 5$. While this value of m is too small to make the distribution a Gaussian or even a Poisson distribution, it has the merit that it is small enough to let us get a good grasp of $P_m(n)$. According to our original notation, we let p stand for the probability of the emission of an electron in one of the short intervals, and we assume that it is wholly unlikely that more than one electron will ever be emitted in one of the short intervals. If now we let

1 ≡ an interval in which an electron is emitted
0 ≡ an interval in which no electron is emitted

then the 32 possible combinations exist that are shown in Table III.

Each of these 32 combinations has a certain probability "weight" $p^n(1 - p)^{5-n}$, where n is the total number of electrons emitted according to that possible arrangement. Now there are C_n^5 combinations giving a total number of n electrons emitted. Therefore

$$P_m(n) = C_n^5 p^n(1 - p)^{5-n} \tag{71}$$

is the probability that n electrons will be emitted. The values of $P_m(n)$ are placed next to each group of combinations in Table III.

[1] 1.005 is used as an approximation to the average value of $R = mp/n$ in the range $0.99\,\bar{n} < n < \bar{n}$.

TABLE III

n	Combinations	$P_m(n)$	n	Combinations	$P_m(n)$
0	00000	$(1-p)^5$		00111	
	00001			01011	
	00010			10011	
1	00100	$5p(1-p)^4$		01101	
	01000			10101	
	10000		3	11001	$10p^3(1-p)^2$
				01110	
	00011			10110	
	00101			11010	
	01001			11100	
	10001				
	00110			01111	
2	01010	$10p^2(1-p)^3$		10111	
	10010		4	11011	$5p^4(1-p)$
	01100			11101	
	10100			11110	
	11000				
			5	11111	p^5

The probability weights

$$p^n(1-p)^{5-n}$$

insert the probability p of the emission of an electron in a short interval into the calculation. To convince ourselves that they do this correctly, let us find, according to Table III, the probability of the emission of an electron in one of the short intervals, say the first. Noting the occurrence of 1's in the first column under Combinations of Table III, we have

Probability of emission of an electron in first interval according to Table III

$$= \frac{p(1-p)^4 + 4p^2(1-p)^3 + 6p^3(1-p)^2 + 4p^4(1-p) + p^5}{(1-p)^5 + 5p(1-p)^4 + 10p^2(1-p)^3 + 10p^3(1-p)^2 + 5p^4(1-p) + p^5}$$

$$= \frac{p[p+(1-p)]^4}{[p+(1-p)]^5} = p \tag{72}$$

Table III is thus in agreement with the definition of p.

In the light of the foregoing discussion it is hoped that the reader will see more clearly the significance of $P_m(n)$ and the reason why it can have such a remarkably sharp peak. In the particular case of the electron-emission problem we have seen that the fundamental assumptions are random emission of constant probability p, with the additional assumption that not more than one electron can be emitted in one of the small intervals. Since the actual values of p and of m do not enter into the Poisson or Gaussian formulas, the error due to this additional assumption is not significant since it can be reduced at will by decreasing the length of the small interval.

For convenience in reference we collect here the three distribution formulas and note the specialization that leads from one to the other.

$$\text{(Bernoulli)} \qquad P_m(n) = \frac{m!}{n!(m-n)!} p^n(1-p)^{m-n} \tag{73}$$

This specializes to

$$\text{(Poisson)} \qquad P_m(n) = \epsilon^{-\bar{n}} \frac{(\bar{n})^n}{n!} \qquad \left.\begin{matrix} (\text{when } m \gg n \\ p \ll 1 \\ m \gg 1) \end{matrix}\right\} \tag{74}$$

This specializes further to

$$\text{(Gaussian)} \quad P_m(n) = \frac{1}{\sqrt{2\pi\bar{n}}} \epsilon^{-\frac{(n-\bar{n})^2}{2\bar{n}}} \qquad \left.\begin{matrix} (\text{when } n \gg 1 \\ \dfrac{n-\bar{n}}{\bar{n}} \ll 1 \\ n-\bar{n} \gg 1) \end{matrix}\right\} \tag{75}$$

7.8 A First Discussion of Fluctuations.[1] At this point we shall consider briefly the probability of fluctuations about the average in the case of the Gaussian distribution formula (57), which we recall here.

$$P_m(n) = \frac{1}{\sqrt{2\pi\bar{n}}} \epsilon^{-\frac{(n-\bar{n})^2}{2\bar{n}}} \tag{76}$$

In this formula, $P_m(n)$ is the probability that an event will occur exactly n times in m independent trials, and $\bar{n}$ is the average value of n.*

According to these definitions,

$$D = n - \bar{n} \tag{77}$$

[1] A brilliant but advanced and somewhat difficult discussion of fluctuation theory is given by S. Chandrasekhar, *Rev. Modern Phys.*, January, 1943.

* It is worth pointing out that the specific meaning of $\bar{n}$ is that, if m trials are repeated a very large number of times, the average value of n per m trials will be found to be $\bar{n}$. We have previously shown in Eq. 27 that

$$\bar{n} = mp$$

The entire number of repetitions of the m trials is called an *ensemble* of repetitions, and $\bar{n}$ is then the average taken over the ensemble, or just the ensemble average. In probability theory, $\bar{n}$ is also frequently called the *expectation* of n.

is the deviation from the average value, and the probability of obtaining a particular deviation D is of course numerically the same as the probability of obtaining the value n, since they are just different ways of saying the same thing. Let us write

$$P'_{\bar{n}}(D)$$

for the probability of obtaining the deviation D for a given value of $\bar{n}$. Then, by Eq. (76),

$$P'_{\bar{n}}(D) = P_m(n) = \frac{1}{\sqrt{2\pi\bar{n}}} \epsilon^{-\frac{(n-\bar{n})^2}{2\bar{n}}} = \frac{1}{\sqrt{2\pi\bar{n}}} \epsilon^{-\frac{D^2}{2\bar{n}}} \tag{78}$$

The fact that n is not always equal to $\bar{n}$, that is, that D is not always zero, is described by saying that the phenomenon in question exhibits fluctuations.[1] In the case of electron emission we know that the emission is not always equal to its average value; rather there are slight fluctuations, which give rise to the shot effect. In a more elementary type of example, when two pennies are tossed, we do not always get one head and one tail but sometimes get two heads and sometimes zero heads. The numbers involved in this last example are too small for a Gaussian distribution, but variations from the average value of one head per two pennies tossed are perfectly good examples of fluctuations.

We shall now examine how fluctuations vary in size with the value of $\bar{n}$. We have already had occasion to note in Sec. 7.6 the small probabilities of appreciable percentage deviations from $\bar{n}$ in a Gaussian distribution when $\bar{n}$ is large. If the value of $\bar{n}$ is doubled, the probability of a sizable percentage deviation is tremendously decreased. Thus, according to Eq. (78),

$$P'_{2\bar{n}}(2D) = \frac{1}{\sqrt{4\pi\bar{n}}} \epsilon^{-\frac{4D^2}{4\bar{n}}} = \frac{1}{\sqrt{2}} \epsilon^{-\frac{\bar{n}}{2}\left(\frac{D}{\bar{n}}\right)^2} P'_{\bar{n}}(D) \tag{79}$$

Consequently, if $D/\bar{n}$ is a sizable value and $\bar{n}$ is a very large number, $P'_{2\bar{n}}(2D)$ is practically vanishingly small as compared with $P'_{\bar{n}}(D)$. This means that if $\bar{n}$ is doubled, the probability of the same percentage fluctuation is greatly decreased.

We shall now show, however, that, if the value of $\bar{n}$ is doubled, the magnitudes of corresponding deviations in the new situation go up by a

[1] Fluctuations are sometimes more specifically described as a time function due to D in cases where random values of n follow one another. We shall not specialize the definition of fluctuations in this manner for our present purposes, however.

factor of $\sqrt{2}$. According to Eq. (76)

$$P'_{2\bar{n}}(\sqrt{2}D) = \frac{1}{\sqrt{4\pi\bar{n}}} \epsilon^{-\frac{2D^2}{4\bar{n}}} = \frac{P'_n(D)}{\sqrt{2}} \tag{80}$$

The significance of this situation will best be seen by reference to Fig. 2. If $\bar{n}$ is doubled, a point A of deviation D in the original distribution goes over to a point A' of deviation $\sqrt{2}\,D$ in the new distribution. Now it may be seen from the figure that values of n in a range of width

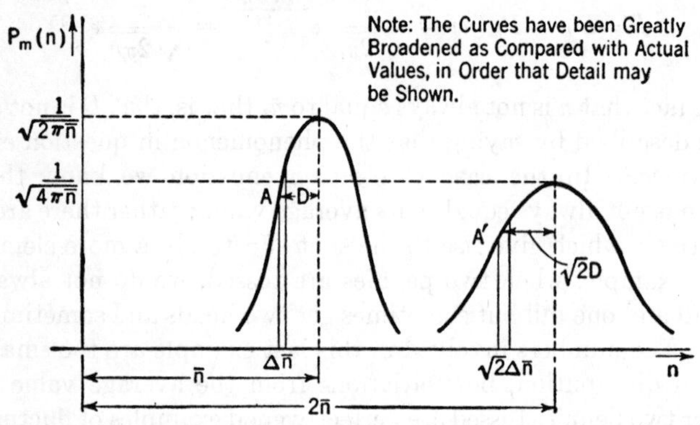

FIG. 2. Change in shape of a Gaussian distribution curve as the number of trials is doubled.

$\Delta\bar{n}$ in the original distribution go over into values of n in a range of width $\sqrt{2}\,\Delta\bar{n}$ in the new distribution. Therefore, even though the probability $P'_{2\bar{n}}(\sqrt{2}D)$ in the new distribution corresponds to the probability $P'_{\bar{n}}(D)$ in the original distribution, the numerical values of probabilities in the new distributions are reduced by a factor $1/\sqrt{2}$, as shown in Eq. (80), since there are $\sqrt{2}$ times as many values of n in corresponding ranges of the new distribution. We have thus shown, in effect, that, when n is doubled, the average deviation goes up as the square root of 2. Equation (80) can readily be generalized to

$$P'_{a\bar{n}}(\sqrt{a}D) = \frac{P'_{\bar{n}}(D)}{\sqrt{a}} \tag{81}$$

which, in view of the foregoing, shows that if $\bar{n}$ goes up by a factor a then the average value of D goes up by a factor $\sqrt{a}$ in a Gaussian distribution.

Finally, we shall derive a simple but very important formula for the average value of D^2 in any Bernoulli distribution, including the

Poisson and Gaussian distributions as special cases. Accordingly, let us write

$$\text{Average value of } D^2 = \overline{D^2} = \overline{(n - \bar{n})^2} = \overline{n^2 - 2\,n\bar{n} + \bar{n}^2}$$
$$= \overline{n^2} - 2\bar{n}\bar{n} + \bar{n}^2 = \overline{n^2} - (\bar{n})^2 \qquad (82)^{1}$$

Now

$$\overline{n^2} = \sum_{n=1}^{n=m} n^2 P_m(n) \qquad (83)$$

To evaluate Eq. (83) we use a procedure similar to that used in Sec. 7.4*b*. Starting from Eq. (21), we have

$$\frac{d}{du}\left[u\frac{d}{du}(q + pu)^m\right] = C_1^m q^{m-1}p + C_2^m q^{m-2}4p^2 + \cdots + C_m^m m^2 p(pu)^{m-1} \qquad (84)$$

By the regular formula of differentiation, we also have

$$\frac{d}{du}\left[u\frac{d}{du}(q + pu)^m\right] = \frac{d}{du}(q + pu)^m + u\frac{d^2}{du^2}(q + pu)^m$$
$$= mp(q + pu)^{m-1} + m(m - 1)p^2(q + pu)^{m-2} \qquad (85)$$

From Eqs. (84) and (85) it follows that

$$C_1^m q^{m-1}p + C_2^m q^{m-2}4p^2 + \cdots + C_m^m m^2 p(pu)^{m-1} = mp(q + pu)^{m-1} + m(m - 1)p^2(q + pu)^{m-2} \qquad (86)$$

As in Sec. 7.4, we now set

$$q = 1 - p \qquad (87)$$

and

$$u = 1 \qquad (88)$$

According to Eqs. (10) and (83), Eq. (86) then becomes

$$\sum_{n=1}^{n=m} n^2 P_m(n) = mp + m(m - 1)p^2 \qquad (89)$$

Now, from Eq. (27), we already know that

$$\bar{n} = mp \qquad (90)$$

so that from Eqs. (89) and (83)

$$\overline{n^2} = \bar{n} + (\bar{n})^2 - p\bar{n} \qquad (90a)$$

[1] $\overline{D^2}$ is sometimes called the "dispersion" of n, and $\sqrt{\overline{D^2}}$ is called the "standard deviation."

Substituting Eqs. (90*a*) and (90) into (82), we obtain

$$\overline{D^2} = \overline{n^2} - (\bar{n})^2 = \bar{n} + (\bar{n})^2 - p\bar{n} - (\bar{n})^2 = \bar{n}(1 - p) \qquad (91)$$

For the special case of a Gaussian distribution, $p \ll 1$, so that Eq. (91) becomes

$$\overline{D^2} = \bar{n} \qquad (92)$$

A simple argument will show that Eq. (92) is actually a consequence of Eq. (81), but we have given a separate derivation since the method and intermediate results are of interest. Equation (92) is sometimes called the law of large numbers. Because of it, percentage deviations from the average become small when the number of trials is large. It is the backbone of fluctuation theory.

Exercise

If 100 pennies are tossed and n represents the number of heads obtained, then $\bar{n} = 50$. Compare the probability of obtaining 48 heads when 100 pennies are tossed with the probability of obtaining 196 heads when 400 pennies are tossed. Compare the result with Eq. (81).

7.9 Superposition of Two or More Probability Distributions. We shall next derive some important results regarding the superposition of two probability distributions. To get a picture of what we are talking about, we shall consider as an example a thermionic tube in which two separate hot cathodes are emitting electrons as shown in Fig. 3. These cathodes have respective probabilities p_1 and p_2 of the emission of an electron in an elementary interval as discussed in Sec. 7.5*c*, for example.

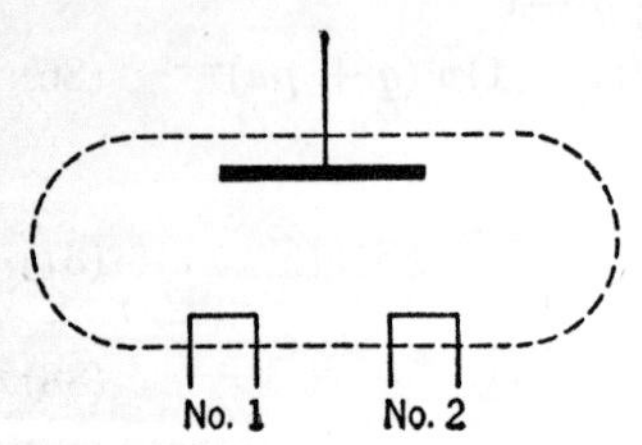

FIG. 3. Two separate cathodes emitting thermionic electrons independently.

In a larger interval, consisting of m elementary intervals, the probability of the emission of n electrons by the respective cathodes may be called

$$P_{1m}(n) \qquad \text{and} \qquad P_{2m}(n)$$

respectively. We now wish to find the probability $P_{3m}(n)$ of the total emission of n electrons by both cathodes together. Taking a numerical case, suppose that we wish to find the probability of the total emission of five electrons. This will occur in the situations

Cathode 1 emits	Cathode 2 emits	Total emission
0	5	5
1	4	5
2	3	5
3	2	5
4	1	5
5	0	5

Now the probability of the simultaneous emission of zero electrons by cathode 1 and five electrons by cathode 2 is

$$P_{1m}(0) \text{ times } P_{2m}(5)$$

and so on, for the other combinations. Therefore

$$\begin{aligned} P_{3m}(5) = P_{1m}(0) \cdot P_{2m}(5) + P_{1m}(1) \cdot P_{2m}(4) + P_{1m}(2)P_{2m}(3) \\ + P_{1m}(3) \cdot P_{2m}(2) + P_{1m}(4)P_{2m}(1) + P_{1m}(5)P_{2m}(0) \end{aligned} \tag{93}$$

In the general case, the equivalent of Eq. (93) may be written

$$P_{3m}(n) = \sum_{n=n_1+n_2} P_{1m}(n_1) \cdot P_{2m}(n_2) \tag{94}$$

where the summation is taken over all values of n_1 and n_2 for which $n_1 + n_2 = n$. Equation (94) is the general equation for the superposition of two probability distributions. However, it is clearly not limited to the foregoing example but holds for any probability distributions.

Let us next find the average value of n in the combined distribution. This is

$$\begin{aligned} \bar{n} &= \sum_{n=0}^{2m} nP_{3m}(n) = \sum_{n=0}^{2m} \sum_{n=n_1+n_2} (n_1 + n_2)P_{1m}(n_1) \cdot P_{2m}(n_2) \\ &= \sum_{n=0}^{n=2m} \sum_{n=n_1+n_2} [n_1P_{1m}(n_1)P_{2m}(n_2) + n_2P_{1m}(n_1)P_{2m}(n_2)] \end{aligned} \tag{95}$$

Therefore

$$\begin{aligned} \bar{n} = \Big[\sum_{n_1=0}^{m} n_1P_{1m}(n_1)\Big]\Big[\sum_{n_2=0}^{m} P_{2m}(n_2)\Big] \\ + \Big[\sum_{n_1=0}^{m} P_{1m}(n_1)\Big]\Big[\sum_{n_2=0}^{m} n_2P_{2m}(n_2)\Big] \end{aligned} \tag{96}$$

The final expression for $\bar{n}$ in Eq. (96) is just a different arrangement of the terms of the expression in (95). Now

$$\sum_{n_1=0}^{m} n_1 P_{1m}(n_1) = \bar{n}_1 \tag{97}$$

$$\sum_{n_2=0}^{m} n_2 P_{2m}(n_2) = \bar{n}_2 \tag{98}$$

and

$$\sum_{n_1=0}^{m} P_{1m}(n_1) = 1 = \sum_{n_2=0}^{m} P_{2m}(n_2) \tag{99}$$

Substituting these values into Eq. (96), we obtain the important formula

$$\bar{n} = \bar{n}_1 + \bar{n}_2 \tag{100}$$

Expressing Eq. (100) in words, we may say that, *if two probability distributions are superimposed, the average value of the new distribution is equal to the sum of the average values of the original distributions.*

Another important relation is obtained by finding the average value of the square of the deviation of the superimposed distributions. Thus

$$\begin{aligned}
\overline{D^2} = \overline{(n - \bar{n})^2} &= \sum_{n=0}^{2m} (n - \bar{n})^2 P_{3m}(n) \\
&= \sum_{n=0}^{2m} \left[(n - \bar{n})^2 \sum_{n=n_1+n_2} P_{1m}(n_1) P_{2m}(n_2) \right] \\
&= \sum_{n=0}^{2m} \sum_{n=n_1+n_2} (n_1 + n_2 - \bar{n}_1 - \bar{n}_2)^2 P_{1m}(n_1) P_{2m}(n_2) \\
&= \sum_{n=0}^{2m} \sum_{n=n_1+n_2} [(n_1 - \bar{n}_1)^2 + 2(n_1 - \bar{n}_1)(n_2 - \bar{n}_2) \\
&\qquad + (n_2 - \bar{n}_2)^2] P_{1m}(n_1) P_{2m}(n_2) \\
&= \left[\sum_{n_1=0}^{m} (n_1 - \bar{n}_1)^2 P_{1m}(n_1) \right] \sum_{n_2=0}^{m} P_{2m}(n_2) \\
&\qquad + 2 \left[\sum_{n_1=0}^{m} (n_1 - \bar{n}_1) P_{1m}(n_1) \right] \left[\sum_{n_2=0}^{m} (n_2 - \bar{n}_2) P_{2m}(n_2) \right] \\
&\qquad + \left[\sum_{n_2=0}^{m} (n_2 - \bar{n}_2)^2 P_{2m}(n_2) \right] \sum_{n_1=0}^{m} P_{1m}(n_1) \\
&= \overline{(n_1 - \bar{n}_1)^2} + 0 + \overline{(n_2 - \bar{n}_2)^2}
\end{aligned} \tag{101}$$

[1]

[1] See Exercise 2 below.

In other words,

$$\overline{(n - \bar{n})^2} = \overline{(n_1 - \bar{n}_1)^2} + \overline{(n_2 - \bar{n}_2)^2} \tag{102}$$

Stated in words, Eq. (102) says that, *if two probability distributions are superimposed, the average value of the squares of the deviations of the new distribution is equal to the sum of the average values of the squares of the deviations of the original distributions.*

Equations (100) and (102) express two of the basic mathematical phenomena used in noise theory.

Exercises

1. Show that

$$\sum_{n=0}^{n=2m} P_{3m}(n) = 1$$

if P_{3m} is defined by Eq. (94) and

$$\sum_{n_1=0}^{m} P_{1m}(n_1) = 1 = \sum_{n_2=0}^{m} P_{2m}(n_2)$$

2. Show that

$$\sum_{n_1=0}^{m} (n_1 - \bar{n}_1)P_{1m}(n_1) = 0 = \sum_{n_2=0}^{m} (n_2 - \bar{n}_2)P_{2m}(n_2)$$

in Eq. (101).

7.10 A Generalized Superposition Theorem for Large Numbers and Continuous Distributions. If n is a function of n_1 and n_2 and if n_1 and n_2 are large numbers in all the important regions under consideration or if they are continuous variables, then the results of the preceding section can be generalized to the following theorem:

If

$$n = An_1 + Bn_2 \tag{103}$$

where n, n_1, and n_2 are stochastic[1] *variables, then*

$$\bar{n} = A\bar{n}_1 + B\bar{n}_2 \tag{104}$$

and

$$\overline{D^2} = A^2\overline{D_1^2} + B^2\overline{D_2^2} \tag{105}$$

[1] The following definition is taken from Uspensky: *Definition:* Variable quantities with a definite range of values each of which, depending on chance, can be attained with a definite probability are called "chance variables" or, using a Greek term, "stochastic variables."

To prove the theorem, let

$$P(n)\,dn = \text{probability of } n \text{ between } n \text{ and } n + dn \tag{106}$$

$$P_1(n_1)\,dn_1 = \text{probability of } n_1 \text{ between } n_1 \text{ and } n_1 + dn_1 \tag{107}$$

and

$$P_2(n_2)\,dn_2 = \text{probability of } n_2 \text{ between } n_2 \text{ and } n_2 + dn_2 \tag{108}$$

where

$$\int_{-\infty}^{+\infty} P(n)\,dn = 1 = \int_{-\infty}^{+\infty} P_1(n_1)\,dn_1 = \int_{-\infty}^{+\infty} P_2(n_2)\,dn_2 \tag{109}$$

For the sake of generality, we have included the possibility that the variables n, n_1, and n_2 may take on negative as well as positive values. If negative values are ruled out, then P is just zero when the variable is negative.

Now according to the second rule in Sec. 7.3,

$$P(n)\,dn = P_1(n_1) \cdot P_2(n_2)\,dn_1\,dn_2 \tag{110}$$

when the element $dn_1\,dn_2$ consists of the values of n_1 and n_2 that correspond to the element dn in accordance with Eq. (103).
Thus

$$\begin{aligned} \bar{n} &= \int_{-\infty}^{+\infty} nP(n)\,dn = \int_{-\infty}^{+\infty}\int_{-\infty}^{+\infty} (An_1 + Bn_2)P_1(n_1)P_2(n_2)\,dn_1\,dn_2 \\ &= \int_{-\infty}^{+\infty} An_1P(n_1)\,dn_1 \int_{-\infty}^{+\infty} P_2(n_2)\,dn_2 \\ &\qquad + \int_{-\infty}^{+\infty} Bn_2P_2(n_2)\,dn_2 \int_{-\infty}^{+\infty} P_1(n_1)\,dn_1 \\ &= A\bar{n}_1 + B\bar{n}_2 \end{aligned} \tag{111}$$

Similarly,

$$\begin{aligned} \overline{D^2} &= \overline{(n - \bar{n})^2} = \int_{-\infty}^{+\infty} (n - \bar{n})^2P(n)\,dn \\ &= \int_{-\infty}^{+\infty}\int_{-\infty}^{+\infty} (An_1 + Bn_2 - A\bar{n}_1 - B\bar{n}_2)^2P(n_1)P(n_2)\,dn_1\,dn_2 \\ &= \int_{-\infty}^{+\infty}\int_{-\infty}^{+\infty} \{[A(n_1 - \bar{n}_1)]^2 + 2[A(n_1 - \bar{n}_1)B(n_2 - \bar{n}_2)] \\ &\qquad + [B(n_2 - \bar{n}_2)]^2\}P(n_1)P(n_2)\,dn_1\,dn_2 \\ &= \int_{-\infty}^{+\infty} [A(n_1 - \bar{n}_1)]^2P(n_1)\,dn_1 \int_{-\infty}^{+\infty} P(n_2)\,dn_2 \\ &\qquad + 2\int_{-\infty}^{+\infty} A(n_1 - \bar{n}_1)P(n_1)\,dn_1 \int_{-\infty}^{+\infty} B(n_2 - \bar{n}_2)P(n_2)\,dn_2 \\ &\qquad + \int_{-\infty}^{+\infty} [B(n_2 - \bar{n}_2)]^2P(n_2)\,dn_2 \int_{-\infty}^{+\infty} P(n_1)\,dn_1 \\ &= A^2\overline{(n_1 - \bar{n}_1)^2} + B^2\overline{(n_2 - \bar{n}_2)^2} \end{aligned} \tag{112}$$

since

$$\int_{-\infty}^{+\infty} A(n_1 - \bar{n}_1)P(n_1)\, dn_1 = 0 = \int_{-\infty}^{+\infty} B(n_2 - \bar{n}_2)P(n_2)\, dn_2 \quad (113)$$

If n_1 and n_2 have only integral values but have Gaussian distributions, the values of n, n_1, and n_2 are very large in all regions of importance, so that Eq. (110) can be used as an accurate approximation.

Using the same method, we can also easily obtain the more general result that if

$$n = A_1 n_1 + A_2 n_2 + \cdots + A_s n_s \quad (114)$$

then

$$\bar{n} = A_1 \bar{n}_1 + A_2 \bar{n}_2 + \cdots + A_s \bar{n}_s \quad (115)$$

and

$$\overline{D^2} = A_1^2 \overline{D_1^2} + A_2^2 \overline{D_2^2} + \cdots + A_s^2 \overline{D_s^2} \quad (116)$$

7.11 Probability Distributions of Identical Functions. *a. Introduction.* So far we have been concerned with the probability distribu-

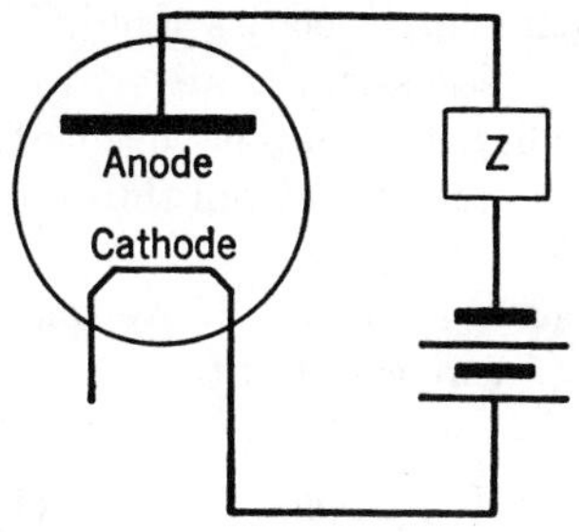

FIG. 4. A diode and external circuit.

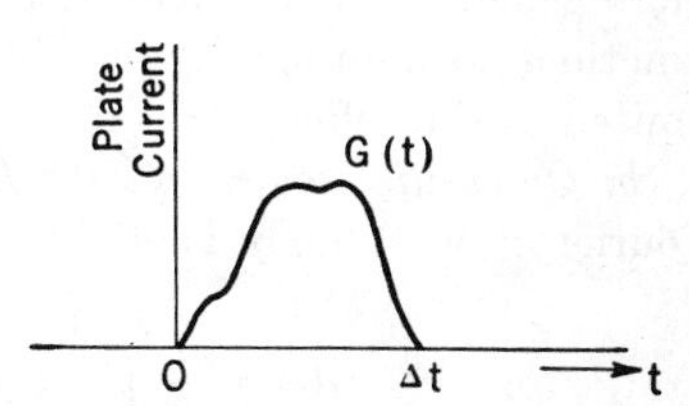

FIG. 5. Plate current due to the passage of a single electron between cathode and anode.

tion of isolated events between which there could be no interaction. We shall now generalize our considerations to cover certain cases in which there is at least a possibility of interaction between the events of which the probability distributions are being studied.

Consider, once more, the emission of electrons, which we have so often used as an example. Up to the present, we have always talked about the fluctuations in electron emission but never really about the fluctuations in plate current. However, the fluctuations in plate current are the real shot effect that is of such great technical importance. The two are very closely connected, but they are by no means the same thing. Thus, if a single electron is emitted from the cathode and moves toward the anode, then if the plate circuit is closed, as shown in Fig. 4, plate current starts to flow in the external plate circuit as soon as the electron leaves the cathode and continues to flow until it arrives at the anode. The actual form of the plate current as a function of time depends on the geometry of the tube and the potential distribution in it and the velocity of the electron. Thus the plate current as a function of time for a single electron may be like $G(t)$, shown in Fig. 5, where Δt represents the transit time of the electron. In the case of an actual tube with a plate current of, say, 100 ma (that is, 6.3×10^{17} electrons per second) and with a transit time of 10^{-8} sec, there will be a constant overlap (*i.e.*, superposition) of the plate currents due to individual electrons. It will now be our problem to find the result of the superposition of functions distributed in occurrence according to some probability distribution and thus learn how to deal with such phenomena as shot effect.

We shall begin our study with the case in which all the functions are of identical form and size. Such a case would be approximated in practice by the temperature-limited shot effect in which the plate voltage is so high that variations in the emission velocities of individual electrons are of little consequence. Our discussion, however, will be more general and will deal with probability distributions of identical functions without specifying what they represent and will thus not be limited to shot effect.

b. Quadratic Content in the Low-frequency Range. If we make a Fourier integral analysis of $G(t)$ in Fig. (5), we can write

$$G(t) = \frac{1}{\pi} \int_0^\infty S(\omega) \cos [\omega t + \phi(\omega)]\, d\omega \tag{117}$$

Since the range of appreciable values of $G(t)$ is limited to the interval $0 < t < \Delta t$, we know (see Sec. 4.19) that $G(t)$ acts like an impulse of strength

$$M = \int_0^\infty G(t)\, dt = \int_0^{\Delta t} G(t)\, dt \tag{118}$$

in the low-frequency range. Therefore, by Eq. (156) of Chap. IV,

$$S(\omega) = M = \int_0^{\Delta t} G(t)\, dt \tag{119}$$

and

$$\phi(\omega) = 0 \tag{120}$$

in the low-frequency range, for which the transit time Δt is inappreciable.

For our purposes at present, it will be more convenient to express

$G(t - T_1)$ as a Fourier series in terms of a long fundamental interval[1] extending from 0 to T (see Fig. 6). Thus we may write (see Sec. 1.8)

$$G(t - T_1) = \frac{a_0}{2} + \sum_{q=1}^{\infty} \left(a_q \cos \frac{2\pi qt}{T} + b_q \sin \frac{2\pi qt}{T} \right) \tag{121}$$

where

$$a_0 = \frac{2}{T} \int_0^T G(t - T_1)\, dt = \frac{2M}{T} \tag{122}$$

$$a_q = \frac{2}{T} \int_0^T G(t - T_1) \cos \left(\frac{2\pi qt}{T} \right) dt = \frac{2M}{T} \cos \frac{2\pi q T_1}{T} \tag{123}$$

$$b_q = \frac{2}{T} \int_0^T G(t - T_1) \sin \frac{2\pi qt}{T}\, dt = \frac{2M}{T} \sin \frac{2\pi q T_1}{T} \tag{124}$$

Substituting these values into Eq. (121), we have

$$G(t - T_1) = \frac{M}{T} + \frac{2M}{T} \sum_{q=1}^{\infty} \cos \left[\frac{2\pi q(t - T_1)}{T} \right] \tag{125}$$

Equation (125) is of course restricted to the low-frequency range in which $G(t)$ may be considered as an impulse.

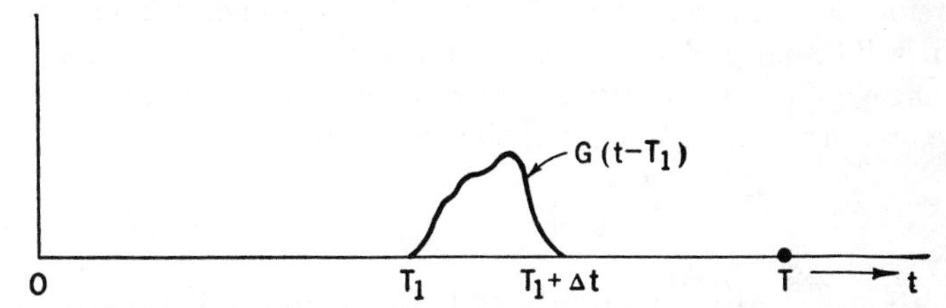

FIG. 6. A long interval of duration T, showing the location of the plate current due to a single electron between T_1 and $T_1 + \Delta t$.

We shall next consider what happens when a whole probability distribution of these functions of the form $G(t)$ and distributed at random along the time axis is superimposed. Let us call the resulting function $I(t)$. We shall be interested particularly in two properties of $I(t)$,

1. Linear content, $\int_0^T I(t)\, dt$, that is, direct-current component

2. Quadratic content, $\int_0^T I^2(t)\, dt$, that is, alternating-current energy

[1] This interval may be thought of as the entire time of observation in the experiment under consideration. The use of a Fourier series thus does not imply that there is any periodicity in the phenomenon.

We shall, of course, be particularly interested in the frequency distribution of the quadratic content.

If we consider some specific Fourier component in $I(t)$

$$C \cos\left(\frac{2\pi qt}{T} - \phi\right) \tag{126}$$

then each individual $G(t - T_1)$ contributes an "elementary" component

$$\frac{2M}{T} \cos \frac{2\pi q(t - T_1)}{T} \tag{127}$$

to Eq. (126). However, these components are not all in phase and so must be added vectorially as described in Sec. 5.4*a*. The phases of

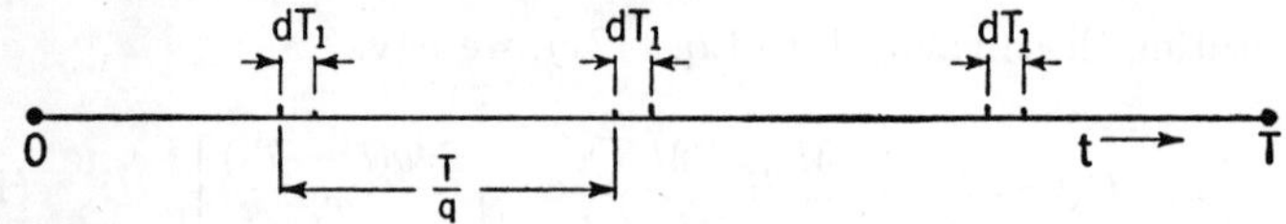

FIG. 7. Intervals at which phases of cos $[2\pi q(t - T_1)]/T$ are repeated.

the "elementary" components depend on the value of T_1. Also, the phases repeat for values of T_1 at distances T/q apart on the time axis. Therefore we may consider the value of ϕ as ranging from 0 to 2π, and it will be our problem to add vectorially all the components in this 2π range. For any particular range of ϕ, between ϕ and $\phi + d\phi$, there are, in the time T, q small time intervals of length

$$dT_1 = \frac{T\,d\phi}{2\pi q} \tag{128}$$[1]

Any $G(t - T_1)$ with its T_1 in these intervals will contribute an "elementary" component in this phase range. Now, if the average number of $G(t)$'s per second is K, then the average value of the number giving rise to phases in the interval between ϕ and $\phi + d\phi$ is

$$\bar{n} = K \cdot q \cdot \frac{T\,d\phi}{2\pi q} = \frac{KT\,d\phi}{2\pi} \tag{129}$$

where n is the number of $G(t)$'s giving rise to phases in the interval between ϕ and $\phi + d\phi$ in any particular trial.[2] Let us now divide the

[1] The value of $d\phi$ here is small but not infinitesimal. $d\phi$ will be considered large enough so that a large number of $G(t - T_1)$'s will have their phase-determining points T_1 between ϕ and $\phi + d\phi$.

[2] The meaning of $\bar{n}$ here as in all the preceding cases is the average value of what would be found for n by investigating the same conditions a very large number of times. In other words, it is an ensemble average.

phase range between 0 and 2π into a large number of equal intervals of size $d\phi$. Then the average value of the sum of the elementary Fourier components of frequency q/T in any particular phase range ϕ to $\phi + d\phi$ will be

$$\frac{KT\,d\phi}{2\pi}\frac{2M}{T}\cos\left(\frac{2\pi qt}{T} - \phi\right) = \frac{KM}{\pi}\cos\left(\frac{2\pi qt}{T} - \phi\right)d\phi \qquad (130)$$

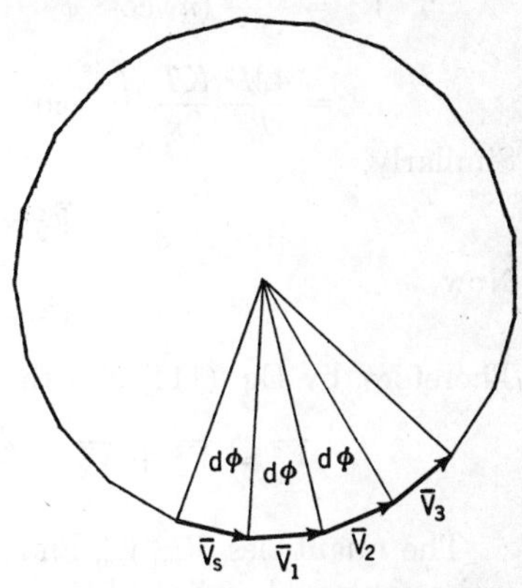

FIG. 8. Vector diagram showing the superposition of the average resultants of the different phase intervals.

Now, if all the average resultants of the type Eq. (130) are added together vectorially for the entire phase range between 0 and 2π, they will form a closed circular polygon as shown in Fig. 8, so that the combination of the *average* resultants is zero. However, if the actual values of n are used instead of their average values, each differential vector is subject to a certain amount of fluctuation about its average length of $(KM/\pi)d\phi$. Let us number the different vectors 1,2, . . . , s and call their lengths $V_1, V_2, \ldots, V_s$. Let us call the length of the combined resultant V.[1] Then we have for the x and y components of these V vectors,

$$V_x = V_{1x} + V_{2x} + \cdots + V_{sx} = V_1\cos\phi_1 + V_2\cos\phi_2 + \cdots + V_s\cos\phi_s$$
$$= \frac{2M\cos\phi_1}{T}n_1 + \frac{2M\cos\phi_2}{T}n_2 + \cdots + \frac{2M\cos\phi_s}{T}n_s \qquad (131)$$
$$V_y = V_{1y} + V_{2y} + \cdots + V_{sy} = V_1\sin\phi_1 + V_2\sin\phi_2 + \cdots + V_s\sin\phi_s$$
$$= \frac{2M\sin\phi_1}{T}n_1 + \frac{2M\sin\phi_2}{T}n_2 + \cdots + \frac{2M\sin\phi_s}{T}n_s \qquad (132)$$

We know from Fig. 8 that the average values of V_x and of V_y are zero. Therefore we may let V_x stand for the deviation of V_x, and we may let V_y stand for the deviation of V_y. It then follows from Eqs. (114), (116), and (131) that

$$\overline{V_x^2} = \frac{4M^2}{T^2}(\overline{D_1^2}\cos^2\phi_1 + \overline{D_2^2}\cos^2\phi_2 + \cdots + \overline{D_s^2}\cos^2\phi_s) \qquad (133)$$

[1] V is thus equal to C in Eq. (126).

and since $n_1, n_2, \ldots, n_s$ have Gaussian distributions, it then follows from Eqs. (133), (92), and (129) that

$$\overline{V_x^2} = \frac{4M^2}{T^2}(\overline{n_1} \cos^2 \phi_1 + \overline{n_2} \cos^2 \phi_2 + \cdots + \overline{n_s} \cos^2 \phi_s)$$

$$= \frac{4M^2}{T^2}\frac{KT}{2\pi}\int_0^{2\pi} \cos^2 \phi \, d\phi = \frac{2M^2K}{T} \tag{134}$$

Similarly,

$$\overline{V_y^2} = \frac{2M^2K}{T} \tag{135}$$

Now

$$V^2 = V_x^2 + V_y^2 \tag{136}$$

Therefore, by Eq. (114) and the foregoing,

$$\overline{V^2} = \overline{V_x^2} + \overline{V_y^2} = \frac{2M^2K}{T} + \frac{2M^2K}{T} = \frac{4M^2K}{T} \tag{137}$$

The quantities V_x^2, V_y^2, and V^2 are essentially fluctuations of the entire circle in Fig. 8, and they may be expected to have distributions somewhat similar to that of D^2 in Eq. (78) rather than n^2. In any individual case, we may thus expect relatively large percentage deviations of D^2 from its average. In particular, it is clear from symmetry and physical considerations that all values of

$$\phi = \tan^{-1}\left(\frac{V_x}{V_y}\right) \tag{138}$$

are equally probable.

It follows from Eq. (137) that the Fourier component in Eq. (126)

$$C \cos\left(\frac{2\pi qt}{T} - \phi\right) = V \cos\left(\frac{2\pi qt}{T} - \phi\right) \tag{139}$$

has an average mean square value of

$$\overline{[(I_q)_{\text{rms}}]^2} = \frac{1}{2}\frac{4M^2K}{T} = \frac{2M^2K}{T} \tag{140}$$

As mentioned in the foregoing paragraph, however, the percentage deviation from the average in any particular case is likely to be large.

In practice, we encounter, not individual Fourier components, but rather the resultant of those in a frequency band of width, say, ΔF. Now the frequency[1] of any Fourier component such as shown in Eq. (139) is

$$F = \frac{q}{T} \tag{141}$$

[1] See also Sec. 3.2 in this connection.

Therefore the number of Fourier harmonics in the bandwidth ΔF is

$$\Delta q = T \, \Delta F \tag{142}$$ [1]

According to Sec. 2.5 the mean square values of Fourier components are separately additive, there being zero average interaction between them. Consequently, the average mean square value of the resultant of the Fourier components in the bandwidth ΔF is

$$\overline{[(I_{\Delta F})_{\text{rms}}]^2} = \Delta q \frac{2M^2K}{T} = T \, \Delta F \frac{2M^2K}{T} = 2M^2K \, \Delta F \tag{143}$$ [2]

It is shown in Sec. 7.15 that as Δq becomes large in comparison with unity, the percentage deviations of this mean square value from its average tend to become very small. Consequently, when Δq is large, there is little likelihood of appreciable deviation from $2M^2K \, \Delta F$ in any actual measurement of $[(I_{\Delta F})_{\text{rms}}]^2$. Equation (143) is of fundamental importance in noise theory, since, as we shall see, it enables us to calculate the noise energy in the bandwidth ΔF.

c. Quadratic Content in the High-frequency Range. In the high-frequency range, *i.e.*, the range in which $G(t)$ cannot be considered as impulsive, the Fourier expansion for $G(t)$ can be written (see Chap. I) as

$$G(t) = \frac{a_0}{2} + \sum_{q=1}^{\infty} C_q \cos\left(\frac{2\pi qt}{T} - \phi_q\right) \tag{144}$$

where

$$a_0 = \frac{2}{T} \int_0^T G(t) \, dt \tag{145}$$

$$C_q = \frac{2}{T} \sqrt{\left[\int_0^T G(t) \cos \frac{2\pi qt}{T} \, dt\right]^2 + \left[\int_0^T G(t) \sin \frac{2\pi qt}{T} \, dt\right]^2} \tag{146}$$

and

$$\phi_q = \tan^{-1} \left[\frac{\int_0^T G(t) \sin (2\pi qt/T) \, dt}{\int_0^T G(t) \cos (2\pi qt/T) \, dt}\right] \tag{147}$$

Then

$$G(t - T_1) = \frac{a_0}{2} + \sum_{q=1}^{\infty} C_q \left[\frac{2\pi q(t - T_1)}{T} - \phi_q\right] \tag{148}$$

Combined resultants for the whole distribution of $G(t - T_1)$'s for any high-frequency harmonic can now clearly be obtained in exactly the

[1] In practice, $T \, \Delta F$ is large enough so that Δq is large in comparison with unity.

[2] This same formula is derived in Sec. 7.20 at the end of the chapter on the basis of true frequency distributions rather than Fourier components.

same way as was done for the low-frequency case in Sec. 7.11*b*, only M is now no longer a constant but varies with frequency. The expression for M is, according to Eqs. (125), (144), and (146),

$$M_q = \sqrt{\left[\int_0^T G(t) \cos \frac{2\pi qt}{T}\, dt\right]^2 + \left[\int_0^T G(t) \sin \frac{2\pi qt}{T}\, dt\right]^2} \tag{149}$$

For zero frequency the value of M is

$$M_0 = \int_0^T G(t)\, dt \tag{150}$$

With this understanding, Eq. (140) then applies to all harmonics, whether of low or high frequency. For the equivalent of Eq. (143) we then have

$$\left.\begin{array}{l}\text{Average of the mean square values of the} \\ \text{resultant of the Fourier components in} \\ \text{bandwidth } \Delta F\end{array}\right\} = \sum_{q/T=F_1}^{q/T=F_1+\Delta F_1} \frac{2M_q^2 K}{T} \tag{151}$$

The right side of Eq. (151) is actually not very useful in practice and can be replaced by its Fourier integral equivalent. Thus

$$\overline{[(I_{\Delta F})_{\text{rms}}]^2} = 2K \int_{F_1}^{F_1+\Delta F} [S(\omega)]^2\, df \tag{152}$$

where

$$S(\omega) = \sqrt{\left[\int_{-\infty}^{+\infty} G(t) \cos \omega t\, dt\right]^2 + \left[\int_{-\infty}^{+\infty} G(t) \sin \omega t\, dt\right]^2} \tag{153}$$

and

$$\omega = 2\pi f$$

d. Total Linear and Quadratic Content. If we let $I(t)$ stand for the resultant of the entire probability distribution of $G(t)$'s, then we have for the average value of the linear content of $I(t)$

$$\overline{\int^T I(t)\, dt} = \bar{N} M_0 = KTM_0 \qquad (154)[1]$$

As previously pointed out, this average value is the average of what would be found for

$$\int_0^T I(t)\, dt$$

if the same conditions were investigated a large number of times. Because of the enormous value of N and its Gaussian distribution, perceptible deviations from the average are completely unlikely, so that we may treat

[1] N stands for the total number of $G(t)$'s in the entire interval from 0 to T and has a Gaussian distribution, so that its percentage fluctuations are small.

$$\overline{\int_0^T I(t)\,dt}$$

as the actual value of what will be found in any practical trial. Therefore, we obtain

$$I_{DC} = \text{direct-current value of } I(t) = \frac{1}{T}\int_0^T I(t)\,dt = KM_0 \tag{155}$$

In other words, the total direct-current component is equal to the sum of the direct-current components of the individual $G(t)$'s. Similarly, according to Eq. (103) of Chap. I in conjunction with the results of the foregoing sections,

$$\overline{\frac{1}{T}\int_0^T I^2(t)\,dt} = M_0^2K^2 + \frac{1}{2}\sum_{q=1}^{\infty}\frac{4M_q^2K}{T} \tag{156}$$

If we let

$$G_{DC} = \frac{1}{T}\int_0^T G(t)\,dt = \frac{M_0}{T} \tag{157}$$

and

$$G_{AC}(t) = G(t) - G_{DC} \tag{158}$$

then according to Eq. (103) of Chap. I and the foregoing

$$\frac{1}{T}\int_0^T G_{AC}^2(t)\,dt = \frac{1}{2}\sum_{q=1}^{\infty}\frac{4M_q^2}{T^2} \tag{159}$$

Substituting Eq. (159) into Eq. (156) we obtain

$$\overline{\frac{1}{T}\int_0^T I^2(t)\,dt} = M_0^2K^2 + K\int_0^T G_{AC}^2(t)\,dt \tag{160}$$

Next let

$$I_{AC}(t) = I(t) - I_{DC} \tag{161}$$

Then

$$\begin{aligned}
\overline{\frac{1}{T}\int_0^T I_{AC}^2(t)\,dt}
&= \overline{\frac{1}{T}\int_0^T [I(t) - I_{DC}]^2\,dt} = \overline{\frac{1}{T}\int_0^T [I^2(t) - 2I(t)I_{DC} + I_{DC}^2]\,dt} \\
&= \overline{\frac{1}{T}\int_0^T [I^2(t) - 2I_{DC}^2 + I_{DC}^2]\,dt} \\
&= \overline{\frac{1}{T}\int_0^T [I^2(t) - I_{DC}^2]\,dt} \\
&= K\int_0^T G_{AC}^2(t)\,dt
\end{aligned} \tag{162}$$

In other words, the average value of total alternating-current energy is equal to the sum of the alternating-current energies of the individual $G(t)$'s. The net result of the random distribution of the $G(t)$'s is thus on the average to cancel out any interaction energy between the elementary functions.

Because of the large number of frequency components that go into the making of

$$\int_0^T [I(t) - I_{DC}]^2\,dt$$

perceptible deviations from the average in any particular case are completely unlikely (see Sec. 7.15), so that Eq. (162) may be taken as the actual value of the total alternating-current quadratic content. In practical problems this is, of course, proportional to the noise energy.

7.12 Superposition of Probability Distributions of Different Classes of Functions. In Sec. 7.11 we dealt with a distribution of $G(t)$'s all of exactly the same form and occurring at an average rate of K per second. We shall now consider the more general case in which there are several types of functions

$$G_a(t),\ G_b(t),\ \cdots,\ G_p(t)$$

having respective average rates of occurrence of

$$K_a,\ K_b,\ \cdots,\ K_p$$

per second. We shall investigate the linear and quadratic content of the resultant and also the frequency distribution of the quadratic content.

Let

$$M_{qr} = \sqrt{\left[\int_0^T G_r(t)\cos\frac{2\pi qt}{T}\,dt\right]^2 + \left[\int_0^T G_r(t)\sin\frac{2\pi qt}{T}\,dt\right]^2} \tag{163}$$

stand for the coefficient of the qth harmonic of $G_r(t)$ in accordance with our previous notation, and let

$$M_{0r} = \int_0^T G_r(t)\,dt \tag{164}$$

Then we can carry through exactly the same steps as in Sec. 7.11 to get the required results. These steps will not be duplicated here. However, the equivalents of the crucial Eqs. (131) to (134) will now be

$$\begin{aligned} V_x = {} & \frac{2}{T}(M_{qa}n_{1a} + M_{qb}n_{1b} + \cdots + M_{qp}n_{1p})\cos\phi_1 \\ & + \frac{2}{T}(M_{qa}n_{2a} + M_{qb}n_{2b} + \cdots + M_{qp}n_{2p})\cos\phi_2 \\ & + \cdots\cdots\cdots\cdots\cdots\cdots \\ & + \frac{2}{T}(M_{qa}n_{sa} + M_{qb}n_{sb} + \cdots + M_{qp}n_{sp})\cos\phi_s \end{aligned} \tag{165}$$

$$\overline{V_x^2} = \frac{4M_{qa}^2}{T^2}(\overline{D_{1a}^2}\cos^2\phi_1 + \overline{D_{2a}^2}\cos^2\phi_2 + \cdots + \overline{D_{sa}^2}\cos^2\phi_s)$$
$$+ \frac{4M_{qb}^2}{T^2}(\overline{D_{1b}^2}\cos^2\phi_1 + \overline{D_{2b}^2}\cos^2\phi_2 + \cdots + \overline{D_{sb}^2}\cos^2\phi_s)$$
$$+ \cdots\cdots\cdots\cdots\cdots\cdots$$
$$+ \frac{4M_{qp}^2}{T^2}(\overline{D_{1p}^2}\cos^2\phi_1 + \overline{D_{2p}^2}\cos^2\phi_2 + \cdots + \overline{D_{sp}^2}\cos^2\phi_s) \quad (166)$$

and

$$\overline{V_x^2} = \frac{4M_{qa}^2}{T^2}(\overline{n_{1a}}\cos^2\phi_1 + \overline{n_{2a}}\cos^2\phi_2 + \cdots + \overline{n_{sa}}\cos^2\phi_s)$$
$$+ \frac{4M_{qb}^2}{T^2}(\overline{n_{1b}}\cos^2\phi_1 + \overline{n_{2b}}\cos^2\phi_2 + \cdots + \overline{n_{sb}}\cos^2\phi_s)$$
$$+ \cdots\cdots\cdots\cdots\cdots\cdots$$
$$+ \frac{4M_{qp}^2}{T^2}(\overline{n_{1p}}\cos^2\phi_1 + \overline{n_{2p}}\cos^2\phi_2 + \cdots + \overline{n_{sp}}\cos^2\phi_s)$$
$$= \frac{4M_{qa}^2}{T^2}\left(\frac{K_aT}{2\pi}\int_0^{2\pi}\cos^2\phi\,d\phi\right) + \frac{4M_{qb}^2}{T^2}\left(\frac{K_bT}{2\pi}\int_0^{2\pi}\cos^2\phi\,d\phi\right)$$
$$+ \cdots + \frac{4M_{qp}^2}{T^2}\left(\frac{K_pT}{2\pi}\int_0^{2\pi}\cos^2\phi\,d\phi\right)$$
$$= \frac{2}{T}(M_{qa}^2K_a + M_{qb}^2K_b + \cdots + M_{qp}^2K_p) \quad (167)$$

For the final results we obtain for the average of the mean square value of the qth Fourier component [equivalent to Eq. (140)]

$$\overline{[(I_q)_{\text{rms}}]^2} = \frac{2}{T}(M_{qa}^2K_a + M_{qb}^2K_b + \cdots + M_{qp}^2K_p) \quad (168)$$

The equivalent of Eq. (143) for the low-frequency range is

$$\overline{[(I_{\Delta F})_{\text{rms}}]^2} = 2(M_a^2K_a + M_b^2K_b + \cdots + M_p^2K_p)\,\Delta F \quad (169)$$

and the equivalent of Eq. (152) for a range of any frequency is

$$\overline{[(I_{\Delta F})_{\text{rms}}]^2} = 2\int_{F_1}^{F_1+\Delta F}\{K_a[S_a(\omega)]^2 + K_b[S_b(\omega)]^2 + \cdots + K_p[S_p(\omega)]^2\}\,df \quad (170)$$

The equivalent of Eq. (155) for the direct-current component is

$$I_{DC} = K_aM_a + K_bM_b + \cdots + K_pM_p \quad (171)$$

and the equivalent of Eq. (162) for the total alternating-current quadratic content is

$$\overline{\frac{1}{T}\int_0^T [I(t) - I_{DC}]^2\,dt} = \int_0^T [K_aG_{a(AC)}^2(t) + K_bG_{b(AC)}^2(t) + \cdots + K_pG_{p(AC)}^2(t)]\,dt \quad (172)$$

The net result of Eqs. (168) to (172) for the superposition of sets of random distributions of functions as described above may be combined into the following rule:

If a number of sets of random distributions of functions are superimposed,

1. *The direct-current components of the sets are additive.*
2. *The alternating-current quadratic contents of the sets are additive for any frequency range.*

This rule is of fundamental importance for the superposition of noise currents or voltages. It is used in the preceding chapter in dealing with the superposition of random noise from different sources and in the next chapter in dealing with space-charge-limited shot effect.

According to the discussion in Sec. 7.15 the probability of any deviation from the average value in the practical application of Eqs. (169) to (172) is so very small that it can be ignored. Consequently, the averaging lines across the quantities on the left sides of these equations can be removed in practice.

7.13 Normal Distributions. Up to the present point in this chapter, we have derived all the formulas we have used. This has been done so that the reader would understand completely the type of reasoning upon which our results and conclusions were based and so that he could use them with complete confidence. We shall now discuss an important generalization of these results, which, however, we shall not derive, since its derivation is more involved mathematically than is justified in a book of this type and, besides, no thoroughly satisfactory derivation has yet been given.

This generalization deals with the question of *normal distributions*. In Sec. 7.6 we derived the Gaussian distribution formula [Eq. (57)] for the probability of a variable (n) having a given value as the result of a particular random process, when the number of independent random events involved became very large. This is a particular case of a very general mathematical phenomena, sometimes called the central-limit theorem,[1] concerning the limiting form of distribution approached by

[1] As far as the author is aware, a completely general proof of the central-limit theorem has never been given. An informative limited proof may be found in Uspensky, "Introduction to Mathematical Probability," pp. 314 *ff*. It appears from Rice, *Bell System Tech. J.*, July, 1944, pp. 330–332, that a more general discussion may be found in H. Cramer, Random Variables and Probability Distributions, *Cambridge Tract* 36 (1937). A related discussion to the general case is also given by Chandrasekhar, *Rev. Modern Phys.* In the absence of a proof of the theorem which precisely specifies its limitations, there is some question as to the range of validity of the results dependent upon it.

the resultant of m random contributions as m approaches infinity. In our derivation of the Gaussian distribution formula, the m random contributions were the results of the m trials to see whether an event occurred whose probability of occurrence in any one trial had a constant value p. This is called a one-dimensional distribution since the results of the m trials were directly additive to give a final value n. An example of a quantity having a two-dimensional distribution is the amplitude V of a particular noise frequency component (see Sec. 7.11*b*), since it is made up of the superposition of a large number of random inphase and quadrature components that are separately additive. Now the central-limit theorem deals with the form of the distribution function in the general case of any number of dimensions as the number m of the individual random contributions approaches infinity.

The form of the distribution function indicated by the central-limit theorem becomes quite simple in the special case when the following two requirements are met:

1. The ensemble average value of the contributions in each dimension is zero.

2. The contributions in the different dimensions are independent of one another.

Then, if the dimensions are x, y, z, etc., the central-limit theorem states that the probability that the resultant will lie in the volume element $dx\,dy\,dz\ \ldots$ is

$$\frac{a}{\sqrt{\pi}}\,\epsilon^{-a^2x^2}\,dx\,\frac{b}{\sqrt{\pi}}\,\epsilon^{-b^2y^2}\,dy\,\frac{c}{\sqrt{\pi}}\,\epsilon^{-c^2z^2}\,dz\ \cdots \tag{173}$$

where a^2, b^2, c^2, etc., are given by the equations

$$a^2 = \frac{1}{2\sigma_x^2}, \qquad b^2 = \frac{1}{2\sigma_y^2}, \text{ etc.} \qquad (174)[1]$$

and σ_x^2 is the ensemble average value of x^2, with corresponding meanings for σ_y, σ_z, etc. It should be pointed out that the above form indicated by the central-limit theorem is not limited to the particular type of random process used by us in deriving the Gaussian distribution but holds for any type of random process.

For the central-limit theorem to be safely applicable it is also necessary that no one of the m random contributions shall be comparable with the

[1] This significance for a^2, etc., follows from the formula

$$\sigma_x^2 = \overline{x^2} = \int_{-\infty}^{+\infty} x^2\,\frac{a}{\sqrt{\pi}}\,\epsilon^{-a^2x^2}\,dx = \frac{1}{2a^2}$$

resultant of all the others, or, more precisely,

$$\lim_{m \to \infty} \frac{u_s}{R_m} = 0$$

where u_s is some particular contribution and R_m is the resultant of all the others.

We may note, as an example of Eq. (173), that the deviation D in Eq. (57) is made up of contributions from the m trials which have an ensemble average value of zero. Since D is obtained by a one-dimensional random process, it then follows from Eq. (173) that its distribution function is

$$P(D) = \frac{a}{\sqrt{\pi}} \epsilon^{-a^2D^2} \tag{175}$$ [1]

We know the ensemble average value of D^2, since by Eq. (92) we have

$$\overline{D^2} = \bar{n} \tag{176}$$

for a Gaussian distribution. Therefore, by Eq. (174),

$$a = \frac{1}{2\bar{n}} \tag{177}$$

Thus Eq. (175) becomes

$$P(D) = \frac{1}{\sqrt{2\pi\bar{n}}} \epsilon^{-\frac{D^2}{2\bar{n}}} \tag{178}$$

which agrees with Eq. (57).

The form of the distribution function specified by the central-limit theorem is called a *normal distribution.*

7.14 Random Noise. *a. The Distribution Function for I_q.* We shall now apply the central-limit theorem to find the probability distribution of the Fourier components in $I(t)$ of Sec. 7.11. Thus we let I_q stand for the amplitude of the qth harmonic and I_{qx} and I_{qy} for its cosine and sine components, *i.e.*,

$$\begin{aligned} I_q &= I_q \cos\left(\frac{2\pi qt}{T} - \phi_q\right) \\ &= I_{qx} \cos\frac{2\pi qt}{T} + I_{qy} \sin\frac{2\pi qt}{T} \end{aligned} \tag{179}$$

where

$$I_q^2 = I_{qx}^2 + I_{qy}^2 \qquad \text{and} \qquad \phi_q = \tan^{-1}\left(\frac{I_{qy}}{I_{qx}}\right) \tag{180}$$

[1] The notation $P(x)\,dx$ stands for the function which gives the probability that the x variable lies between x and $x + dx$. $P(x)$ is not a specific function like $\sin x$ or $\log x$ because the form of $P(x)$ depends on the nature of x.

According to the derivation in Sec. 7.11*b*, I_{qx} and I_{qy} are each the resultant of a very large number of random contributions no one of which is comparable with the resultant of all the others, and furthermore the contributions of the x and y components are independent of each other and

$$\overline{I_{qx}} = 0 = \overline{I_{qy}} \tag{181}$$

Therefore the central-limit theorem applies to $\mathbf{I}_q$. Consequently,

$$P(I_{qx})\,dI_{qx} = \frac{a}{\sqrt{\pi}}\,\epsilon^{-a^2I_{qx}^2} \quad \text{and} \quad P(I_{qy})\,dI_{qy} = \frac{b}{\sqrt{\pi}}\,\epsilon^{-b^2I_{qy}^2}\,dI_{qy} \tag{182}$$

According to Eqs. (174), (134), and (135)

$$a^2 = \frac{T}{4M^2K} \quad \text{and} \quad b^2 = \frac{T}{4M^2K} \tag{183}$$

The distribution of I_q itself is two-dimensional. In order to find the form of the distribution for I_q, we shall therefore transform from rectangular to polar coordinates. It then follows that

$$dI_{qx}\,dI_{qy} = I_q\,dI_q\,d\phi \tag{184}$$

Therefore

$$\begin{aligned}\int_{-\infty}^{+\infty}\int_{-\infty}^{+\infty} &P(I_{qx})P(I_{qy})\,dI_{qx}\,dI_{qy} \\ &= \frac{T}{4\pi M^2K}\int_{I_q=0}^{\infty}\int_{\phi=0}^{2\pi}\epsilon^{-\frac{TI_q^2}{4M^2K}}\,I_q\,dI_q\,d\phi \\ &= \frac{T}{2M^2K}\int_{I_q=0}^{\infty} I_q\epsilon^{-\frac{TI_q^2}{4M^2K}}\,dI_q \\ &= \int_{I_q=0}^{\infty}\frac{TI_q}{2M^2K}\,\epsilon^{-\frac{TI_q^2}{4M^2K}}\,dI_q = \int_{I_q=0}^{\infty}P(I_q)dI_q \end{aligned} \tag{185}$$

For a two-dimensional normal distribution, such as that of I_q, the form of the distribution function is thus

$$P(I_q)\,dI_q = 2A^2I_q\epsilon^{-A^2I_q^2}\,dI_q \tag{186}$$

where

$$A^2 = \frac{1}{\overline{I_q^2}} = \frac{T}{4M^2K} \tag{187}$$ [1]

[1] This follows from the formula of integration

$$\int_0^\infty r^2 2A^2re^{-A^2r^2}dr = \frac{1}{A^2}$$

in the above case. We note from Eq. (187) that $1/A^2$ is a measure of the noise energy.

$P(I_q)$ has a maximum when

$$\frac{d[P(I_q)]}{dI_q} = 2A^2\epsilon^{-A^2I_q^2} + 2A^2I_q\epsilon^{-A^2I_q^2}(-2A^2I_q) = 0 \qquad (188)$$

i.e., when

$$I_q = \frac{1}{\sqrt{2A^2}} = \frac{\sqrt{\overline{I_q^2}}}{\sqrt{2}} = \sqrt{\frac{2M^2K}{T}} \qquad (189)$$

Thus, while we cannot predict the exact value of I_q in any particular case, we do know that its most probable value is given by Eq. (189). Futhermore, the average value of its square is given by Eq. (187).

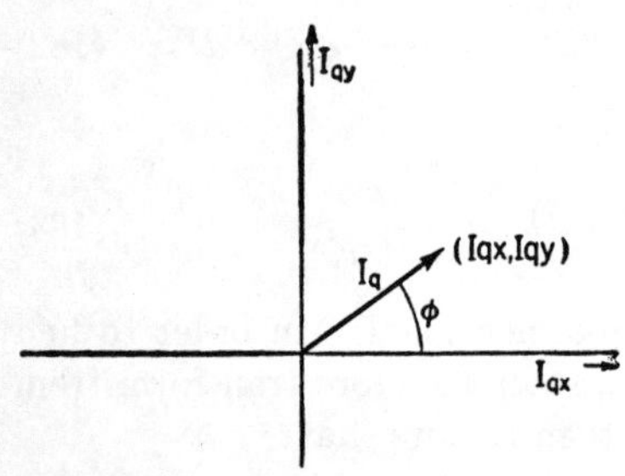

Fig. 9. Representation of I_q in rectangular and polar coordinates.

The quantity $\overline{I_q^2}$ is not the square of an rms value averaged over time but rather is the average obtained for the square of the peak current I_q when a large number of trials are made. The ensemble average of the mean square values averaged over time of the qth Fourier component of $I(t)$ of Sec. 7.11*b* is thus, from Eq. (187),

$$\frac{\overline{I_q^2}}{2} = \frac{2M^2K}{T} \qquad (190)$$

Equation (190) gives the ensemble average of the quadratic content of the qth Fourier component.

b. Definition of Random Noise. The foregoing study of I_q suggests the following definition of random noise: *Definition: Any stochastic function of time of specified length whose Fourier series components each have a two-dimensional normal distribution and random phase will be called random noise, provided that the quadratic content of no single component is an appreciable percentage of the total.*[1]

According to this definition, random noise will still be random noise even after going through a linear transmission system having any selectivity characteristic whatever.

[1] The random phase requirement means that the average values of the sine and cosine components are equal at every frequency. The requirement regarding the smallness of every component in the above definition is equivalent to saying that the number of components must be large and that there is no appreciable direct-current component.

It is shown at appropriate places in the following chapters that both shot noise and thermal noise are random noise, in accordance with the foregoing definition. This definition is more general than is usually necessary. For most purposes we can restrict our considerations to *white* random noise. In the latter case the average value of I_q^2 is independent of q.

c. The Distribution Function for the Amplitude of Random Noise. Let us next find the distribution function for the amplitude of $I(t)$ for a particular[1] time t, where $I(t)$ is any random noise. Now $I(t)$ is the resultant of the superposition of contributions

$$I_q \cos\left(\frac{2\pi qt}{T} - \phi_q\right)$$

from each Fourier component. These contributions are random since they depend on random values of I_q and ϕ_q. Furthermore, the average value of $I(t)$ is zero, since positive and negative values of any size are equally probable. If T, the total length of the observation time, is made sufficiently long so that there are a very large number of Fourier harmonics used in the superposition of which $I(t)$ is the resultant, then the conditions required for the central-limit theorem to be applicable are fulfilled. Therefore, for any particular value of t, it follows that

$$P(I) = \frac{1}{\sigma_I \sqrt{2\pi}} \epsilon^{-\frac{I^2}{2\sigma_I^2}} \tag{191}$$

where

$$\sigma_I^2 = \overline{I^2} \tag{192}$$

The distribution is one-dimensional, for all the components that go into the making of $I(t)$ are directly additive if the proper sign is used.

For the particular case studied in Sec. 7.11*b*,

$$\overline{I^2} = 2M^2K\,\Delta F \tag{193}$$

so that Eq. (191), becomes

$$P(I) = \frac{1}{\sqrt{4\pi M^2K\,\Delta F}} \epsilon^{-\frac{I^2}{4M^2K\,\Delta F}} \tag{194}$$

d. The Principle of Low-frequency Composition. Suppose that we have two functions $g_1(t)$ and $g_2(t)$ whose appearance is the same except in the very fine details. We shall express this mathematically by

[1] The meaning of a particular value of time t in the case of a stochastic function like $I(t)$ refers to a particular length of time from the beginning of the interval of length T. Repeated trials are then made of intervals of length T to find the stochastic distributions.

saying that

$$\int_{t_a}^{t_b} g_1(t)\, dt = \int_{t_a}^{t_b} g_2(t)\, dt \tag{195}$$

in *every* interval of length $t_b - t_a$ which is short enough so that $\cos(2\pi nt/T)$ and $\sin(2\pi nt/T)$ do not vary perceptibly in the interval $t_b - t_a$. Let us next divide the whole interval T into short intervals of length $t_b - t_a$. It then follows from the formula

$$a_{n1} - a_{n2} = \frac{2}{T}\int_0^T [g_1(t) - g_2(t)] \cos\frac{2\pi nt}{T}\, dt$$
$$= \frac{2}{T}\sum \cos\frac{2\pi nt_a}{T}\int_{t_a}^{t_b} [g_1(t) - g_2(t)]\, dt = 0 \quad (196)[1]$$

and the corresponding formula for $b_{n1} - b_{n2}$ for the difference between the Fourier coefficients that the two functions have the same frequency composition for frequencies below (n/T). Similarly, if the frequency composition is the same below $F = n/T$, then Eq. (195) holds. We shall call this proposition and its converse the *principle of low-frequency composition.* It follows from this principle that the fine structure of a function contributes only components of high frequency to its Fourier composition.

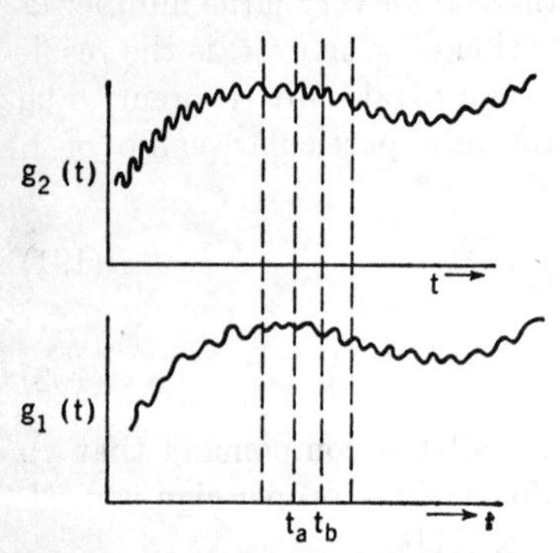

Fig. 10. Two functions differing only in fine details.

e. Demonstration that the Ensemble Distribution of the Amplitude of Random Noise Is Also a Time Distribution. Description of Random Noise as a Function of Time. We shall now demonstrate that the ensemble distribution of the amplitude of random noise is also its time distribution. In other words, we shall show that the fraction of time which I spends in the range between I and $I + dI$ in an actual case of sufficient duration is proportional to $P(I)$.

Let us divide the long interval T in which random noise is being studied into very short intervals of equal length t_0, these latter intervals being so short that I is effectively constant for the duration of any one of them in any particular trial of an ensemble.[2] Now the

[1] The summation in Eq. (196) is taken over all the intervals of length $t_b - t_a$.

[2] All random noise has an upper frequency limit above which it has essentially

probability distribution of I in any particular t_0 is exactly the same as the distribution in every other t_0 and is equal to $P(I)$ itself since all values of time have the same probability of having any particular noise amplitude in the random noise that we have been studying. It follows that, *on the average, the fraction of time which I spends in the*

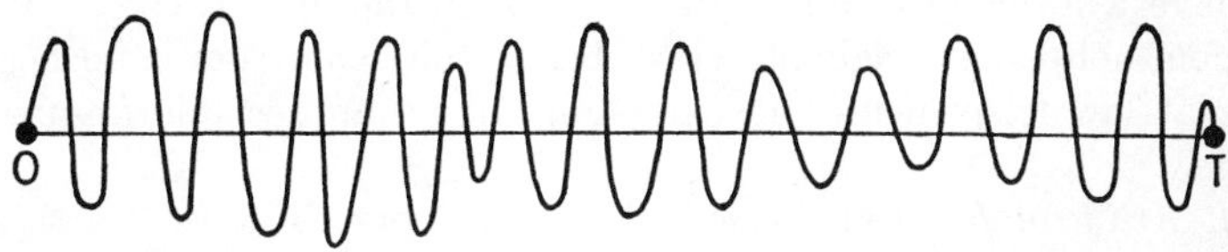

FIG. 11. The result of one particular determination of the values of $I(t)$ in the range from 0 to T for a given set of experimental conditions. Many such trials would make up an ensemble. (The random noise shown in Fig. 11 is not white noise, but rather is the noise in a narrow frequency channel.)

range between I and $I + dI$ is proportional to $P(I)$ itself. While there are fluctuations from this average condition, if the interval T is made long enough, the fluctuations will be small.

So far, in our discussion of random noise we have spoken only of probability distributions. In the light of the preceding paragraphs, we can now specify the conditions under which we should describe a particular signal of finite duration, such as a particular oscillogram, as random noise. Thus if

1. The signal has a very large number of Fourier series components
2. The ratio of the quadratic content of any one component in comparison with the total is vanishingly small
3. The phases of the components are distributed at random.
4. There is no direct-current component

then we shall describe the signal as random noise.[1] Such a signal will have the amplitude distribution and other properties that we have

---

no components, so that it follows from the principle of low-frequency composition that a sufficiently small interval t_0 exists in which I is effectively constant. The high-frequency limit to shot noise is brought about by finite transit time, the high-frequency limit to thermal noise is due to quantum effects, while the high-frequency limit to artificial random noises is ensured by their finite energy content.

[1] This definition requires clarification for those who have not read the earlier parts of the present chapter. The fundamental period used in the Fourier series is the total time of observation of the signal. Thus, a snapshot oscilloscope picture of a 10-μsec interval of thermal noise of 1 mc bandwidth would not be classified as random noise because the early Fourier series components each have an appreciable percentage of the total quadratic content. However, if the interval of observation is extended to 1,000 μsec, then the signal in the picture would be classified as random noise.

already found for random noise. The only other information necessary to specify it completely is a knowledge of how much quadratic content it has as a function of frequency, or, in common terminology, a knowledge of its power vs. frequency spectrum.

If the power vs. frequency function is a constant, the noise is said to have a *white* spectrum, by analogy with the optical case. Most random noise as it originally arises has a white spectrum band beginning at low frequencies and extending for an appreciable frequency range.

f. Artificial Random Noise. We shall apply the term "artificial random noise" to man-made random noise such as film-scratch noise, which is usually the resultant of the superposition of a large number of individual, but not necessarily identical, functions that occur at random intervals. Probably man-made noise is never truly random, for there is usually some regularity in it. However, some such noise is close enough to true random noise so that the superposition laws of random noise can be applied to it.

Since the individual functions referred to above are usually of short duration, they may be considered as impulsive in the low-frequency range. Consequently, the value of I_q for any particular *low-frequency* harmonic will have a two-dimensional probability distribution, the value of σ^2 being the same for all low-frequency harmonics. This type of random noise will therefore have a uniform energy distribution in the low-frequency range.

g. Superposition Laws. Random noise has certain characteristic superposition laws, which will now be stated and proved.

1. *The superposition of two or more random-noise functions gives another random-noise function.* This follows directly from the definition in Sec. 7.14*b*, since the superposition process just adds infinitesimal Fourier components of a given frequency together, which still leaves the components infinitesimal. Therefore, by the central-limit theorem, the resultant function still has a two-dimensional normal distribution.

2. *If two or more random-noise functions are superimposed, the ensemble averages of their squares are additive.*

The proof of this follows directly from Eq. (116), for the average value of any random-noise function is zero, so that the actual values may be considered as fluctuations. Thus since

$$I = I_1 + I_2 + \cdots + I_n \tag{197}$$

and all the I's are stochastic functions, it follows that

$$\overline{I^2} = \overline{I_1^2} + \overline{I_2^2} + \cdots + \overline{I_n^2} \tag{198}$$

From Eqs. (191) and (198) we also obtain

$$P(I) = \frac{1}{\sqrt{2\pi(\sigma_1^2 + \sigma_2^2 + \cdots + \sigma_n^2)}} \epsilon^{\frac{I^2}{2(\sigma_1^2+\sigma_2^2+\cdots+\sigma_n^2)}} \tag{199}$$

3. *If two or more random-noise functions are superimposed, the quadratic contents are additive.*

The proof follows directly from Eq. (198) and the fact demonstrated in Sec. 7.14*e* that the ensemble distributions of I, I_1, I_2, etc., are also their time distributions. Consequently,

$$\int_0^T I^2\,dt = \int_0^T I_1^2\,dt + \int_0^T I_2^2\,dt + \cdots + \int_0^T I_n^2\,dt \tag{200}$$

7.15 The Crowding of Values of the Resultant around the Average as the Number of Dimensions in a Normal Distribution Is Increased. In Section 7.14*a* we found that in a two-dimensional distribution in which a vectorial law of addition applies, *i.e.*,

$$r^2 = x^2 + y^2 \tag{201}$$

the distribution of the resultant has a maximum for a value of r which is determined by the average values of x^2 and y^2. We shall now show that, as the number of dimensions is increased, this maximum tends to become very sharp. This has important applications in noise problems.

For simplicity we shall study the symmetrical case in which the standard deviations σ are the same in each dimension. Suppose that we are dealing with an N-dimensional distribution, and let us call the coordinates

$$x_1, x_2, \cdots, x_N$$

We shall assume that N is an even number, since this is the usual case of interest.

Then

$$r^2 = x_1^2 + x_2^2 + \cdots + x_N^2 \tag{202}$$

Now, we know by definition that

$$\int_0^\infty P(r)\,dr = 1 \tag{203}$$

and we know by geometry that

$$\int_{-\infty}^{+\infty} \cdots \int_{-\infty}^{+\infty} P(x_1)P(x_2) \cdots P(x_N)\,dx_1\,dx_2 \cdots dx_N$$

$$= \frac{a_1a_2 \cdots a_N}{(\sqrt{\pi})^N} \int_{-\infty}^{+\infty} \cdots \int_{-\infty}^{+\infty} \epsilon^{-(a_1^2x_1^2+a_2^2x_2^2+\cdots+a_N^2x_N^2)}\,dx_1\,dx_2 \cdots dx_N$$

$$= \int_0^\infty Ar^{N-1}\epsilon^{-a^2r^2}\,dr \tag{204}$$

since by hypothesis

$$a_1^2 = a_2^2 = \cdots = a_N^2 = \text{say } a^2 \tag{205}$$

Since N is an even number,

$$\int_0^\infty A r^{N-1} \epsilon^{-a^2 r^2}\, dr = \frac{A\left[\left(\frac{N-2}{2}\right)!\right]}{2a^N} \tag{206}$$

so that by Eq. (203)

$$A = \frac{2a^N}{\left(\frac{N-2}{2}\right)!} \tag{207}$$

Thus

$$P(r) = \frac{2a^N}{\left(\frac{N-2}{2}\right)!} r^{N-1} \epsilon^{-a^2 r^2} \tag{208}$$

$P(r)$ has a maximum when

$$\frac{d[P(r)]}{dr} = \frac{2a^N}{\left(\frac{N-2}{2}\right)!} [\epsilon^{-a^2 r^2}(N-1) r^{N-2} + r^{N-1} \epsilon^{-a^2 r^2}(-2a^2 r)] = 0 \tag{209}$$

i.e., when

$$(N-1) - 2a^2 r^2 = 0 \tag{210}$$

or

$$r = \frac{1}{a}\sqrt{\frac{N-1}{2}} \tag{211}$$

To show that the maximum is sharp when N is large, we need only note that r^{N-1} decreases rapidly on the low-r side of the maximum, so that low values of r are improbable; and $\epsilon^{-a^2 r^2}$ decreases rapidly on the high-r side, so that large values of r are improbable. When N increases, the value of r for maximum $P(r)$ increases according to Eq. (211), so that the maximum moves out to a region in which $\epsilon^{-a^2 r^2}$ is decreasing more rapidly. The maximum thus becomes sharper on both the high- and low-r sides as N increases. The reader can work out some numerical cases as exercises.

The most common application of the foregoing mathematical phenomenon in our work occurs in the calculation of the energy in the superposition of different frequency components, each of which has a normal distribution. Each frequency component adds two dimensions (one inphase and one quadrature) to the over-all picture. Consequently, when the number of frequency components is large, appreciable deviations from the average energy value are extremely improbable. Therefore, if the time of observation T is long enough so that there are a large number of Fourier components in the frequency band ΔF, then the power or energy measured in ΔF will show no appreciable fluctuations in practice.

7.16 Coherence. When two identical signals are added in phase, it is well known that the energy (quadratic content) of the resultant is equal to four times that of either signal taken separately. On the other hand, if the two signals are added out of phase, the resultant has zero energy. In general, if we have two signals $E_1(t)$ and $E_2(t)$ and the two are superimposed, the resultant quadratic content is

$$\begin{aligned}\int[E_1(t) + E_2(t)]^2dt &= \int[E_1^2(t) + 2E_1(t)E_2(t) + E_2^2(t)]\,dt \\ &= \int[E_1^2(t) + E_2^2(t)]\,dt + \int 2E_1(t)E_2(t)\,dt \qquad (212)\end{aligned}$$

The first integral on the right of Eq. (212) represents the quadratic contents of the two signals taken separately, while the second integral represents an interaction quadratic content. The ratio

$$\frac{\int 2E_1(t)E_2(t)\,dt}{\int 2|E_1(t)||E_2(t)|dt} = H_{12} \qquad (213)$$

will be called the coherence ratio between the signals $E_1(t)$ and $E_2(t)$. The value of the coherence ratio thus must lie between -1 and $+1$. The coherence ratio represents a normalized version of the interaction quadratic content.

In accordance with the foregoing definition, we see that two independent noise signals have a zero coherence ratio, since we know that their quadratic contents are directly additive. Furthermore if the integration is carried out over a sufficiently long time, two signals of different frequencies

$$C_1 \cos \omega_1 t \qquad \text{and} \qquad C_2 \cos \omega_2 t$$

have a zero coherence ratio. Two signals of the same frequency but 90 deg out of phase will likewise have a zero coherence ratio if the integration is extended over a very large number of cycles. Signals having a zero coherence ratio are called *orthogonal.* Signals having a coherence ratio of $+1$ or -1 may be called *unicoherent.*

Any signal can be divided into Fourier series components (each component having a sine and a cosine term). Therefore, if two signals are considered over a long period of time, it follows that they can be separated into orthogonal and unicoherent components. We can therefore state the following rule:

The resultant average quadratic content in the superposition of a number of signals is equal to the sum of the average quadratic contents of the individual signals plus twice the sum of the average values of the products of the unicoherent components, each product taken with proper sign.

As an example, let us find the average quadratic content in the superposition of $C_1 \cos \omega t$ and $C_2 \cos (\omega t + \phi)$. Here the unicoherent components are

$$C_1 \cos \omega t \qquad \text{and} \qquad C_2 \cos \phi \cos \omega t$$

and the only orthogonal component is

$$-C_2 \sin \phi \sin \omega t$$

The total average quadratic content is therefore

$$\frac{C_1^2}{2} + \frac{C_2^2}{2} \cos^2 \phi + \frac{C_2^2}{2} \sin^2 \phi + 2\frac{C_1C_2}{2} \cos \phi = \frac{C_1^2}{2} + \frac{C_2^2}{2} + C_1C_2 \cos \phi \tag{214}$$

It is a general practical fact that any two signals arising from independent sources are orthogonal. Even in the case of signals of presumably the same frequency, if the signals are independent there will always be a wandering of the phase between them so that over a long time the average value of the interaction term $C_1C_2 \cos \phi$ in Eq. (214) will be zero.

The different sidebands of a modulated wave are orthogonal. This is true regardless of the type of modulation, since the sidebands are of different frequencies. Nevertheless, the sidebands have definitely specified amplitude, phase, and frequency relationships with respect to each other. On the basis of these relationships, as we have seen in the last chapter, it is possible to obtain improved signal-to-noise ratios. It is therefore reasonable to call these sidebands coherent, even though their interaction energy is zero. We thus arrive at the following general definitions:

Any two signals, or any two parts of the same signal, which have a specified relationship between their detailed values (i.e., *between their amplitudes as a function of time or between the phases of their frequency components*) *are coherent. Two signals, or two parts of the same signal, are incoherent if they are independent of each other* (i.e., *if there is no specified relation between their detailed values*).

On the basis of these definitions, all incoherent signals are orthogonal, but orthogonal signals are not necessarily incoherent.

Since the quadratic contents of incoherent signals are additive, any deviation from exact addition is an indication that the signals are not independent. In particular, any decrease (or increase) in the normal fluctuations of a random process can be brought about only by the introduction of some coherence whose effect is to make the process no longer random.

For example, in Sec. 7.11, we derived the formula

$$\overline{[(I_{\Delta F})_{\text{rms}}]^2} = 2M^2K\,\Delta F \tag{215}$$

for the fluctuation in the resultant of a large number of identical impulsive functions occurring at random, but at the average rate of K per second, and of impulsive strength M. Since the quadratic content in the bandwidth ΔF of a single impulse is $2M^2\,\Delta F$, Eq. (215) states that the quadratic contents of random impulses are additive, *i.e.*, their average interaction energy is zero. Applying Eq. (215) to the case of shot effect, we have

$$M = e = \text{electronic charge} \tag{216}$$

and

$$MK = I = \text{plate current} \tag{217}$$

Thus

$$\overline{[(I_{\Delta F})_{\text{rms}}]^2} = 2eI\,\Delta F \tag{218}$$

Now, in the presence of space charge or when there is an external load impedance, the actual fluctuations in place current are *less* than the amount given by Eq. (218). We can therefore conclude that the presence of space charge or the external impedance must introduce coherence between the impulses which make up the plate current. To state this in other words, we may conclude that both space charge and external impedances cause interaction between electrons traveling in a tube so that the arrival of individual electrons at the anode is no longer a random process. Nevertheless, in the case of shot effect (see Sec. 8.4) the anode current is still random noise in accordance with the definitions in Sec. 7.14, since its wave form is unchanged by these coherent influences and only its magnitude has been affected. Coherent influences of such types are thus quite similar to regeneration or degeneration.

Exercises

1. Discuss the amount and effects of coherence when a chorus of n persons is singing a song.

2. If a number of people are speaking at random in a room, the question arises as to whether the addition of more speakers will tend to increase the general noise level or whether it will tend to decrease it, owing to phase reinforcement and cancellation. Show that the average noise level (measured in terms of sound energy, which is proportional to amplitude squared) is directly proportional to the number of people speaking, if each is speaking with the same average loudness.

7.17 The Envelope of a Noise Signal and of a Noise plus Carrier Signal.[1] In many cases in radio engineering in which random noise is important, the noise passes through a radio-frequency transmission system which is quite narrow, say perhaps 10 to 30 kc wide for audio or 3 to 6 mc wide for television. The noise or noise plus signal then passes through a detector, so that what is really important is the envelope of the noise or noise plus signal. We shall therefore now calculate the probability distribution function of the amplitude of the envelope of a noise function and of a noise plus carrier signal.

a. Noise. A noise signal according to Sec. 7.14*a* consists of frequency components of the form

$$i_q = I_q \cos\left(\frac{2\pi qt}{T} - \phi_q\right) \tag{219}$$

where I_q has a two-dimensional normal distribution and ϕ_q is a random phase. In order to find the envelope of the noise signal, we express i_q as a modulated carrier in the form

$$\begin{aligned} i_q &= I_q \cos\left[2\pi\left(\frac{q}{T} - F\right)t + 2\pi Ft + \phi_q\right] \\ &= I_q \cos\left[2\pi\left(\frac{q}{T} - F\right)t + \phi_q\right] \cos 2\pi Ft \\ &\qquad - I_q \sin\left[2\pi\left(\frac{q}{T} - F\right)t + \phi_q\right] \sin 2\pi Ft \end{aligned} \tag{220}$$

In Eq. (220) F is the carrier frequency, which may be chosen in the center of the pass band, although this particular choice is not necessary. The term with $\cos 2\pi Ft$ as a factor may be considered the inphase component and the term with $\sin 2\pi Ft$ as a factor may be considered the quadrature component of Eq. (220) in accordance with the terminology of Chap. V. The total noise signal may then be expressed

$$\begin{aligned} i_N &= I_c \cos 2\pi Ft - I_s \sin 2\pi Ft \\ &= R_N \cos(2\pi Ft + \theta) \end{aligned} \tag{221}$$

where

$$I_c = \sum I_q \cos\left[2\pi\left(\frac{q}{T} - F\right)t + \phi_q\right] \tag{222}$$

[1] The methods used in this and the following two sections are due to S. O. Rice, *Bell System Tech. J.*, July, 1944.

and

$$I_s = \sum I_q \sin \left[2\pi \left(\frac{q}{T} - F \right) t + \phi_q \right] \tag{223}$$

and the summation is taken over all values of q in the pass band. Furthermore,

$$R_N = \sqrt{I_c^2 + I_s^2} \tag{224}$$

where R_N is the amplitude of the envelope.

Both I_c and I_s satisfy the conditions required by the central-limit theorem, so that each has a one-dimensional normal distribution. Consequently, R_N has a two-dimensional normal distribution, which may be expressed, according to Eq. (186), as

$$P(R_N)\,dR_N = 2A^2 R_N \epsilon^{-A^2 R_N^2}\,dR_N \tag{225}$$

where

$$A^2 = \frac{1}{\overline{R_N^2}} \tag{226}$$

From Eq. (221) it also follows that

$$\overline{i_N^2} = \overline{\tfrac{1}{2} R_N^2} \tag{227}$$

since the average value of the $\cos^2$ is $\frac{1}{2}$ and since, according to Sec. 7.14*e*, an ensemble distribution of random noise may be considered a time distribution. Therefore

$$A^2 = \frac{1}{2(\text{mean square total radio-frequency noise signal})} \tag{228}$$

Equation (225), with the value of A^2 given by Eq. (228), is the desired probability distribution of the envelope amplitude of random noise.

For future reference we now also note that from Eqs. (226) and (224) it follows that

$$\overline{I_c^2} = \overline{I_s^2} = \frac{1}{2A^2} \tag{229}$$

Therefore the distributions of I_c and I_s are, according to Eq. (174),

$$P(I_c)\,dI_c = \frac{A}{\sqrt{\pi}}\,\epsilon^{-A^2 I_c^2}\,dI_c \tag{230}$$

and

$$P(I_s)\,dI_s = \frac{A}{\sqrt{\pi}}\,\epsilon^{-A^2 I_s^2}\,dI_s \tag{231}$$

b. Noise plus Carrier. Let us next consider the case in which we have a carrier in addition to the noise, and let the carrier be

$$K \cos 2\pi F t \tag{232}$$

The coefficient of the inphase component is now

$$I_c' = K + I_c \tag{233}$$

and that of the quadrature component is

$$I_s' = I_s \tag{234}$$

The amplitude of the envelope is

$$R = \sqrt{I_c'^2 + I_s'^2} \tag{235}$$

so that

$$I_c' = R \cos \theta \tag{236}$$

and

$$I_s' = R \sin \theta \tag{237}$$

where

$$\theta = \tan^{-1}\left(\frac{I_s'}{I_c'}\right) \tag{238}$$

The probability distribution of I_s' is the same as that of I_s, namely,

$$P(I_s')\,dI_s' = \frac{A}{\sqrt{\pi}}\,\epsilon^{-A^2 I_s'^2}\,dI_s' \tag{239}$$

Since K is a constant, the probability distribution of I_c is, according to Eqs. (230) and (233),

$$P(I_c')\,dI_c' = \frac{A}{\sqrt{\pi}}\,\epsilon^{-A^2(I_c'-K)^2}\,dI_c' \tag{240}$$

According to the method used in Eq. (185) it then follows from Eqs. (239) and (240) that

$$\begin{aligned} P(R)\,dR &= \int_{\theta=0}^{\theta=2\pi} \frac{A^2}{\pi}\,\epsilon^{-A^2[I_s'^2+(I_c'-K)^2]}\,R\,dR\,d\theta \\ &= \int_{\theta=0}^{2\pi} \frac{A^2}{\pi}\,\epsilon^{-A^2(R^2-2KR\cos\theta+K^2)}\,R\,dR\,d\theta \\ &= \frac{A^2 R}{\pi}\,\epsilon^{-A^2(R^2+K^2)}\left(\int_0^{2\pi} \epsilon^{2A^2KR\cos\theta}\,d\theta\right)dR \\ &= 2A^2 R\epsilon^{-A^2(R^2+K^2)} I_0(2A^2KR)\,dR \end{aligned} \tag{241}$$ [1]

where I_0 is the modified Bessel function of the first kind of zero order (discussed in Appendix E).

[1] This follows from the formula

$$\frac{1}{2\pi}\int_0^{2\pi} \epsilon^{z\cos\theta}\,d\theta = I_0(z)$$

Equation (241) is the desired probability distribution for the amplitude of the envelope of a combined random noise plus carrier signal. The value of A^2 is given in Eq. (228).[1]

Exercise

In certain low-frequency amplifiers, the noise and signal are superimposed and observed directly without a detection process. For such a case, find the probability distribution of a superimposed direct-current pulse and random noise. This will be the analogue of Eq. (241).

7.18 Linear and Low-frequency Quadratic Content of the Rectified Envelope of Noise and Noise Plus Carrier Signals (Linear Detection). We shall next determine the output of a linear detector when the input is either pure noise or noise plus carrier. We are interested in finding

1. The direct-current output (diode current), since this can then be used as a measure of the noise and the carrier.

2. The mean square value of the low-frequency alternating-current output, since this is a measure of the output energy (audio, video, or other signal).

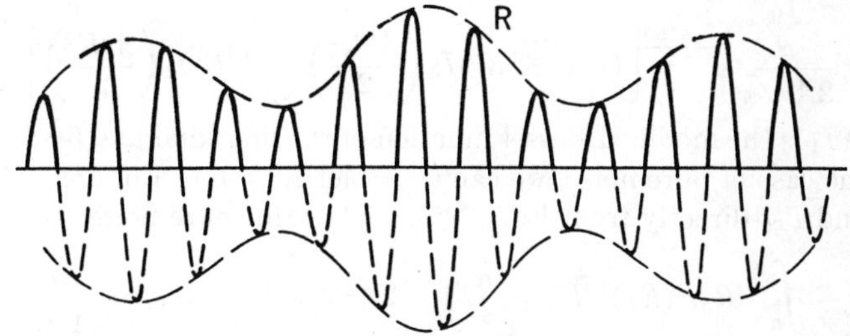

FIG. 12. A modulated carrier showing the envelope and indicating the portion passed by a linear rectifier.

Let us suppose that the linear rectifier has a characteristic

$$\left.\begin{aligned} I &= 0 \qquad (\text{when } V < 0) \\ &= \alpha V \qquad (\text{when } V > 0) \end{aligned}\right\} \tag{242}$$

where V is the input signal amplitude and I is the output signal amplitude. In Fig. 12 is a diagram of the envelope R of the signal, and the

[1] Since

$$\text{Rms value of carrier} = \frac{K}{\sqrt{2}}$$

and

$$\text{Rms value of noise} = \frac{1}{\sqrt{2}A}$$

it follows that

$$\frac{\text{Rms noise}}{\text{Rms carrier}} = \frac{1}{AK}$$

actual radio-frequency signal is also shown. Now

$$\frac{1}{2\pi}\int_0^\pi \sin x\, dx = \frac{1}{\pi} \tag{243}$$

Consequently, a glance at Fig. 12 shows that the total of direct-current plus low-frequency output of the rectifier is

$$I_{TL} = \frac{\alpha R}{\pi} = I_{DC} + I_{AC} \tag{244}$$

where the subscript $_{TL}$ is an abbreviation of "total low" and I_{AC} in Eq. (244) stands for the low-frequency (*i.e.*, excluding radio-frequency) components in the output.

To find I_{DC}, we need only find the average value of I_{TL}. Thus, according to Eq. (241), for noise plus a carrier

$$\begin{aligned} I_{DC} &= \frac{\alpha}{\pi}\int_0^\infty RP(R)\, dR \\ &= \frac{\alpha}{\pi}\int_0^\infty 2A^2R^2\epsilon^{-A^2(R^2+K^2)}I_0(2A^2KR)\, dR \\ &= \frac{\alpha}{2A\sqrt{\pi}}\epsilon^{-\frac{A^2K^2}{2}}\left[(1 + A^2K^2)I_0\left(\frac{A^2K^2}{2}\right) + A^2K^2I_1\left(\frac{A^2K^2}{2}\right)\right] \end{aligned} \tag{245}$$ [1]

where I_1 is the modified Bessel function of the first kind and first order. For the case of pure noise, we can either let $K = 0$ in Eq. (245), or we can find I_{DC} directly from Eq. (225). Thus, for pure noise,

$$I_{DC} = \frac{\alpha}{\pi}\int_0^\infty R_NP(R_N)\, dR_N = \frac{\alpha}{\pi}\int_0^\infty 2A^2R_N^2\epsilon^{-A^2R_N^2}\, dR_N = \frac{\alpha}{2A\sqrt{\pi}} \tag{246}$$ [2]

This is also the value of Eq. (245) when $K = 0$. The value of A is given in Eq. (228).

[1] This follows from the formula

$$\int_0^\infty z^2\epsilon^{-A^2z^2}I_0(2A^2Kz)\, dz = \frac{\sqrt{\pi}}{4A^3}\epsilon^{\frac{A^2K^2}{2}}\left[(1 + A^2K^2)I_0\left(\frac{A^2K^2}{2}\right) + A^2K^2I_1\left(\frac{A^2K^2}{2}\right)\right]$$

Equation (245) is credited by Rice to W. R. Bennett and D. O. North.

[2] This same value of I_{DC} should be obtainable by direct rectification of the noise amplitude given in Eq. (191), since the direct current should not depend upon whether the noise is considered as a modulated carrier or not. The rectified direct current according to Eq. (191) is

$$\begin{aligned} \alpha\int_0^\infty IP(I)\, dI &= \alpha\int_0^\infty \frac{I}{\sigma_I\sqrt{2\pi}}\epsilon^{-\frac{I^2}{2\sigma_I^2}}\, dI \\ &= \frac{\alpha\sigma_I}{\sqrt{2\pi}} = \frac{\alpha}{2A\sqrt{\pi}} \end{aligned}$$

since $\sigma_I = 1/A\sqrt{2}$ according to Eqs. (192) and (228). This agrees with Eq. (246).

Equations (246) and (245) allow noise and noise plus signal to be measured with a diode meter. Equation (245) is plotted as a function of K in Chap. VI (Fig. 22).

Let us next determine the low-frequency quadratic content of these rectified envelopes, namely, $\overline{I_{AC}^2}$. According to Eq. (244),

$$\begin{aligned} \overline{I_{TL}^2} &= \overline{(I_{DC} + I_{AC})^2} = I_{DC}^2 + 2I_{DC}\overline{I_{AC}} + \overline{I_{AC}^2} \\ &= I_{DC}^2 + \overline{I_{AC}^2} \end{aligned} \tag{247}$$

since

$$\overline{I_{AC}} = 0 \tag{248}$$

Thus

$$\overline{I_{AC}^2} = \overline{I_{TL}^2} - I_{DC}^2 \tag{249}$$

Now, according to Eqs. (244) and (241),

$$\begin{aligned} \overline{I_{TL}^2} &= \int_0^\infty \left(\frac{\alpha R}{\pi}\right)^2 P(R)\, dR \\ &= \frac{\alpha^2}{\pi^2} \int_0^\infty 2A^2R^3\, \epsilon^{-A^2(R^2+K^2)}\, I_0(2A^2KR)\, dR \\ &= \frac{\alpha^2}{\pi^2}\left(K^2 + \frac{1}{A^2}\right) \end{aligned} \tag{250}$$[1]

Combining Eqs. (249), (250), and (245), we obtain

$$\overline{I_{AC}^2} = \frac{\alpha^2}{\pi^2}\left(K^2 + \frac{1}{A^2}\right) - \frac{\alpha^2}{4A^2\pi}\,\epsilon^{-A^2K^2} \left[(1 + A^2K^2)I_0\left(\frac{A^2K^2}{2}\right) + A^2K^2I_1\left(\frac{A^2K^2}{2}\right)\right]^2 \tag{251}$$

Equation (251) is plotted as a function of K in Chap. VI (Fig. 23). For very large and for very small values of K the values that it gives for $\overline{I_{AC}^2}$ become much simpler. Thus, when A^2K^2 is very small [see Eqs. (15) and (16) of Appendix E],

$$I_0\left(\frac{A^2K^2}{2}\right) = 1 + \frac{A^4K^4}{8} + \cdots \tag{252}$$

and

$$I_1\left(\frac{A^2K^2}{2}\right) = \frac{A^2K^2}{4} + \cdots \tag{253}$$

so that Eq. (251) becomes

$$\overline{I_{AC}^2} = \frac{\alpha^2}{\pi^2}\left(K^2 + \frac{1}{A^2}\right) - \frac{\alpha^2}{4A^2\pi}\,\epsilon^{-A^2K^2}\left(1 + A^2K^2 + \frac{3}{8}A^4K^4 + \cdots\right)^2 \tag{254}$$

[1] This follows from the integration formula

$$\int_0^\infty 2A^2x^3\epsilon^{-A^2(x^2+K^2)}\, I_0(2A^2Kx)\, dx = K^2 + \frac{1}{A^2}$$

If $K = 0$, Eq. (254) reduces to

$$\overline{I_{AC}^2} = \frac{\alpha^2}{A^2}\left(\frac{1}{\pi^2} - \frac{1}{4\pi}\right) = \frac{\alpha^2}{4\pi^2 A^2}(4 - \pi) \tag{255}$$

This same value could also have been obtained by using Eqs. (225), (244), (246), and (249) for the case of pure noise.

When A^2K^2 is very large, we can use the asymptotic expansions for the Bessel functions [Eq. (21) of Appendix E]. We thus obtain, for large values of A^2K^2,

$$I_0\left(\frac{A^2K^2}{2}\right) = \frac{\epsilon^{\frac{A^2K^2}{2}}}{AK\sqrt{\pi}}\left(1 + \frac{1}{4A^2K^2} + \cdots\right) \tag{256}$$

and

$$I_1\left(\frac{A^2K^2}{2}\right) = \frac{\epsilon^{\frac{A^2K^2}{2}}}{AK\sqrt{\pi}}\left(1 - \frac{3}{4A^2K^2} + \cdots\right) \tag{257}$$

Substitution of these values into Eq. (251) gives

$$\begin{aligned}\overline{I_{AC}^2} &= \frac{\alpha^2}{\pi^2 A^2}(1 + K^2A^2) - \frac{\alpha^2}{4A^2\pi}\left[\frac{4}{\pi}A^2K^2 + \frac{2}{\pi} + \cdots\left(\frac{1}{A^2K^2}\right)\right] \\ &= \frac{\alpha^2}{2\pi^2 A^2}\end{aligned} \tag{258}$$

We thus see that for large values of K, the carrier level, the output signal is independent of K and depends only on the radio-frequency noise $1/2A^2$.

The ratio of Eq. (258) to (255) gives the increase in apparent noise that is always observed in a radio receiver when a carrier is tuned in. This ratio is

$$\frac{\alpha^2/2\pi^2A^2}{\alpha^2/(4\pi^2A^2)(4 - \pi)} = \frac{2}{4 - \pi} = 2.33 \tag{259}$$

The ratio given in Eq. (259) is actually the minimum value that can be observed for the ratio of noise with and without a carrier. In actual receivers two characteristics tend to increase this ratio, often manyfold. One of these characteristics is the frequency characteristic of the low-frequency amplifier. Thus, if the carrier is located at the center of the pass band of the noise and the carrier is of large amplitude, the low-frequency noise output is pretty well confined to a band extending from zero frequency to a frequency of one-half the width of the radio-frequency noise pass band. The reason for this is that the low-frequency noise in this case arises from beating of the carrier with the separate noise components. However, when the carrier is absent, the beating of noise components gives rise to important frequencies extending from zero up to the entire width of the pass band, although the output does fall off at the higher frequencies. Furthermore, the asymmetrical noise sidebands, which practically give rise only to frequency modulation when a large carrier is present, will, in the absence of a carrier, also give rise to AM harmonics of the noise beat frequencies, thus still further extending the low-frequency range. Consequently, unless the low-frequency amplifier has a very wide pass band, it will act to increase the ratio given in Eq. (259).

The other characteristic of a receiver that tends to increase the ratio in Eq. (259) is nonlinearity of the detector at low amplitudes. This will make the detector relatively insensitive at the low amplitudes that may occur when noise alone is present, thus often causing a manyfold increase in the ratio given by Eq. (259). For this same reason it is important that large signal levels shall be present, when Eq. (245) is used to evaluate noise measured with a diode meter.

Exercises

1. When K is large, express the effective percentage of noise modulation in terms of A and K.

2. Find the output of a linear detector for an input wave

$$K(1 + m \cos \alpha t) \cos \omega t$$

Answer:

$$I_{TL} = \frac{\alpha K}{\pi} + \frac{\alpha m K}{\pi} \cos \alpha t$$

$$I_{AC}^2 = \frac{\alpha^2 m^2 K^2}{2\pi^2}$$

$$I_{DC} = \frac{\alpha K}{\pi}$$

7.19 Effect of a Quadratic Transmission System on Random Noise and the Envelope of Noise Plus Carrier (Square-law Detection). We shall next determine what happens when noise or noise plus carrier passes through a quadratic transmission system (square-law-type detector) such as the curved portion of a vacuum-tube characteristic. Let us assume that the characteristic of the transmission system is

$$I = \alpha V^2 + \beta V + \gamma \tag{260}$$

where V is the amplitude of the input signal, I is the amplitude of the output signal, and α, β, and γ are constants of the transmission system. Let the input signal consist either of pure random noise or noise plus a carrier. In either case, as shown in Sec. 7.17, the input may be considered a modulated carrier

$$V = R \cos (2\pi F t + \phi) \tag{261}$$

where R is the envelope and F is the carrier frequency. The notation of Sec. 7.17 will be used in the following discussion.

From Eqs. (260) and (261) it follows that

$$I = \alpha R^2 \cos^2 (2\pi Ft + \phi) + \beta R \cos (2\pi Ft + \phi) + \gamma$$
$$= \frac{\alpha R^2}{2} + \frac{\alpha R^2}{2} \cos (4\pi Ft + 2\phi) + \beta R \cos (2\pi Ft + \phi) + \gamma \quad (262)$$

Now suppose that we have a filter to remove high frequencies, in the carrier range or higher. Then Eq. (262) reduces to

$$I' = \frac{\alpha R^2}{2} + \gamma \quad (263)$$

where I' is that portion of I from which the high frequencies have been removed.

If we let R be the envelope of carrier plus noise as given by Eq. (241), then the direct-current component of the output is

$$I_{DC} = \overline{\frac{\alpha R^2}{2}} + \gamma = \frac{\alpha}{2} \int_0^\infty 2A^2R^3\epsilon^{-A^2(R^2+K^2)}\, I_0(2A^2KR)\, dR + \gamma$$
$$= \frac{\alpha}{2}\left(K^2 + \frac{1}{A^2}\right) + \gamma \quad (264)$$

The integral in Eq. (264) has previously been evaluated in Eq. (250). If there is no carrier, then K is just set equal to zero in Eq. (264). The value of A^2 is given in Eq. (228).

To find the alternating-current quadratic content (power) of I', we first note that according to Eq. (249)

$$\overline{I'^2_{AC}} = \overline{I^2_{TL}} - I^2_{DC} \quad (265)$$

where $\overline{I^2_{TL}}$ is the average value of I'^2. Thus

$$\overline{I^2_{TL}} = \overline{\frac{\alpha^2 R^4}{4}} + 2\gamma \overline{\frac{\alpha R^2}{2}} + \gamma^2$$
$$= \frac{\alpha^2}{4} \int_0^\infty 2A^2R^5\epsilon^{-A^2(R^2+K^2)}\, I_0(2A^2KR)\, dR$$
$$+ \alpha\gamma \int_0^\infty 2A^2R^3\epsilon^{-A^2(R^2+K^2)}\, I_0(2A^2KR)\, dR + \gamma^2$$
$$= \frac{\alpha^2}{4}\left(\frac{2}{A^4} + \frac{4K^2}{A^2} + K^4\right) + \alpha\gamma\left(K^2 + \frac{1}{A^2}\right) + \gamma^2 \quad (266)[1]$$

[1] The first integral is evaluated by the formula

$$\int_0^\infty 2A^2x^5\epsilon^{-A^2(x^2+K^2)}\, I_0(2A^2Kx)\, dx = \frac{2}{A^4} + \frac{4K^2}{A^2} + K^4$$

The second integral has been evaluated previously. General formulas for evalu-

Consequently,

$$\overline{I_{AC}^2} = \overline{I_{TL}^2} - I_{DC}^2 = \frac{\alpha^2}{4}\left(\frac{1}{A^4} + \frac{2K^2}{A^2}\right) \tag{267}$$

In Eq. (267), K is the carrier amplitude, and $1/2A^2$ is the mean square value of the total radio-frequency noise signal. For pure noise, we

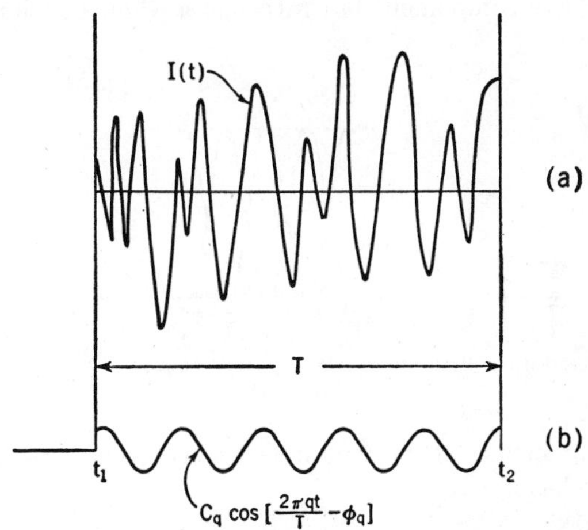

FIG. 13. The random-noise current $I(t)$ and its qth Fourier harmonic $C_q \cos\left(\frac{2\pi qt}{T} - \phi_q\right)$.

just set $K = 0$ in Eq. (267). As in the case of the linear detector, the pure noise terms have a wider frequency spectrum than the original frequency band, so that narrowing the band of the low-frequency amplifier will discriminate against noise.

Exercise

Using Eq. (191) for the amplitude distribution of random noise, show that $I_{DC} = (\alpha/2A^2) + \gamma$ for random noise passing through a quadratic transmission system.

7.20 Relation between Fourier Harmonics and Frequency Composition in a Signal of Finite Duration. Before closing Chap. VII we shall discuss briefly the relation between the Fourier series components and frequency composition of random-noise currents. In Fig. 13 is shown diagrammatically the total current $I(t)$ and its qth

ating this type of integral are given by Rice in his equations 3.10-12 and 4B-1. It should be noted that, when n is an even integer, Rice's series 4B-1 terminates with the $\left(\frac{n}{2} + 1\right)$th term.

Fourier harmonic

$$C_q \cos\left(\frac{2\pi qt}{T} - \phi_q\right)$$

Since T is finite, the qth Fourier harmonic is just a wave train of finite length; and according to the discussion in Sec. 3.2 it consists not of a single frequency component, but rather of a whole distribution of fre-

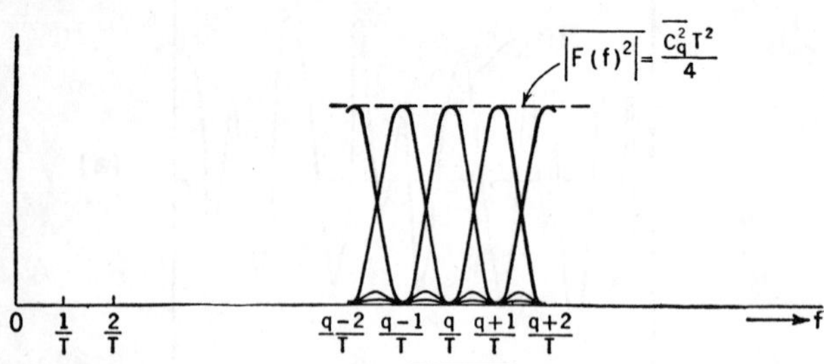

FIG. 14. Superposition of the functions $\overline{|F_{q+n}(f)|^2}$ to give $\overline{|F(f)|^2}$ in accordance with Eq. (271).

quency components. However, if the wave train consists of many complete cycles of

$$C_q \cos\left(\frac{2\pi qt}{T} - \phi_q\right)$$

the frequency distribution is sharply peaked in the neighborhood of the frequency q/T. Consequently, it is customary to speak of the qth Fourier component as having a frequency q/T, especially when q is large, but it should be kept in mind that each Fourier component really represents a distribution of frequency components.

For many theoretical as well as practical purposes it is desirable to have an expression for the actual frequency distribution of $I(t)$, not just the amplitudes of its Fourier series components. We shall therefore proceed to find the frequency distribution. Our method will be to find the complex frequency distribution $F(f)$ of each Fourier series component and then add these frequency distributions for all the Fourier series components. According to Eq. (33) of Chap. IV this will give us the frequency distribution of $I(t)$.

Let us first find the frequency distribution $F_q(f)$ of the general Fourier component

$$C_q \cos\left(\frac{2\pi qt}{T} - \phi_q\right)$$

Thus

$$F_q(f) = \int_0^T C_q \cos\left(\frac{2\pi qt}{T} - \phi_q\right)\cos 2\pi ft\,dt - j\int_0^T C_q \cos\left(\frac{2\pi qt}{T} - \phi_q\right)\sin 2\pi ft\,dt$$

$$= \left\{\frac{C_q}{4\pi\left(f + \frac{q}{T}\right)}\sin\left[2\pi\left(f + \frac{q}{T}\right)t - \phi_q\right] + \frac{C_q}{4\pi\left(f - \frac{q}{T}\right)}\sin\left[2\pi\left(f - \frac{q}{T}\right)t + \phi_q\right]\right\}\Bigg|_0^T$$
$$+ j\left\{\frac{C_q}{4\pi\left(f + \frac{q}{T}\right)}\cos\left[2\pi\left(f + \frac{q}{T}\right)t - \phi_q\right] + \frac{C_q}{4\pi\left(f - \frac{q}{T}\right)}\cos\left[2\pi\left(f - \frac{q}{T}\right)t + \phi_q\right]\right\}\Bigg|_0^T \quad (268)$$

For the high Fourier series harmonics, q is a large number, so that the first terms inside the braces in Eq. (268) become negligible in comparison with the second and the second are appreciable only in the neighborhood of $f = q/T$. Under these circumstances, we have approximately

$$F_q(f) = \frac{C_q}{4\pi\left(f - \frac{q}{T}\right)}\left\{\sin\left[2\pi\left(f - \frac{q}{T}\right)T + \phi_q\right] - \sin\phi_q\right\} + \frac{jC_q}{4\pi\left(f - \frac{q}{T}\right)}\left\{\cos\left[2\pi\left(f - \frac{q}{T}\right)T + \phi_q\right] - \cos\phi_q\right\} \quad (269)$$

After a little trigonometric manipulation,[1] this reduces to

$$F_q(f) = \frac{C_q}{4\pi\left(f - \frac{q}{T}\right)}\left\{2 - 2\cos\left[2\pi\left(f - \frac{q}{T}\right)T\right]\right\}^{1/2} \epsilon^{-j\tan^{-1}\left[\pi\left(f - \frac{q}{T}\right)T + \phi_q\right]} \quad (270)$$

In Fig. 14 we have plotted

$$\overline{|F(f)|^2}$$

[1] Using Eqs. (24) and (26) of Appendix C.

as a function of f. Since ϕ_q in Eq. (270) is a random phase angle, the values of $\overline{|F_q(f)|^2}$ for the different values of q will be additive just like the values of the quadratic content of random noise. Consequently, for any frequency f the total value of $\overline{|F(f)|^2}$ will be

$$\overline{|F(f)|^2} = \overline{|F_q(f)|^2} + \overline{|F_{q+1}(f)|^2} + \overline{|F_{q+2}(f)|^2} + \cdots + \overline{|F_{q-1}(f)|^2} + \overline{|F_{q-2}(f)|^2} + \cdots \qquad (271)^1$$

Now we note that

$$\overline{|F_{q+n}(f)|^2} = \frac{\overline{(C_{q+n})^2}}{\{4\pi[f - (q+n)f_0]\}^2}\{2 - 2\cos[2\pi fT - 2\pi(q+n)]\}$$
$$= \frac{\overline{(C_{q+n})^2}}{\{4\pi[f - (q+n)f_0]\}^2}(2 - 2\cos 2\pi fT) \qquad (272)$$

where

$$f_0 = \frac{1}{T} \qquad (273)$$

Therefore

$$\overline{|F(f)|^2} = (2 - 2\cos 2\pi fT) \sum_{q=-\infty}^{+\infty} \frac{\overline{(C_q)^2}}{[4\pi(f - qf_0)]^2} \qquad (274)$$

Now the case of greatest interest (see Sec. 9.5) is that in which we consider the range of frequencies in which q is a large number and $\overline{C_q^2}$ is a constant for all values of q. We shall therefore consider this case first. In this case, physical reasoning tells us that $\overline{|F(f)|^2}$ should be independent of frequency. There are two general cases in which we can find the value of $\overline{|F(f)|^2}$. First of all, if f is one of the Fourier harmonic frequencies,

$$f = nf_0 = \frac{n}{T} \qquad (275)$$

where n is an integer. Then Eq. (274) becomes indeterminate, so that the operation in Eq. (272) is no longer justified and we must write the equation in its original form

$$\overline{|F(f)|^2} = \sum_{q=1}^{\infty} \frac{\overline{C_q^2}}{\left[4\pi\left(f - \frac{q}{T}\right)\right]^2}\left\{2 - 2\cos\left[2\pi\left(f - \frac{q}{T}\right)T\right]\right\} \qquad (276)$$

For this case,

$$\cos\left[2\pi\left(f - \frac{q}{T}\right)T\right] = \cos[2\pi(n-q)] = 1 \qquad (277)$$

so that all the terms in Eq. (276) vanish except when $q = n$. When

[1] The averaging bar over a quantity stands for an ensemble average, as has been customary in this chapter.

$q = n$, the corresponding term in Eq. (276) becomes

$$\frac{\overline{C_q^2}}{[4\pi(q - q)f_0]^2}\{2 - 2 \cos [2\pi(q - q)]\} \tag{278}$$

which is indeterminate. To evaluate this term, we expand the cosine in a power series and obtain

$$\begin{aligned}\overline{|F(f)|^2} &= \frac{\overline{C_q^2}}{[4\pi(q - q)f_0]^2}\left\{2 - 2\left[1 - \frac{(2\pi)^2(q - q)^2}{2} + \cdots\right]\right\} \\ &= \frac{\overline{C_q^2}}{4f_0^2} = \frac{\overline{C_q^2}T^2}{4}\end{aligned} \tag{279}$$

Equation (279) shows that $\overline{|F(f)|^2}$ has the value $\frac{\overline{C_q^2}T^2}{4}$ for all integral multiples of f_0. As already stated, physical reasoning tells us that $\overline{|F(f)|^2}$ must be independent of frequency, so that we must then have

$$\overline{|F(f)|^2} = \frac{\overline{C_q^2}T^2}{4} \tag{280}$$

for all frequencies, if $\overline{C_q^2}$ is a constant for all values of q. It would be preferable to have a mathematical proof of this statement, but the author has been unable to sum the series (274) for all values of f, in order to prove it. However, if

$$f = (n + \tfrac{1}{2})f_0 \tag{281}$$

i.e., midway between the Fourier series harmonics, we can also sum the series Eq. (274). In that case

$$\cos 2\pi fT = -1 \tag{282}$$

and

$$\begin{aligned}\overline{|F(f)|^2} &= 4 \sum_{q=-\infty}^{+\infty} \frac{\overline{C_q^2}}{[4\pi(n - q + \frac{1}{2})f_0]^2} \\ &= \frac{4\overline{C_q^2}}{(4\pi)^2f_0^2}\left\{\begin{array}{l}\frac{1}{(\frac{1}{2})^2} + \frac{1}{(\frac{3}{2})^2} + \frac{1}{(\frac{5}{2})^2} + \cdots \\ + \frac{1}{(-\frac{1}{2})^2} + \frac{1}{(-\frac{3}{2})^2} + \frac{1}{(-\frac{5}{2})^2} + \cdots\end{array}\right\} \\ &= \frac{4\overline{C_q^2}}{(4\pi)^2f_0^2}\, 8\left(1 + \frac{1}{3^2} + \frac{1}{5^2} + \cdots\right) \\ &= \frac{4\overline{C_q^2}}{(4\pi)^2f_0^2}\, 8\,\frac{\pi^2}{8} = \frac{\overline{C_q^2}}{4f_0^2} = \frac{\overline{C_q^2}T^2}{4}\end{aligned} \tag{283}$$ [1]

[1] The series

$$1 + \frac{1}{3^2} + \frac{1}{5^2} + \frac{1}{7^2} + \cdots = \frac{\pi^2}{8}$$

To show this, we need only substitute $x = \pi$ in Eq. (29) of Chap. I.

Thus, midway between the harmonics, we also get the value given by Eq. (280). If we could sum the series (274), it would undoubtedly give the same value of $\overline{|F(f)|^2}$ for all values of f.

Let us next find the value of $\overline{[(I_{\Delta F})_{\text{rms}}]^2}$ in terms of the frequency composition. If we include all frequency components of $I(t)$, then, by the Fourier integral energy theorem,

$$\overline{(I_{\text{rms}})^2} = \frac{1}{T}\int_0^T \overline{I^2(t)}\, dt = \frac{2}{T}\int_0^\infty \overline{|F(f)|^2}\, df \tag{284}$$

Consequently,

$$\begin{aligned}\overline{[(I_{\Delta F})_{\text{rms}}]^2} &= \frac{2}{T}\int_{F_1}^{F_1+\Delta F} \overline{|F(f)^2|}\, df = \frac{2}{T}\int_{F_1}^{F_1+\Delta F} \frac{\overline{C_q^2}T^2}{4}\, df \\ &= \tfrac{1}{2}\overline{C_q^2}T\, \Delta F\end{aligned} \tag{285}$$

According to Eq. (137),

$$\overline{C_q^2} = \frac{4M^2K}{T} \tag{286}$$

Substituting this value into Eq. (285), we obtain

$$\overline{[(I_{\Delta F})_{\text{rms}}]^2} = 2M^2K\, \Delta F \tag{287}$$

in agreement with Eq. (143). It thus appears that we get the same answer for $\overline{[(I_{\Delta F})_{\text{rms}}]^2}$ whether we consider the random-noise signal in terms of its Fourier series components or whether we consider it in terms of its frequency composition.

Finally, it may be pointed out that all the discussion in the foregoing chapter concerning Fourier series components and frequency composition does not require that the current $I(t)$ shall be periodic (see Fig. 13a). The reader should refer to Sec. 1.2 to see that the derivation of the original Fourier series expansion does not assume that the function is periodic. A periodic function has the advantage in Fourier series analysis that the same Fourier expansion derived for one interval can be extended outside this interval (see Sec. 1.4). However, Fourier analysis is not in any way limited to periodic functions, and the reader should not get the impression that there is any assumed periodicity in the random noise analyzed in the foregoing chapter.

7.21 General. In the foregoing pages, we have developed those portions of the mathematical theory of probability and of random noise which are used in this book. For particular problems on the wave form and frequency distribution of noise under special circumstances, more advanced mathematical methods involving the correlation function and the theory of matrices are required.[1] However, the results thus attainable have not appeared to the author to be of sufficient value as yet to justify including the necessary mathematical background in the present book.

The theory of probability is of great intellectual interest. When the number of trials involved is very large, the mathematical phenomena that emerge, such as normal distributions, are amazingly simple.

[1] A discussion of these is given in Rice, *Bell System Tech. J.*, July, 1944.

CHAPTER VIII

NOISE III: SHOT EFFECT

8.1 Introduction. The phenomenon of thermionic emission is of the greatest importance in radio engineering and has been the subject of an extensive literature. Owing to the fact that this emission takes place in terms of electrons, which have a finite charge and are emitted at random times, the emission current is never completely steady but exhibits minute fluctuations. The result of these fluctuations in

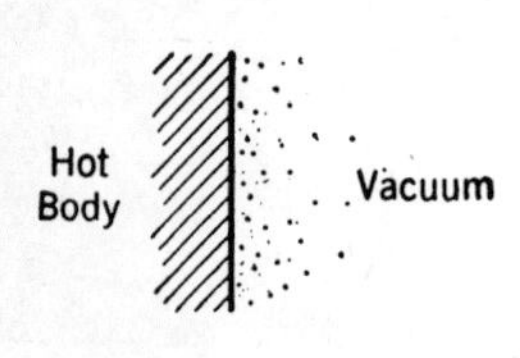

FIG. 1. Thermionic emission of electrons.

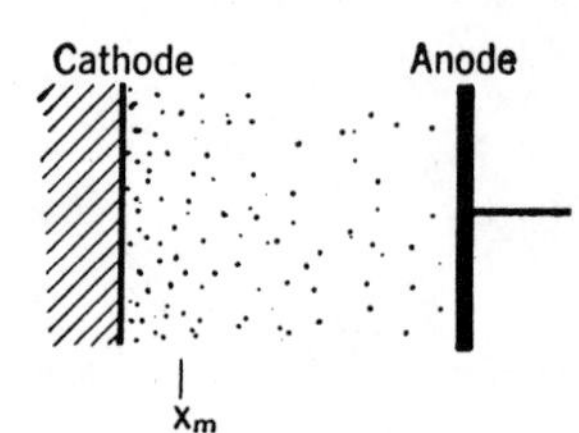

FIG. 2. Distribution of electron density in a diode.

emission on the circuits in which the thermionic emitter operates is called *shot effect.*[1]

Our interest in shot effect arises from the fact that it places a limit upon the useful amount of amplification possible in an amplifier. The methods used and the results derived in the mathematical analysis of shot effect are the subject matter of the present chapter.

8.2 Thermionic Emission and Space-charge Effects. The theory of thermionic emission shows that a hot body will emit electrons into a vacuum of such an amount as to give an emission current per unit area

$$I_c = AT^2\epsilon^{-\frac{b_0}{T}} \tag{1}$$

where A and b_0 are characteristic constants of the emitting material, T is its absolute temperature, and $\epsilon = 2.71828 \ldots$. The theory

[1] Shot effect was first noted and correctly interpreted by W. Schottky, *Ann. Physik*, **57**, 541–567, 1918. He called it shot effect as a description of the noise that it caused in an amplifier.

also shows that the electrons are not all emitted with the same velocity. Rather, the emission velocities have a normal distribution.[1]

In particular, if

s = electron velocity perpendicular to the emitting surface
m = mass of an electron
κ = charge of an electron
k = Boltzmann's constant[2]
T = absolute temperature of cathode
I_c = emission current per unit area of emitting surface
dI_{cs} = portion of emission current whose electron velocities are between s and $s + ds$

then

$$\frac{dI_{cs}}{I_c} = \frac{m}{kT} \epsilon^{\frac{-ms^2}{2kT}} s\, ds \tag{2}$$

If the emitting material is the cathode of a diode and if the anode voltage is sufficiently high, all the emitted electrons will reach the anode and thus become part of the anode, or plate, current. However, if the anode voltage is not very high, the emitted electrons will form a charged "cloud" of electrons (called a *space charge*) in front of the surface of the cathode. This charged cloud will repel electrons and will therefore tend to slow down electrons emitted from the cathode and moving toward the anode, at the same time as the electric field due to the anode voltage tends to make them go faster. The net result is shown by the potential distribution curves (B_1 and B_2) in Fig. 3. Near the cathode the potential at first falls, reaching a minimum at x_m, after which it rises until it reaches the anode potential. Thus, between 0 and x_m, the space-charge field is stronger than the anode field so that electrons emitted from the cathode are slowed down; if their velocity reaches zero before they get to x_m, the electric field then gives them velocity toward the cathode so that they ultimately return to the cathode without becoming part of the anode current. On the other hand, those electrons having sufficient emission velocity so that their velocity has not been reduced to zero by the time they reach x_m will cross x_m into the region of rising voltage where the anode field is stronger than the space-charge field so that the resultant acceleration is in the direction of the anode. These electrons will consequently reach the anode and thus become part of the anode current.

[1] See Section 7.13 for a discussion of normal distributions.
[2] See Sec. 9.2 for the meaning and numerical value of Boltzmann's constant.

The net result of space charge is thus to produce a potential barrier at x_m, called the *virtual cathode*. Those emitted electrons which have sufficient emission velocity to cross this barrier will ultimately reach the anode and become part of the external current. Those emitted electrons which do not have sufficient emission velocity to cross this barrier will ultimately return to the cathode and will thus not become part of the anode current.

In Fig. 3 are shown potential distribution curves for various anode voltages. When the anode voltage becomes sufficient high, the virtual

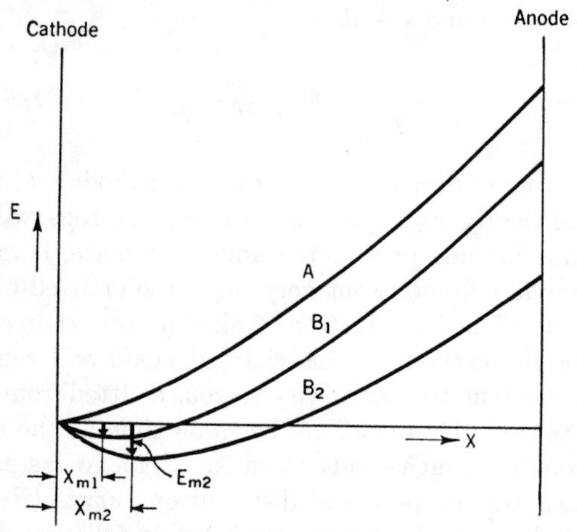

FIG. 3. Potential distribution in a diode for various anode voltages.

cathode becomes coincident with the actual cathode so that the entire emission current reaches the anode.

In Fig. 4 are shown curves giving the anode current vs. anode voltage for various temperatures. The rising portion of these curves is called the *space-charge portion*, since it corresponds to the case in which the virtual cathode is removed from the actual cathode so that increasing the anode voltage will increase the anode current. The flat portions of these curves are called the *temperature-limited portions*. These portions correspond to the case in which the virtual cathode is coincident with the actual cathode so that the entire emission current becomes anode current. In these portions, increasing the anode voltage will not increase the anode current, for the entire emission current already reaches the anode. The anode current in the temperature-limited range is thus determined solely by the emission current, which, according to Eq. (1), is a function only of the temperature, for a given cathode.[1]

Since shot-effect theory is simplest in the temperature-limited case, we shall analyze that case first. We shall then return to a discussion of space charge.

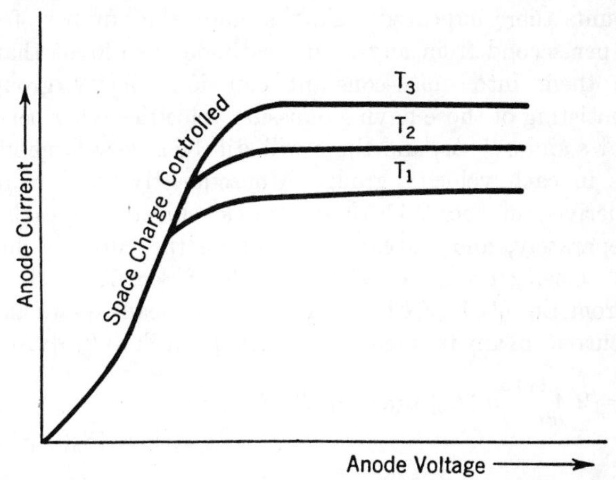

FIG. 4. Anode current in a diode for various cathode temperatures.

8.3 Shot Effect in Diodes in the Temperature-limited Case. When a diode is operated in the temperature-limited condition, as mentioned in the previous section, all the electrons emitted from the cathode reach the anode and become part of the anode current. During the entire time of flight of the electron between the cathode and the anode, there is current flowing in the anode circuit, as already explained in Sec. 7.11*a*, due to charges that the electron induces on the surfaces of the cathode and anode. If i_1 is the current induced in the anode circuit by the flight of some particular electron, then the form of i_1 as a function of time will be something like that shown in Fig. 5, the exact form of the curve depending upon the geometry of the diode, the potential distribution within it, and the emission velocity of the

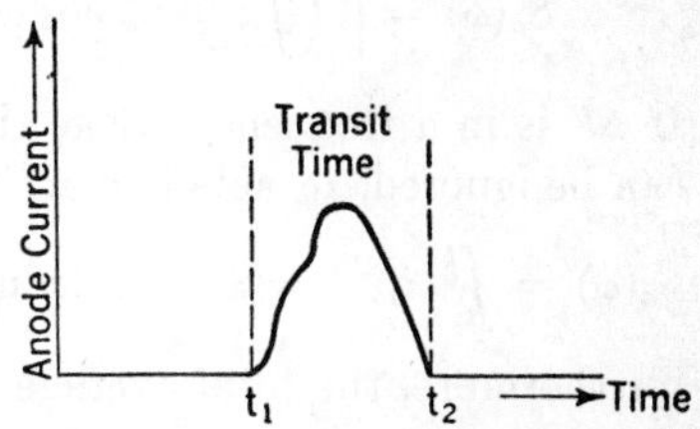

FIG. 5. Anode current due to the flight of a single electron (not a scale drawing).

[1] In an oxide-coated cathode, the anode current is never truly limited. Temperature-limited theory will therefore never apply exactly to oxide-coated cathodes.

electron. However, electrical theory tells us that we must have

$$\int_{t_1}^{t_2} i_1\,dt = \kappa = \text{charge of an electron} \tag{3}$$

The emission of electrons from the cathode, as already discussed in Sec. 7.5c, is a random process and is therefore subject to fluctuations of the amounts there indicated. Furthermore, the number of electrons emitted per second from any actual cathode is so great that we can separate them into quasi-constant emission-velocity groups, each group consisting of those having emission velocities lying between any particular s and $s + \Delta s$, and there will still be a very large number of electrons in each velocity group. Consequently we can apply the results derived in Sec. 7.11 to the anode currents of each velocity group separately, and we can superimpose the currents due to the different velocity groups by the methods of Sec. 7.12. It therefore follows from Eq. (170) of Chap. VII that the mean square anode fluctuation current in any frequency band, ΔF, from F_1 to $F_1 + \Delta F$, is

$$(I_{\Delta F})^2_{\text{rms}} = 2 \int_{F_1}^{F_1+\Delta F} \{K_a[S_a(\omega)]^2 + K_b[S_b(\omega)]^2 + \cdots + K_p[S_p(\omega)]^2\}\,dF \tag{4}$$ [1]

The different subscripts $a, b, \ldots, p$ refer to the different velocity groups; K_a, K_b, etc., refer to the number of electrons emitted per second in the different groups; and

$$S_a(\omega) = \left[\left(\int_{-\infty}^{+\infty} i_{1a} \cos \omega t\,dt\right)^2 + \left(\int_{-\infty}^{+\infty} i_{1a} \sin \omega t\,dt\right)^2\right]^{1/2} \tag{5}$$

If ΔF is in a frequency range that is low enough so that transit time can be ignored, i_{1a} acts like an impulse, so that

$$S_a(\omega) = \int_{t_1}^{t_2} i_{1a}\,dt = \kappa = \text{electronic charge} = S_b(\omega) = \cdots = S_p(\omega) \tag{6}$$

Furthermore, the total average anode current is

$$I = (K_a + K_b + \cdots + K_p)\kappa = \text{total average anode current} \tag{7}$$

Consequently, it follows from Eqs. (4), (6), and (7) that the mean square anode fluctuation current in the frequency band ΔF is

$$(I_{\Delta F})^2_{\text{rms}} = 2\kappa I\,\Delta F \tag{8}$$ [2]

[1] $(I_{\Delta F})^2_{\text{rms}}$ in this chapter has the same meaning as $\overline{[(I_{\Delta F})_{\text{rms}}]^2}$ in the last chapter. The average bar is omitted because it was shown that the likelihood of any appreciable fluctuation from the average, in practice, is exceedingly small.

[2] This formula shows very clearly the effect of the finite electronic charge on current fluctuations. If the charge of an electron (that is, κ) became vanishingly

Equation (8) is the desired equation for the shot effect of the anode current for a diode operated in the temperature-limited range. The derivation has been made under the assumption that the transit time is negligibly short in the frequency range of interest. Even when this assumption is not justified, Eq. (4) still holds and can be used as a starting point for investigation. However, except at very high frequencies, the assumption of negligible transit time is justifiable, and Eq. (8) can be used for the temperature-limited case.

It is noteworthy that the velocity distribution of the electrons turns out to be of no importance in this case. This is because the transit time has been assumed to be negligible, regardless of the initial velocity.

Exercise

Show that if interaction between the current impulses due to the individual electrons can be neglected, then Eq. (8) of this chapter is a direct consequence of Eq. (92) of Chap. VII. The result of the analysis in Sec. 7.11 shows that the above-mentioned interaction is negligible.

8.4 The Reduction of Shot Noise by Space Charge. In Eq. (8) we found the amount of shot noise in a temperature-limited diode. We shall next see how space charge affects the shot noise. Because of space charge, not all the electrons emitted by the cathode reach the anode. Rather, only those having a sufficient initial velocity to get past the virtual cathode will reach the anode. The rest will return to the cathode. The necessary velocity s_c to reach the virtual cathode is given by the equation

$$\tfrac{1}{2}ms_c^2 = \kappa E_m \tag{9}$$

according to the conservation of energy. It therefore follows from Eq. (2) that the total anode current is

$$\begin{aligned} I &= \int_{s=\sqrt{\frac{2\kappa E_m}{m}}}^{\infty} \frac{m}{kT} I_c \epsilon^{-\frac{ms^2}{2kT}} s\, ds \\ &= -I_c \epsilon^{-\frac{ms^2}{2kT}} \Big|_{\sqrt{\frac{2\kappa E_m}{m}}}^{\infty} = I_c \epsilon^{-\frac{\kappa E_m}{kT}} \end{aligned} \tag{10}$$

The emission current I_c is the result of a random process and therefore has fluctuations. In the temperature-limited case, all the emission current becomes anode current, so that the shot effect for the low-frequency range in the temperature-limited case given by Eq. (8) is

---

small, then for the same average current I the fluctuation currents would also become vanishingly small.

also a measure of the fluctuations of the emission current in the low-frequency range, since transit time was neglected. Furthermore, these fluctuations in emission current are essentially unaffected by anything which happens external to the cathode, so that the same fluctuations in emission will occur even if space charge is present. However, space charge can affect the extent to which these fluctuations are converted into fluctuations in the anode current. In particular, a change (*i.e.*, fluctuation) in the cathode current will change the location of the virtual cathode and consequently the magnitude of E_m.[1] This in turn changes the percentage of the average cathode current I_c that will reach the anode according to Eq. (10). It is clear that the sign of the change in E_m will be such as to decrease any fluctuation in I_c as it is transferred into a fluctuation in anode current.

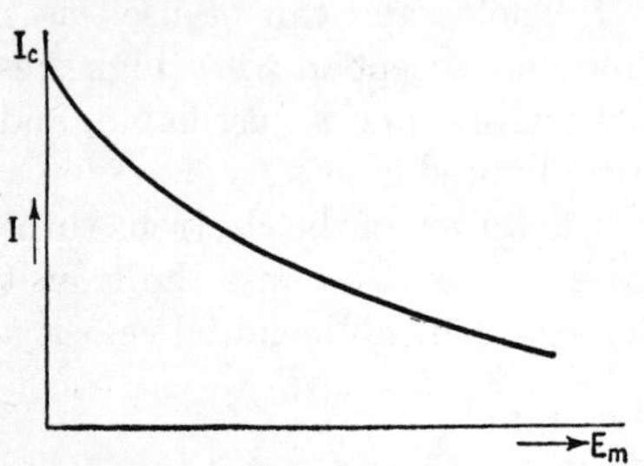

FIG. 6. Variation of anode current in a diode as a function of the potential of the virtual cathode.

The calculation of the actual amount of the decrease in cathode-current fluctuations caused by space charge as these fluctuations are transformed into anode-current fluctuations is a complicated matter. The reader is referred elsewhere[2] for the details since they require tedious manipulations in space-charge theory that are outside the scope of this book. The result of the calculation shows that, under the space-charge operating conditions of usual interest in a tube,

$$(I_{\Delta F})^2_{\text{rms}} = 3\left(1 - \frac{\pi}{4}\right) 4kTg\,\Delta F = (0.644)4kTg\,\Delta F \qquad (11)^3$$

where g is the anode conductance of the diode (which varies with anode voltage) and T is the cathode temperature. However, if the value of the anode voltage is reduced to the potential of the virtual cathode, the fluctuation current becomes

$$(I_{\Delta F})^2_{\text{rms}} = 2kTg\,\Delta F \qquad (11a)$$

[1] In this chapter we shall use the term "motion of the virtual cathode" synonymous with the term "change in the potential E_m."

[2] NORTH, D. O., *R.C.A. Rev.*, April, 1940, p. 441; RACK, A. J., *Bell System Tech. J.*, October, 1938, p. 592.

[3] Equation (11) for the space-charge-reduced shot noise is a good form for practical use, since $T = 1000°$ abs approximately in most modern oxide-coated cathodes.

On the other hand, when the anode voltage is raised so high that the diode goes into temperature-limited operation, the virtual cathode becomes coincident with the actual cathode and can no longer be moved by minute fluctuations in emission. The entire fluctuations of the cathode current then appear as fluctuations in the anode current, provided that transit time can be neglected, and the shot effect is then given by Eq. (8).

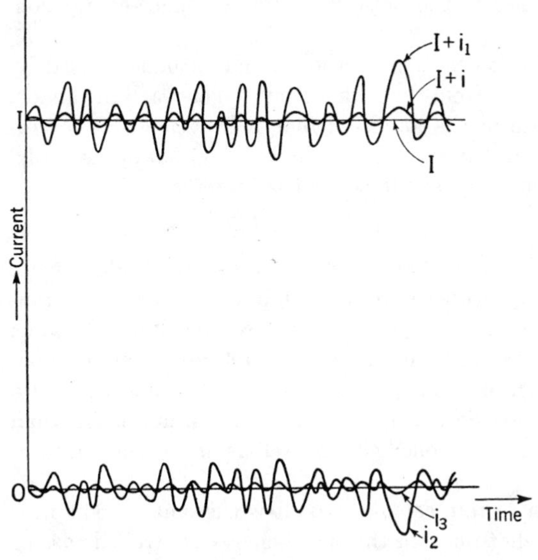

$I + i$ is the actual instantaneous anode current.
I is the average anode current.
$I + i_1$ is the anode current which would flow in the absence of motion of the virtual cathode.
i_2 is anode current due to motion of virtual cathode which is caused by the fluctuating current i_1 (i_2 is coherent with i_3 but is 180 deg out of phase with it).
i_3 is the anode current due to motion of the virtual cathode caused by fluctuation in the emission of electrons which have insufficient emission velocity to cross the virtual cathode.
$i = i_1 + i_2 + i_3$.

FIG. 7. Important components in space-charge-reduced shot effect.

The derivation of Eq. (8) is such that it must give the correct value for the mean square fluctuation current, provided that I is due to the superposition of impulses occurring at random times. The fact that the anode-current fluctuations in the presence of space charge are less than indicated by the $2\kappa I\,\Delta F$ value is therefore evidence that there is a certain amount of coherence between the impulses of anode current due to the individual electrons. This matter has already been mentioned in Sec. 7.16. The over-all situation[1] is shown in Fig. 7. There I is the average anode current and $I + i_1$ is the anode current exhibiting a pure random amount of fluctuation. Thus the square of the rms value of the portion of i_1 in the frequency band ΔF is $2\kappa I\,\Delta F$. i_2 is the anode current due to motion of the virtual cathode caused by

[1] A more detailed discussion is given in Sec. 8.7.

the fluctuating current i_1, i_3 is the anode current due to motion of the virtual cathode caused by fluctuations in the emission of electrons that have insufficient emission velocity to cross the virtual cathode, and $I + i$ is the actual instantaneous plate current, where

$$i = i_1 + i_2 + i_3 \tag{12}$$

We note that i_2 is coherent with i_1. It is almost equal in magnitude to i_1 but is in the opposite direction and thus acts like a degenerative current. It is the cause of the noise reduction in space-charge-controlled operation.

The current i_3, due to motion of the virtual cathode caused by electrons that are emitted from the cathode but never reach the anode, causes a small increase in the anode-current fluctuations. The current i_3 is incoherent with i_1 and i_2. The quadratic content of the actual fluctuating component of the anode current is therefore

$$\int i^2\,dt = \int (i_1 + i_2)^2\,dt + \int i_3^2\,dt \tag{12a}$$

It is worth pointing out that both i_1 and i_3 are random noise since they arise from the superposition of impulses occurring at random times. Furthermore, $i_1 + i_2$ is random noise since it has the same wave shape as i_1, but reduced amplitude. Therefore, the actual fluctuating current i, which is the superposition of $i_1 + i_2$ and i_3, is also random noise according to Sec. 7.14*g*. Therefore, shot noise is random noise in the space-charge-controlled case as well as in the temperature-limited case.

For convenience in certain calculations, it is customary to express the magnitude of the shot noise in the space-charge-controlled case as

$$(I_{\Delta F})^2_{\text{rms}} = \Gamma^2(2\kappa I\,\Delta F) \tag{13}$$

where $I_{\Delta F}$ is the portion of i in the frequency band ΔF and Γ^2 is a positive constant less than 1 that takes into account the space-charge effects.[1] The value of Γ^2 depends upon the particular space-charge conditions which exist in the tube. In some cases calculated by North the value of Γ^2 is less than 0.02 so that the reduction of shot effect by space charge can be very great. Because of the complicated nature of the detailed expression for Γ^2, Eq. (13) is too cumbersome for practical use, and Eq. (11) is used instead.[2]

[1] When $\Gamma^2 = 1$, there is no space-charge reduction of the shot effect. We accordingly call $2\kappa I\,\Delta F$ the magnitude of the "free" shot effect.

[2] The derivation of Eq. (11) is actually obtained from Eq. (13) under the special conditions prevalent in space-charge operation when the anode voltage is not too low (see D. O. North, *R.C.A. Rev.*, April, 1940).

The reader may wonder to what extent the foregoing theory agrees with experiment. This matter is discussed at length by D. O. North. Shot-noise formulas for the temperature-limited case agree very well with experimental data. The agreement is also quite good when the theory is applied to space-charge-limited triodes operated under normal circumstances, which is the most important case. However, for many space-charge-limited diodes and for triodes operated outside their normal ratings, the measured values of shot noise are higher than those predicted by theory. It is believed that these discrepancies are due to certain effects discussed by North,[1] which have not been taken into account in the foregoing theory.

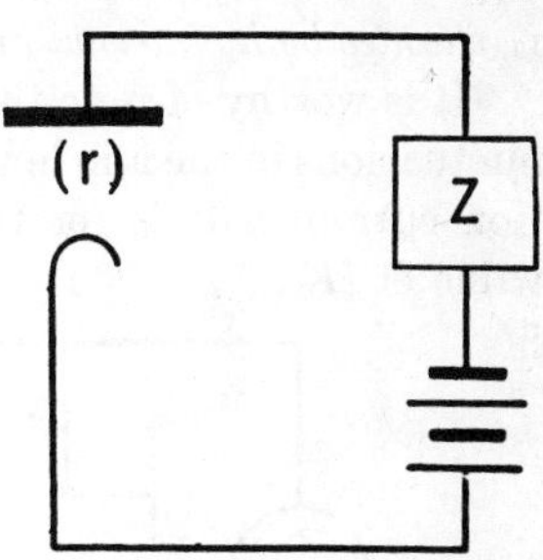

FIG. 8. Diode with load in its anode circuit.

8.5 The Current-generator Representation and the Shunting Effect of Internal Impedance.[2] In Fig. 8 is shown a diode with an external impedance between its anode and the source of anode voltage. In this case, any fluctuations in the anode current will cause fluctuations in the voltage drop across Z. This in turn will cause fluctuations in the anode voltage, which in their turn will affect the anode current. We shall now determine quantitatively the effect of the external impedance on anode-current fluctuations.

Let

i_0 = fluctuating portion of anode current if anode voltage is maintained always at its average value

i = actual fluctuating portion of anode current in presence of Z

r = internal alternating-current impedance of diode

Then

Zi = reduction in anode voltage due to fluctuating current

Consequently,

$\frac{Zi}{r}$ = reduction in fluctuating current due to fluctuations in the anode voltage

Thus

$$i_0 - i = \frac{Z}{r} i \tag{14}$$

[1] See North, *R.C.A. Rev.*, April, 1940.

[2] In the other sections of this chapter, it is assumed, unless otherwise stated, that the electrode potentials are constant and do not fluctuate. This is equivalent to assuming that they are grounded to alternating current for all frequencies.

Solving Eq. (14), we obtain

$$i = \frac{i_0}{1 + (Z/r)} = i_0 \left(\frac{r}{r + Z} \right) \tag{15}$$

As defined above, i_0 is the fluctuating current that would be obtained if the anode voltage were maintained constant. The formulas of Sec. 8.3 and 8.4 thus give i_0, since they did not take into account any current fluctuations due to anode-voltage fluctuations. Thus, according to Eq. (15), *a diode acts like a constant-current generator of strength i_0, shunted by its internal impedance* r, as shown in Fig. 9.

It is worthy of note that the changes in current fluctuations due to fluctuations in the anode voltage are coherent with the original fluctuation current. It is for this reason that they are able to reduce the value of $(I_{\Delta F})^2_{\text{rms}}$.

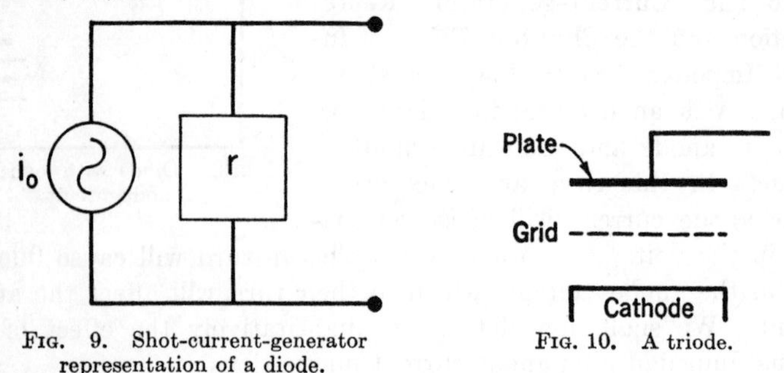

FIG. 9. Shot-current-generator representation of a diode.

FIG. 10. A triode.

8.6 Shot Effect in Triodes. In Secs. 8.3 and 8.4 we dealt with the shot effect in diodes, since that is the simplest theoretical case. We shall now see how the results there obtained are modified when we deal with the more important practical case of a triode. In Fig. 10 is shown a diagram of a triode. For simplicity, let us assume that the grid is at negative potential so that there is no grid conduction current. If now the triode is operated in the temperature-limited condition, all the cathode emission current now becomes plate current. Consequently, all the fluctuations in emission current become fluctuations in plate current, so that Eq. (8) gives the correct value for plate-current fluctuations, *i.e.*,

$$(I_{\Delta F})^2_{\text{rms}} = 2\kappa I \,\Delta F \tag{16}$$

where I is now the plate current and κ is the electronic charge. As pointed out in Sec. 8.5, Eq. (16), like Eq. (8), must be modified when the external plate impedance is not zero. The triode in the temperature-limited case is thus no more complicated than the diode.

Let us next consider the space-charge-limited case. In this case, just as for the diode, the virtual cathode moves coherently with the plate-current fluctuations, causing a reduction of shot noise. However, since the space-charge potential conditions are different for the case of a triode, Eq. (11) is replaced by another equation. In this case it is

$$(I_{\Delta F})^2_{\text{rms}} = \frac{0.644}{\sigma} 4kT_c g_m \Delta F \tag{17}$$[1]

where g_m is now the transconductance of the tube, T_c is the cathode temperature, and σ is a tube parameter given approximately by the equation

$$\sigma = \left[1 + \frac{1}{\mu}\left(1 + \frac{4}{3}y\right)\right]^{-1} \tag{18}$$

In Eq. (18)

$$y = \frac{\text{grid-anode spacing}}{\text{grid-cathode spacing}} \tag{19}$$

The value of σ usually lies between 0.5 and 1.0.

Equation (13) will of course apply to the case of the triode also, with Γ^2 a positive constant less than one. However, as in the case of the diode, the formulation of Γ^2 is very complicated, so that Eq. (17) is the equation for practical use. In Chap. VI, the way in which Eq. (17) is used and further transformed for practical purposes is discussed in detail.

The current-generator representation and the shunting effect of the internal plate impedance, derived for the diode in Sec. 8.5, will clearly apply equally well to a triode.

8.7 Shot Effect in Multicollector Tubes. It is widely known that triodes have a tendency to be "quieter" than tetrodes and pentodes. In the case of tetrodes, it was at first thought that the excess noise might be introduced by secondary emission from the screen grid. While there is no doubt an effect of this kind, it is only a part of the story, for the same type of excess noise is also present in pentodes, where the suppressor grid should eliminate secondary emission. D. O. North[2] has developed a comprehensive and quantitative theory showing how the excess noise is due to the division of the tube current between the collector electodes, when the tube is in space-charge-limited operation. Because of the practical importance of North's theory and because it is a good example of the use of the methods developed in Chap. VII, we shall discuss it in some detail.

[1] NORTH, D. O., *R.C.A. Rev.*, April, 1940.

[2] *R.C.A. Rev.*, October, 1940, p. 244.

As a first step in the development of North's theory, we shall have to analyze the reduction of shot effect by space charge in more detail. It will be necessary for us to use a rather involved notation and to draw some careful distinctions. However, if the reader will follow the derivation, he will find that the final result is surprisingly simple.

As pointed out in Sec. 8.2, the electrons emitted from the cathode do not all have the same velocity; rather they have a velocity distribution as given by Eq. (2). The exact velocity distribution is not important for our present purposes, so long as we keep in mind that there is a velocity distribution. Since the time that an electron spends in the space-charge region is dependent upon its initial velocity, the effect of the electron upon the location of the virtual cathode will also depend upon its initial velocity. Accordingly, we theoretically divide the total instantaneous emission current i_c into parts i_{cs} whose electrons lie in narrow ranges of velocities. Then

$$i_c = \sum_s i_{cs} \tag{20}$$

where the summation is taken over the entire range of electron emission velocities. The individual current components i_{cs} may now be considered to consist of electrons having essentially the same emission velocities and thus the same effect on the space-charge conditions. Furthermore, if I_c is the average total emission current and I_{cs} the average emission current of electrons with the velocity s, then

$$I_c = \sum_s I_{cs} \tag{21}$$

Now the emission of electrons, of any velocity class, from the cathode is a random process, so that according to Eq. (8) and Sec. 7.11 we can write

$$\overline{(\Delta i_c)^2_{\Delta F}} = \sum_s \overline{(\Delta i_{cs})^2_{\Delta F}} = \sum_s 2\kappa I_{cs}\,\Delta F = 2\kappa I_c\,\Delta F \tag{22}$$ [1]

where

$$\Delta i_c = i_c - I_c \qquad \text{and} \qquad \Delta i_{cs} = i_{cs} - I_{cs} \tag{23}$$

Equation (22) gives the quadratic content of the fluctuating component of the emission current and shows how it is divided between the currents consisting of electrons of various velocity classes. We may call this a "free" shot effect since its magnitude is determined entirely by the random emission process. By way of distinction, the space-charge-

[1] The subscript rms is omitted in this section.

reduced shot effects of the currents in the external circuits of the various collector electrodes will be called "reduced" shot effects.

Let us next consider a multicollector tube such as is shown in Fig. 11*a*. In this tube a certain number of the emitted electrons do not have sufficient emission velocity to pass the virtual cathode. These electrons return directly to the cathode without going through any external circuit. The rest of the emitted electrons get past the virtual cathode and go to one of the collector electrodes.[1] The algebraic sum of the currents to all the collector electrodes will be called I_t (t for total). Electrons that do not have sufficient velocity to pass the virtual cathode will be called α-electrons, while those which do have sufficient velocity to get past will be called β-electrons. Accordingly,

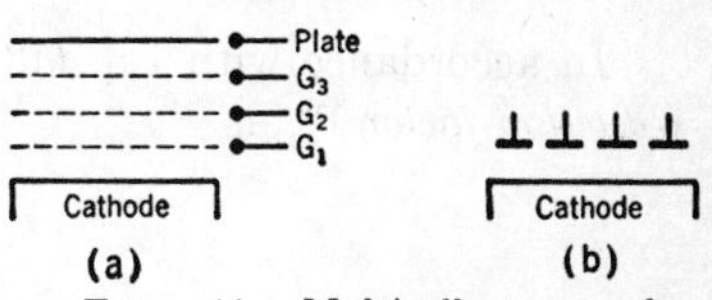

FIG. 11. Multicollector tubes showing superposition (*a*) and independence (*b*) of the electron streams.

$$I_c = \sum_\alpha I_{cs} + \sum_\beta I_{cs} \tag{24}$$

$$I_t = \sum_\beta I_{cs} \tag{25}$$

where the significance of the α and β under the summation signs is now obvious.

In the discussion of the reduction of shot effect by space charge in Sec. 8.4, it was pointed out that any fluctuation in emission of electrons of any velocity class causes a minute change in location of the virtual cathode, which thus causes a change in anode current. We may express this mathematically by writing

$$\Delta i_t = \sum_\beta \Delta i_{cs}\,(1 + b_s) + \sum_\alpha \Delta i_{cs} b_s \tag{26}$$

where b_s is a function of s. The quantity $b_s\,\Delta i_{cs}$ is the change in i_t due to the change in location of the virtual cathode caused by Δi_{cs}. Since this quantity is small, it is proportional to Δi_{cs}. The magnitude of b_s is less than unity for all values of s and the sign of b_s is negative.

It follows from Eqs. (8) and (26) of this chapter and Eq. (198) of Chap. VII that

[1] For the purposes of this discussion, the suppressor grid in a pentode is also considered one of the collector electrodes.

$$\begin{aligned}\overline{(\Delta i_t)^2_{\Delta F}} &= \sum_\beta (1 + b_s)^2 \overline{(\Delta i_{cs})^2_{\Delta F}} + \sum_\alpha b_s^2 \overline{(\Delta i_{cs})^2_{\Delta F}} \\ &= \sum_\beta (1 + b_s)^2 2\kappa I_{cs}\, \Delta F + \sum_\alpha b_s^2 2\kappa I_{cs}\, \Delta F \end{aligned} \tag{27}$$

In accordance with Eq. (13) we now define the *space-charge noise-reduction factor* Γ^2, as

$$\Gamma^2 = \frac{\overline{(\Delta i_t)^2_{\Delta F}}}{2\kappa I_t\, \Delta F} \tag{28}$$

From Eqs. (27) and (28) it follows that

$$\Gamma^2 = \frac{\sum_\beta (1 + b_s)^2 I_{cs} + \sum_\alpha b_s^2 I_{cs}}{I_t} \tag{29}$$

In order to find numerical values of Γ^2, it is first necessary to evaluate b_s from space-charge theory. This has been done by North, but it will not be necessary for our present purposes.

Consider next some particular collector electrode, say the nth, and let us call the instantaneous current that goes to this electrode i_n and its average value I_n. If now the electron streams that go to the different collector electrodes are practically independent, as shown in Fig. 11*b*, then there will be no interaction between the fluctuating currents of the different electrodes. Accordingly, the mean square fluctuating current to the nth electrode would be

$$\overline{(\Delta i_n)^2_{\Delta F}} = \Gamma^2 2\kappa I_n\, \Delta F \tag{30}$$

where Γ^2 is given by Eq. (29).

In actual tubes, however, the most usual case is just the opposite, namely, that shown in Fig. 11*a*, in which the current streams to the different electrodes are practically superimposed. In this case a shift in the location of the virtual cathode due to a fluctuation in current to the nth electrode will consequently change the current to every electrode by the same amount as an equal shift caused by a current fluctuation in any other electrode. The fluctuation current to the nth electrode is therefore given by the formula

$$\Delta i_n = \sum_\beta \left(1 + \frac{I_n}{I_t} b_s\right) \Delta i_{cns} + \sum_\beta \frac{I_n}{I_t} b_s\, \Delta i_{c(-n)s} + \sum_\alpha \frac{I_n}{I_t} b_s\, \Delta i_{cs} \tag{31}$$

whose terms will now be explained.

In Eq. (31), for any electron emission velocity s, Δi_{cns} represents the fluctuation current that would go to the nth electrode in the absence of motion of the virtual cathode. However, owing to the motion of the virtual cathode, a quantity $(I_n/I_t)b_s$ times the original fluctuation current, and coherent with it, is added to the original fluctuation current. The reason why this multiplier is $(I_n/I_t)b_s$ rather than b_s itself is that I_n receives only a fraction I_n/I_t of the current flowing in the tube. Thus in Eq. (31) the first term on the right represents the effects of the fluctuations in emission of the current that would have gone to the nth electrode in the absence of motion of the virtual cathode. In a similar manner, the second term on the right of Eq. (31) represents the effect of the fluctuations in emission of the current that would have gone to all the electrodes except the nth in the absence of motion of the virtual cathode. Finally, the third term on the right of Eq. (31) represents the effect of emitted electrons that do not have sufficient emission velocity to cross the virtual cathode.

From Eqs. (8) and (31) above and Eq. (198) of Chap. VII, it follows that

$$\begin{aligned}\overline{(\Delta i_n)^2_{\Delta F}} &= \sum_\beta \left(1 + \frac{I_n}{I_t} b_s\right)^2 \overline{(\Delta i_{cns})^2_{\Delta F}} + \sum_\beta \left(\frac{I_n}{I_t} b_s\right)^2 \overline{[\Delta i_{c(-n)s}]^2_{\Delta F}} \\ &\qquad + \sum_\alpha \left(\frac{I_n}{I_t} b_s\right)^2 \overline{(\Delta i_{cs})^2_{\Delta F}} \\ &= \sum_\beta \left(1 + \frac{I_n}{I_t} b_s\right)^2 2\kappa \frac{I_n}{I_t} I_{cs}\,\Delta F + \sum_\beta \left(\frac{I_n}{I_t} b_s\right)^2 2\kappa \frac{I_t - I_n}{I_t} I_{cs}\,\Delta F \\ &\qquad + \sum_\alpha \left(\frac{I_n}{I_t} b_s\right)^2 2\kappa I_{cs}\,\Delta F \\ &= \left[1 - \frac{I_n}{I_t}(1 - \Gamma^2)\right] I_n 2\kappa\,\Delta F \end{aligned} \tag{32}$$

where Γ^2 is defined in Eq. (29) and use is made of Eq. (25). We can also write Eq. (32) in the form

$$\overline{(\Delta i_n)^2_{\Delta F}} = \Gamma_n^2 2\kappa I_n\,\Delta F \tag{33}$$

where

$$\Gamma_n^2 = 1 - \frac{I_n}{I_t}(1 - \Gamma^2) \tag{34}$$

Comparison of Eq. (13) or (28) with Eqs. (33) and (34) shows the effect on shot noise of division of current between the collector electrodes. The value of Γ_n^2 rises monotonically[1] for decreasing values of I_n/I_t. When $I_n/I_t = 1$, then $\Gamma_n^2 = \Gamma^2$ so that the shot effect of current in the circuit of the nth electrode is equal to the space-charge-reduced value of that of I_t. However, as I_n/I_t approaches zero, Γ_n^2 approaches unity and the shot effect of current in the circuit of the nth electrode approaches its free value.

The practical use and significance of Eqs. (33) and (34) are discussed in Chap. VI. However, as a general interpretation of the foregoing results we may say that division of the space current between different electrodes decreases the amount by which space charge reduces the shot noise. The principal reason for this is that in this case only part of the coherent currents due to motion of the virtual cathode (which reduce shot effect in a triode) will now go to the electrodes with the currents of which they are coherent.

Equations (33) and (34) apply to tubes of the type in which the space-current streams to the different electrodes are essentially superimposed, as shown in Fig. 11*a*. However, they cannot be expected to apply to tubes with aligned grids of the "beam" type without a more detailed examination of each particular case. They will definitely not apply to tubes such as those shown in Fig. 11*b* in which the space-current streams to the different electrodes are not superimposed.

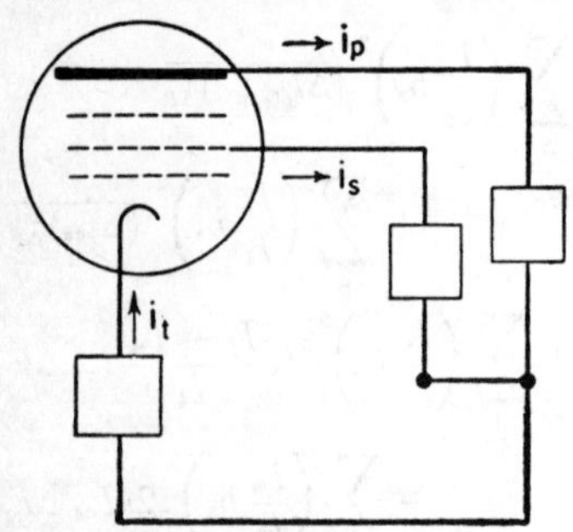

FIG. 12. Schematic diagram showing variational components of some electrode currents in a pentode.

It is interesting to note that the current in the cathode circuit of a multicollector tube, such as i_t in Fig. 12, shows no loss in the value of Γ^2, since all the coherent noise-reduction currents due to motion of the virtual cathode are fully utilized in the cathode current. Consequently it follows from item 5 of the next paragraph that there is generally less shot current in the cathode circuit than in the circuit of any collector electrode.

For tubes to which Eqs. (33) and (34) do apply, D. O. North[2] has listed the following conclusions:

1. No fluctuation current is greater then the free shot effect for the current considered.

[1] Monotonic variation is variation without maxima or minima.

[2] *R.C.A. Rev.*, April, 1940.

2. The smaller the fraction of the total current an electrode collects, the more nearly the noise in that current approaches the free shot effect.

3. For vanishingly small Γ, the mean-square fluctuation in the current collected at any electrode is equal to the product of the free shot effect for said current and the fraction of the total current not collected at said electrode.

4. The ratio of actual noise to free shot effect in a divided portion of the total current exceeds the corresponding ratio for the total current itself.

5. The noise in the current of an electrode exceeds the noise in the total current provided

$$\frac{\Gamma^2}{1 - \Gamma^2} < \frac{I_n}{I_t} < 1.$$

In conventional tubes this is usually true for all collector electrodes.

6. With constant Γ, the noise in a given collector electrode current is a maximum (against variations in I_n) when

$$\frac{I_n}{I_t} = \frac{1}{2(1 - \Gamma^2)}.$$

In other words, provided $\Gamma^2 < \frac{1}{2}$, the noise in no collector lead should exceed

$$\frac{1}{4(1 - \Gamma^2)} I_t \cdot 2\kappa \Delta F$$

8.8 Shot Effect at Frequencies for Which Transit Time is Important. *a. Introduction—Temperature-limited Diode.* Up to the present, we have considered only the shot effect at frequencies for which transit time is unimportant. This allowed very considerable simplification of the problem to be made. However, we shall now consider the frequency ranges for which this approximation cannot be made. A satisfactory quantitative theory of shot effect in this frequency range does not appear in the literature. However, we shall outline the basis of a general theory and shall show the general way in which shot effect may be expected to vary with frequency.

In Sec. 8.3 we derived a formula, namely, Eq. (8), for the shot effect at low frequencies in the temperature-limited case. This formula was derived on the assumption that the current due to an individual electron, such as is shown in Fig. 5, could be considered an impulse of strength κ. It is obvious that, at frequencies for which the transit time is an appreciable fraction of a period, this assumption is no longer tenable and that, in accordance with Eqs. (4) and (5), the shot effect due to pulses of current of the type shown in Fig. 5 will fall with frequency after the transit angle[1] has reached the order of magnitude

[1] The transit angle is 2π times the frequency times the transit time.

of a radian. We may thus expect the shot effect of a temperature-limited diode to fall with frequency after the transit angle has reached the order of magnitude of a radian.

b. Space-charge-controlled Diode. If the diode is space-charge-controlled, we shall now show that the shot effect may be expected to rise as the transit angles become appreciable. The rise of the shot effect with frequency in the case of a space-charge-controlled diode is due to several obvious causes. When we first considered space-charge

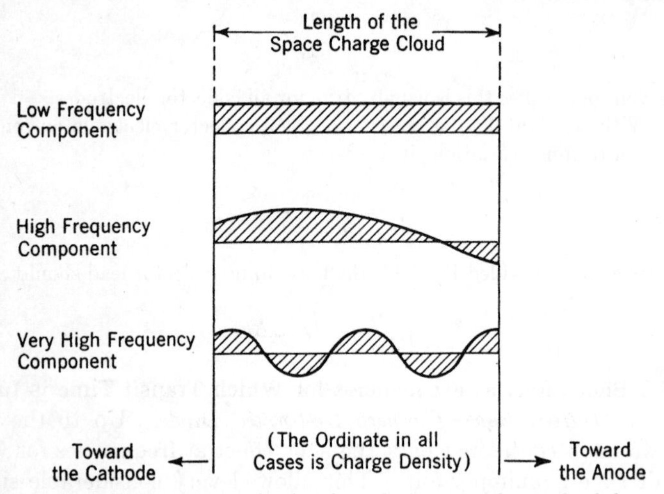

FIG. 13. Variation in charge density through the space-charge cloud due to components of different frequencies in the emission-current fluctuations. (This figure refers to electrons of a particular emission velocity. For other emission velocities, the curves are similar, but the distances between wave nodes increase with the emission velocity. The total space charge is obtained by the superposition of the space-charge curves due to electrons of all emission velocities.)

noise reduction, it was pointed out that a fluctuation in emission current causes a corresponding fluctuation in space charge. The latter largely cancels the fluctuation in emission current before it is transformed into a fluctuation in plate current. However, if we consider a very high frequency component of the fluctuation in emission current, its effect is not in the same phase throughout the space-charge cloud (see Fig. 13). Consequently, at very high frequencies, when the average transit time of electrons through the space-charge cloud is many cycles, there is a general cancellation between the effects of positive and negative phases of the fluctuation and the potential of the virtual cathode is almost unchanged. The space-charge noise-reduction effect thus deteriorates as the frequency rises. Furthermore, a phase difference arises between the original fluctuation current and the coherent current, due to fluctuation of the virtual-cathode potential. This further decreases the magnitude of the space-charge noise-reduction effect.

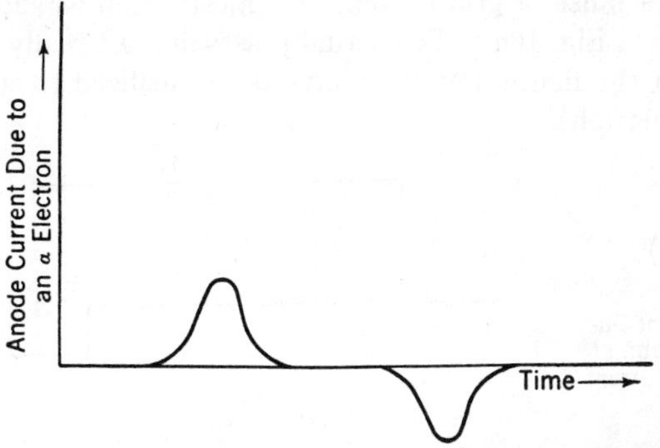

FIG. 14. Doublet-impulse type of current due to an α-electron.

The second cause of the rise of shot noise with frequency lies in the α-electrons. The effect on noise due to the motion of the virtual cathode that is induced by fluctuation in the emission of α-electrons is included in the derivation of Eq. (11). However, an additional effect, which is inconsequental at low frequencies but which becomes more important at high frequencies, will now be considered. The α-electrons never reach the anode but return to the cathode. Consequently, the pulses that they cause in the anode current are of a doublet-impulse type, as shown in Fig. 14. Such pulses have a rising frequency characteristic[1] up to a frequency at which their duration is equal to many radians, after which it eventually declines. In a wide region of high frequencies these doublet impulses may therefore be expected to make a substantial contribution to the shot noise.

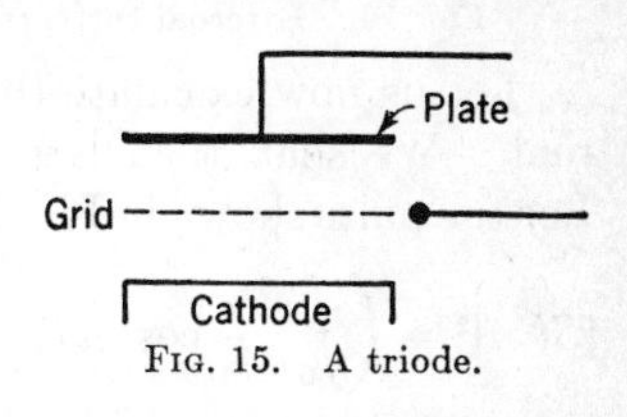

FIG. 15. A triode.

As a consequence of all the foregoing reasons, the shot effect of a space-controlled diode may thus be expected to rise with frequency as transit angles become appreciable, ultimately equaling and even exceeding the "free" value of shot noise.

c. Grid-current Fluctuations Induced by Plate-current Fluctuations in a Negative-grid Triode. Let us next consider the case of a negative-grid triode. Consider the case of an electron that goes from the

[1] See Sec. 4.18.

cathode to the plate in the triode shown in Fig. 15. As the electron approaches the grid, its image in the grid causes a pulse of grid current as shown between 0 and τ_1 in Fig. 16*a*. Then, after the electron has passed through the grid and travels toward the plate, its image in the grid causes a pulse of grid current of opposite sign as shown between $\tau - \tau_2$ and τ in Fig. 16*a*. The actual pulses are not really rectangular, as shown in the figure, but they have been idealized to simplify some future calculations.

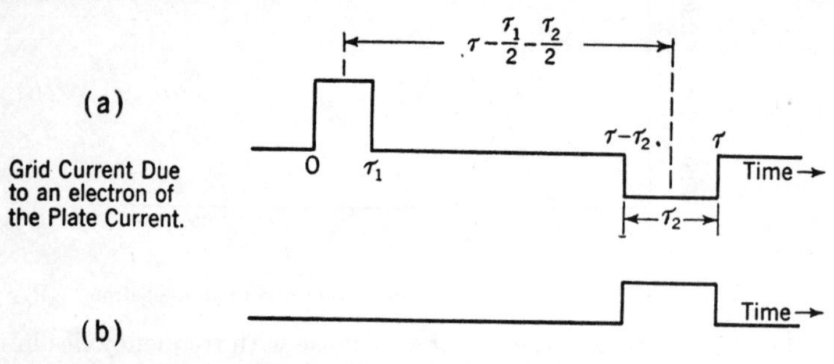

FIG. 16. External currents due to the flight of an electron in a triode.

Let us now calculate the frequency characteristic of this grid current. We shall then later calculate its effect on the plate current. For the pulse shown in Fig. 16*a* we may write (for a high-μ triode)

$$[S(\omega)]^2 = \left(\int_0^{\tau_1} \frac{\kappa}{\tau_1} \cos \omega t \, dt - \int_{\tau-\tau_2}^{\tau} \frac{\kappa}{\tau_2} \cos \omega t \, dt\right)^2 + \left(\int_0^{\tau_1} \frac{\kappa}{\tau_1} \sin \omega t \, dt - \int_{\tau-\tau_2}^{\tau} \frac{\kappa}{\tau_2} \sin \omega t \, dt\right)^2 \quad (35)$$

where κ is the charge of an electron. After integration we obtain

$$[S(\omega)]^2 = \left\{\frac{\kappa}{\omega\tau_1} \sin \omega\tau_1 - \frac{\kappa}{\omega\tau_2} \sin \omega\tau + \frac{\kappa}{\omega\tau_2} \sin [\omega(\tau - \tau_2)]\right\}^2 + \left\{-\frac{\kappa}{\omega\tau_1} (\cos \omega\tau_1 - 1) + \frac{\kappa}{\omega\tau_2} \cos \omega\tau - \frac{\kappa}{\omega\tau_2} \cos [\omega(\tau - \tau_2)]\right\}^2 \quad (36)$$

When the frequencies are low enough so that we can write

$$\left.\begin{aligned} \sin x &= x \\ \cos x &= 1 - \frac{x^2}{2} \end{aligned}\right\} \qquad \text{(approx)}$$

Eq. (36) reduces to

$$S(\omega) = \kappa\omega\left(\tau - \frac{\tau_1}{2} - \frac{\tau_2}{2}\right) \tag{37}$$

Thus, for small transit angles Eq. (37) shows that the frequency content of each grid-current doublet impulse rises directly with frequency. On the other hand, when the frequency is extremely high, Eq. (36) shows that $S(\omega)$ will fall proportionally to frequency.

In the range of frequencies for which Eq. (37) holds, the value of $S(\omega)$ in the plate current for a single electron is just

$$S(\omega)_p = \kappa \tag{38}$$

as is obvious from our earlier analysis of impulses. In this same range of frequencies, the total plate current is approximately that due to the superposition of the pulses of the individual electrons which arrive at the plate. Since the same electrons give rise to the grid current, the quadratic content of the grid current in any bandwidth ΔF in this range is therefore

$$\omega^2\left(\tau - \frac{\tau_1}{2} - \frac{\tau_2}{2}\right)^2$$

times the quadratic content of the plate current. Therefore, from (16), (17), (37), and (38), we have for the grid current, approximately,

$$\begin{aligned}\overline{(I_{\Delta F})^2_{\text{rms}}} &= \Gamma^2(2\kappa i_p\,\Delta F)\omega^2\left(\tau - \frac{\tau_1}{2} - \frac{\tau_2}{2}\right)^2 \\ &= \omega^2\left(\tau - \frac{\tau_1}{2} - \frac{\tau_2}{2}\right)^2 \frac{0.644}{\sigma}\,4kT_c g_m\,\Delta F\end{aligned} \tag{39}$$

As the value of the transit angle

$$\omega\left(\tau - \frac{\tau_1}{2} - \frac{\tau_2}{2}\right)$$

becomes appreciable, the grid-current fluctuations thus approach the order of magnitude of the plate-current fluctuations. However, before investigating the effect of these grid-current fluctuations on the tube noise, we shall first determine the effect of transit time on the grid impedance of a tube.

d. Effect of Electron Transit Time On Grid Impedance.[1] A sine wave of voltage

$$\Delta e_g = \Delta E_g \sin \omega t \tag{40}$$

[1] NORTH, D. D., *Proc. I.R.E.*, **24**, 108, 1936; FERRIS, W. R., *Proc. I.R.E.*, **24**, 82, 1936; LLEWELLYN, F. B., *B.S.T. J.*, **14**, 659, 1935.

on the grid, due to any cause (either signal or fluctuation noise), will cause a change in potential of the virtual cathode, giving rise to a change in plate current

$$\Delta i_p = g_m \, \Delta e_g = g_m \, \Delta E_g \sin \omega t \tag{41}$$

where g_m is the transconductance of the tube. The phase of Δi_p given by Eq. (41) is its phase at the virtual cathode. Its phase at any other location[1] in the tube is shown by the equation

$$\Delta i_p = g_m \, \Delta E_g \sin [\omega(t - T)] \tag{42}$$

where T is the transit time required for electrons to move from the virtual cathode to the location of interest.

To find an approximate value for the grid current, we shall again use the idealization shown in Fig. 16a for the grid current due to passage of a single electron of the plate-current stream. Then we have as an approximate expression for the grid current

$$\begin{aligned} \Delta i_g &= \Delta i_p \left(\text{at } \frac{\tau_1}{2}\right) - \Delta i_p \left(\text{at } \tau - \frac{\tau_2}{2}\right) \\ &= g_m \, \Delta E_g \left\{ \sin \left[\omega \left(t - \frac{\tau_1}{2} - T_0 \right) \right] - \sin \left[\omega \left(t - \tau + \frac{\tau_2}{2} - T_0 \right) \right] \right\} \end{aligned} \tag{43}$$

where T_0 is the transit time between the point designated as 0 in Fig. 16a and the virtual cathode. If the transit angles involved are small, we can treat Eq. (43) as a differential effect. Thus

$$\begin{aligned} \sin & \left[\omega \left(t - \frac{\tau_1}{2} - T_0 \right) \right] - \sin \left[\omega \left(t - \tau + \frac{\tau_2}{2} - T_0 \right) \right] \\ &= \sin \left\{ \omega \left[t - T_0 - \left(\frac{\tau}{2} - \frac{\tau_2}{4} + \frac{\tau_1}{4} \right) + \left(\frac{\tau}{2} - \frac{\tau_2}{4} - \frac{\tau_1}{4} \right) \right] \right\} \\ &\quad - \sin \left\{ \omega \left[t - T_0 - \left(\frac{\tau}{2} - \frac{\tau_2}{4} + \frac{\tau_1}{4} \right) - \left(\frac{\tau}{2} - \frac{\tau_2}{4} - \frac{\tau_1}{4} \right) \right] \right\} \\ &= 2 \cos \left[\omega \left(t - T_0 - \frac{\tau}{2} + \frac{\tau_2}{4} - \frac{\tau_1}{4} \right) \right] \sin \left[\omega \left(\frac{\tau}{2} - \frac{\tau_2}{4} - \frac{\tau_1}{4} \right) \right] \end{aligned} \tag{44}$$

$$\begin{aligned} \sin & \left[\omega \left(t - \frac{\tau_1}{2} - T_0 \right) \right] - \sin \left[\omega \left(t - \tau + \frac{\tau_2}{2} - T_0 \right) \right] \\ &= \omega \left(\tau - \frac{\tau_2}{2} - \frac{\tau_1}{2} \right) \cos \left[\omega \left(t - T_0 - \frac{\tau}{2} + \frac{\tau_2}{4} - \frac{\tau_1}{4} \right) \right] \text{(approx)} \end{aligned} \tag{45}$$

[1] When we speak of the phase of Δi_p at a particular location, we mean the phase of the current made up of the Δi_p electrons as they pass the location in question.

Substituting Eq. (45) into Eq. (43), we obtain

$$\Delta i_g = g_m \, \Delta E_g \omega \left(\tau - \frac{\tau_2}{2} - \frac{\tau_1}{2}\right) \cos \left[\omega \left(t - T_0 - \frac{\tau}{2} + \frac{\tau_2}{4} - \frac{\tau_1}{4}\right)\right] \quad (46)$$

From Eqs. (40) and (46) we obtain for the grid admittance in complex form

$$\frac{\Delta i_g}{\Delta e_g} = g_m \omega \left(\tau - \frac{\tau_2}{2} - \frac{\tau_1}{2}\right) \epsilon^{j\left[\frac{\pi}{2} - \omega\left(T_0 + \frac{\tau}{2} - \frac{\tau_2}{4} + \frac{\tau_1}{4}\right)\right]} \quad (47)$$

$$= j g_m \omega \left(\tau - \frac{\tau_2}{2} - \frac{\tau_1}{2}\right) \left[1 - j\omega \left(T_0 + \frac{\tau}{2} - \frac{\tau_2}{4} + \frac{\tau_1}{4}\right)\right] \text{(approx)} \quad (48)$$

$$= j g_m \omega \left(\tau - \frac{\tau_2}{2} - \frac{\tau_1}{2}\right) + g_m \omega^2 \left(\tau - \frac{\tau_2}{2} - \frac{\tau_1}{2}\right) \left(T_0 + \frac{\tau}{2} - \frac{\tau_2}{4} + \frac{\tau_1}{4}\right) \quad (49)$$

if we neglect higher power terms in $\omega \left(T_0 + \frac{\tau}{2} - \frac{\tau_2}{4} + \frac{\tau_1}{4}\right)$. The effect of space charge is thus to increase the input capacity by an amount

$$g_m \left(\tau - \frac{\tau_2}{2} - \frac{\tau_1}{2}\right) \quad (50)$$

and to cause an inphase input conductance, usually called g_g, where

$$g_g = g_m \omega^2 \left(\tau - \frac{\tau_2}{2} - \frac{\tau_1}{2}\right) \left(T_0 + \frac{\tau}{2} - \frac{\tau_2}{4} + \frac{\tau_1}{4}\right) \quad (51)$$

The expressions (50) and (51) are only approximate since they have assumed the idealized form shown in Fig. 16*a* for the grid current due to a single electron, and they have neglected changes in this wave shape due to the presence of the grid voltage. Nevertheless, the above expressions give a good idea of the effects of electron transit time on the circuit. Equation (50) shows that there is an apparent increase in the grid-to-cathode capacity, *i.e.*, a difference between the cold and hot capacity, which is independent of frequency. In addition, according to Eq. (51), there is input conductance that is proportional to the square of the frequency and to the product of the two transit times $\tau - \frac{\tau_2}{2} - \frac{\tau_1}{2}$ and $T_0 + \frac{\tau}{2} - \frac{\tau_2}{4} + \frac{\tau_1}{4}$. This input conductance is the grid-circuit loading, which, as is well known, limits the tuned input impedance that can be developed between grid and cathode of a tube at high frequencies.[1]

e. The Grid-induced Shot Effect. According to Eq. (39), the grid-current fluctuations due to transit time have a quadratic content of amount

$$\overline{(I_{\Delta F})^2_{\text{rms}}} = \frac{0.644}{\sigma} 4kT_c g_m \, \Delta F \, \omega^2 \left(\tau - \frac{\tau_1}{2} - \frac{\tau_2}{2}\right)^2 \tag{52}$$

Substituting Eq. (51) into (52), we obtain

$$\overline{(I_{\Delta F})^2_{\text{rms}}} = \frac{0.644}{\sigma} \frac{\tau - \dfrac{\tau_1}{2} - \dfrac{\tau_2}{2}}{T_0 + \dfrac{\tau}{2} - \dfrac{\tau_2}{4} + \dfrac{\tau_1}{4}} 4kT_c g_g \, \Delta F \tag{53}$$

for the grid fluctuation current in terms of the grid conductance. North and Ferris[2] state that they have derived a formula

$$\overline{(I_{\Delta F})^2_{\text{rms}}} = 1.43(4kT_c g_g \, \Delta F) \tag{54}$$

which agrees rather well with experiment. The derivation of the approximate formula (53) given here indicates that their result is reasonable.

Now if Δi_g is an induced fluctuation in the grid current, then

$$\Delta e_g = Z_g \, \Delta i_g \tag{55}$$

is the corresponding fluctuation in the grid voltage, where Z_g is the external impedance between grid and cathode of the tube. Therefore, if we consider the plate grounded for radio frequency, as is usual in calculating shot-current generation, we obtain

$$\Delta i_p = g_m Z_g \, \Delta i_g \tag{56}$$

as the fluctuation in plate current corresponding to Eq. (55). It then follows from Eq. (52) that the fluctuations in plate current due to the grid induction effect are given by the equation

$$\overline{(I_{\Delta F})^2_{\text{rms (plate)}}} = (g_m Z_g)^2 \frac{0.644}{\sigma} 4kT_c g_m \, \Delta F \omega^2 \left(\tau - \frac{\tau_1}{2} - \frac{\tau_2}{2}\right)^2 \tag{57}$$

[1] The significance of the two transit times can be seen from Fig. 16*a* in conjunction with the definition of T_0. Thus $T_0 + \frac{\tau}{2} - \frac{\tau_2}{4} + \frac{\tau_1}{4}$ is the transit time between the virtual cathode and the mid-point between the τ_1 and τ_2 blocks. Furthermore $\tau - \frac{\tau_2}{2} - \frac{\tau_1}{2}$ is the transit time between the mid-points of the τ_1 and τ_2 blocks.

[2] *Proc. I.R.E.*, February, 1941, p. 49.

Looking back at subsection *d*, we see that according to the approximations we have used the fluctuations in Eq. (57) are 90 deg out of phase with the original fluctuations in plate current which caused them, provided that Z_g is resistive. When this is the case, the quadratic content of Eq. (57) can be added directly to that of Eq. (17) to get the total shot noise in the plate current. When Z_g is not resistive, there is coherence between the fluctuations indicated by Eqs. (57) and (17) and this fact must be taken into account.

Comparing Eq. (57) with Eq. (17), we see that for the highest frequencies for which Eq. (57) is valid the grid-induced shot effect in the presence of space charge may well exceed the low-frequency value of shot effect given by Eq. (17). In any case, the general effect of grid-induced shot noise will be to cause a large increase in shot noise when transit times become appreciable. At very high frequencies, when space-charge noise-reduction effects deteriorate, the grid-induced shot noise increases (in line with the increase of the original plate-current fluctuations) to values much higher even than that given by Eq. (57). According to the foregoing theory there should be a cyclic effect of rise and fall of shot noise as the transit time $\omega\left(\tau - \frac{\tau_1}{2} - \frac{\tau_2}{2}\right)$ goes through complete periods. This cyclic effect is superimposed upon the general rise in noise due to the deterioration of space-charge noise reduction.

Exercise

Since no electrons actually strike the grid despite the existence of input conductance at high frequencies in a negative-grid triode, where does the dissipation due to grid conductance occur? Show the relation between this phenomenon and the question of coherence discussed in Sec. 7.16.

8.9 Magnetic Fluctuation Noise. Another type of fluctuation noise that may appear in amplifiers is magnetic fluctuation noise, sometimes called Barkhausen effect. It has certain mathematical and physical similarities to shot effect. When a piece of iron is being magnetized, it is not a uniform and continuous magnetic material but rather consists of minute regions of magnetization, which line up as semi-independent units in the magnetic field. When there is a change of the applied field strength, certain of these regions grow at the expense of others. This activity is subject to probability fluctuations, and the magnetization process is therefore not uniform, but rather has minute random fluctuations superimposed upon it. These random fluctuations in magnetization give rise to random noise currents in any coil that is threaded by the magnetic lines from the iron.

The most important practical example of Barkhausen effect is the case of a modern radio receiver of the type having a loop antenna and an iron-core power transformer. In such a receiver the iron of the power transformer is magnetized and demagnetized at the power frequency (60 cycles/sec in the United States). The magnetic fluctuation noise generated in the iron core during the magnetization cycles is picked up by the loop antenna; and if the coupling between the loop and the power transformer is not kept very low, this noise may limit the sensitivity of the receiver. To reduce the coupling, it may be necessary to use extra shielding on the transformer and to turn it in such a direction that its stray lines do not thread the loop.

An idealized model of the magnetization process which will readily allow us to apply the methods developed in the present chapter to the calculation of magnetic fluctuation noise is the following. We will assume that the magnetic material is made up of a large number of elementary magnetic particles and that the magnetization process consists of the alignment of these particles in the magnetic field. To simplify our mathematics, we shall analyze the case of an iron-core coil representing the power transformer and having an inductance L and carrying a current

$$i = I \sin \omega t \tag{58}$$

We shall assume that the magnetic energy of the transformer is practically all in the iron but that there is a small stray mutual M between the iron-core coil and an air-core loop antenna. The voltage generated in the loop we shall call e_2, so that

$$e_2 = \frac{d}{dt}(Mi) \tag{59}$$

With these simplifications, we are now ready to proceed with the analysis.

According to standard magnetic theory[1]

$$B = H + 4\pi J = H + 4\pi sH = H(1 + 4\pi s) = \mu H \tag{60}$$

Thus

$$\mu = 1 + 4\pi s \tag{61}$$

where H = magnetic-field strength in the core
μ = permeability of the core

[1] A standard textbook covering magnetism on an engineer's level is S. G. Starling's "Electricity and Magnetism." See especially pp. 269–270 and pp. 561–575. We shall use the system of C.G.S. units used by Starling.

B = magnetic induction in the core
s = magnetic susceptibility of the core
$J = sH$ = magnetic moment per unit volume

Suppose we let
V = volume of the iron core
m = magnetic moment of an elementary magnetic particle
n = total number of elementary magnetic particles lined up by the field strength H in the volume V

According to magnetic theory, as long as μ is constant, the ratio of n/H has a constant probability.

Then the total magnetic moment is

$$sHV = nm \tag{62}$$

Furthermore, the total magnetic energy is approximately

$$\frac{1}{2}Li^2 = \frac{BHV}{8\pi}\text{ (approx)} = \frac{(1 + 4\pi s)H^2V}{8\pi} = \frac{sH^2V}{2}\text{ (approx)}$$
$$= \frac{nmH}{2} \tag{63}$$

These approximations are reasonably accurate if the μ is high.

Next, let us assume that

$$Mi = N = Cn \tag{64}$$

where N is the number of magnetic lines threading the loop and C is a constant of proportionality. The accuracy of Eq. (64) will depend upon the magnetic configuration. However, by using it, we shall in any case get a good idea of the order of magnitude of magnetic fluctuation noise and of the way in which it varies with the different parameters involved.

For a unit fluctuation in n the corresponding voltage impulse is

$$\int e_2\,dt = \Delta N = C\,\Delta n = \frac{N}{n}\,\Delta n = \frac{Mi}{n}\,\Delta n = \frac{Mi}{n} \tag{65}$$

where the fluctuation in n is

$$\Delta n = 1 \tag{66}$$

We can now find the formula for the fluctuations in secondary voltage by the same methods as those used in deriving the temperature-limited shot effect. Thus, iM/n corresponds to the electronic charge, and $e_2 = M\,di/dt$ corresponds to the average anode current. Without repeating the steps in the derivation, we can write

$$\overline{\Delta e_2^2} = 2\left(\frac{Mi}{n}\right)\left(M\frac{di}{dt}\right)\Delta F$$
$$= 2Mi\frac{mH}{Li^2}M\frac{di}{dt}\Delta F$$
$$= 2\frac{M^2}{L}\frac{H}{i}m\frac{di}{dt}\Delta F \tag{67}$$

For the particular primary current given by Eq. (58),

$$\frac{di}{dt} = \omega I \cos \omega t \tag{68}$$

so that Eq. (67) becomes

$$\overline{\Delta e_2^2} = 2\frac{M^2}{L}\frac{H}{i}m\omega I \cos \omega t\, \Delta F \tag{69}$$

Equation (69) shows how the magnetic fluctuation noise varies with the different parameters. M is the mutual inductance between the loop and the iron-core coil, L and H/i are constants of the coil, ω is 2π times the power frequency, I is the peak value of the power current, and ΔF is the bandwidth of the receiver. The constant m in Eq. (69) is the magnetic moment of an elementary magnetic particle of the type aligned in the magnetization cycle. If Eq. (69) is used to calculate m from the observed magnetic fluctuation noise in a loop receiver, the value found for m corresponds to magnetic particles of microscopic but far larger than atomic size. The exact value found for m does not have very much significance, since the model used in the derivation of Eq. (69) was so highly idealized, and since coherent interaction between elementary magnetic regions was neglected.

CHAPTER IX

NOISE IV: THERMAL NOISE[1]

9.1 The Two Laws of Thermodynamics. In this chapter we shall briefly review the statistical theory of thermodynamics, and on the basis of this we shall derive the formulas for thermal noise. As a first step, we recall the two laws of thermodynamics.

The first law of thermodynamics is essentially a restatement of the conservation of energy and says that if an amount of heat energy dQ flows into a system, and during the process the system does an amount of work dW on the outside world, then, if dU is the increase in energy contained in the system,

$$dU = dQ - dW \tag{1}$$

The differential form is employed in Eq. (1) as a convenience for use in the second law, although as far as the first law is concerned the quantities involved need not be infinitesimal.

The second law of thermodynamics determines the amount of thermal energy in a system and the way and the extent to which it can be transformed into other types of energy. There are several equivalent formal statements of the second law, such as

1. Heat will not flow of itself from a body of lower temperature to a body of higher temperature.

2. It is impossible to perform a cyclic process whose only effects will be the removal of thermal energy from a body and its conversion into work.

We shall not here go through all the reasoning carried out in thermodynamics by means of which it is shown that these laws lead to the final results which we shall use. Instead, we shall merely outline and interpret the results.

In thermodynamics, a quantity S is defined by the equations

$$dS = \frac{dQ}{T} \qquad \text{or} \qquad S = \int \frac{dQ}{T} + S_0 \tag{2}$$ [2]

[1] It is expected that the reader already has a general knowledge of thermal noise, such as may be obtained from Chap. VI.

[2] Throughout this chapter, the temperature T will always mean the absolute temperature, *i.e.*, centigrade temperature plus 273.1°.

where dQ represents heat which enters a system, T is the temperature at which it enters, and the integral in Eq. (2) is taken from an initial state 1 to a final state 2 along a reversible path.[1] The quantity S in Eq. (2) is called the *entropy* of the system, and it is proved in thermodynamics that the entropy of a system in a given state (*i.e.*, given temperature, pressure, volume, etc.) has a definite value which is independent of the manner in which the system arrived at that state. It is further shown that the quantity

$$TS = \text{temperature} \times \text{entropy}$$

represents what may be called the "bound energy" or "thermal energy" of the system; and this energy cannot be removed from the system and transformed into work[2] unless there is some means of lowering the temperature of the system, such as by letting it deliver heat to another system at lower temperature. The difference between the total energy U of the system and the thermal energy TS is called the "free energy" or "available energy" ψ of the system at the temperature T. Thus

$$\psi = U - TS \tag{3}$$

The available energy ψ is the energy which can be removed from the system at the temperature T and can be used to perform work on other systems.

9.2 Statistical Interpretation of the Results of Thermodynamics.[3] During the general period of the second half of the nineteenth century a statistical theory of thermodynamics was developed.[4] This theory is called *statistical mechanics*. According to statistical mechanics, the

[1] A reversible path is one whose direction of operation can be reversed by infinitesimal changes in the external conditions. Operations along a reversible path consequently take place with only infinitesimal speed. If the path in Eq. (2) is not reversible, which is usually the case in practice, then it may be shown that

$$S - S_0 > \int \frac{dQ}{T}$$

We shall not go into the details of thermodynamics here, such as the real meaning of cyclic processes and reversible paths, since they are not necessary for the use that we shall make of thermodynamics.

[2] Latent heats can be removed from a system, but they cannot be transformed into work at the temperature of the system, so that they do not represent available energy.

[3] In order to read the remainder of this chapter, the reader should be acquainted with the ideas and terminology of Chapter VII.

[4] By such men as Maxwell, Boltzmann, and Gibbs.

thermal energy of a system consists of the energy associated with the to-and-fro irregular motions of the individual atoms, molecules, or electrons in a system with respect to each other. These motions are essentially random in nature, and for this reason it is impossible to get at the energy associated with them in order to convert this energy into other types except to the extent that is permitted by the laws of thermodynamics.[1] The theory points out that the macroscopic[2] (*i.e.*, large-scale) properties of a system are statistical in nature and are subject to fluctuations. In particular, it is shown that any property (for example, the pressure) which determines the state of a system is subject to fluctuations; and if the free energy can be expressed as a pure quadratic function of these fluctuations, then the fluctuations have a normal distribution. Thus, the probability that a property shall have a value lying between x and $x + dx$ is

$$P(x)\,dx = B\epsilon^{-a^2(x-x_0)^2}\,dx \tag{4}$$

where x_0 is the most probable value of x. If x has a one-dimensional normal distribution, then B is a constant; otherwise, it is a function of x. Statistical mechanics also shows the connections between Eq. (4) and the laws of thermodynamics. Thus, it shows that for the exponent in Eq. (4),

$$-a^2(x - x_0)^2 = \frac{S - S_0}{k} \qquad (5)^3$$

where S is the entropy corresponding to the value x for the observable property, S_0 is the entropy corresponding to x_0, and k is a universal constant, called Boltzmann's constant or the gas constant per molecule. The value of k is

$$k = 1.371 \times 10^{-16} \text{ erg/deg} = 1.371 \times 10^{-23} \text{ watt-sec/deg}$$

[1] While thermal energy cannot be converted into work without a change in temperature, if a second and cooler system is present so that the original system can have its temperature decreased by transfer of heat to the cooler system, a certain amount of its thermal energy can be converted into work. Thus

$$d(TS) = T\,dS + S\,dT = dQ + S\,dT$$

and the quantity

$$-\int S\,dT$$

represents work that can be obtained from the system in the course of lowering its temperature.

[2] As distinguished from microscopic properties, which pertain to the individual atoms, molecules, or electrons.

[3] It follows from Eqs. (4) and (5) that S_0 is a maximum value of S. Thus the most probable state of a system is that in which the entropy is a maximum.

It follows from Eqs. (4) and (5) that

$$P(x)\,dx = B\epsilon^{\frac{S-S_0}{k}}\,dx \tag{6}$$

The entropy of a system is thus intimately tied up with its statistical properties.[1]

9.3 The Equipartition Theorem. Suppose that the free energy of a system includes a term which is a positive quadratic function of some variable y, where y is the measure of the fluctuation (from the most probable state) of some property of the system. Let us further suppose that, except for this term, y does not otherwise appear in the thermal or the free energy.[2] Then we may write

$$\psi = \psi_0 + b^2y^2 \tag{7}$$

where ψ_0 is independent of y; and, from Eq. (3)

$$S = \frac{U - \psi}{T} = \frac{U - \psi_0 - b^2y^2}{T} \tag{8}$$

Substituting Eq. (8) into Eq. (6), we have

$$P(y)\,dy = B\epsilon^{-\frac{b^2y^2}{kT}}\,dy \tag{9}$$

where B is a constant. Since by definition

$$\int_{-\infty}^{+\infty} P(y)\,dy = 1 \tag{10}$$

it follows that

$$\int_{-\infty}^{+\infty} B\epsilon^{-\frac{b^2y^2}{kT}}\,dy = \frac{B}{b}\sqrt{\pi kT} = 1 \tag{11}$$

or

$$B = \frac{b}{\sqrt{\pi kT}} \tag{12}$$

[1] While the foregoing discussion gives us the equations we shall require, it is completely inadequate for the reader who has had no previous acquaintance with fluctuation phenomena in physics and their relation to thermodynamics. Such readers are strongly advised to get additional knowledge of the subject from a textbook on statistical mechanics, such as R. C. Tolman, "Statistical Mechanics." A more advanced but very fine discussion is also given by S. Chandrasekhar, *Rev. Modern Phys.*, January, 1943.

[2] y may, for example, be the charge on the condenser C, in Fig. 1, due to thermal noise in R. Then

$$\psi - \psi_0 = \frac{1}{2C}y^2$$

The ensemble average value of b^2y^2 is then

$$\int_{-\infty}^{+\infty} b^2y^2 \frac{b}{\sqrt{\pi kT}} \epsilon^{-\frac{b^2y^2}{kT}}\, dy = \frac{b}{\sqrt{\pi kT}} b^2 \frac{1}{2} \sqrt{\frac{\pi k^3T^3}{b^6}}$$
$$= \frac{kT}{2} \tag{13}$$

Equation (13) tells us that the average value of the free-energy fluctuations, due to a term of the type of b^2y^2, is $\frac{1}{2}kT$. If the free energy consists of the sum of n independent quadratic terms of the type of b^2y^2, then, by following the same procedure as that used above, we should find the average value of the total free-energy fluctuations to be $n\frac{1}{2}kT$. This result is called the *equipartition theorem*. It is very useful in practice.

With the aid of the foregoing very brief outline of some of thermodynamics and its statistical interpretation, and in conjunction with the fluctuation theory developed in Chap. VII, we shall next derive the laws and formulas for thermal noise.

9.4 Thermal Noise—Introduction.[1] In the beginning of the twentieth century, von Smoluckowski and Einstein used the fluctuation theory of statistical mechanics to explain such known natural fluctuation phenomena as the Brownian movement and the opalescence of liquids in the critical state. They also pointed out that fluctuation phenomena due to thermal energy would appear in a variety of other ways, among them as fluctuations of electric current in a circuit. This matter, however, was of no practical interest until 1928, when J. B. Johnson[2] showed that such fluctuation currents were observable in a high-gain amplifier and actually set a limit to its sensitivity. Working in conjunction with Johnson, H. Nyquist also derived the now well-known formula for the noise power developed in a given frequency band. The researches of Johnson and Nyquist in thermal noise are among the classical investigations of radio engineering.

In beginning the study of thermal noise let us consider a vacuum tube with a grid resistor R, and let the input capacity of the tube be C. Let us consider fluctuations in the entropy of the R-C circuit as indicated by the free energy that is stored in the input capacity of the tube. Since there is no free energy in the resistor itself, the variations

[1] An interesting and stimulating account of thermal-noise experiments and theory will be found in the first chapter of Moullin, "Spontaneous Fluctuations of Voltage."

[2] Johnson, J. B., *Phys. Rev.*, **32**, 97, 1928; Nyquist, H., *Phys. Rev.*, **32**, 110, 1928.

in entropy are, according to Eq. (3), just the negative of the energy delivered to the capacitor divided by the temperature so that

$$S - S_0 = -\frac{1}{2}\frac{CE^2}{T} \tag{14}$$

where E is the thermal-noise voltage across C. Letting E be the x of Eq. (6) for our problem, we then have

$$P(E)\,dE = B\epsilon^{-\frac{CE^2}{2kT}}\,dE \tag{15}$$

The voltage E, as in Sec. 7.14, has a one-dimensional distribution so that B is a constant. Therefore, since

$$\int_{-\infty}^{+\infty} P(E)\,dE = \int_{-\infty}^{+\infty} B\epsilon^{-\frac{CE^2}{2kT}}\,dE = B\sqrt{\frac{2\pi kT}{C}} = 1 \tag{16}$$

it follows that

$$B = \sqrt{\frac{C}{2\pi kT}} \tag{17}$$

Since $P(E)$ measures the probability of finding the voltage between E and $E + dE$, then according to Sec. 7.14e, it also represents the fraction of time that the voltage will be between E and $E + dE$. Therefore, the mean square value of the voltage is

$$\begin{aligned}\int_{-\infty}^{+\infty} E^2P(E)\,dE &= \int_{-\infty}^{+\infty}\sqrt{\frac{C}{2\pi kT}}\,E^2\epsilon^{-\frac{CE^2}{2kT}}\,dE \\ &= \sqrt{\frac{C}{2\pi kT}}\,\frac{1}{2}\sqrt{\frac{\pi 8k^3T^3}{C^3}} = \frac{kT}{C}\end{aligned} \tag{18}$$

The answer given by Eq. (18) for the mean square value of the thermal-noise voltage is unfortunately not in a very useful form. In practice, there is usually a tuned amplifier following the source of thermal noise, and thus it would be desirable to know the frequency distribution of the thermal noise. This will be obtained in the next section. For the present, however, we shall consider further some general matters pertaining to thermal noise.

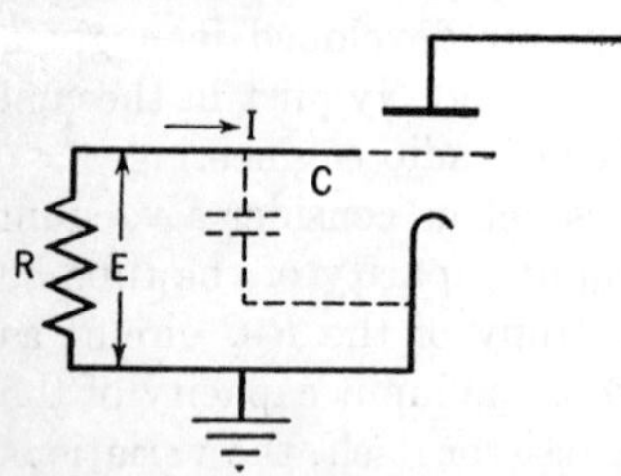

FIG. 1. Example of a resistor which stores free energy in a capacitor.

One point that we note immediately is that, since the capacitor is considered as the storage medium for the free energy of the resistor, we could have predicted from the equipartition theorem that the mean square voltage across the capacitor would be kT/C, for the energy of the capacitor is $\frac{1}{2}CE^2$, so that we should have

$$\overline{\tfrac{1}{2}CE^2} = \tfrac{1}{2}kT \tag{19}$$

We have gone through the detailed derivation, however, in order to show the significance of the equipartition theorem.

Finally, before taking up Nyquist's derivation of the formula for thermal-noise voltage, we may point out that, if it is assumed that a resistor is a voltage generator of thermal noise of an amount which is equally distributed throughout the frequency range, then the above methods are sufficient to determine the amount of noise per megacycle. To show this let

$$A^2\,df \tag{20}$$

be the mean square voltage in an infinitesimal bandwidth df generated in the resistor. Then the amount of this appearing across the capacitor will be

$$A^2\,df\,\frac{(1/2\pi fC)^2}{R^2 + (1/2\pi fC)^2} = \frac{A^2\,df}{4\pi^2f^2C^2R^2 + 1} \tag{21}$$

Since, according to the Fourier integral energy theorem, mean square voltages of different frequencies may be added directly, the total mean square voltage across the capacitor will be

$$\begin{aligned} \int_0^\infty \frac{A^2\,df}{4\pi^2f^2C^2R^2 + 1} &= \frac{A^2}{2\pi CR}\tan^{-1}(2\pi fCR)\Big|_{f=0}^{f=\infty} \\ &= \frac{A^2}{2\pi CR}\frac{\pi}{2} = \frac{A^2}{4CR} \end{aligned} \tag{22}$$

From Eq. (18) we also know that the value of the mean square voltage is kT/C, so that

$$\frac{A^2}{4CR} = \frac{kT}{C} \tag{23}$$

or

$$A^2 = 4RkT \tag{24}$$

Thus, the mean square noise voltage generated in a resistance R in a band of width Δf is

$$A^2\,\Delta f = 4RkT\,\Delta f \tag{25}$$

This is Nyquist's formula, but it has been derived under the thus far unproved assumption that a resistor is a noise-voltage generator which generates equal amounts of voltage throughout the frequency range. We shall next give a derivation that does not require this assumption.

9.5 Derivation of the Thermal-noise Formula of Nyquist.[1,2] The derivation in the preceding section suggests that, if, in place of a capacitor, we use a free-energy storage medium which is not selective to frequency, it will enable us to determine directly the frequency

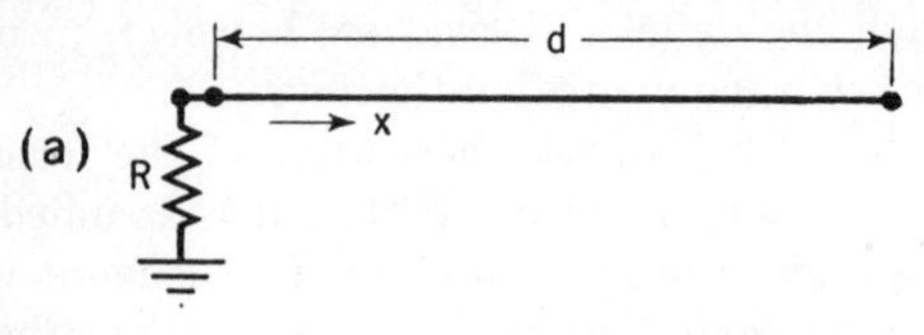

FIG. 2. The storage of thermal-noise energy in a lossless transmission line.

distribution in thermal noise. Such a medium is available, at least theoretically, in the form of a lossless transmission line. Accordingly, let us connect a resistor R to a lossless transmission line of surge impedance R, as shown in Fig. 2, and let the line be open-circuited at its far end. Then the resistor will deliver noise energy into the line. This will be in the form of an electric wave that flows along the line. Since the line is open at the far end, there will be complete reflection of the energy there; and since R is the surge impedance of the line, the reflected wave will be completely absorbed again at the resistor. In Fig. 2*b* is shown a diagram of the voltage E_f of the forward wave, and in Fig. 2*c* is a diagram of the voltage E_b of the reflected (back) wave. According to the fundamental form of Fourier's theorem, each of these voltages can be expanded in a Fourier series of the form

$$E_f = a_{f0} + \sum_{q=1}^{\infty} \left(a_{fq} \cos \frac{2\pi q x}{d} + b_{fq} \sin \frac{2\pi q x}{d} \right) \tag{26}$$

[1] The derivation given here has been altered somewhat from Nyquist's, but the use of a transmission line as an energy storage medium, which is the crux of the matter, is still the same.

It is recommended that the student read Sec. 7.20 as a preliminary to this section.

[2] The method, used in this section, of applying the second law of thermodynamics to highly idealized elements in a physical process has a time-honored position in the history of physics. The reader who has had no previous acquaintance with it should not be led by its artificiality to belittle its reliability or its importance. The method has had many great successes in the past, a most notable achievement being that it led Planck to the original formulation of the quantum theory.

$$E_b = a_{b0} + \sum_{q=1}^{\infty} \left(a_{bq} \cos \frac{2\pi q x}{d} + b_{bq} \sin \frac{2\pi q x}{d} \right) \tag{27}$$

where d is the length of the line; and the corresponding currents can be obtained by dividing these voltages by the surge impedance of the line

$$Z_0 = \sqrt{\frac{L}{C}} = R \tag{28}$$

where L is the series inductance per unit length of the line and C is the shunt capacity per unit length.

The energy of the qth Fourier harmonic of either the forward or the backward wave is

$$\int_0^d \frac{1}{2} \left(C + \frac{L}{Z_0^2} \right) \left(a_q \cos \frac{2\pi q x}{d} + b_q \sin \frac{2\pi q x}{d} \right)^2 dx = \frac{C(a_q^2 + b_q^2)d}{2} = \frac{(a_q^2 + b_q^2)d}{2Rv} \tag{29}$$[1]

where

$$v = \frac{1}{\sqrt{LC}} \tag{30}$$

is the velocity of traveling waves along the line. The total energy in the transmission line is then

$$\text{Energy} = \frac{d}{Rv} (a_{f0}^2 + a_{b0}^2) + \frac{d}{2Rv} \sum_{q=1}^{\infty} (a_{fq}^2 + b_{fq}^2 + a_{bq}^2 + b_{bq}^2) \tag{31}$$

Now all the a and b components are independent of each other, and each has a one-dimensional probability distribution. Therefore, if the transmission line is considered as the storage medium for the free energy of the resistor, it follows from the equipartition theorem that

$$\frac{d}{2Rv} \overline{(a_{fq}^2 + b_{fq}^2 + a_{bq}^2 + b_{bq}^2)} = 4 \left(\frac{1}{2} kT \right) = 2kT \tag{32}$$

As far as the forward wave alone is concerned, the average energy of the qth harmonic is

$$\frac{d}{2Rv} \overline{(a_{fq}^2 + b_{fq}^2)} = kT \tag{33}$$

[1] The energy per unit length of a transmission line is

$$\tfrac{1}{2}CE^2 + \tfrac{1}{2}LI^2$$

and the energy delivered by the resistor into the line per second comprising the qth harmonic is

$$\frac{v}{d}\left[\frac{d}{2Rv}\,\overline{(a_{fq}^2 + b_{fq}^2)}\right] = \frac{\overline{a_{fq}^2 + b_{fq}^2}}{2R} = \frac{vkT}{d} \tag{34}$$

At this point, we should realize that the qth harmonic of the Fourier expansion of Fig. 2b consists not of a single frequency, but rather of a narrow band of frequencies, since it is a wave train of finite length (see Fig. 4 of Chap. III and Sec. 7.20). This band centers about the frequency

$$F_q = q\frac{v}{d} \tag{35}$$

which is the local frequency of the qth Fourier harmonic.

If the line is very long so that its fundamental frequency

$$F_1 = \frac{v}{d} \tag{36}$$

is very low, then there will be many line harmonics in any given frequency band ΔF of interest. Each of these line harmonics will be at the center of a band of frequencies of the noise energy, and the bands will overlap to give a smooth energy vs. frequency curve.[1] The number of harmonics in a frequency band of width ΔF will be

$$\frac{\Delta F}{F_1} \tag{37}$$

so that the total noise energy delivered by the resistor into the line per second in the frequency band ΔF is

$$\frac{\Delta F}{F_1}\frac{vkT}{d} = \Delta FkT \tag{38}$$

Equation (38) is a very important result. It is the rate at which thermal-noise energy is delivered by a resistor R into another resistor[2]

[1] It is clear physically that this curve will be smooth since it cannot be affected by the line length, because the properties of the forward wave are independent of line length.

[2] The transmission line acts like a resistor to the forward wave, even though an open line *in the steady state* would look like a pure reactance. A transmission line acts like a pure resistance of magnitude Z_0 to the forward wave and to the backward wave taken separately, regardless of the termination of the line. The termination determines the magnitude and phase of the reflected wave, but not the ratio of current to voltage in it.

of the same size. An equal amount of noise power is delivered by the second resistor (the line) to the first (*i.e.*, by the back wave), so that thermal equilibrium is not disturbed. The peculiar properties of a transmission line, which allow us theoretically to separate the forward and backward wave, *i.e.*, the noise energy leaving and entering the resistor, and which allow us to express this energy in terms of its frequency components, make a transmission line ideally well suited to our purposes.

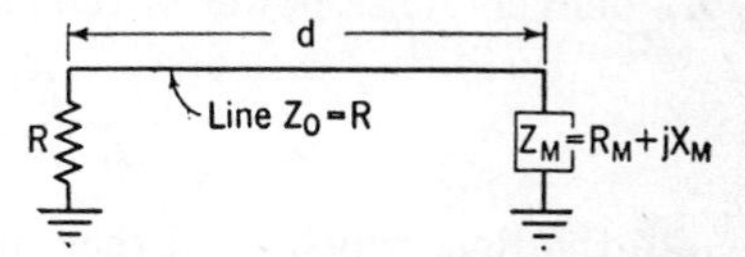

FIG. 3. A transmission line terminated by its surge impedance at one end and by an arbitrary impedance at the other end.

Now that we know how much energy the resistor sends into the line, let us next terminate the far end of the line with an impedance

$$Z_M = R_M + jX_M \tag{39}$$

as shown in Fig. 3, and let Z_M be at the same temperature T as R. When the noise energy of the forward wave from R arrives at Z_M, a fraction of it equal to $|K|^2$ times the original value is reflected, where K is the voltage-reflection coefficient. We know from transmission-line theory that

$$K = \frac{Z_M - R}{Z_M + R} = \frac{(R_M - R) + jX_M}{(R_M + R) + jX_M} \tag{40}$$

so that

$$|K|^2 = \frac{(R_M - R)^2 + X_M^2}{(R_M + R)^2 + X_M^2} \tag{41}$$

Furthermore, a fraction

$$1 - |K|^2 = \frac{4RR_M}{(R_M + R)^2 + X_M^2} \tag{42}$$

of the forward wave is absorbed in Z_M.

In order to simplify our analysis, we shall assume that Z_M is of a band-pass nature, being infinite except in a narrow frequency band, ΔF. Thus, except in the band ΔF, the line will be open-circuited at the Z_M end and will behave as in the case previously analyzed. We shall next concentrate on what happens in the relatively narrow frequency band ΔF, in order to get at the heart of the thermal-noise question.

Now we have assumed that R and Z_M are at the same temperature. Then, according to the second law of thermodynamics, the thermal-noise energy going from Z_M to R must equal the thermal-noise energy going from R to Z_M. Otherwise, R would get colder while Z_M got warmer, or vice versa, in violation of the second law. Accordingly, we conclude from Eqs. (42) and (38) that the terminating impedance Z_M delivers noise power of the amount

$$\frac{4RR_MkT\,\Delta F}{(R_M + R)^2 + X_M^2} \tag{43}$$

into the line, which is all then absorbed at R. The values of R, R_M, and X_M in Eq. (43) are their values for the frequency range ΔF.

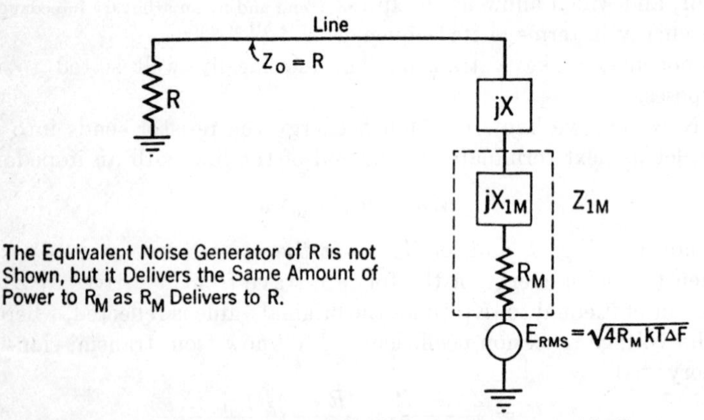

FIG. 4. Circuit of operation of the thermal noise generated in Z_{1M}.

The form of Eq. (43) shows that the thermal-noise power delivered by Z_M into a resistance R is the equivalent of what would occur if there were a thermal-noise generator in Z_M, delivering a voltage of magnitude E such that

$$\overline{E^2} = 4R_MkT\,\Delta F \tag{44}$$

By dividing the reactance X_M of Fig. 3 into two parts X and X_{1M}, as shown in Fig. 4, such that

$$X_M = X + X_{1M} \tag{45}$$

it follows that a general impedance

$$Z_{1M} = R_M + jX_{1M} \tag{46}$$

will deliver an amount of noise power into another general impedance

$$Z = R + jX \tag{47}$$

as though Z_{1M} were a voltage generator with a voltage of the amount shown in Eq. (44). We see that $\overline{E^2}$ is proportional to R_M, to the temperature T, and to the bandwidth ΔF, and that it is independent of the location of ΔF in the frequency band since the absolute frequency does not appear in Eq. (44). Furthermore E does not depend on the load impedance $R + jX$, nor does it depend on the reactance X_{1M} of the generating impedance. The latter fact shows that resistances alone are sources of noise voltage, a fact that can also easily be shown by other means.

Equation (44) is Nyquist's famous formula for thermal noise.

We note here that R_M is the resistive component of an impedance in the frequency range ΔF and that the derivation of Eq. (44) would hold just as well if R_M is due to the power factor of a condenser or any other cause. Equation (44) is not limited to any specific type of R_M.

According to Sec. 6.4 this equation can also be written in the equivalent current-generator form

$$\overline{I^2} = 4G_M kT\,\Delta F \tag{44a}$$

where G_M is the real part of $1/Z_M$, that is, G_M is the conductance of Z_M. In this case the impedance Z_M is in shunt with the current generator.

It may be noted that, since according to Eq. (44) the total mean square voltage has equal contributions from every frequency band of width ΔF, the total mean square voltage in the complete frequency range from $F = 0$ to $F = \infty$ should be infinite. A similar difficulty arises in the theory of heat radiation in physics when the simple equations (4) to (6) of classical statistical mechanics are used. However, if these equations are revised in accordance with quantum theory, the results are essentially unchanged up to a frequency of the order of

$$F = \frac{kT}{h} \qquad (48)^{1}$$

but above this frequency the energies involved decrease rapidly. In our case, if

[1] In quantum theory the energy per degree of freedom is

$$\frac{hv}{\epsilon^{\frac{hv}{kT}} - 1} \qquad \text{(where } v \text{ is frequency)}$$

instead of kT, as in classical statistical mechanics. The kT result for classical statistical mechanics is a consequence of the equipartition theorm in conjunction with the fact that each degree of freedom contributes two quadratic terms to the total energy.

$$T = 293^\circ \text{ (that is, } 20^\circ\text{C)}$$
$$k = 1.37 \times 10^{-16} \text{ erg/deg}$$
$$h = 6.6 \times 10^{-27} \text{ erg-sec (the quantum constant)}$$

then

$$F = \frac{kT}{h} = 6.1 \times 10^{12} \text{ cycles} = 6{,}100{,}000 \text{ mc} \tag{49}$$

Consequently, we may expect that Nyquist's formula gives the correct value for thermal-noise voltage up to frequencies of the order of those indicated by Eq. (48) and (49). This includes all frequencies of interest in radio engineering at present. Above these frequencies, it is to be expected that the classical statistical mechanics upon which our results were based will give erroneous results and that the true results will show a falling off of energy with frequency in accordance with quantum theory.

In concluding this section, we note that it follows from Eqs. (4), (26), and (29) that thermal noise is random noise in accordance with the definition in Sec. 7.14.

9.6 Thermal Noise as Fluctuation Noise of the Conduction Electrons.[1] In the foregoing section, we have derived Nyquist's formula for thermal noise from the statistical theory of thermodynamics without any recourse as to the nature of the mechanism that produces thermal noise. This is highly desirable from the standpoint of rigor, since it does not make our results depend upon any particular theory of electrical conduction. It is nevertheless of interest to know whether or not the modern theory of electrical conduction supplies a mechanism that generates thermal noise of the correct amount. This we shall now investigate, with no attempt at great accuracy, however, but only with the purpose of seeing whether thermodynamic and conduction theories are in general agreement.

According to the theory of metallic conduction, any metal has a large number of free electrons moving about in it. In the absence of an external emf, these electrons derive their velocities from collisions with the atoms of the metal. The motion of the free electrons is thus essentially thermal in nature. In any metal the atoms are so close together that an electron can travel only a short distance before it collides with an atom. During the collision the speed and direction of the electron motion are completely changed. The average distance

[1] The discussion presented here is a development of a corresponding discussion given by Moullin, "Spontaneous Fluctuations of Voltage," p. 66–67. Moullin attributes the original development to D. A. Bell and states that Bell has published a further development of the theory in *J.I.E.E.*, **82,** 529, 1938.

between collisions in the electron's travels is known as the *mean free path* of free electrons in the metal in question. The numerical value of this mean free path for free electrons is a physical characteristic of a metal. Furthermore, the number of free electrons per cubic centimeter is also a physical characteristic of a metal. It is shown in Drude's theory of metallic conduction that the specific resistivity of a metal is given by the formula

$$\rho = \frac{6kT}{N\kappa^2 D\bar{v}} \tag{50}$$[1]

where D = mean free path
N = number of free electrons per cubic centimeter
κ = electronic charge
$\bar{v}$ = average thermal velocity of free electrons
ρ = specific resistivity

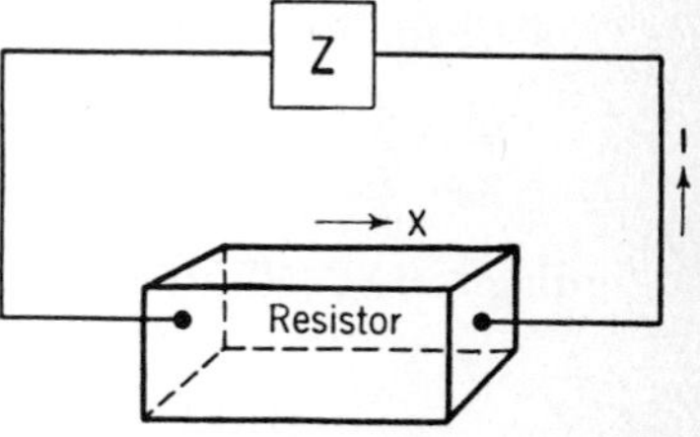

FIG. 5. A metallic resistor connected to an external circuit.

Let us now consider the metallic resistor, shown in Fig. 5, in which there are free electrons traveling with thermal velocities, and let us suppose that the resistor is located in a closed circuit. Then because of electrical and magnetic induction, the current i that flows in the resistor will also flow in the external circuit.[2] Let us now calculate the fluctuation current i that flows in the resistor owing to the thermal velocities of the free electrons.

As an electron travels between one collision and another, it creates an equivalent current in the resistor in the direction around the circuit. This equivalent current is of the order of magnitude of

$$\frac{\kappa v_x}{d} \tag{51}$$

where d is the length of the resistor. That is, on the average, an electron traveling with a velocity component v_x in the x direction will cause approximately the same induction effects as a current $\kappa v_x/d$ flowing through the entire length d of the resistor. Electronic flights between collisions are thus on the average equivalent to current impulses of strength

[1] JEANS, J. H., "Dynamical Theory of Gases," p. 303.

[2] Another way of saying this is to say that the motion of electrons inside the resistor will induce a general motion of the entire "cloud" of free electrons in the circuit in such a way that the external current i will be uniform around the circuit.

$$\pm \int \frac{\kappa \overline{|v_x|}}{d}\, dt = \pm \frac{\kappa \overline{|v_x|} \tau}{d} = \pm \frac{\kappa D}{d} \frac{\overline{|v_x|}}{\bar{v}} = \pm \frac{\kappa D}{2d} \qquad (52)^{1}$$

where $\tau = D/\bar{v}$ = average time between collisions

$\overline{|v_x|}$ = average of the absolute values of v_x

Now the average number of impulses per second due to each free electron is $1/\tau$, and the total number of free electrons in the resistor is NdA,

where d = length of the resistor

A = area of cross section of the resistor

Consequently, the total number of impulses per second due to the thermal motion of the free electrons is $(N/\tau)\, dA$.[2] Therefore, by Eq. (143) of Chap. VII, the fluctuation current due to these impulses is

$$\overline{(I_{\Delta F})^2_{\text{rms}}} = 2 \frac{\kappa^2 D^2}{4d^2} \frac{N}{\tau}\, dA\, \Delta F \qquad (53)$$

According to Eq. (50), the resistance R of the resistor is

$$R = \rho \frac{d}{A} = \frac{6kT}{N\kappa^2 D\bar{v}} \frac{d}{A} = \frac{6kT\tau}{N\kappa^2 D^2} \frac{1}{A} \qquad (54)$$

Substituting Eq. (54) into (53), we obtain the formula

$$\overline{(I_{\Delta F})^2_{\text{rms}}} = \frac{3kT}{R} \Delta F \qquad (55)$$

for the fluctuation current. This fluctuation current either can be absorbed in the resistor itself or else will flow in the external circuit. Thus, the thermal motion of the free electrons in the resistor R will cause fluctuation currents as indicated in Fig. 6a or fluctuation voltages as shown in the equivalent form in Fig. 6b. Since these fluctua-

[1] It may be shown [by integration of Eqs. (90) and (92) of Tolman, "Statistical Mechanics") that

$$\overline{|v_x|} = \sqrt{\frac{2kT}{\pi m}} \qquad \text{and} \qquad \bar{v} = \sqrt{\frac{8kT}{\pi m}}$$

so that

$$\frac{\overline{|v_x|}}{\bar{v}} = \frac{1}{2}$$

[2] Approximately half of these impulses will be in one direction around the circuit, and half will be in the opposite direction. However, except at zero frequency, this fact will affect only the phase of the frequency components and not their magnitudes, so that we can ignore it, since we are considering the components to be of random phase in any case.

tions are of nearly the same magnitude as the thermal noise generated in a resistor, according to the thermodynamic theory, we conclude that the theory of metallic conduction supplies a fairly satisfactory mechanism for the generation of thermal noise in metallic resistors. If we refined the methods of calculation and averaging used in this section, it is quite likely that an even better agreement with the Nyquist formula would be obtained. In any case, the Nyquist formula is based upon a rigorous theoretical foundation, and furthermore it agrees with experiment, so that it is the formula to be used in calculating thermal noise.

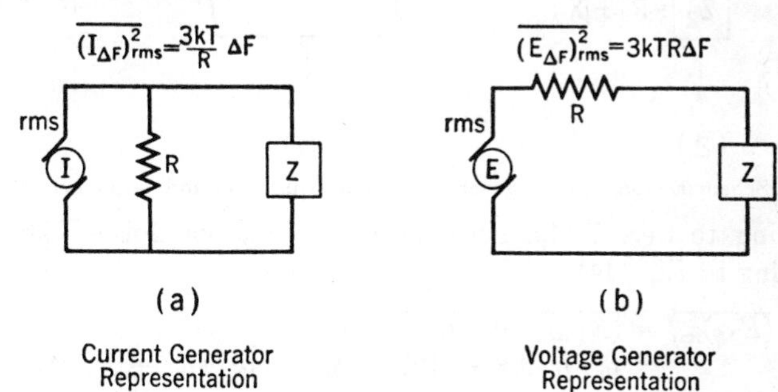

FIG. 6. Magnitude of thermal noise in a metallic resistor according to Drude's theory of metallic conduction.

It would seem that an accurate calculation from a correct theory of metallic conduction would have to yield the true value of thermal noise. It would be of considerable interest to make such a calculation based on the quantum-mechanical theory of metallic conduction, and compare it with a derivation of the Nyquist type revised in accordance with quantum statistics. A comparison with experiment in any frequency range in which the two methods of calculation give different results, if there turned out to be such a frequency range, might yield important information concerning metallic conduction and radiation theory.

9.7 Further Discussion of Thermal Noise.[1] *a. Consistency of Nyquist's Formula in Complex Networks.* For the Nyquist formula to be of general validity, it is necessary that it should be self-consistent when applied to a complex network. Since all networks are made up of combinations of series and parallel sections, a general test of the consistency of the formula would be given by testing it in the circuits shown in Fig. 7. Let us therefore make such a test.

[1] Further information on the subjects discussed in this section will be found in Moullin, "Spontaneous Fluctuations of Voltage."

The total impedance in Fig. 7*a* is

$$Z = Z_1 + Z_2 = (R_1 + R_2) + j(X_1 + X_2)$$

The total thermal-noise voltage generated is obtained by adding the quadratic contents of the noise voltages generated in Z_1 and Z_2,

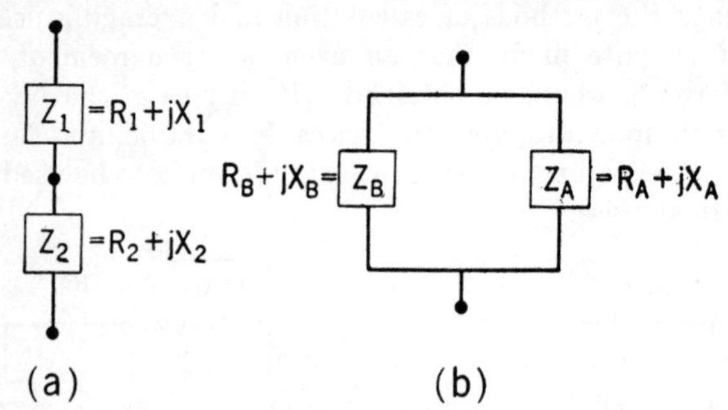

FIG. 7. Schematic diagrams of general impedances in series and parallel combinations.

according to Sec. 7.14*g*, since both are random noise. Therefore, according to Eq. (44),

$$\begin{aligned}\overline{(E_{\Delta F})^2_{\text{rms}}} &= \overline{(E_{1\,\Delta F})^2} + \overline{(E_{2\,\Delta F})^2} \\ &= 4kTR_1\,\Delta F + 4kTR_2\,\Delta F = 4kT(R_1 + R_2)\,\Delta F \end{aligned} \tag{56}$$

This is also the value that would be obtained by applying Eq. (44) to Z directly. Therefore Eq. (44) leads to consistent results when applied to series circuits.

Consider next the parallel circuit in Fig. 7*b*. Here the answer can best be obtained by using Eq. (44) and the equivalent current-generator representation (see Section 6.4). Thus, we have for the admittance

$$\begin{aligned} Y = G + jS = \frac{1}{Z} &= Y_A + Y_B = \frac{1}{Z_A} + \frac{1}{Z_B} \\ &= (G_A + jS_A) + (G_B + jS_B) = (G_A + G_B) + j(S_A + S_B) \end{aligned} \tag{57}$$

The total thermal-noise current generated in Y is obtained by adding the quadratic contents of the noise currents generated in Y_1 and Y_2. Thus

$$\begin{aligned}\overline{(I_{\Delta F})^2_{\text{rms}}} &= \overline{(I_{A\,\Delta F})^2_{\text{rms}}} + \overline{(I_{B\,\Delta F})^2_{\text{rms}}} \\ &= 4kTG_A\,\Delta F + 4kTG_B\,\Delta F \\ &= 4kT(G_A + G_B)\,\Delta F \end{aligned} \tag{58}$$

This is likewise the value that would be obtained by applying Eq. (44*a*) directly to Fig. 7*b* as a whole. Thus Nyquist's formula also leads to consistent results when parallel impedances are present.

Exercise

Show that according to Eq. (44) the thermal-noise power absorbed by Z_B from Z_A in Fig. 7*b* is equal to the thermal-noise power absorbed by Z_A from Z_B. If this were not the case, one impedance would steadily get warmer while the other got cooler, and this condition would violate the second law of thermodynamics.

b. Reactances Generate No Thermal Noise. According to the discussion in Sec. 9.5 reactances generate no thermal noise. There is an obvious physical reason for this, namely, that pure reactances of themselves do not contain numerous individual elements in statistical equilibrium, like the free electrons in a resistor, and therefore they cannot be expected to be the source of statistical fluctuations. From the point of view of the electron theory of conduction the reason why reactances generate no thermal noise is that there are no sudden interruptions to the motion of an electron in a pure reactance such as are caused by its collisions with the atoms of a resistor. The most convincing argument is, of course, the fact that, as the calculation of thermal noise in Sec. 9.5 shows, the voltage generated is independent of the size of the reactance. The matter is, however, so fundamental that F. C. Williams has made an independent experimental investigation to confirm it. He showed that in a circuit consisting of a resistor and a capacitor, the thermal-noise voltage generated is proportional to the temperature of the resistor but is independent of the temperature of the capacitor.

An independent theoretical verification of the fact that reactances generate no thermal noise can be obtained by applying the second law of thermodynamics directly to Fig. 8. If either reactance in Fig. 8 generated a thermal-noise voltage, it would send power into the resistor. Since over a long period of time a reactance cannot absorb any average power, it would therefore continually get cooler, while the resistor got warmer. This would violate the second law of thermodynamics.

c. Superposition of Direct Current or a Signal on Thermal Noise. In most cases in which thermal noise is of interest the thermal noise is superimposed upon a signal which it is desired to transmit. It is therefore of interest to know whether or not the presence of the signal affects the amount of thermal or other fluctuation noise generated. This problem cannot be handled by the thermodynamic arguments that we have previously used for pure thermal noise, since we are no longer dealing with a system in thermal equilibrium because of the I^2R generation of heat by the signal current I. Our information must therefore come from a theory of the detailed mechanism involved and of course, from experimental results.

The matter has been investigated experimentally by Moullin and is discussed in his book "Spontaneous Fluctuations of Voltage." He concludes from his measurements that a superimposed steady current has no effect on the thermal-noise current generated, provided that the circuit elements involved, particularly resistors, are of stable form. Thus, there are certain commercial resistors available whose resistance involves numerous granular contacts. Such resistors (called "crazy-

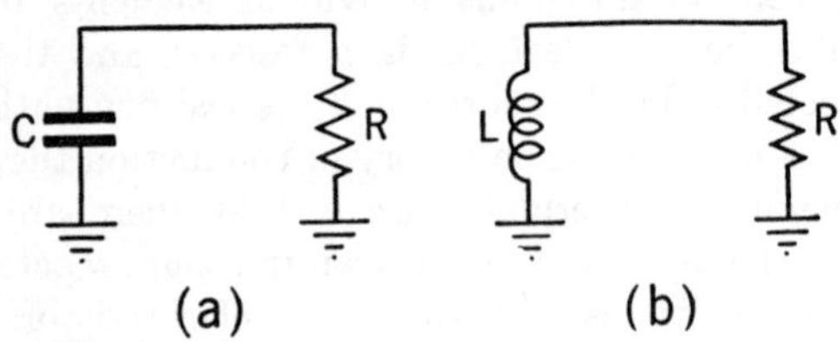

FIG. 8. Simple circuits containing a resistance and a reactance.

contact" resistors by the British) will generate extra noise when current is flowing through them, the extra noise actually being due to resistance variation rather than to any new emf. Except for noise of this type, which can be avoided by using high-quality resistors, the experimental evidence indicates that a superimposed signal or direct current has no effect on thermal noise.

Purely from the point of view of noise theory we can say that, if the impedances involved are *linear*, then the principle of superposition indicates that the frequency components of signal and thermal noise will be independent of each other except for cases in which the two have some frequency components in common. For such frequencies the frequency components will add vectorially. However, owing to the random phases of the frequency components of a thermal-noise signal, there will be no average change in thermal-noise power due to the presence of the signal. On the other hand, if the signal generates fluctuation noise of its own, it may be added directly to the thermal noise on a power basis.

The matter thus seems to be reduced to a question of whether or not the signal generates an *independent* fluctuation noise of its own. Now, since electric current is electronic in nature, the finite size of an electron, in conjunction with the random fluctuations in the density of distribution of electrons in a conductor, will always introduce some statistical fluctuations, similar to shot effect. However, the cloud of free electrons in a metal will behave as a buffer, just like the space charge in a tube, and will introduce coherent fluctuations which will largely cancel the effect of the original fluctuations. In order to get an approximate value for the final residual increase in noise, we refer to the analysis in Sec. 9.6 and note that the effect of the superimposed signal is to increase the ratio of $\overline{|v_x|}/\bar{v}$ in Eq. (52). Now according to the electron theory of conduction, signal currents are ordinarily due to average drift velocities of the electrons in the direction of the emf of the order of magnitude of 1 cm/sec. On the other hand, the average thermal velocity at 20°C is around 5×10^6 cm/sec. The factor of increase in $\overline{|v_x|}/\bar{v}$ due to the signal is around the ratio of the drift velocity to the thermal velocity. As just pointed out, this ratio is exceedingly small. The increase in fluctuation noise due to the signal is consequently only a negligible fraction of the ordinary thermal noise and is too small to be detected experimentally.

d. Parts of Circuits at Different Temperatures. If parts of a circuit or network are at different temperatures, then we can just calculate the noise voltage due to each resistor at its own temperature and solve the circuit or network equation on that basis, remembering that the quadratic contents of noise signals are additive in any frequency range. The only other question involved is then whether or not a temperature gradient will cause the generation of any additional noise voltage. As far as the author is aware, this matter has never been investigated in detail. It is, of course, known that a temperature gradient will cause a flow of heat and also a generation of direct-current electric voltage (the Thomson effect). According to electron theory, this direct-current voltage is due to an average resultant drift velocity of the electrons caused by the temperature gradient. Using a similar argument to that of Sec. 9.7*c*, it follows that the fractional increase in the thermal noise, due to the temperature gradient, will be too small to be detected experimentally.

9.8 Thermal Noise and Radiation Resistance. The input circuit of a radio receiver is invariably connected to an antenna. Since the antenna has radiation resistance, the thermal noise generated in this radiation resistance is likely to be an important part of the total receiver noise. It is therefore important to consider the thermal noise developed in the antenna's radiation resistance.

The entire difficulty in calculating the thermal noise developed in the radiation resistance of an antenna is the difficulty in determining the effective temperature of this resistance. If the antenna were surrounded by a distant enclosure all at the same temperature T as the antenna itself, then it must follow from thermodynamic reasoning that the temperature of the radiation resistance would just be T. However, actual antennas are not surrounding by enclosures of uniform temperature, so that the problem is not a simple one.

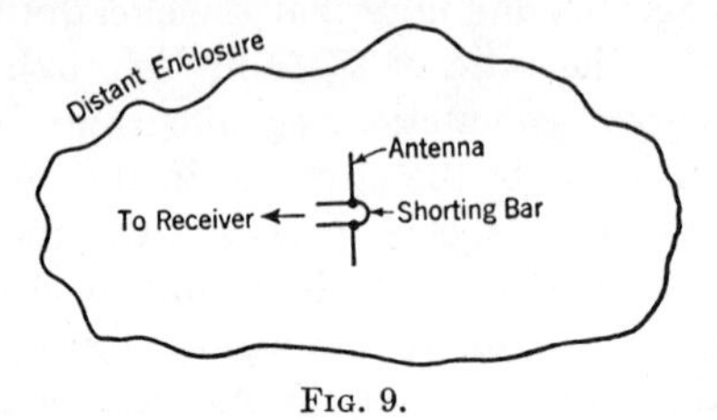

FIG. 9.

To get at the heart of the problem, we shall first show that the noise power of the radiation resistance originates not in the antenna, but rather in its surroundings, whether near or distant, which are capable of radiating power to the antenna. To show this, consider the idealized antenna shown in Fig. 9, which has radiation resistance and reactance but no ohmic resistance. Let us first consider the case in which the antenna is not connected to any circuits. In this case, if i_A is the antenna current (at its mid-terminal), the antenna will receive power of amount $i_A^2 R_A$, where R_A is the radiation resistance, and radiate power of the same amount. The antenna thus is not the source of any power but merely acts to reflect or scatter the power that comes to it from the outside. If the antenna has ohmic resistance R_0, then it will also have free electrons traveling in interrupted paths, so that it will generate a thermal-noise voltage $4kTR_0 \, \Delta F$ of its own; but, in the absence of such ohmic resistance, the antenna will not be the original source of any thermal-noise power.

If the antenna is connected to the antenna circuit of a radio receiver, then it will deliver some of the thermal-noise power that it receives from the outside to the receiver. The amount of this noise power that it delivers can be determined by assuming that it is a source of voltage of quadratic content

$$\overline{(E_{\Delta F})^2_{\text{rms}}} = 4kR_A T_S \, \Delta F \tag{59}$$

delivered through the antenna impedance Z_A. The mean thermal temperature T_S of the radiation resistance is then an average temperature of the antenna's surroundings that can radiate power to it. In estimating this average the various directions must be given weights proportional to the efficiency of radiation and reception of the antenna in these directions. The value of T_S is consequently a kind of weighted average of the earth's surface temperature, the effective temperature of the Heaviside layer, and the mean thermal temperature of galactic space.

In practice, it is impossible to separate the thermal noise due to radiation resistance from other random noise picked up by the antenna, such as atmospherics, interstellar interference, and man-made random noise. Consequently, the entire random-noise voltage appearing at the antenna terminals, except that due to the ohmic resistance of the antenna, is lumped together into a voltage $(E'_{\Delta F})_{\text{rms}}$ and the *effective temperature* T_A of the radiation resistance is determined by the equation

$$T_A = \frac{(E'_{\Delta F})^2_{\text{rms}}}{4kR_A\,\Delta F} \tag{60}$$

As thus defined, T_A is a measure of the noisiness of the antenna in its operating location. It depends upon the directional receiving pattern of the antenna as installed and upon the wavelength. In the broadcast band, owing to atmospherics, T_A is much higher than room temperature. At higher frequencies, particularly above 50 mc, the intensity of atmospherics declines; but while T_A may fall, it continues well above room temperature for a variety of causes. Among these are interstellar interference and, in urban localities in the daytime, diathermy.[1]

[1] Very recently, elaborate and ingenious techniques have been evolved to measure the effective temperatures of various areas and layers of the sun by means of the thermal noise radiated from the regions in question. Investigations are also being made of the Milky Way. While there is still a wide divergence of opinion in the interpretation of the results, there is no doubt that they are important.

of the Brownian lever, and the mean thermal temperature of gas [illegible]

[illegible] In practice, it is impossible to separate the thermal noise [illegible] from the other random noise picked up by the [illegible] components of [illegible] interference, and man-made random noises. [illegible] the equivalent noise voltage [illegible] resistance of the [illegible] and the [illegible] is determined by the equation

[illegible]

[illegible] of the antenna [illegible] and [illegible] absolute [illegible]

[illegible]

APPENDIX A

TABLE OF PRINCIPAL SYMBOLS, NOTATIONS, AND ABBREVIATIONS

Symbol	Meaning	Page defined or first used
$=$	"Equals"	3
$\equiv$	"Is identical with"	40
$<$	"Is less than"	21
$>$	"Is greater than"	126
$\rightarrow$	"Approaches"	80
$\leqq$	"Is less than or equal to"	7
$\geqq$	"Is greater than or equal to"	7
$\ll$	"Is much less than" or "is negligible in comparison with"	297
$\gg$	"Is much greater than"	25
$!$	"Factorial"	287
∞	"Infinity"	3
$\sim$	"Is similar to," "is proportional to," "is of the order of magnitude of," or "cycles per second"	300
$\int$	Symbol of integration	4
$\int_a^b$	The definite integral from a to b	4
Σ	Symbol of summation	3
$\sqrt{\ }$	Square-root sign	48
$\sum_{p=1}^{n}$	Summation from $p = 1$ to $p = n$	3
$\bar{n}$	Average value of n or "ensemble average" value of n	292
$\overline{f(t)}$	Ensemble average of $f(t)$	318
$\bar{G}(t)$	A function related to $G(t)$	73
$*$	Symbol of complex conjugate, that is, z^* = complex conjugate of z	23
$\vert\ \vert$	Absolute value sign, that is, $\vert k\vert$ is the absolute value of k	4
$f(x)$	A function of x	3
$f(x,y)$	A function of x and y	112

TABLE OF PRINCIPLE SYMBOLS, NOTATIONS, AND ABBREVIATIONS—*Continued*

Symbol	Meaning	Page defined or first used
σ_x^2	Ensemble average of x^2	323
$P(x)$	The probability of x	324
g_g	Input conductance of a tube	265
R_{eq}	Equivalent grid noise resistance	226
R_A	Radiation resistance of antenna	239
AM	Amplitude modulation	149
FM	Frequency modulation	149
PM	Phase modulation	149
$J_n(x)$, $I_n(x)$	Bessel functions of x	417
$\mathrm{Si}(x)$	Sine integral function of x	74
$\mathrm{Ci}(x)$	Cosine integral function of x	92
$\delta(t)$	The impulse function (of argument t)	125
Δx	Increment or small change (in x)	125
ΔF	Bandwidth in cycles/sec, deviation frequency	212, 147
$U(t)$	The unit-step function (of argument t)	124
$\delta'(t)$, $\delta''(t)$, etc.	Impulse functions of higher order	129
$P_m(n)$	The probability that an event will occur n times in m independent trials	290
$P'_{\bar{n}}(D)$	The probability of a fluctuation D from an average $\bar{n}$	303
P_n^n	Permutation symbol	287
C_m^n	Combination symbol	287
$G(t)$, $F(f)$, $S(\omega)$, $\phi(\omega)$, $\Omega(\omega)$, $a(\omega)$, $b(\omega)$	See Fourier integral formulas at conclusion of Chap. III	66
a_n, b_n	Fourier series coefficients	3
g_m	Transconductance of a tube	225
g_c	Conversion conductance of a tube	230
a, b, c, d, k / A, B, C, D, K	Constants	3
u, v, w, x, y, z / U, V, W, X, Y, Z	Variables	3
a	Amplitude (variable with time)	142
A	Fixed amplitude	115
c, C	Capacity, capacity per unit length	33
D	(1) Maximum deviation frequency	166
	(2) A fluctuation	302
e, E	Voltage	36
f	Frequency	58
F	(1) Complex frequency-distribution function	59

TABLE OF PRINCIPLE SYMBOLS, NOTATIONS, AND ABBREVIATIONS—*Continued*

Symbol	Meaning	Page defined or first used
F	(2) Frequency, especially carrier frequency	142
	(3) Noise figure	255
g, G	Conductance, conductance per unit length	223
H	Magnetic-field strength	378
i, I	Current	43
j	$\sqrt{-1}$	21
J	See Bessel functions	417
k	A constant; Boltzmann's constant	46, 212
l, L	Inductance, inductance per unit length	33
m	(1) An integer	287
	(2) Modulation factor	142
M	Mutual inductance	240
n, N	An integer	3, 318
N	(1) Noise voltage or power	251
	(2) Number of magnetic flux lines	379
p	(1) Probability of occurrence	290
	(2) A number (an integer)	5
q	A number (an integer)	5
Q	(1) Quality factor	136
	(2) Quantity of heat	381
r, R	Resistance or resistance per unit length	33
s	(1) Electron velocity	353
	(2) Magnetic susceptibility	379
S	(1) Signal voltage or power	251
	(2) Entropy	381
t	A variable, usually time	25
t_0, t_1, t_2, etc.	Particular values of t	25
T	Period $= \frac{1}{f}$	20
T, T_1, etc.	Particular values of t	25
T	Temperature	212
U	Total energy of a system	381
v, V	Velocity	116
x, X	Reactance	136
y, Y	Admittance	178
z, Z	(1) Impedance	69
	(2) Any complex quantity	22
α	Type of electrons that do not get past the virtual cathode	365
β	Type of electrons that get past the virtual cathode	365

TABLE OF PRINCIPAL SYMBOLS, NOTATIONS, AND ABBREVIATIONS—*Continued*

Symbol	Meaning	Page defined or first used
Γ^2	Space-charge noise-reduction factor	225
δ	See impulse function	125
Δ	Symbol for an increment or small part	125
ϵ	The number 2.71828 . . . , which is the base of natural logarithms	10
θ	(1) An angle or phase angle	11
	(2) Phase of a complex quantity	21
κ	Electronic charge = 1.60×10^{-19} coulomb	224
λ	Wavelength	116
μ	(1) Amplification factor of a tube	363
	(2) Modulation frequency	142
	(3) Magnetic permeability	378
π	The number 3.14159 . . .	3
ρ	Specific resistivity	395
σ	A tube-structure constant	225
τ	An auxiliary time variable	372
ϕ	(1) An angle or phase angle	4
	(2) Phase of a complex quantity	178
ψ	(1) A phase angle	171
	(2) Free energy	382
ω	Angular velocity = $2\pi \times$ frequency	36
Ω	The Fourier transform (of a time function) expressed as a function of ω	60

APPENDIX B[1]

SHORT TABLE OF INTEGRALS

(The following brief table includes principally those integrals which are of particular use in connection with the present book. For a more extensive list, the reader should consult the various standard tables of integrals.)

$$(1)\quad \int au\,dx = a\int u\,dx$$

$$(2)\quad \int (u+v)\,dx = \int u\,dx + \int v\,dx$$

$$(3)\quad \int (u-v)\,dx = \int u\,dx - \int v\,dx$$

$$(4)\quad \int \frac{dz}{dy}\frac{dy}{dx}\,dx = z + C$$

$$(5)\quad \int u\frac{dv}{dx}\,dx = uv - \int v\frac{du}{dx}\,dx$$

$$(6)\quad \int x^n\,dx = \frac{x^{n+1}}{n+1} + C$$

$$(7)\quad \int \epsilon^{bx}\,dx = \frac{\epsilon^{bx}}{b} + C$$

$$(8)\quad \int a^{bx}\,dx = \frac{a^{bx}}{b\log_\epsilon a} + C$$

$$(9)\quad \int \frac{dx}{x} = \log_\epsilon x + C = \log_\epsilon kx$$

$$(10)\quad \int \sin x\,dx = -\cos x + C$$

$$(11)\quad \int \cos x\,dx = \sin x + C$$

$$(12)\quad \int \tan x\,dx = -\log\cos x + C$$

$$(13)\quad \int \cot x\,dx = \log\sin x + C$$

[1] All logarithms in this table have the base ϵ.

(14) $\int \sec^2 x dx = \tan x + C$

(15) $\int \csc^2 x dx = -\cot x + C$

(16) $\int \tan x \sec x \, dx = \sec x + C$

(17) $\int \cot x \csc x \, dx = -\csc x + C$

(18) $\int \frac{dx}{a^2 + x^2} = \frac{1}{a} \tan^{-1}\left(\frac{x}{a}\right) + C = -\frac{1}{a} \cot^{-1}\left(\frac{x}{a}\right) + C'$

where $C' = C + \frac{\pi}{2}$

(19) $\int \frac{dx}{\sqrt{a^2 - x^2}} = \sin^{-1}\left(\frac{x}{a}\right) + C = -\cos^{-1}\left(\frac{x}{a}\right) + C'$

(20) $\int \frac{dx}{x\sqrt{x^2 - a^2}} = \frac{1}{a} \sec^{-1}\left(\frac{x}{a}\right) + C = -\frac{1}{a} \csc^{-1}\left(\frac{x}{a}\right) + C'$

(21) $\int \sinh x \, dx = \cosh x + C$

(22) $\int \cosh x \, dx = \sinh x + C$

(23) $\int \frac{dx}{\sqrt{x^2 + a^2}} = \sinh^{-1}\left(\frac{x}{a}\right) + C = \log_\epsilon (x + \sqrt{x^2 + a^2}) + C$

(24) $\int \frac{dx}{\sqrt{x^2 - a^2}} = \cosh^{-1}\left(\frac{x}{a}\right) + C = \log_\epsilon (x + \sqrt{x^2 - a^2}) + C$

(25) $\int \frac{dx}{a^2 - x^2} = \frac{1}{a} \tanh^{-1}\left(\frac{x}{a}\right) + C = \frac{1}{2a} \log_\epsilon \left(\frac{a + x}{a - x}\right) + C$

(26) $\int \frac{dx}{x^2 - a^2} = -\frac{1}{a} \coth^{-1}\left(\frac{x}{a}\right) + C = \frac{1}{2a} \log_\epsilon \left(\frac{x - a}{x + a}\right) + C$

(27) $\int \frac{dx}{x\sqrt{a^2 - x^2}} = \frac{-1}{a} \operatorname{sech}^{-1}\left(\frac{x}{a}\right) + C$

$$= \frac{-1}{a} \log_\epsilon \left(\frac{a + \sqrt{a^2 - x^2}}{x}\right) + C$$

(28) $\int \frac{dx}{x\sqrt{a^2 + x^2}} = -\frac{1}{a} \operatorname{csch}^{-1}\left(\frac{x}{a}\right) + C$

$$= \frac{1}{a} \log_\epsilon \left(\frac{a + \sqrt{a^2 + x^2}}{x}\right) + C$$

(29) $\int \sin^2 x \, dx = \frac{x}{2} - \frac{1}{2} \cos x \sin x + C = \frac{x}{2} - \frac{1}{4} \sin 2x + C$

(30) $$\int \cos^2 x\,dx = \frac{x}{2} + \frac{1}{2}\cos x \sin x + C = \frac{x}{2} + \frac{1}{4}\sin 2x + C$$

(31) $$\int \sin mx \sin nx\,dx = \frac{\sin[(m-n)x]}{2(m-n)} - \frac{\sin[(m+n)x]}{2(m+n)} + C \qquad (m^2 \neq n^2)$$

(32) $$\int \cos mx \cos nx\,dx = \frac{\sin[(m-n)x]}{2(m-n)} + \frac{\sin[(m+n)x]}{2(m+n)} + C \qquad (m^2 \neq n^2)$$

(33) $$\int \sin mx \cos nx\,dx = -\frac{\cos[(m-n)x]}{2(m-n)} - \frac{\cos[(m+n)x]}{2(m+n)} + C$$

(34) $$\int x \sin x\,dx = \sin x - x\cos x + C$$

(35) $$\int x \cos x\,dx = \cos x + x \sin x + C$$

(36) $$\int \epsilon^{ax} \sin bx\,dx = \frac{\epsilon^{ax}(a \sin bx - b \cos bx)}{a^2 + b^2} + C$$

(37) $$\int \epsilon^{ax} \cos bx\,dx = \frac{\epsilon^{ax}(a \cos bx + b \sin bx)}{a^2 + b^2} + C$$

(38) $$\int_0^\infty \epsilon^{-ax^2}\,dx = \frac{1}{2}\sqrt{\frac{\pi}{a}}$$

(39) $$\int_0^\infty \epsilon^{-ax^2}x^2\,dx = \frac{1}{4}\sqrt{\frac{\pi}{a^3}}$$

(40) $$\int_0^\infty \epsilon^{-ax^2}x^4\,dx = \frac{3}{8}\sqrt{\frac{\pi}{a^5}}$$

(41) $$\int_0^\infty \epsilon^{-ax^2}x\,dx = \frac{1}{2a}$$

(42) $$\int_0^\infty \epsilon^{-ax^2}x^3\,dx = \frac{1}{2a^2}$$

(43) $$\int_0^\infty \epsilon^{-ax^2}x^5\,dx = \frac{1}{a^3}$$

(44) $$\int_0^\infty \epsilon^{-ax^2}x^{2k}\,dx = \frac{1\cdot 3 \cdots (2k-1)}{2^{k+1}}\sqrt{\frac{\pi}{a^{2k+1}}}$$

(45) $$\int_0^\infty \epsilon^{-ax^2}x^{2k+1}\,dx = \frac{k!}{2a^{k+1}}$$

(46) $$\int \epsilon^{ax}\,dx = \frac{\epsilon^{ax}}{a} + C$$

(47) $$\int \epsilon^{ax}x\,dx = \frac{\epsilon^{ax}}{a^2}(ax - 1) + C$$

(48) $\int \epsilon^{ax} x^m \, dx = \frac{x^m \epsilon^{ax}}{a} - \frac{m}{a} \int \epsilon^{ax} x^{m-1} \, dx$

(49) $\int_0^x \frac{\sin x}{x} \, dx = \mathrm{Si}(x)$

(50) $\int_x^\infty \frac{\cos x}{x} \, dx = -\mathrm{Ci}(x)$

(51) $\int_0^\infty x^{n-1} \epsilon^{-x} \, dx = \Gamma(n) = (n-1)!$ (if n is an integer)

(52) $\int_0^x \epsilon^{-x^2} \, dx = \frac{\sqrt{\pi}}{2} \operatorname{erf}(x)$

(53) $\int_x^\infty \epsilon^{-x^2} \, dx = \frac{\sqrt{\pi}}{2} \operatorname{erfc}(x)$

(54) $\frac{1}{\pi} \int_0^\pi \cos (n\phi - x \sin \phi) \, d\phi = J_n(x)$ (where n is any positive integer, including zero)

(55) $\frac{1}{\pi} \int_0^\pi \sin (x \sin \phi) \sin n\phi \, d\phi = \begin{cases} J_n(x) & \text{(if } n \text{ is an odd positive integer)} \\ 0 & \text{(if } n \text{ is an even positive integer)} \end{cases}$

(56) $\frac{1}{\pi} \int_0^\pi \cos (x \sin \phi) \cos n\phi \, d\phi = \begin{cases} J_n(x) & \text{(if } n \text{ is an even positive integer)} \\ 0 & \text{(if } n \text{ is an odd positive integer)} \end{cases}$

(57) $\frac{1}{\pi} \int_0^\pi \cos (x \sin \phi) \, d\phi = J_0(x)$

(58) $\int_0^\infty \frac{\sin mx}{x} \, dx = \frac{\pi}{2}$ (if m is positive)

(59) $\int_0^\infty \frac{\cos bx}{1 + x^2} \, dx = \begin{cases} \frac{\pi}{2} \epsilon^{-b} & \text{(if } b \text{ is a positive integer)} \\ \frac{\pi}{2} \epsilon^{b} & \text{(if } b \text{ is a negative integer)} \end{cases}$

(60) $\int_0^\infty \frac{\tan x}{x} \, dx = \frac{\pi}{2}$

(61) $\frac{1}{2\pi} \int_0^{2\pi} \epsilon^{x \cos \phi} \, d\phi = I_0(x)$

APPENDIX C

TABLE OF TRIGONOMETRIC IDENTITIES

(1) $\sin A = \dfrac{1}{\csc A}$

(2) $\cos A = \dfrac{1}{\sec A}$

(3) $\tan A = \dfrac{1}{\cot A} = \dfrac{\sin A}{\cos A}$

(4) $\sin A = \cos\left(\dfrac{\pi}{2} - A\right) = \sin(\pi - A) = -\sin(-A)$
$= -\cos\left(A + \dfrac{\pi}{2}\right)$

(5) $\cos A = \sin\left(\dfrac{\pi}{2} - A\right) = -\cos(\pi - A) = \cos(-A)$
$= \sin\left(A + \dfrac{\pi}{2}\right)$

(6) $\tan A = \cot\left(\dfrac{\pi}{2} - A\right) = -\tan(\pi - A) = -\tan(-A)$
$= \tan(A + \pi)$

(7) $\cot A = \tan\left(\dfrac{\pi}{2} - A\right) = -\cot(\pi - A) = -\cot(-A)$
$= \cot(A + \pi)$

(8) $\sin^2 A + \cos^2 A = 1$

(9) $1 + \tan^2 A = \sec^2 A$

(10) $1 + \cot^2 A = \csc^2 A$

(11) $\sin(A + B) = \sin A \cos B + \cos A \sin B$

(12) $\sin(A - B) = \sin A \cos B - \cos A \sin B$

(13) $\cos(A + B) = \cos A \cos B - \sin A \sin B$

(14) $\cos(A - B) = \cos A \cos B + \sin A \sin B$

(15) $\tan(A + B) = \dfrac{\tan A + \tan B}{1 - \tan A \tan B}$

(16) $\tan(A - B) = \dfrac{\tan A - \tan B}{1 + \tan A \tan B}$

(17) $\sin 2A = 2 \sin A \cos A$

(18) $\cos 2A = \cos^2 A - \sin^2 A = 2\cos^2 A - 1 = 1 - 2\sin^2 A$

(19) $\tan 2A = \dfrac{2\tan A}{1 - \tan^2 A}$

(20) $\sin \dfrac{1}{2} A = \pm \sqrt{\dfrac{1 - \cos A}{2}}$

(21) $\cos \dfrac{1}{2} A = \pm \sqrt{\dfrac{1 + \cos A}{2}}$

(22) $\tan \dfrac{1}{2} A = \pm \sqrt{\dfrac{1 - \cos A}{1 + \cos A}} = \dfrac{1 - \cos A}{\sin A} = \dfrac{\sin A}{1 + \cos A}$

(23) $\sin A + \sin B = 2 \sin \frac{1}{2}(A + B) \cos \frac{1}{2}(A - B)$

(24) $\sin A - \sin B = 2 \sin \frac{1}{2}(A - B) \cos \frac{1}{2}(A + B)$

(25) $\cos A + \cos B = 2 \cos \frac{1}{2}(A + B) \cos \frac{1}{2}(A - B)$

(26) $\cos A - \cos B = -2 \sin \frac{1}{2}(A + B) \sin \frac{1}{2}(A - B)$

(27) $\tan A \pm \tan B = \dfrac{\sin (A \pm B)}{\cos A \cos B}$

(28) $\cot A \pm \cot B = \dfrac{\pm \sin (A + B)}{\sin A \sin B}$

(29) $\sin^2 A - \sin^2 B = \sin (A + B) \sin (A - B)$

(30) $\cos^2 A - \cos^2 B = -\sin (A + B) \sin (A - B)$

(31) $\cos^2 A - \sin^2 B = \cos (A + B) \cos (A - B)$

(32) $\sin^2 A = \dfrac{1 - \cos 2A}{2}$

(33) $\cos^2 A = \dfrac{1 + \cos 2A}{2}$

(34) $\sin^3 A = \frac{3}{4} \sin A - \frac{1}{4} \sin 3A$

(35) $\cos^3 A = \frac{1}{4} \cos 3A + \frac{3}{4} \cos A$

(36) $\cos^2 A \cos B = \frac{1}{2} \cos B + \frac{1}{4}[\cos (2A + B) + \cos (2A - B)]$

(37) $\cos^2 A \sin B = \frac{1}{2} \sin B + \frac{1}{4}[\sin (2A + B) - \sin (2A - B)]$

(38) $\cos A \sin^2 B = \frac{1}{2} \cos A + \frac{1}{4}[\cos (2B + A) + \cos (2B - A)]$

(39) $\sin^2 A \sin B = \frac{1}{2} \sin B + \frac{1}{4}[\sin (2A - B) - \sin (2A + B)]$

(40) $\cos A \cos B = \frac{1}{2}[\cos (A + B) + \cos (A - B)]$

(41) $\cos A \sin B = \frac{1}{2}[\sin (A + B) - \sin (A - B)]$
$= \frac{1}{2}[\sin(A + B) + \sin (B - A)]$

(42) $\sin A \sin B = \frac{1}{2}[\cos (A - B) - \cos (A + B)]$

(43) $\sin 3A = 3 \sin A - 4 \sin^3 A$

(44) $\cos 3A = 4 \cos^3 A - 3 \cos A$

(45) $\sin 4A = 8 \cos^3 A \sin A - 4 \cos A \sin A$

(46) $\cos 4A = 8 \cos^4 A - 8 \cos^2 A + 1$

(47) $\sin^{-1} A = \dfrac{\pi}{2} - \cos^{-1} A$

(48) $\tan^{-1} A = \dfrac{\pi}{2} - \cot^{-1} A$

(49) $\sin^{-1} A = \pm 2\pi n + \sin^{-1} A$ (where n is integral)

(50) $\cos^{-1} A - \pm 2\pi n + \cos^{-1} A$ (where n is integral)

(51) $\tan^{-1} A = \pm \pi n + \tan^{-1} A$ (where n is integral)

(52) $\cot^{-1} A = \pm \pi n + \cot^{-1} A$ (where n is integral)

(53) $\sin^{-1} A + \sin^{-1} B = \sin^{-1} (A \sqrt{1 - B^2} + B \sqrt{1 - A^2})$

(54) $\sin^{-1} A - \sin^{-1} B = \sin^{-1} (A \sqrt{1 - B^2} - B \sqrt{1 - A^2})$

(55) $\cos^{-1} A + \cos^{-1} B = \cos^{-1} [AB - \sqrt{(1 - A^2)(1 - B^2)}]$

(56) $\cos^{-1} A - \cos^{-1} B = \cos^{-1} [AB + \sqrt{(1 - A^2)(1 - B^2)}]$

(57) $\tan^{-1} A + \tan^{-1} B = \tan^{-1} \left(\dfrac{A + B}{1 - AB}\right)$

(58) $\tan^{-1} A - \tan^{-1} B = \tan^{-1} \left(\dfrac{A - B}{1 + AB}\right)$

APPENDIX D

SAMPLE TABLE OF FOURIER PAIRS

$$G(g) = \int_{-\infty}^{+\infty} F(f)\epsilon^{j2\pi fg}\, df$$

$$F(f) = \int_{-\infty}^{+\infty} G(g)\epsilon^{-j2\pi fg}\, dg$$

$$\omega = 2\pi f$$

No.	$F(f)$	$G(g)$	Remarks
1	$F_1 \pm F_2 \pm \cdots + F_n$	$G_1 \pm G_2 \pm \cdots \pm G_n$	Superposition theorem of Sec. 4.6
2	$kF(f)$	$kG(g)$	
3	$\frac{\epsilon^{-j(\omega-\omega_0)T_1}}{2j(\omega-\omega_0)} - \frac{\epsilon^{-j(\omega-\omega_0)T_2}}{2j(\omega-\omega_0)} + \frac{\epsilon^{-j(\omega+\omega_0)T_1}}{2j(\omega+\omega_0)} - \frac{\epsilon^{-j(\omega+\omega_0)T_2}}{2j(\omega+\omega_0)}$	$\cos \omega_0 g$ $(T_1 < g < T_2)$	Example in Sec. 3.2
4	$\frac{K}{\omega}[\sin \omega T + j(\cos \omega T - 1)]$	K $(0 < g < T)$	Example in Sec. 3.4
5	$\frac{k(\epsilon^{j\omega T_2} - \epsilon^{-j\omega T_1})}{-j\omega}$ $(-\omega_s < \omega < \omega_s)$	$\frac{k}{\pi}\{\mathrm{Si}[\omega_s(g - T_1)]$ $-\mathrm{Si}[\omega_s(g - T_2)]\}$	Example in Sec. 4.5 assuming zero phase shift
6	$\epsilon^{-\frac{\pi^2 f^2}{k^2}}$	$\frac{k}{\sqrt{\pi}}\epsilon^{-k^2g^2}$	
7	$\epsilon^{-\pi f^2}$	$\epsilon^{-\pi g^2}$	Special case of pair 6 when $k = \sqrt{\pi}$
8	1 $(-f_0 < f < +f_0)$	$\frac{1}{\pi g}\sin 2\pi f_0 g$	Example in Sec. 4.18

APPENDIX E

BESSEL FUNCTIONS

Bessel functions have considerable importance in many branches of radio engineering and are studied in some detail in the author's "Transformation Calculus." For the reader who is unacquainted with them and for reference purposes, certain of their fundamental properties and formulas are listed below.

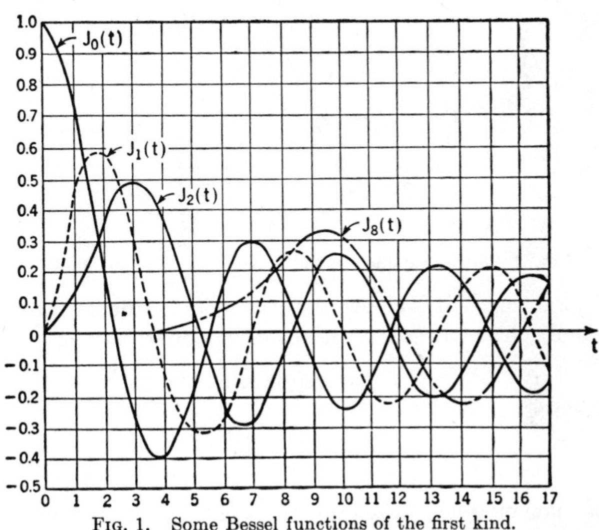

FIG. 1. Some Bessel functions of the first kind.

A Bessel function is very much like a damped sine or damped cosine wave. However, while all sine and cosine waves are similar in shape, each different type of Bessel function has a different shape. The different Bessel functions are distinguished by different subscripts, called *orders*. Thus, $J_0(x)$, $J_1(x)$, and $J_2(x)$ are called Bessel functions of the first kind of zero order, of the first order, and of the second order, respectively. The capital J indicates that the Bessel function is of the first kind. The variable x in the above cases is usually called the argument of the Bessel function in question. For example, $J_1(x)$ is called a Bessel function of the first kind, of the first order, and of argument x. Curves of some Bessel functions of the first kind are shown in Fig. 1.

Closely related to the Bessel functions are a group of functions $I_0(x)$, $I_1(x)$, $I_2(x)$, etc., which are known as modified Bessel functions.

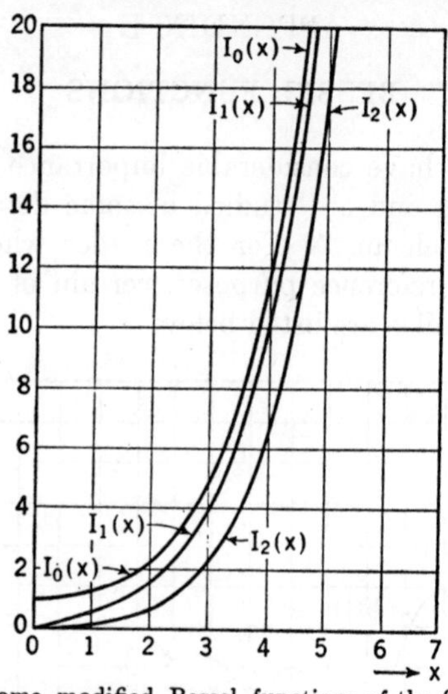

FIG. 2. Some modified Bessel functions of the first kind.

In the general theory it is shown that the modified Bessel functions are complex multiples of Bessel functions of imaginary argument. Thus,

$$I_0(x) = J_0[(\sqrt{-1})x] \tag{1}$$

and in general

$$I_n(x) = \frac{J_n[(\sqrt{-1})x]}{(\sqrt{-1})^n} \tag{2}$$

Curves of some modified Bessel functions of the first kind are shown in Fig. 2.

There are certain relations between trigonometric functions and Bessel functions that can be derived and that are very important in modulation theory. We record them here for reference.

$$\cos (x \sin \phi) = J_0(x) + 2[J_2(x) \cos 2\phi + J_4(x) \cos 4\phi + \cdots] \tag{3}$$

$$\sin (x \sin \phi) = 2[J_1(x) \sin \phi + J_3(x) \sin 3\phi + J_5(x) \sin 5\phi + \cdots] \tag{4}$$

$$\cos (x \cos \phi) = J_0(x) - 2[J_2(x) \cos 2\phi - J_4(x) \cos 4\phi + J_6(x) \cos 6\phi - J_8(x) \cos 8\phi + \cdots] \tag{5}$$

$$\sin(x \cos \phi) = 2[J_1(x) \cos \phi - J_3(x) \cos 3\phi + J_5(x) \cos 5\phi - J_7(x) \cos 7\phi + \cdots] \quad (6)$$

Because of the importance of the series (3) to (6) in modulation theory, Fig. 3, showing some Bessel functions of constant argument and variable order, is of considerable interest.

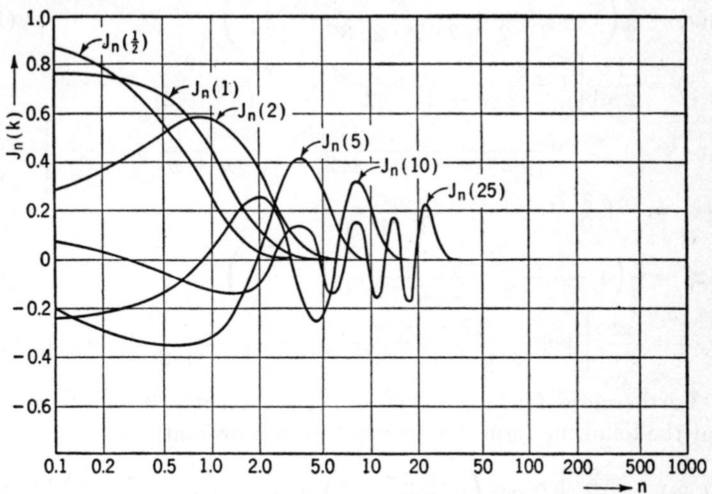

FIG. 3. Curves of Bessel functions of constant argument and variable order.

The above relations show that the Bessel functions of integral order are particularly important in modulation theory. For Bessel functions of integral order, we also have the following relations:

$$J_n(-x) = (-1)^n J_n(x) \quad (7)$$

$$J_{-n}(x) = (-1)^n J_n(x) \quad (8)$$

$$J_0(x) = \frac{1}{\pi} \int_0^\pi \cos(x \sin \phi)\, d\phi \quad (9)$$

and, if n is positive,

$$J_n(x) = \frac{1}{\pi} \int_0^\pi \cos(n\phi - x \sin \phi)\, d\phi \quad (10)$$

Another relation that we have found useful in the study of paired echoes in Chap. IV is

$$\epsilon^{jx \sin \phi} = \sum_{k=-\infty}^{+\infty} J_k(x) \epsilon^{jk\phi}$$

$$= J_0(x) + [J_1(x)\epsilon^{j\phi} + J_{-1}(x)\epsilon^{-j\phi}] + [J_2(x)\epsilon^{j2\phi} + J_{-2}(x)\epsilon^{-j2\phi}] + \cdots \quad (11)$$

Just as the trigonometric functions can be expanded in power series, so also can the Bessel functions be expanded in power series. Thus, we have

$$J_0(x) = 1 - \frac{x^2}{2^2} + \frac{x^4}{2^2 \cdot 4^2} - \frac{x^6}{2^2 \cdot 4^2 \cdot 6^2} + \cdots \tag{12}$$

$$J_1(x) = \frac{x}{2}\left(1 - \frac{x^2}{2^2 \cdot 2} + \frac{x^4}{2 \cdot 2^4 \cdot 2 \cdot 3} - \cdots\right) \tag{13}$$

$$J_n(x) = \frac{x^n}{2^n n!}\left[1 - \frac{x^2}{2^2(n+1)} + \frac{x^4}{2 \cdot 2^4(n+1)(n+2)} + \cdots + \frac{(-1)^p x^{2p}}{p! 2^{2p}(n+1)(n+2) \cdots (n+p)} + \cdots\right] \tag{14}$$

$$I_0(x) = 1 + \frac{x^2}{2^2} + \frac{x^4}{2^2 \cdot 4^2} + \frac{x^6}{2^2 \cdot 4^2 \cdot 6^2} + \cdots \tag{15}$$

$$I_1(x) = \frac{x}{2}\left(1 + \frac{x^2}{2^2 \cdot 2} + \frac{x^4}{2 \cdot 2^4 \cdot 2 \cdot 3} + \cdots\right) \tag{16}$$

$$I_n(x) = \frac{x^n}{2^n n!}\left[1 + \frac{x^2}{2^2(n+1)} + \frac{x^4}{(2 \cdot 2^4(n+1)(n+2)} + \cdots\right] \tag{17}$$

Furthermore, for large values of the argument x, it may be shown that the following formulas are excellent approximations:

$$J_n(x) = \frac{2}{\sqrt{\pi x}}\left[U \cos\left(x - \frac{n\pi}{2} - \frac{\pi}{4}\right) + V \sin\left(x - \frac{n\pi}{2} - \frac{\pi}{4}\right)\right] \tag{18}$$

where

$$U = 1 - \frac{(1^2 - 4n^2)(3^2 - 4n^2)}{2!(8x)^2} + \frac{(1^2 - 4n^2) \cdots (7^2 - 4n^2)}{4!(8x)^4} - \cdots \tag{19}$$

and

$$V = \frac{1 - 4n^2}{8x} - \frac{(1 - 4n^2)(3^2 - 4n^2)(5^2 - 4n^2)}{3!(8x)^3} + \cdots \tag{20}$$

$$I_n(x) = \frac{\epsilon^x}{\sqrt{2\pi x}}\left[1 + \frac{1^2 - 4n^2}{8x} + \frac{(1^2 - 4n^2)(3^2 - 4n^2)}{2!(8x)^2} + \cdots\right] \tag{21}$$

For very large values of x, Eqs. (18) and (21) reduce further to the very simple forms

$$J_n(x) = \sqrt{\frac{2}{\pi x}} \cos\left(x - \frac{n\pi}{2} - \frac{\pi}{4}\right) \tag{22}$$

and

$$I_n(x) = \frac{\epsilon^x}{\sqrt{2\pi x}} \tag{23}$$

APPENDIX F

TABLE OF BESSEL FUNCTIONS OF THE FIRST KIND OF CONSTANT INTEGRAL ARGUMENT AND VARIABLE INTEGRAL ORDER[1]

p	$J_p(1)$	$J_p(2)$	$J_p(3)$	$J_p(4)$	$J_p(5)$
0	+0.76520	+0.22389	−0.26005	−0.39714	−0.17760
1	+0.44005	+0.57672	+0.33906	−0.06604	−0.32758
2	+0.11490	+0.35283	+0.48609	+0.36413	+0.04657
3	+0.01956	+0.12894	+0.30906	+0.43017	+0.36483
4	$+0.0^{2}2477$	+0.03400	+0.13203	+0.28113	+0.39123
5	$+0.0^{3}2498$	$+0.0^{2}7040$	+0.04303	+0.13208	+0.26114
6	$+0.0^{4}2094$	$+0.0^{2}1202$	+0.01139	+0.04909	+0.13105
7	$+0.0^{5}1502$	$+0.0^{3}1749$	$+0.0^{2}2547$	+0.01518	+0.05338
8	$+0.0^{7}9422$	$+0.0^{4}2218$	$+0.0^{3}4934$	$+0.0^{2}4029$	+0.01841
9	$+0.0^{8}5249$	$+0.0^{5}2492$	$+0.0^{4}8440$	$+0.0^{3}3986$	$+0.0^{2}5520$
10	$+0.0^{9}2631$	$+0.0^{6}2515$	$+0.0^{4}1293$	$+0.0^{3}1950$	$+0.0^{2}1468$
11	$+0.0^{10}1198$	$+0.0^{7}2304$	$+0.0^{5}1794$	$+0.0^{4}3660$	$+0.0^{3}3509$
12	$+0.0^{12}5000$	$+0.0^{8}1933$	$+0.0^{6}2276$	$+0.0^{5}6264$	$+0.0^{4}7628$
13	$+0.0^{13}1926$	$+0.0^{9}1495$	$+0.0^{7}2659$	$+0.0^{6}9859$	$+0.0^{4}1521$
14	$+0.0^{15}689$	$+0.0^{10}1073$	$+0.0^{8}2880$	$+0.0^{6}1436$	$+0.0^{5}2801$

[1] Appendix F is of particular use in determining the sideband magnitudes in frequency and phase modulation. The values of $J_p(30)$, $J_p(31)$, $J_p(32)$, and $J_p(33)$ did not appear in the earlier tables of Jahnke-Emde and of Gray, Matthews, and MacRoberts. These values were obtained through the courtesy of Mr. John A. Harr from the proof sheets of the magnificent new tables of Bessel functions being published by the Computation Laboratory of Harvard University.

p	$J_p(6)$	$J_p(7)$	$J_p(8)$	$J_p(9)$	$J_p(10)$
0	$+0.1506$	$+0.3001$	$+0.1717$	-0.09033	-0.2459
1	-0.2767	$-0.0^{2}4683$	$+0.2346$	$+0.2453$	$+0.04347$
2	-0.2429	-0.3014	-0.1130	$+0.1448$	$+0.2546$
3	$+0.1148$	-0.1676	-0.2911	-0.1809	$+0.05838$
4	$+0.3576$	$+0.1578$	-0.1054	-0.2655	-0.2196
5	$+0.3621$	$+0.3479$	$+0.1858$	-0.05504	-0.2341
6	$+0.2458$	$+0.3392$	$+0.3376$	$+0.2043$	-0.01446
7	$+0.1296$	$+0.2336$	$+0.3206$	$+0.3275$	$+0.2167$
8	$+0.05653$	$+0.1280$	$+0.2235$	$+0.3051$	$+0.3179$
9	$+0.02117$	$+0.05892$	$+0.1263$	$+0.2149$	$+0.2919$
10	$+0.0^{2}6964$	$+0.02354$	$+0.06077$	$+0.1247$	$+0.2075$
11	$+0.0^{2}2048$	$+0.0^{2}8335$	$+0.02560$	$+0.06222$	$+0.1231$
12	$+0.0^{3}5452$	$+0.0^{2}2656$	$+0.0^{2}9624$	$+0.02739$	$+0.06337$
13	$+0.0^{3}1327$	$+0.0^{3}7702$	$+0.0^{2}3275$	$+0.01083$	$+0.02897$
14	$+0.0^{4}2976$	$+0.0^{3}2052$	$+0.0^{2}1019$	$+0.0^{2}3895$	$+0.01196$
15	$+0.0^{5}6192$	$+0.0^{4}5059$	$+0.0^{3}2926$	$+0.0^{2}1286$	$+0.0^{2}4508$
16	$+0.0^{5}1202$	$+0.0^{4}1161$	$+0.0^{4}7801$	$+0.0^{3}3933$	$+0.0^{2}1567$
17	$+0.0^{6}2187$	$+0.0^{5}2494$	$+0.0^{4}1942$	$+0.0^{3}1120$	$+0.0^{3}5056$
18	$+0.0^{7}3746$	$+0.0^{6}5037$	$+0.0^{5}4538$	$+0.0^{4}2988$	$+0.0^{3}1524$
19	$+0.0^{8}6062$	$+0.0^{7}9598$	$+0.0^{6}9992$	$+0.0^{5}7497$	$+0.0^{4}4315$

p	$J_p(11)$	$J_p(12)$	$J_p(13)$	$J_p(14)$	$J_p(15)$
0	-0.1712	$+0.04769$	$+0.2069$	$+0.1711$	-0.01422
1	-0.1768	-0.2234	-0.07032	$+0.1334$	$+0.2051$
2	$+0.1390$	-0.08493	-0.2177	-0.1520	$+0.04157$
3	$+0.2273$	$+0.1951$	$+0.0^{2}3320$	-0.1768	-0.1940
4	-0.01504	$+0.1825$	$+0.2193$	$+0.07624$	-0.1192
5	-0.2383	-0.07347	$+0.1316$	$+0.2204$	$+0.1305$
6	-0.2016	-0.2437	-0.1180	$+0.08117$	$+0.2061$
7	$+0.01838$	-0.1703	-0.2406	-0.1508	$+0.03446$
8	$+0.2250$	$+0.04510$	-0.1410	-0.2320	-0.1740
9	$+0.3089$	$+0.2304$	$+0.06698$	-0.1143	-0.2200
10	$+0.2804$	$+0.3005$	$+0.2338$	$+0.08501$	-0.09007
11	$+0.2010$	$+0.2704$	$+0.2927$	$+0.2357$	$+0.09995$
12	$+0.1216$	$+0.1953$	$+0.2615$	$+0.2855$	$+0.2367$
13	$+0.06429$	$+0.1201$	$+0.1901$	$+0.2536$	$+0.2787$
14	$+0.03037$	$+0.06504$	$+0.1188$	$+0.1855$	$+0.2464$
15	$+0.01301$	$+0.03161$	$+0.06564$	$+0.1174$	$+0.1813$
16	$+0.0^{2}5110$	$+0.01399$	$+0.03272$	$+0.06613$	$+0.1162$
17	$+0.0^{2}1856$	$+0.0^{2}5698$	$+0.01491$	$+0.03372$	$+0.06653$
18	$+0.0^{3}6280$	$+0.0^{2}2152$	$+0.0^{2}6269$	$+0.01577$	$+0.03463$
19	$+0.0^{3}1990$	$+0.0^{3}7590$	$+0.0^{2}2452$	$+0.0^{2}6824$	$+0.01657$
20	$+0.0^{4}5931$	$+0.0^{3}2512$	$+0.0^{3}8971$	$+0.0^{2}2753$	$+0.0^{2}7360$
21	$+0.0^{4}1670$	$+0.0^{4}7839$	$+0.0^{3}3087$	$+0.0^{2}1041$	$+0.0^{2}3054$
22	$+0.0^{5}4458$	$+0.0^{4}2315$	$+0.0^{3}1004$	$+0.0^{3}3711$	$+0.0^{2}1190$
23	$+0.0^{5}1132$	$+0.0^{5}6491$	$+0.0^{4}3092$	$+0.0^{3}1251$	$+0.0^{3}4379$
24	$+0.0^{6}2738$	$+0.0^{5}1733$	$+0.0^{5}9060$	$+0.0^{4}4006$	$+0.0^{3}1527$

p	$J_p(16)$	$J_p(17)$	$J_p(18)$	$J_p(19)$	$J_p(20)$
0	−0.1749	−0.1699	−0.01336	+0.1466	+0.1670
1	+0.09040	−0.09767	−0.1880	−0.1057	+0.06683
2	+0.1862	+0.1584	$-0.0^{2}7533$	−0.1578	−0.1603
3	−0.04385	+0.1349	+0.1863	+0.07249	−0.09890
4	−0.2026	−0.1107	+0.06964	+0.1806	+0.1307
5	−0.05747	−0.1870	−0.1554	$+0.0^{2}3572$	+0.1512
6	+0.1667	$+0.0^{3}7153$	−0.1560	−0.1788	−0.05509
7	+0.1825	+0.1875	+0.05140	−0.1165	−0.1842
8	$-0.0^{2}7021$	+0.1537	+0.1959	+0.09294	−0.07387
9	−0.1895	−0.04286	+0.1228	+0.1947	+0.1251
10	−0.2062	−0.1991	−0.07317	+0.09155	+0.1865
11	−0.06822	−0.1914	−0.2041	−0.09837	+0.06136
12	+0.1124	−0.04857	−0.1762	−0.2055	−0.1190
13	+0.2368	+0.1228	−0.03092	−0.1612	−0.2041
14	+0.2724	+0.2364	+0.1316	−0.01507	−0.1464
15	+0.2399	+0.2666	+0.2356	+0.1389	$-0.0^{3}8121$
16	+0.1775	+0.2340	+0.2611	+0.2345	+0.1452
17	+0.1150	+0.1739	+0.2286	+0.2559	+0.2331
18	+0.06685	+0.1138	+0.1706	+0.2235	+0.2511
19	+0.03544	+0.06710	+0.1127	+0.1676	+0.2189
20	+0.01733	+0.03619	+0.06731	+0.1116	+0.1647
21	$+0.0^{2}7879$	+0.01804	+0.03686	+0.06746	+0.1106
22	$+0.0^{2}3354$	$+0.0^{2}8380$	+0.01871	+0.03748	+0.06758
23	$+0.0^{2}1343$	$+0.0^{2}3651$	$+0.0^{2}8864$	+0.01934	+0.03805
24	$+0.0^{3}5087$	$+0.0^{2}1500$	$+0.0^{2}3946$	$+0.0^{2}9331$	+0.01993
25	$+0.0^{3}1828$	$+0.0^{3}5831$	$+0.0^{2}1658$	$+0.0^{2}4237$	$+0.0^{2}9781$
26	$+0.0^{4}6253$	$+0.0^{3}2154$	$+0.0^{3}6607$	$+0.0^{2}1819$	$+0.0^{2}4524$
27	$+0.0^{4}2042$	$+0.0^{4}7586$	$+0.0^{3}2504$	$+0.0^{3}7412$	$+0.0^{2}1981$
28	$+0.0^{5}6380$	$+0.0^{4}2553$	$+0.0^{4}9057$	$+0.0^{3}2877$	$+0.0^{3}8242$
29	$+0.0^{5}1912$	$+0.0^{5}8228$	$+0.0^{4}3133$	$+0.0^{3}1066$	$+0.0^{3}3270$

p	$J_p(21)$	$J_p(22)$	$J_p(23)$	$J_p(24)$
0	$+0.03658$	-0.1207	-0.1624	-0.05623
1	$+0.1711$	$+0.1172$	-0.03952	-0.1540
2	-0.02028	$+0.1313$	$+0.1590$	$+0.04339$
3	-0.1750	-0.09330	$+0.06717$	$+0.1613$
4	-0.02971	-0.1568	-0.1415	$-0.0^{2}3076$
5	$+0.1637$	$+0.03630$	-0.1164	-0.1623
6	$+0.1076$	$+0.1733$	$+0.09086$	-0.06455
7	-0.1022	$+0.05820$	$+0.1638$	$+0.1300$
8	-0.1757	-0.1362	$+0.0^{2}8829$	$+0.1404$
9	-0.3175	-0.1573	-0.1576	-0.03643
10	$+0.1485$	$+0.0^{2}7547$	-0.1322	-0.1677
11	$+0.1732$	$+0.1641$	$+0.04268$	-0.1033
12	$+0.03293$	$+0.1566$	$+0.1730$	$+0.07299$
13	-0.1356	$+0.0^{2}6688$	$+0.1379$	$+0.1763$
14	-0.2008	-0.1487	-0.01718	$+0.1180$
15	-0.1321	-0.1959	-0.1588	-0.03863
16	$+0.01202$	-0.1185	-0.1899	-0.1663
17	$+0.1505$	$+0.02358$	-0.1055	-0.1831
18	$+0.2316$	$+0.1549$	$+0.03402$	-0.09311
19	$+0.2465$	$+0.2299$	$+0.1587$	$+0.04345$
20	$+0.2145$	$+0.2422$	$+0.2282$	$+0.1619$
21	$+0.1621$	$+0.2105$	$+0.2381$	$+0.2264$
22	$+0.1097$	$+0.1596$	$+0.2067$	$+0.2343$
23	$+0.06767$	$+0.1087$	$+0.1573$	$+0.2031$
24	$+0.03857$	$+0.06773$	$+0.1078$	$+0.1550$
25	$+0.02049$	$+0.03905$	$+0.06777$	$+0.1070$
26	$+0.01022$	$+0.02102$	$+0.03949$	$+0.06778$
27	$+0.0^{2}4806$	$+0.01064$	$+0.02152$	$+0.03990$
28	$+0.0^{2}2143$	$+0.0^{2}5084$	$+0.01104$	$+0.02200$
29	$+0.0^{3}9094$	$+0.0^{2}2307$	$+0.0^{2}5357$	$+0.01143$
30	$+0.0^{3}3682$	$+0.0^{3}9965$	$+0.0^{2}2470$	$+0.0^{2}5626$
31	$+0.0^{3}1427$	$+0.0^{3}4113$	$+0.0^{2}1085$	$+0.0^{2}2633$
32	$+0.0^{4}5304$	$+0.0^{3}1626$	$+0.0^{3}4561$	$+0.0^{2}1176$
33	$+0.0^{4}1895$	$+0.0^{4}6171$	$+0.0^{3}1837$	$+0.0^{3}5024$
34	$+0.0^{5}6521$	$+0.0^{4}2253$	$+0.0^{4}7110$	$+0.0^{3}2060$

p	$J_p(25)$	$J_p(26)$	$J_p(27)$	$J_p(28)$	$J_p(29)$
0	+0.0963	+0.1560	+0.0727	−0.0732	−0.1478
1	−0.1254	+0.0150	+0.1366	+0.1306	+0.0069
2	−0.1063	−0.1548	−0.0626	+0.0825	+0.1483
3	+0.1083	−0.0389	−0.1459	−0.1188	+0.0135
4	+0.1323	+0.1459	+0.0302	−0.1079	−0.1455
5	−0.0660	+0.0838	+0.1548	+0.0879	−0.0537
6	−0.1587	−0.1137	+0.0271	+0.1393	+0.1270
7	−0.0102	−0.1362	−0.1428	−0.0282	+0.1062
8	+0.1530	+0.0403	−0.1012	−0.1534	−0.0757
9	+0.1081	+0.1610	+0.0828	−0.0595	−0.1480
10	−0.0752	+0.0712	+0.1564	+0.1152	−0.0161
11	−0.1682	−0.1063	+0.0330	+0.1418	+0.1369
12	−0.0729	−0.1611	−0.1295	−0.0038	+0.1200
13	+0.0983	−0.0424	−0.1481	−0.1450	−0.0376
14	+0.1751	+0.1187	−0.0131	−0.1309	−0.1537
15	+0.0978	+0.1702	+0.1345	+0.0142	−0.1108
16	−0.0577	+0.0777	+0.1625	+0.1461	+0.0391
17	−0.1717	−0.0745	+0.0582	+0.1527	+0.1539
18	−0.1758	−0.1752	−0.0893	+0.0394	+0.1414
19	−0.0814	−0.1681	−0.1772	−0.1021	+0.0216
20	+0.0520	−0.0704	−0.1601	−0.1779	−0.1131
21	+0.1646	+0.0597	−0.0600	−0.1521	−0.1776
22	+0.2246	+0.1669	+0.0668	−0.0502	−0.1441
23	+0.2306	+0.2227	+0.1688	+0.0732	−0.0410
24	+0.1998	+0.2271	+0.2209	+0.1704	+0.0790
25	+0.1529	+0.1966	+0.2238	+0.2190	+0.1718
26	+0.1061	+0.1510	+0.1936	+0.2207	+0.2172
27	+0.06778	+0.1053	+0.1491	+0.1908	+0.2176
28	+0.04028	+0.06776	+0.1045	+0.1473	+0.1881
29	+0.02245	+0.04063	+0.06773	+0.1038	+0.1456
30	+0.01181	+0.02288	+0.04096	+0.06769	+0.1030
31	$+0.0^{2}5889$	+0.01217	+0.02329	+0.04126	+0.06763
32	$+0.0^{2}2795$	$+0.0^{2}6147$	+0.01253	+0.02368	+0.04155
33	$+0.0^{2}1267$	$+0.0^{2}2957$	$+0.0^{2}6400$	+0.01287	+0.02405
34	$+0.0^{3}550$	$+0.0^{2}1360$	$+0.0^{2}3118$	$+0.0^{2}6648$	+0.01320

p	$J_p(30)$	$J_p(31)$	$J_p(32)$	$J_p(33)$
0	−0.08637	+0.05121	+0.13808	+0.09727
1	−0.11875	−0.13302	−0.02659	+0.10062
2	+0.07845	−0.05979	−0.13974	−0.09117
3	+0.12921	+0.12531	+0.00912	−0.11167
4	−0.05261	+0.08404	+0.14145	+0.07087
5	−0.14324	−0.10362	+0.02624	+0.12885
6	+0.00486	−0.11747	−0.13325	−0.03182
7	+0.14519	+0.05815	−0.07621	−0.14042
8	+0.06289	+0.14373	+0.09991	−0.02775
9	−0.11164	+0.01603	+0.12616	+0.12697
10	−0.12988	−0.13442	−0.02894	+0.09701
11	+0.02506	−0.10276	−0.14425	−0.06818
12	+0.14825	+0.06150	−0.07023	−0.14246
13	+0.09354	+0.15037	+0.09158	−0.03543
14	−0.06718	+0.06462	+0.14464	+0.11454
15	−0.15625	−0.09200	+0.03498	+0.13262
16	−0.08907	−0.15365	−0.11184	+0.00602
17	+0.06124	−0.06661	−0.14683	−0.12678
18	+0.15848	+0.08060	−0.04416	−0.13664
19	+0.12893	+0.16021	+0.09715	−0.02228
20	+0.00483	+0.11578	+0.15952	+0.11098
21	−0.12248	−0.01081	+0.10225	+0.15681
22	−0.17631	−0.13043	−0.02531	+0.08859
23	−0.13610	−0.17431	−0.13706	−0.03869
24	−0.03238	−0.12823	−0.17171	−0.14252
25	+0.08429	−0.02424	−0.12051	−0.16861
26	+0.17287	+0.08914	−0.01658	−0.11295
27	+0.21535	+0.17376	+0.09356	−0.00937
28	+0.21476	+0.21354	+0.17447	+0.09761
29	+0.18553	+0.21199	+0.21176	+0.17502
30	+0.14394	+0.18309	+0.20934	+0.21000
31	+0.10234	+0.14237	+0.18076	+0.20680
32	+0.06757	+0.10166	+0.14087	+0.17853
33	+0.04181	+0.06750	+0.10099	+0.13944
34	+0.02441	+0.04205	+0.06742	+0.10035
35	+0.01352	+0.02475	+0.04228	+0.06734
36	+0.00713	+0.01382	+0.02507	+0.04250

INDEX

SOME DOVER SCIENCE BOOKS

CHANCE, LUCK AND STATISTICS: THE SCIENCE OF CHANCE,
Horace C. Levinson
Theory of probability and science of statistics in simple, non-technical language. Part I deals with theory of probability, covering odd superstitions in regard to "luck," the meaning of betting odds, the law of mathematical expectation, gambling, and applications in poker, roulette, lotteries, dice, bridge, and other games of chance. Part II discusses the misuse of statistics, the concept of statistical probabilities, normal and skew frequency distributions, and statistics applied to various fields—birth rates, stock speculation, insurance rates, advertising, etc. "Presented in an easy humorous style which I consider the best kind of expository writing," Prof. A. C. Cohen, Industry Quality Control. Enlarged revised edition. Formerly titled *The Science of Chance.* Preface and two new appendices by the author. xiv + 365pp. 5⅜ x 8. 21007-3 Paperbound $2.00

BASIC ELECTRONICS,
prepared by the U.S. Navy Training Publications Center
A thorough and comprehensive manual on the fundamentals of electronics. Written clearly, it is equally useful for self-study or course work for those with a knowledge of the principles of basic electricity. Partial contents: Operating Principles of the Electron Tube; Introduction to Transistors; Power Supplies for Electronic Equipment; Tuned Circuits; Electron-Tube Amplifiers; Audio Power Amplifiers; Oscillators; Transmitters; Transmission Lines; Antennas and Propagation; Introduction to Computers; and related topics. Appendix. Index. Hundreds of illustrations and diagrams. vi + 471pp. 6½ x 9¼.
61076-4 Paperbound $2.95

BASIC THEORY AND APPLICATION OF TRANSISTORS,
prepared by the U.S. Department of the Army
An introductory manual prepared for an army training program. One of the finest available surveys of theory and application of transistor design and operation. Minimal knowledge of physics and theory of electron tubes required. Suitable for textbook use, course supplement, or home study. Chapters: Introduction; fundamental theory of transistors; transistor amplifier fundamentals; parameters, equivalent circuits, and characteristic curves; bias stabilization; transistor analysis and comparison using characteristic curves and charts; audio amplifiers; tuned amplifiers; wide-band amplifiers; oscillators; pulse and switching circuits; modulation, mixing, and demodulation; and additional semiconductor devices. Unabridged, corrected edition. 240 schematic drawings, photographs, wiring diagrams, etc. 2 Appendices. Glossary. Index. 263pp. 6½ x 9¼. 60380-6 Paperbound $1.75

GUIDE TO THE LITERATURE OF MATHEMATICS AND PHYSICS,
N. G. Parke III
Over 5000 entries included under approximately 120 major subject headings of selected most important books, monographs, periodicals, articles in English, plus important works in German, French, Italian, Spanish, Russian (many recently available works). Covers every branch of physics, math, related engineering. Includes author, title, edition, publisher, place, date, number of volumes, number of pages. A 40-page introduction on the basic problems of research and study provides useful information on the organization and use of libraries, the psychology of learning, etc. This reference work will save you hours of time. 2nd revised edition. Indices of authors, subjects, 464pp. 5⅜ x 8.
60447-0 Paperbound $2.75

THE RISE OF THE NEW PHYSICS (formerly THE DECLINE OF MECHANISM), *A. d'Abro*

This authoritative and comprehensive 2-volume exposition is unique in scientific publishing. Written for intelligent readers not familiar with higher mathematics, it is the only thorough explanation in non-technical language of modern mathematical-physical theory. Combining both history and exposition, it ranges from classical Newtonian concepts up through the electronic theories of Dirac and Heisenberg, the statistical mechanics of Fermi, and Einstein's relativity theories. "A must for anyone doing serious study in the physical sciences," *J. of Franklin Inst.* 97 illustrations. 991pp. 2 volumes.
20003-5, 20004-3 Two volume set, paperbound $5.50

THE STRANGE STORY OF THE QUANTUM, AN ACCOUNT FOR THE GENERAL READER OF THE GROWTH OF IDEAS UNDERLYING OUR PRESENT ATOMIC KNOWLEDGE, *B. Hoffmann*

Presents lucidly and expertly, with barest amount of mathematics, the problems and theories which led to modern quantum physics. Dr. Hoffmann begins with the closing years of the 19th century, when certain trifling discrepancies were noticed, and with illuminating analogies and examples takes you through the brilliant concepts of Planck, Einstein, Pauli, de Broglie, Bohr, Schroedinger, Heisenberg, Dirac, Sommerfeld, Feynman, etc. This edition includes a new, long postscript carrying the story through 1958. "Of the books attempting an account of the history and contents of our modern atomic physics which have come to my attention, this is the best," H. Margenau, Yale University, in *American Journal of Physics.* 32 tables and line illustrations. Index. 275pp. 5⅜ x 8.
20518-5 Paperbound $2.00

GREAT IDEAS AND THEORIES OF MODERN COSMOLOGY, *Jagjit Singh*

The theories of Jeans, Eddington, Milne, Kant, Bondi, Gold, Newton, Einstein, Gamow, Hoyle, Dirac, Kuiper, Hubble, Weizsäcker and many others on such cosmological questions as the origin of the universe, space and time, planet formation, "continuous creation," the birth, life, and death of the stars, the origin of the galaxies, etc. By the author of the popular *Great Ideas of Modern Mathematics.* A gifted popularizer of science, he makes the most difficult abstractions crystal-clear even to the most non-mathematical reader. Index. xii + 276pp. 5⅜ x 8½. 20925-3 Paperbound $2.50

GREAT IDEAS OF MODERN MATHEMATICS: THEIR NATURE AND USE, *Jagjit Singh*

Reader with only high school math will understand main mathematical ideas of modern physics, astronomy, genetics, psychology, evolution, etc., better than many who use them as tools, but comprehend little of their basic structure. Author uses his wide knowledge of non-mathematical fields in brilliant exposition of differential equations, matrices, group theory, logic, statistics, problems of mathematical foundations, imaginary numbers, vectors, etc. Original publications, appendices. indexes. 65 illustr. 322pp. 5⅜ x 8. 20587-8 Paperbound $2.25

THE MATHEMATICS OF GREAT AMATEURS, *Julian L. Coolidge*

Great discoveries made by poets, theologians, philosophers, artists and other non-mathematicians: Omar Khayyam, Leonardo da Vinci, Albrecht Dürer, John Napier, Pascal, Diderot, Bolzano, etc. Surprising accounts of what can result from a non-professional preoccupation with the oldest of sciences. 56 figures. viii + 211pp. 5⅜ x 8½. 61009-8 Paperbound $2.00

COLLEGE ALGEBRA, *H. B. Fine*
Standard college text that gives a systematic and deductive structure to algebra; comprehensive, connected, with emphasis on theory. Discusses the commutative, associative, and distributive laws of number in unusual detail, and goes on with undetermined coefficients, quadratic equations, progressions, logarithms, permutations, probability, power series, and much more. Still most valuable elementary-intermediate text on the science and structure of algebra. Index. 1560 problems, all with answers. x + 631pp. 5⅜ x 8. 60211-7 Paperbound $2.75

HIGHER MATHEMATICS FOR STUDENTS OF CHEMISTRY AND PHYSICS, *J. W. Mellor*
Not abstract, but practical, building its problems out of familiar laboratory material, this covers differential calculus, coordinate, analytical geometry, functions, integral calculus, infinite series, numerical equations, differential equations, Fourier's theorem, probability, theory of errors, calculus of variations, determinants. "If the reader is not familiar with this book, it will repay him to examine it," *Chem. & Engineering News.* 800 problems. 189 figures. Bibliography. xxi + 641pp. 5⅜ x 8. 60193-5 Paperbound $3.50

TRIGONOMETRY REFRESHER FOR TECHNICAL MEN, *A. A. Klaf*
A modern question and answer text on plane and spherical trigonometry. Part I covers plane trigonometry: angles, quadrants, trigonometrical functions, graphical representation, interpolation, equations, logarithms, solution of triangles, slide rules, etc. Part II discusses applications to navigation, surveying, elasticity, architecture, and engineering. Small angles, periodic functions, vectors, polar coordinates, De Moivre's theorem, fully covered. Part III is devoted to spherical trigonometry and the solution of spherical triangles, with applications to terrestrial and astronomical problems. Special time-savers for numerical calculation. 913 questions answered for you! 1738 problems; answers to odd numbers. 494 figures. 14 pages of functions, formulae. Index. x + 629pp. 5⅜ x 8. 20371-9 Paperbound $3.00

CALCULUS REFRESHER FOR TECHNICAL MEN, *A. A. Klaf*
Not an ordinary textbook but a unique refresher for engineers, technicians, and students. An examination of the most important aspects of differential and integral calculus by means of 756 key questions. Part I covers simple differential calculus: constants, variables, functions, increments, derivatives, logarithms, curvature, etc. Part II treats fundamental concepts of integration: inspection, substitution, transformation, reduction, areas and volumes, mean value, successive and partial integration, double and triple integration. Stresses practical aspects! A 50 page section gives applications to civil and nautical engineering, electricity, stress and strain, elasticity, industrial engineering, and similar fields. 756 questions answered. 556 problems; solutions to odd numbers. 36 pages of constants, formulae. Index. v + 431pp. 5⅜ x 8. 20370-0 Paperbound $2.25

INTRODUCTION TO THE THEORY OF GROUPS OF FINITE ORDER, *R. Carmichael*
Examines fundamental theorems and their application. Beginning with sets, systems, permutations, etc., it progresses in easy stages through important types of groups: Abelian, prime power, permutation, etc. Except 1 chapter where matrices are desirable, no higher math needed. 783 exercises, problems. Index. xvi + 447pp. 5⅜ x 8. 60300-8 Paperbound $3.00

FIVE VOLUME "THEORY OF FUNCTIONS" SET BY KONRAD KNOPP

This five-volume set, prepared by Konrad Knopp, provides a complete and readily followed account of theory of functions. Proofs are given concisely, yet without sacrifice of completeness or rigor. These volumes are used as texts by such universities as M.I.T., University of Chicago, N. Y. City College, and many others. "Excellent introduction . . . remarkably readable, concise, clear, rigorous," *Journal of the American Statistical Association.*

ELEMENTS OF THE THEORY OF FUNCTIONS,
Konrad Knopp
This book provides the student with background for further volumes in this set, or texts on a similar level. Partial contents: foundations, system of complex numbers and the Gaussian plane of numbers, Riemann sphere of numbers, mapping by linear functions, normal forms, the logarithm, the cyclometric functions and binomial series. "Not only for the young student, but also for the student who knows all about what is in it," *Mathematical Journal.* Bibliography. Index. 140pp. 5⅜ x 8. 60154-4 Paperbound $1.50

THEORY OF FUNCTIONS, PART I,
Konrad Knopp
With volume II, this book provides coverage of basic concepts and theorems. Partial contents: numbers and points, functions of a complex variable, integral of a continuous function, Cauchy's integral theorem, Cauchy's integral formulae, series with variable terms, expansion of analytic functions in power series, analytic continuation and complete definition of analytic functions, entire transcendental functions, Laurent expansion, types of singularities. Bibliography. Index. vii + 146pp. 5⅜ x 8. 60156-0 Paperbound $1.50

THEORY OF FUNCTIONS, PART II,
Konrad Knopp
Application and further development of general theory, special topics. Single valued functions. Entire, Weierstrass, Meromorphic functions. Riemann surfaces. Algebraic functions. Analytical configuration, Riemann surface. Bibliography. Index. x + 150pp. 5⅜ x 8. 60157-9 Paperbound $1.50

PROBLEM BOOK IN THE THEORY OF FUNCTIONS, VOLUME 1.
Konrad Knopp
Problems in elementary theory, for use with Knopp's *Theory of Functions,* or any other text, arranged according to increasing difficulty. Fundamental concepts, sequences of numbers and infinite series, complex variable, integral theorems, development in series, conformal mapping. 182 problems. Answers. viii + 126pp. 5⅜ x 8. 60158-7 Paperbound $1.50

PROBLEM BOOK IN THE THEORY OF FUNCTIONS, VOLUME 2,
Konrad Knopp
Advanced theory of functions, to be used either with Knopp's *Theory of Functions,* or any other comparable text. Singularities, entire & meromorphic functions, periodic, analytic, continuation, multiple-valued functions, Riemann surfaces, conformal mapping. Includes a section of additional elementary problems. "The difficult task of selecting from the immense material of the modern theory of functions the problems just within the reach of the beginner is here masterfully accomplished," *Am. Math. Soc.* Answers. 138pp. 5⅜ x 8.
60159-5 Paperbound $1.50

NUMERICAL SOLUTIONS OF DIFFERENTIAL EQUATIONS,
H. Levy & E. A. Baggott

Comprehensive collection of methods for solving ordinary differential equations of first and higher order. All must pass 2 requirements: easy to grasp and practical, more rapid than school methods. Partial contents: graphical integration of differential equations, graphical methods for detailed solution. Numerical solution. Simultaneous equations and equations of 2nd and higher orders. "Should be in the hands of all in research in applied mathematics, teaching," *Nature.* 21 figures. viii + 238pp. 5⅜ x 8. 60168-4 Paperbound $1.85

ELEMENTARY STATISTICS, WITH APPLICATIONS IN MEDICINE AND THE BIOLOGICAL SCIENCES, *F. E. Croxton*

A sound introduction to statistics for anyone in the physical sciences, assuming no prior acquaintance and requiring only a modest knowledge of math. All basic formulas carefully explained and illustrated; all necessary reference tables included. From basic terms and concepts, the study proceeds to frequency distribution, linear, non-linear, and multiple correlation, skewness, kurtosis, etc. A large section deals with reliability and significance of statistical methods. Containing concrete examples from medicine and biology, this book will prove unusually helpful to workers in those fields who increasingly must evaluate, check, and interpret statistics. Formerly titled "Elementary Statistics with Applications in Medicine." 101 charts. 57 tables. 14 appendices. Index. vi + 376pp. 5⅜ x 8. 60506-X Paperbound $2.25

INTRODUCTION TO SYMBOLIC LOGIC,
S. Langer

No special knowledge of math required—probably the clearest book ever written on symbolic logic, suitable for the layman, general scientist, and philosopher. You start with simple symbols and advance to a knowledge of the Boole-Schroeder and Russell-Whitehead systems. Forms, logical structure, classes, the calculus of propositions, logic of the syllogism, etc. are all covered. "One of the clearest and simplest introductions," *Mathematics Gazette.* Second enlarged, revised edition. 368pp. 5⅜ x 8. 60164-1 Paperbound $2.25

A SHORT ACCOUNT OF THE HISTORY OF MATHEMATICS,
W. W. R. Ball

Most readable non-technical history of mathematics treats lives, discoveries of every important figure from Egyptian, Phoenician, mathematicians to late 19th century. Discusses schools of Ionia, Pythagoras, Athens, Cyzicus, Alexandria, Byzantium, systems of numeration; primitive arithmetic; Middle Ages, Renaissance, including Arabs, Bacon, Regiomontanus, Tartaglia, Cardan, Stevinus, Galileo, Kepler; modern mathematics of Descartes, Pascal, Wallis, Huygens, Newton, Leibnitz, d'Alembert, Euler, Lambert, Laplace, Legendre, Gauss, Hermite, Weierstrass, scores more. Index. 25 figures. 546pp. 5⅜ x 8.
20630-0 Paperbound $2.75

INTRODUCTION TO NONLINEAR DIFFERENTIAL AND INTEGRAL EQUATIONS,
Harold T. Davis

Aspects of the problem of nonlinear equations, transformations that lead to equations solvable by classical means, results in special cases, and useful generalizations. Thorough, but easily followed by mathematically sophisticated reader who knows little about non-linear equations. 137 problems for student to solve. xv + 566pp. 5⅜ x 8½. 60971-5 Paperbound $2.75

AN INTRODUCTION TO THE GEOMETRY OF N DIMENSIONS,
D. H. Y. Sommerville
An introduction presupposing no prior knowledge of the field, the only book in English devoted exclusively to higher dimensional geometry. Discusses fundamental ideas of incidence, parallelism, perpendicularity, angles between linear space; enumerative geometry; analytical geometry from projective and metric points of view; polytopes; elementary ideas in analysis situs; content of hyper-spacial figures. Bibliography. Index. 60 diagrams. 196pp. 5⅜ x 8.
60494-2 Paperbound $1.50

ELEMENTARY CONCEPTS OF TOPOLOGY, *P. Alexandroff*
First English translation of the famous brief introduction to topology for the beginner or for the mathematician not undertaking extensive study. This unusually useful intuitive approach deals primarily with the concepts of complex, cycle, and homology, and is wholly consistent with current investigations. Ranges from basic concepts of set-theoretic topology to the concept of Betti groups. "Glowing example of harmony between intuition and thought," David Hilbert. Translated by A. E. Farley. Introduction by D. Hilbert. Index. 25 figures. 73pp. 5⅜ x 8. 60747-X Paperbound $1.25

ELEMENTS OF NON-EUCLIDEAN GEOMETRY,
D. M. Y. Sommerville
Unique in proceeding step-by-step, in the manner of traditional geometry. Enables the student with only a good knowledge of high school algebra and geometry to grasp elementary hyperbolic, elliptic, analytic non-Euclidean geometries; space curvature and its philosophical implications; theory of radical axes; homothetic centres and systems of circles; parataxy and parallelism; absolute measure; Gauss' proof of the defect area theorem; geodesic representation; much more, all with exceptional clarity. 126 problems at chapter endings provide progressive practice and familiarity. 133 figures. Index. xvi + 274pp. 5⅜ x 8. 60460-8 Paperbound $2.00

INTRODUCTION TO THE THEORY OF NUMBERS, *L. E. Dickson*
Thorough, comprehensive approach with adequate coverage of classical literature, an introductory volume beginners can follow. Chapters on divisibility, congruences, quadratic residues & reciprocity. Diophantine equations, etc. Full treatment of binary quadratic forms without usual restriction to integral coefficients. Covers infinitude of primes, least residues. Fermat's theorem. Euler's phi function, Legendre's symbol, Gauss's lemma, automorphs, reduced forms, recent theorems of Thue & Siegel, many more. Much material not readily available elsewhere. 239 problems. Index. I figure. viii + 183pp. 5⅜ x 8.
60342-3 Paperbound $1.75

MATHEMATICAL TABLES AND FORMULAS,
compiled by Robert D. Carmichael and Edwin R. Smith
Valuable collection for students, etc. Contains all tables necessary in college algebra and trigonometry, such as five-place common logarithms, logarithmic sines and tangents of small angles, logarithmic trigonometric functions, natural trigonometric functions, four-place antilogarithms, tables for changing from sexagesimal to circular and from circular to sexagesimal measure of angles, etc. Also many tables and formulas not ordinarily accessible, including powers, roots, and reciprocals, exponential and hyperbolic functions, ten-place logarithms of prime numbers, and formulas and theorems from analytical and elementary geometry and from calculus. Explanatory introduction. viii + 269pp. 5⅜ x 8½. 60111-0 Paperbound $1.50

A SOURCE BOOK IN MATHEMATICS,
D. E. Smith
Great discoveries in math, from Renaissance to end of 19th century, in English translation. Read announcements by Dedekind, Gauss, Delamain, Pascal, Fermat, Newton, Abel, Lobachevsky, Bolyai, Riemann, De Moivre, Legendre, Laplace, others of discoveries about imaginary numbers, number congruence, slide rule, equations, symbolism, cubic algebraic equations, non-Euclidean forms of geometry, calculus, function theory, quaternions, etc. Succinct selections from 125 different treatises, articles, most unavailable elsewhere in English. Each article preceded by biographical introduction. Vol. I: Fields of Number, Algebra. Index. 32 illus. 338pp. 5⅜ x 8. Vol. II: Fields of Geometry, Probability, Calculus, Functions, Quaternions. 83 illus. 432pp. 5⅜ x 8.
60552-3, 60553-1 Two volume set, paperbound $5.00

FOUNDATIONS OF PHYSICS,
R. B. Lindsay & H. Margenau
Excellent bridge between semi-popular works & technical treatises. A discussion of methods of physical description, construction of theory; valuable for physicist with elementary calculus who is interested in ideas that give meaning to data, tools of modern physics. Contents include symbolism; mathematical equations; space & time foundations of mechanics; probability; physics & continua; electron theory; special & general relativity; quantum mechanics; causality. "Thorough and yet not overdetailed. Unreservedly recommended," *Nature* (London). Unabridged, corrected edition. List of recommended readings. 35 illustrations. xi + 537pp. 5⅜ x 8. 60377-6 Paperbound $3.50

FUNDAMENTAL FORMULAS OF PHYSICS,
ed. by D. H. Menzel
High useful, full, inexpensive reference and study text, ranging from simple to highly sophisticated operations. Mathematics integrated into text—each chapter stands as short textbook of field represented. Vol. 1: Statistics, Physical Constants, Special Theory of Relativity, Hydrodynamics, Aerodynamics, Boundary Value Problems in Math, Physics, Viscosity, Electromagnetic Theory, etc. Vol. 2: Sound, Acoustics, Geometrical Optics, Electron Optics, High-Energy Phenomena, Magnetism, Biophysics, much more. Index. Total of 800pp. 5⅜ x 8.
60595-7, 60596-5 Two volume set, paperbound $4.75

THEORETICAL PHYSICS,
A. S. Kompaneyets
One of the very few thorough studies of the subject in this price range. Provides advanced students with a comprehensive theoretical background. Especially strong on recent experimentation and developments in quantum theory. Contents: Mechanics (Generalized Coordinates, Lagrange's Equation, Collision of Particles, etc.), Electrodynamics (Vector Analysis, Maxwell's equations, Transmission of Signals, Theory of Relativity, etc.), Quantum Mechanics (the Inadequacy of Classical Mechanics, the Wave Equation, Motion in a Central Field, Quantum Theory of Radiation, Quantum Theories of Dispersion and Scattering, etc.), and Statistical Physics (Equilibrium Distribution of Molecules in an Ideal Gas, Boltzmann Statistics, Bose and Fermi Distribution. Thermodynamic Quantities, etc.). Revised to 1961. Translated by George Yankovsky, authorized by Kompaneyets. 137 exercises. 56 figures. 529pp. 5⅜ x 8½.
60972-3 Paperbound $3.50

MATHEMATICAL PHYSICS, *D. H. Menzel*
Thorough one-volume treatment of the mathematical techniques vital for classical mechanics, electromagnetic theory, quantum theory, and relativity. Written by the Harvard Professor of Astrophysics for junior, senior, and graduate courses, it gives clear explanations of all those aspects of function theory, vectors, matrices, dyadics, tensors, partial differential equations, etc., necessary for the understanding of the various physical theories. Electron theory, relativity, and other topics seldom presented appear here in considerable detail. Scores of definition, conversion factors, dimensional constants, etc. "More detailed than normal for an advanced text . . . excellent set of sections on Dyadics, Matrices, and Tensors," *Journal of the Franklin Institute*. Index. 193 problems, with answers. x + 412pp. 5⅜ x 8. 60056-4 Paperbound $2.50

THE THEORY OF SOUND, *Lord Rayleigh*
Most vibrating systems likely to be encountered in practice can be tackled successfully by the methods set forth by the great Nobel laureate, Lord Rayleigh. Complete coverage of experimental, mathematical aspects of sound theory. Partial contents: Harmonic motions, vibrating systems in general, lateral vibrations of bars, curved plates or shells, applications of Laplace's functions to acoustical problems, fluid friction, plane vortex-sheet, vibrations of solid bodies, etc. This is the first inexpensive edition of this great reference and study work. Bibliography, Historical introduction by R. B. Lindsay. Total of 1040pp. 97 figures. 5⅜ x 8. 60292-3, 60293-1 Two volume set, paperbound $6.00

HYDRODYNAMICS, *Horace Lamb*
Internationally famous complete coverage of standard reference work on dynamics of liquids & gases. Fundamental theorems, equations, methods, solutions, background, for classical hydrodynamics. Chapters include Equations of Motion, Integration of Equations in Special Gases, Irrotational Motion, Motion of Liquid in 2 Dimensions, Motion of Solids through Liquid-Dynamical Theory, Vortex Motion, Tidal Waves, Surface Waves, Waves of Expansion, Viscosity, Rotating Masses of Liquids. Excellently planned, arranged; clear, lucid presentation. 6th enlarged, revised edition. Index. Over 900 footnotes, mostly bibliographical. 119 figures. xv + 738pp. 6⅛ x 9¼. 60256-7 Paperbound $4.00

DYNAMICAL THEORY OF GASES, *James Jeans*
Divided into mathematical and physical chapters for the convenience of those not expert in mathematics, this volume discusses the mathematical theory of gas in a steady state, thermodynamics, Boltzmann and Maxwell, kinetic theory, quantum theory, exponentials, etc. 4th enlarged edition, with new material on quantum theory, quantum dynamics, etc. Indexes. 28 figures. 444pp. 6⅛ x 9¼.
60136-6 Paperbound $2.75

THERMODYNAMICS, *Enrico Fermi*
Unabridged reproduction of 1937 edition. Elementary in treatment; remarkable for clarity, organization. Requires no knowledge of advanced math beyond calculus, only familiarity with fundamentals of thermometry, calorimetry. Partial Contents: Thermodynamic systems; First & Second laws of thermodynamics; Entropy; Thermodynamic potentials: phase rule, reversible electric cell; Gaseous reactions: van't Hoff reaction box, principle of LeChatelier; Thermodynamics of dilute solutions: osmotic & vapor pressures, boiling & freezing points; Entropy constant. Index. 25 problems. 24 illustrations. x + 160pp. 5⅜ x 8. 60361-X Paperbound $2.00

CELESTIAL OBJECTS FOR COMMON TELESCOPES,
Rev. T. W. Webb
Classic handbook for the use and pleasure of the amateur astronomer. Of inestimable aid in locating and identifying thousands of celestial objects. Vol I, The Solar System: discussions of the principle and operation of the telescope, procedures of observations and telescope-photography, spectroscopy, etc., precise location information of sun, moon, planets, meteors. Vol. II, The Stars: alphabetical listing of constellations, information on double stars, clusters, stars with unusual spectra, variables, and nebulae, etc. Nearly 4,000 objects noted. Edited and extensively revised by Margaret W. Mayall, director of the American Assn. of Variable Star Observers. New Index by Mrs. Mayall giving the location of all objects mentioned in the text for Epoch 2000. New Precession Table added. New appendices on the planetary satellites, constellation names and abbreviations, and solar system data. Total of 46 illustrations. Total of xxxix + 606pp. 5⅜ x 8. 20917-2, 20918-0 Two volume set, paperbound $5.00

PLANETARY THEORY,
E. W. Brown and C. A. Shook
Provides a clear presentation of basic methods for calculating planetary orbits for today's astronomer. Begins with a careful exposition of specialized mathematical topics essential for handling perturbation theory and then goes on to indicate how most of the previous methods reduce ultimately to two general calculation methods: obtaining expressions either for the coordinates of planetary positions or for the elements which determine the perturbed paths. An example of each is given and worked in detail. Corrected edition. Preface. Appendix. Index. xii + 302pp. 5⅜ x 8½. 61133-7 Paperbound $2.25

STAR NAMES AND THEIR MEANINGS,
Richard Hinckley Allen
An unusual book documenting the various attributions of names to the individual stars over the centuries. Here is a treasure-house of information on a topic not normally delved into even by professional astronomers; provides a fascinating background to the stars in folk-lore, literary references, ancient writings, star catalogs and maps over the centuries. Constellation-by-constellation analysis covers hundreds of stars and other asterisms, including the Pleiades, Hyades, Andromedan Nebula, etc. Introduction. Indices. List of authors and authorities. xx + 563pp. 5⅜ x 8½. 21079-0 Paperbound $3.00

A SHORT HISTORY OF ASTRONOMY, *A. Berry*
Popular standard work for over 50 years, this thorough and accurate volume covers the science from primitive times to the end of the 19th century. After the Greeks and the Middle Ages, individual chapters analyze Copernicus, Brahe, Galileo, Kepler, and Newton, and the mixed reception of their discoveries. Post-Newtonian achievements are then discussed in unusual detail: Halley, Bradley, Lagrange, Laplace, Herschel, Bessel, etc. 2 Indexes. 104 illustrations, 9 portraits. xxxi + 440pp. 5⅜ x 8. 20210-0 Paperbound $2.75

SOME THEORY OF SAMPLING, *W. E. Deming*
The purpose of this book is to make sampling techniques understandable to and useable by social scientists, industrial managers, and natural scientists who are finding statistics increasingly part of their work. Over 200 exercises, plus dozens of actual applications. 61 tables. 90 figs. xix + 602pp. 5⅜ x 8½.
61755-6 Paperbound $3.50

PRINCIPLES OF STRATIGRAPHY,
A. W. Grabau
Classic of 20th century geology, unmatched in scope and comprehensiveness. Nearly 600 pages cover the structure and origins of every kind of sedimentary, hydrogenic, oceanic, pyroclastic, atmoclastic, hydroclastic, marine hydroclastic, and bioclastic rock; metamorphism; erosion; etc. Includes also the constitution of the atmosphere; morphology of oceans, rivers, glaciers; volcanic activities; faults and earthquakes; and fundamental principles of paleontology (nearly 200 pages). New introduction by Prof. M. Kay, Columbia U. 1277 bibliographical entries. 264 diagrams. Tables, maps, etc. Two volume set. Total of xxxii + 1185pp. 5⅜ x 8. 60686-4, 60687-2 Two volume set, paperbound $6.25

SNOW CRYSTALS, *W. A. Bentley and W. J. Humphreys*
Over 200 pages of Bentley's famous microphotographs of snow flakes—the product of painstaking, methodical work at his Jericho, Vermont studio. The pictures, which also include plates of frost, glaze and dew on vegetation, spider webs, windowpanes; sleet; graupel or soft hail, were chosen both for their scientific interest and their aesthetic qualities. The wonder of nature's diversity is exhibited in the intricate, beautiful patterns of the snow flakes. Introductory text by W. J. Humphreys. Selected bibliography. 2,453 illustrations. 224pp. 8 x 10¼. 20287-9 Paperbound $3.25

THE BIRTH AND DEVELOPMENT OF THE GEOLOGICAL SCIENCES,
F. D. Adams
Most thorough history of the earth sciences ever written. Geological thought from earliest times to the end of the 19th century, covering over 300 early thinkers & systems: fossils & their explanation, vulcanists vs. neptunists, figured stones & paleontology, generation of stones, dozens of similar topics. 91 illustrations, including medieval, renaissance woodcuts, etc. Index. 632 footnotes, mostly bibliographical. 511pp. 5⅜ x 8. 20005-1 Paperbound $2.75

ORGANIC CHEMISTRY, *F. C. Whitmore*
The entire subject of organic chemistry for the practicing chemist and the advanced student. Storehouse of facts, theories, processes found elsewhere only in specialized journals. Covers aliphatic compounds (500 pages on the properties and synthetic preparation of hydrocarbons, halides, proteins, ketones, etc.), alicyclic compounds, aromatic compounds, heterocyclic compounds, organophosphorus and organometallic compounds. Methods of synthetic preparation analyzed critically throughout. Includes much of biochemical interest. "The scope of this volume is astonishing," *Industrial and Engineering Chemistry*. 12,000-reference index. 2387-item bibliography. Total of x + 1005pp. 5⅜ x 8. 60700-3, 60701-1 Two volume set, paperbound $4.50

THE PHASE RULE AND ITS APPLICATION,
Alexander Findlay
Covering chemical phenomena of 1, 2, 3, 4, and multiple component systems, this "standard work on the subject" (*Nature*, London), has been completely revised and brought up to date by A. N. Campbell and N. O. Smith. Brand new material has been added on such matters as binary, tertiary liquid equilibria, solid solutions in ternary systems, quinary systems of salts and water. Completely revised to triangular coordinates in ternary systems, clarified graphic representation, solid models, etc. 9th revised edition. Author, subject indexes. 236 figures. 505 footnotes, mostly bibliographic. xii + 494pp. 5⅜ x 8. 60091-2 Paperbound $2.75

A COURSE IN MATHEMATICAL ANALYSIS,
Edouard Goursat

Trans. by E. R. Hedrick, O. Dunkel, H. G. Bergmann. Classic study of fundamental material thoroughly treated. Extremely lucid exposition of wide range of subject matter for student with one year of calculus. Vol. 1: Derivatives and differentials, definite integrals, expansions in series, applications to geometry. 52 figures, 556pp. 60554-X Paperbound $3.00. Vol. 2, Part I: Functions of a complex variable, conformal representations, doubly periodic functions, natural boundaries, etc. 38 figures, 269pp. 60555-8 Paperbound $2.25. Vol. 2, Part II: Differential equations, Cauchy-Lipschitz method, nonlinear differential equations, simultaneous equations, etc. 308pp. 60556-6 Paperbound $2.50. Vol. 3, Part I: Variation of solutions, partial differential equations of the second order. 15 figures, 339pp. 61176-0 Paperbound $3.00. Vol. 3, Part II: Integral equations, calculus of variations. 13 figures, 389pp. 61177-9 Paperbound $3.00 60554-X, 60555-8, 60556-6 61176-0, 61177-9 Six volume set,
paperbound $13.75

PLANETS, STARS AND GALAXIES,
A. E. Fanning

Descriptive astronomy for beginners: the solar system; neighboring galaxies; seasons; quasars; fly-by results from Mars, Venus, Moon; radio astronomy; etc. all simply explained. Revised up to 1966 by author and Prof. D. H. Menzel, former Director, Harvard College Observatory. 29 photos, 16 figures. 189pp. 5⅜ x 8½. 21680-2 Paperbound $1.50

GREAT IDEAS IN INFORMATION THEORY, LANGUAGE AND CYBERNETICS,
Jagjit Singh

Winner of Unesco's Kalinga Prize covers language, metalanguages, analog and digital computers, neural systems, work of McCulloch, Pitts, von Neumann, Turing, other important topics. No advanced mathematics needed, yet a full discussion without compromise or distortion. 118 figures. ix + 338pp. 5⅜ x 8½.
21694-2 Paperbound $2.25

GEOMETRIC EXERCISES IN PAPER FOLDING,
T. Sundara Row

Regular polygons, circles and other curves can be folded or pricked on paper, then used to demonstrate geometric propositions, work out proofs, set up well-known problems. 89 illustrations, photographs of actually folded sheets. xii + 148pp. 5⅜ x 8½. 21594-6 Paperbound $1.00

VISUAL ILLUSIONS, THEIR CAUSES, CHARACTERISTICS AND APPLICATIONS,
M. Luckiesh

The visual process, the structure of the eye, geometric, perspective illusions, influence of angles, illusions of depth and distance, color illusions, lighting effects, illusions in nature, special uses in painting, decoration, architecture, magic, camouflage. New introduction by W. H. Ittleson covers modern developments in this area. 100 illustrations. xxi + 252pp. 5⅜ x 8.
21530-X Paperbound $1.50

ATOMS AND MOLECULES SIMPLY EXPLAINED,
B. C. Saunders and R. E. D. Clark

Introduction to chemical phenomena and their applications: cohesion, particles, crystals, tailoring big molecules, chemist as architect, with applications in radioactivity, color photography, synthetics, biochemistry, polymers, and many other important areas. Non technical. 95 figures. x + 299pp. 5⅜ x 8½.
21282-3 Paperbound $1.50

THE PRINCIPLES OF ELECTROCHEMISTRY,
D. A. MacInnes

Basic equations for almost every subfield of electrochemistry from first principles, referring at all times to the soundest and most recent theories and results; unusually useful as text or as reference. Covers coulometers and Faraday's Law, electrolytic conductance, the Debye-Hueckel method for the theoretical calculation of activity coefficients, concentration cells, standard electrode potentials, thermodynamic ionization constants, pH, potentiometric titrations, irreversible phenomena. Planck's equation, and much more. 2 indices. Appendix. 585-item bibliography. 137 figures. 94 tables. ii + 478pp. 5⅝ x 8⅜.
60052-1 Paperbound $3.00

MATHEMATICS OF MODERN ENGINEERING,
E. G. Keller and R. E. Doherty

Written for the Advanced Course in Engineering of the General Electric Corporation, deals with the engineering use of determinants, tensors, the Heaviside operational calculus, dyadics, the calculus of variations, etc. Presents underlying principles fully, but emphasis is on the perennial engineering attack of set-up and solve. Indexes. Over 185 figures and tables. Hundreds of exercises, problems, and worked-out examples. References. Total of xxxiii + 623pp. 5⅜ x 8. 60734-8, 60735-6 Two volume set, paperbound $3.70

AERODYNAMIC THEORY: A GENERAL REVIEW OF PROGRESS,
William F. Durand, editor-in-chief

A monumental joint effort by the world's leading authorities prepared under a grant of the Guggenheim Fund for the Promotion of Aeronautics. Never equalled for breadth, depth, reliability. Contains discussions of special mathematical topics not usually taught in the engineering or technical courses. Also: an extended two-part treatise on Fluid Mechanics, discussions of aerodynamics of perfect fluids, analyses of experiments with wind tunnels, applied airfoil theory, the nonlifting system of the airplane, the air propeller, hydrodynamics of boats and floats, the aerodynamics of cooling, etc. Contributing experts include Munk, Giacomelli, Prandtl, Toussaint, Von Karman, Klemperer, among others. Unabridged republication. 6 volumes. Total of 1,012 figures, 12 plates, 2,186pp. Bibliographies. Notes. Indices. 5⅜ x 8½. 61709-2, 61710-6, 61711-4, 61712-2, 61713-0, 61715-9 Six volume set, paperbound $13.50

FUNDAMENTALS OF HYDRO- AND AEROMECHANICS,
L. Prandtl and O. G. Tietjens

The well-known standard work based upon Prandtl's lectures at Goettingen. Wherever possible hydrodynamics theory is referred to practical considerations in hydraulics, with the view of unifying theory and experience. Presentation is extremely clear and though primarily physical, mathematical proofs are rigorous and use vector analysis to a considerable extent. An Engineering Society Monograph, 1934. 186 figures. Index. xvi + 270pp. 5⅜ x 8.
60374-1 Paperbound $2.25

APPLIED HYDRO- AND AEROMECHANICS,
L. Prandtl and O. G. Tietjens

Presents for the most part methods which will be valuable to engineers. Covers flow in pipes, boundary layers, airfoil theory, entry conditions, turbulent flow in pipes, and the boundary layer, determining drag from measurements of pressure and velocity, etc. Unabridged, unaltered. An Engineering Society Monograph. 1934. Index. 226 figures, 28 photographic plates illustrating flow patterns. xvi + 311pp. 5⅜ x 8. 60375-X Paperbound $2.50